D1317672

THE TEACHING OF
SECONDARY MATHEMATICS

CURRICULUM AND METHODS IN EDUCATION
Arno A. Bellack, *Consulting Editor*

The Teaching of
Secondary Mathematics

CHARLES H. BUTLER

Professor of Mathematics
Western Michigan University

F. LYNWOOD WREN

Professor of Mathematics
San Fernando Valley State College

JULIA A. SEARS PROFESSOR OF MATHEMATICS, EMERITUS
GEORGE PEABODY COLLEGE FOR TEACHERS

THIRD EDITION

New York   Toronto   London   1960
McGRAW-HILL BOOK COMPANY, INC.

THE TEACHING OF SECONDARY MATHEMATICS

THE MAPLE PRESS COMPANY, YORK, PA.

PREFACE

Justification for the publication of a new edition of a book does not reside merely in a lapse of time. On the other hand, if the intervening years have been characterized by significant changes and developments with respect to the subject, then it becomes important to bring these into focus. We feel that the generous reception which the first and second editions of this book have enjoyed implies an obligation on our part to keep it abreast of the times.

The decade which has elapsed since publication of the second edition has been marked by a profound change in the climate of opinion, in both lay and professional circles, respecting mathematical education in the secondary schools. As an important element in our culture and as a key instrument for a rapidly expanding technology, mathematics has come to be recognized in fuller measure than at any time in the past half century. Equally evident has been the concern whether the curriculum, content, and instructional practices in mathematics as commonly found in our schools are fully adequate and appropriate for a contemporary educational program.

This concern has been motivated both by the practical demands of modern technology and by the insistence on the part of teachers and mathematicians that mathematics should be viewed as a live and growing and exciting subject in its own right. Interest is reflected in current books and articles, in recent and contemporary recommendations of important committees, and in the provision of opportunities and substantial inducements to mathematics teachers to improve their mastery of the subject. This is something of which mathematics teachers must be or become aware, since it provides a new perspective in terms of which many will need to broaden their mathematical backgrounds and reexamine their instructional practices.

In Part I of this new edition we have tried to bring together some of the most significant contemporary thought respecting the program in secondary mathematics and the broad instructional problems involved in making it effective. This first half of the book has been almost completely rewritten, and it represents a radical revision of the second edition. Four of the chapters are completely new.

In Part II (Part III of the second edition) the revision consists mainly of the expansion of existing chapters and the addition of two new ones. Subscribing to the spirit of modern mathematics does not imply wholesale abandonment of the present courses, but rather the gradual improvement of them. Hence, in revising this second half of the book, we have had two main objectives. One has been to retain the material of the second edition that we believe will continue to be helpful to teachers; the other has been to exhibit and illustrate, in the context of familiar subject matter, some of the newer concepts and newer emphases in teaching that we believe will soon be reflected in mathematics textbooks and courses of study for the secondary schools.

We feel that this is a book which will be helpful not only to prospective teachers of mathematics while they are still in college but to experienced teachers as well.

For their kind permission to quote from published sources in the present revision, we wish to express our appreciation to the publishers, organizations, and journals named below and to all individual authors from whose works such quotations have been taken:

American Book Company, New York; Henry Holt and Company, Inc., New York; Houghton Mifflin Company, Boston; McGraw-Hill Book Company, Inc., New York; The Macmillan Company, New York; W. W. Norton & Company, Inc., New York; Rinehart & Company, Inc., New York; University of Chicago Press, Chicago; Central Association of Science and Mathematics Teachers and its official journal, *School Science and Mathematics;* College Entrance Examination Board and its Commission on Mathematics; George Peabody College for Teachers, Nashville, Tenn.; National Association of Secondary School Principals; National Council of Teachers of Mathematics and its official journal, *Mathematics Teacher,* as well as certain issues of its *Yearbook;* U.S. Office of Education; Progressive Education Association; Society for the Promotion of Engineering Education; *Holiday;* and *Look.*

Charles H. Butler
F. Lynwood Wren

CONTENTS

PART I

THE PROGRAM AND
THE IMPROVEMENT OF INSTRUCTION
IN SECONDARY MATHEMATICS

1

THE EVOLVING PROGRAM OF
SECONDARY MATHEMATICS

The American public secondary school, which had its beginning in the third decade of the nineteenth century, was preceded by two other significant institutions of secondary education, viz., the Latin grammar school and the academy. The discrimination between the respective periods for which each of these schools represents the predominant educational pattern is not altogether distinct and clear-cut. The transition from the influence of one educational philosophy to that of another has been characterized by a somewhat deliberate effort at reform under the persistent demands of social change. The development of the new institutions and the gradual fading from prominence of the old have been merely the outward evidences of the efforts of educational leaders to keep abreast of the demands of a changing social order. Such a pattern of educational evolution continues to exercise influence in the shaping of the curriculum content and the instructional procedure in the schools of today.

In the three centuries of American secondary education many significant changes have taken place. The early aristocratic policy of selecting students from among a favored few has been replaced by the modern democratic policy of opening the doors of educational opportunity to students from all levels of society. The fundamental philosphy has changed from one which demanded an institution whose principal function was preparation for a single profession to one which calls for an institution whose chief aim is twofold in nature, viz., the provision of terminal training that is functional for all individuals and the provision of propaedeutic training for those who can, and desire to, derive profit from further study in institutions of higher learning.

Mathematics and the Changing Educational Program. In the early, frontier days the need for mathematics and the motivation for its development were rather limited. The farmer and the ordinary worker needed little beyond the ability to add and subtract. Those boys who aspired to enter some form of trade experience needed to know something of sim-

3

ple computation, along with a slight knowledge of common measure, a few very simple fractions, and the use of English and other European moneys. The seafaring man needed to know the basic principles of navigation; the clergyman found astronomy necessary in fixing the dates of religious festivals; and the public official, when fixing territorial boundaries, found surest recourse in surveying. From this meager source flowed the shallow stream of mathematics in sixteenth-century America. Consequently, it is not surprising that mathematics received little attention in the early elementary schools. They were established for the primary purpose of teaching writing and reading, with an occasional reference to ciphering. In fact, one who could qualify as an "arithmeticker" was likely to be considered as especially endowed, although the sobriquet implied no more than that the individual was able to perform the simplest of computations.

It was not until the latter part of the nineteenth century that real progress began to take place in the development of mathematics in America. By that time there was a fair-sized group of native talent working in the field of mathematics, and there were major influences shaping up to promote significant development in mathematical research. As most important among these influences we might list the vision of the presidents of certain outstanding universities and their appreciation of the need for promotion of interest in mathematics in this country, the founding of the American Mathematical Society, and a closer contact with European scholars. Many of the young men of that era who were interested in mathematics pursued advanced study and sought advanced degrees in mathematics in European universities, in particular, those of Berlin, Göttingen, and Leipzig. Furthermore, many European mathematicians were imported to this country to teach in our universities, some temporarily and others on a permanent basis.

It was well that the leaders in the field of mathematics should have become so concerned with the promotion of mathematical research in this country. The research worker is the producer of mathematics. It is he who must stay out on the frontier in the expansion of the effectiveness, usefulness, and significance of the field of mathematics as an important aspect of our culture and social structure. The investments of effort and planning made by these early leaders have paid excellent dividends to the stockholders in American culture, for today the American corps of mathematicians occupies the vanguard of mathematical thought.

Thus we see that, during the course of approximately four centuries, vision and scholarly effort have produced a strong and impressive superstructure of enlightened research in the field of mathematics in our country. But what of the understructure of effective teaching and intelligent subject-matter planning at the elementary and secondary levels?

While the events of recent years have created an international feeling of awe and admiration in the contemplation of the marvelous accomplishments of mathematical research, there have been many pointed expressions of concern over faulty teaching of and deficient curricula in mathematics at the elementary and secondary levels.

Early Arithmetic.   Arithmetic, the only mathematical study of importance in the secondary schools of the United States during the colonial period, made its entrance to the curriculum of the Latin grammar school through the early writing school.   Later, in the eighteenth century, we find a tendency toward more general recognition of the value of arithmetic as a school subject.   This was due partially to the rise of commercial interests and also to the tendency of the people to be more hospitable toward a subject not supported by tradition.[1]   The subject matter of the course was logical in arrangement and consisted primarily of a series of rules to be memorized and dogmatically applied according to rather definite classifications.   No attempt was made to adapt the instruction to the pupil, and very little change was made in the nature or content of the subject matter.   Under such a system of instruction, the only arithmetic studied was ciphering, which consisted largely of the manipulation of integers.

Textbooks were not generally used until the latter part of the eighteenth century.   The master dictated the problems to be solved and stated the rule or rules to be used.   No special directions or explanations were given. The rules and problems were recorded in cipher books.   In describing two such books used in the study of arithmetic in the state of Illinois between 1804 and 1808, Breslich states that the subject taught was but little more than a mechanical manipulation of figures and a study of rules dogmatically applied.[2]

By the methods of colonial times each problem was solved as being one of a certain type or as belonging to a particular case, and few pupils were able to solve a problem unless they knew under which case it came.   This system and these methods of attack were applied to problems on a variety of subjects.   Such an instructional program placed the emphasis almost entirely on the rote memorization of rules and paid very little attention, if any, to basic understanding of concepts and techniques or to the significant characteristics of effective reasoning.

Mental Discipline.   The curriculum of the academy was much broader in its scope than was that of the Latin grammar school and, in general, was less dominated by college entrance requirements.   An examination

---

[1] Elmer E. Brown, "The Making of Our Middle Schools" (New York: Longmans, Green & Co., Inc., 1902), p. 134.

[2] E. R. Breslich, Arithmetic One Hundred Years Ago, *Elementary School Journal*, **25** (1924–1925) 664–674.

of the annual reports made to the Regents of the University of the State of New York reveals that many different subjects appeared in various academy curricula during the period from 1787 to 1870; among them were arithmetic, algebra, astronomy, bookkeeping, conic sections, civil engineering, plane geometry, analytic geometry, leveling, logarithms, mapping, mensuration, navigation, nautical astronomy, statistics, surveying, and trigonometry.[1] The particular attention which was given to mathematics during this period was due in part to the possibility of practical applications but principally to the idea of mental discipline, which occupied a very prominent place in educational thought during the early years of American education and exerted a profound influence upon curriculum making and methods of teaching. The attitude prevalent in the minds of textbook writers and teachers of this period was well stated by Joseph Ray:[2]

The object of the study of mathematics is twofold—the acquisition of useful knowledge and the cultivation and discipline of the mental powers. A parent often inquires "Why should my son study mathematics? I do not expect him to be a surveyor, an engineer, or an astronomer." Yet the parent is very desirous that his son should be able to reason correctly, and to exercise, in all his relations in life, the energies of a cultivated and disciplined mind. This is, indeed, of more value than the mere attainment of any branch of knowledge.

The more extreme views on mental discipline did not go unchallenged, especially in the Middle West. The pioneer life made it necessary for the individual to rely upon his ability to develop the natural resources of this new country, and this called for a type of education which placed more emphasis on the utilitarian values than on the disciplinary or the cultural values. Although the number of mathematical subjects in the curriculum remained fairly uniform throughout the life of the academy, the nature and purpose of instruction underwent considerable change.

Foreign Influences. The English influence predominated in the American schools from the time of the Revolution until 1820. Many of the instructors in the American colleges and academies had received their training in England, and the majority of the texts either were English editions or were copied rather closely from English authors. Hutton's "Mathematics," Bonnycastle's "Algebra," and Playfair's "Euclid" are three of the most frequently mentioned texts of this early period.[3]

[1] From Paul Monroe, "Principles of Secondary Education" (New York: The Macmillan Company, 1914), p. 54. By permission of The Macmillan Company, publishers.

[2] Joseph Ray, "New Elementary Algebra" (New York: American Book Company, 1848), p. iii.

[3] F. Cajori, "The Teaching and History of Mathematics in the United States" (Washington, D.C.: Government Printing Office, 1890), pp. 55–56.

The period of French influence may be dated from the appointment of Claude Crozet, who had been trained in the École Polytechnique of Paris, as professor of mathematics at the United States Military Academy in 1817. For a period of approximately fifty years from this date texts by French authors were the most popular for general use, although they never entirely displaced the older English texts.

Contemporaneous with the influx of French mathematics was the revival of interest in elementary education under the influence of the Pestalozzian school. The first incorporation of Pestalozzian ideas in the preparation of an arithmetic text was in Warren Colburn's "Intellectual Arithmetic upon the Inductive Method of Instruction," otherwise known as the "First Lessons."[1] This text, published first in 1821, marked the beginning of a new epoch in arithmetic and the teaching of arithmetic. The pupil was now supposed to replace the studying and memorizing of rules that he did not always fully understand with the setting up of his own rules as generalizations of his actual experiences. He was introduced to new topics by means of practical problems and questions, the order of presentation always being from the concrete to the abstract.[2] Colburn published a more advanced book in 1822 as a "sequel" to his "First Lessons." This text was designed as a practical arithmetic to be studied after the more elementary text. It consisted of topics usually found in the earlier advanced arithmetics except for certain omissions—in particular, the rule of three, rule of position, and powers and roots. The method of presentation was the same in the two texts.[3]

The period from 1821 to 1857 was one of rapid development for the study of arithmetic. One hundred and ninety-five texts on the subject were published during that time; of that number, forty-six were designed for use in colleges and academies and four were direct translations from the French.[4] During the period from 1860 to 1892 there was no essential change in aim or content and there were few modifications in the methods of teaching.[5] In contrast with the previous period, however, there was significant change in the organization and presentation of subject matter. The arithmetics of the latter period were combinations of the old, as found in colonial arithmetics, and the new, as found in the works of Colburn. The old arithmetics generally rejected reasoning; Colburn's arithmetics

[1] *Ibid.*, p. 106.

[2] Walter S. Monroe, "Development of Arithmetic as a School Subject" (U.S. Office of Education Bulletin 10, 1917), pp. 63–70, 80–88.

[3] Walter S. Monroe, Analysis of Colburn's Arithmetics, *Elementary School Teacher*, **13** (1912–1913), 239–246.

[4] J. M. Greenwood, "American Textbooks on Arithmetic," *Annual Report of the Commissioner of Education* (Washington, D.C.: Government Printing Office, 1897–1898), vol. I, pp. 796–868.

[5] Walter S. Monroe, "Development of Arithmetic as a School Subject," p. 90.

rejected rules and encouraged reasoning; the texts of the period 1860 to 1892 gave rules but at the same time gave demonstrations and encouraged pupils to think.

The Pestalozzian influence for reform in content selection and instructional technique was felt in algebra and geometry as well as in arithmetic. Colburn, who published his "Introduction to Algebra upon the Inductive Method of Instruction" in 1832, advanced new ideas on methods of instruction in algebra. His idea was to make the transition from arithmetic to algebra as gradual as possible. Because the learner was expected to derive most knowledge from solving the problems himself, the explanations were made as brief as was consistent with giving what was required. The problems were designed to exercise the learner in reasoning instead of making him a mere listener.[1] Geometry, before the nineteenth century, was taught dogmatically, and the students merely memorized and worked by rule. Although there still remain traces of the dogmatic method of instruction, during the first half of the twentieth century there was a definite increase in emphasis on original exercises with less rote memorization of theorems. In still more recent years this new trend toward greater geometric understanding has been augmented by a marked emphasis on more careful and specific attention to the postulational structure of geometry, more intelligent recognition of the relative educational values of both three-dimensional and two-dimensional geometry, and more thoughtful evaluation of the relative significance and effectiveness of the synthetic and analytic techniques of geometric proof.

The Public High School. By 1860 the educational philosophy which was to shape the program of the public high school had begun to predominate over that which had fostered both the Latin grammar school and the academy. There was now a strong tendency toward expansion in both number and content of courses offered, as well as an attempt to blend intellectual and practical training in the same school. Curricula were organized and expanded rapidly with no particular plan or definite educational objective in view. By 1890 this unrest had reached its highest point.[2] This awkward and unsystematic expansion of the curriculum offered sufficient reason for a demand for reform, and mathematics received its share of the attack. Dissatisfaction arose from several sources relative to the results achieved in the teaching of secondary mathematics. Complaints came from the teachers of mathematics themselves that the subject was not being grasped by the pupils. A study of a large number of represent-

[1] H. G. Meserve, Mathematics One Hundred Years Ago, *Mathematics Teacher*, **21** (1928), 339.

[2] I. L. Kandel, "History of Secondary Education" (Boston: Houghton Mifflin Company, 1930), p. 461.

ative high schools revealed that the largest percentages of failures were in Latin and mathematics.[1] College faculties were not hesitant in letting it be known that students entered their freshman classes with poor mathematical training. Businessmen were doubtful of the opportunity for the application of high school mathematics, as taught, to problems of everyday life.

The Committee of Ten. The Committee of Ten on Secondary School Subjects agreed that a radical change in the teaching of mathematics was necessary. The Subcommittee on Mathematics recommended that a course in concrete geometry, with numerous exercises, be introduced into the grammar school and that systematic algebra should be begun at the age of fourteen. The committee suggested that demonstrative geometry should follow the first year of algebra, that it should be taught along with algebra for the next two years, and that work in solid geometry might be incorporated. Formal algebra was to be studied for 5 hours a week during the first year and for $2\frac{1}{2}$ hours a week for the two following years, during which time it was to parallel work in geometry. Special emphasis was to be placed on literal as well as numerical coefficients. The committee also suggested that those who did not expect to go to college might, after the first year of algebra, turn to bookkeeping and the technical parts of arithmetic, while boys planning to attend scientific schools might profitably spend a year on trigonometry and some more advanced topics of algebra. A hope was expressed by the committee that a place might be found in the high school or college course for at least the essentials of modern synthetic or projective geometry.[2]

The Committee on College Entrance Requirements. In order to bring about a better articulation between the secondary schools and colleges, the Committee on College Entrance Requirements in 1899 recommended the following course:

Seventh Grade: Concrete Geometry and Introduction to Algebra; Eighth Grade: Introduction to Demonstrative Geometry and Algebra; Ninth and Tenth Grades: Algebra and Plane Geometry; Eleventh Grade: Solid Geometry and Plane Trigonometry; Twelfth Grade: Advanced Algebra and Mathematics reviewed.

Algebra for the seventh and eighth grades was to begin with literal arithmetic, which was to be followed by simple polynomials and fractional expressions, equations of the first degree with numerical coefficients in one

---

[1] F. P. O'Brien, "The High School Failures," *Contributions to Education* 102 (New York: Bureau of Publications, Teachers College, Columbia University, 1919), p. 21.

[2] "Report of the Committee of Ten on Secondary School Subjects" (New York: American Book Company, 1894), pp. 105–116.

and two unknowns, the four fundamental operations for rational algebraic expressions, and simple factoring. One-half of the time of the seventh grade was to be devoted to concrete geometry, while in the eighth grade one-half of the time was to be spent on demonstrative geometry. The important objective of such work was to awaken an interest in demonstrative geometry. The committee recommended that an equal amount of time be devoted to algebra and geometry in the ninth and tenth grades.[1]

The International Commission. Another influence for change in the curriculum of secondary mathematics was that due to the reports of the International Commission on the Teaching of Mathematics, which were published by the United States Bureau of Education between the years 1911 and 1918. Committee III of the commission, in its study of "Mathematics in the Public General Secondary Schools of the United States," found that every high school offered algebra and geometry for at least one year each. One-half of the schools gave algebra for an extra half year and less than twenty per cent gave algebra for the full two years. There were very few schools that offered algebra for two and one-half years, and only the larger high schools had courses in solid geometry, plane trigonometry, and advanced algebra.[2]

The sequence in practically all the textbooks in geometry was that of Legendre. Geometrical constructions by the Euclidean method[3] were usually given a logical place among other propositions. The original exercises, which ranged from 600 in one text to 1,200 in another, were rigidly confined to the subject matter of the text.

[1] A. F. Nightingale, "Report of the Committee on College Entrance Requirements," *Proceedings and Addresses of National Education Association*, 38th Annual Meeting, 1899, pp. 648–651.

[2] Report of Committees III and IV of the International Commission, "Mathematics in the Public and Private Secondary Schools of the United States" (U.S. Office of Education, Bulletin 16, 1911), pp. 17–22.

[3] The first three postulates stated by Euclid in his famous "Elements" are: "Let it be granted,

"*a.* That a straight line may be drawn from any one point to any other point:

"*b.* That a terminated straight line may be produced to any length in a straight line:

"*c.* And that a circle may be described from any centre, at any distance from that centre."

The first two of these postulates enable us to draw a straight line, but not lines of a prescribed length except insofar as a line might be drawn to connect two given points. In other words, these two postulates permit all operations possible with an unmarked straightedge. The third postulate allows the use of the compasses for the drawing of a circle with a given center and passing through a given point, i.e., with a fixed radius.

Thus "geometrical constructions by the Euclidean method" are those constructions which can be performed by using only the unmarked straightedge and compasses.

For further discussion see Hilda P. Hudson, "Ruler and Compasses" (New York: Longmans, Green & Co., Inc., 1916).

In addition to subjects usually recognized as secondary school subjects, several high schools offered a course in commercial arithmetic similar to the course frequently given in the elementary school except that the problems were somewhat more difficult and more closely related to commercial life.[1]

In their analysis of the report of Committees III and IV, the American Commissioners of the International Commission found[2] the following very marked tendencies for change in curriculum and method:

1. To omit geometric proofs that are either obvious or too difficult
2. To transfer the more difficult portions of the algebraic matter hitherto given in the first year of the high school to a later year
3. To avoid algebraic manipulations of greater complexity than is requisite to prepare pupils thoroughly for the work that lies beyond
4. To give more prominence to the equation
5. To introduce more problems from physics and other sciences and from practical life
6. To modify the conception of the aim of the teaching to conform to what is understood to be the outcome of recent psychologic research concerning the value of "formal discipline"
7. To attach greater importance to the utilitarian possibilities of mathematics

After their general survey of the field of secondary mathematics, the commission felt[3] that there were two main needs which were dominant, namely,

The need for the better preparation of teachers and the need to reduce, if not eliminate, the waste of effort involved in independent and often inadequate treatment of fundamental and broad questions by separate schools, colleges, or local systems.

In their study of elementary mathematics in the college the commission found that calculus had become primarily a sophomore study and that it was serving somewhat as "a boundary line between two styles of teaching," the recitation method and the lecture or lecture-quiz method. This difference in the educational problem before and after calculus was further emphasized by the proposal, on the part of some, to relegate the first two years of college work to the high school and, on the part of others, to take care of this work in "a junior college leading to an appropriate degree." The organization of subject matter was still largely compartmentalized, but there was developing a tendency toward fusion with more emphasis

---

[1] Report of Committees III and IV of the International Commission, *op. cit.*, p. 22.

[2] "Report of the American Commissioners of the International Commission on the Teaching of Mathematics" (U.S. Office of Education Bulletin 14, 1912), pp. 29–31.

[3] *Ibid.*, pp. 39–40.

on practical applications. The general outline of material was algebra, trigonometry, analytic geometry, and calculus, with a prerequisite of elementary algebra through quadratics, plane geometry, and sometimes solid geometry. The changing complexion of the school population was recognized as a cause for readjustment of content and instructional technique in the freshman year.[1]

The National Committee of Fifteen on Geometry Syllabus. In 1908 the Mathematics Round Table of the Secondary Department of the National Education Association unanimously called for a committee to study and report upon the problem of a syllabus for geometry. During the same year the American Federation of Teachers of the Mathematical and Natural Sciences authorized the appointment of such a committee, and in 1909 the Secondary Department of the National Education Association authorized the committee to proceed as a joint committee of the association and federation.

In its report[2] the committee recommended that reasonable attention be given to concrete exercises but with no diminishing attention to the logical structure of geometry. It suggested that there be "a quickening of the logical sense" through a distribution of emphasis designed to economize on the time and energy spent in the mastery of theorems and to provide more time and opportunity for the study of geometry in its more concrete relations. It pointed out that there are some terms in geometry which it is best to accept as undefined and recommended that definitions be introduced when needed rather than massed at one place in the text or course of study. The desirability of the use of certain informal proofs was mentioned, as well as the advisability of excluding limits and incommensurables from the requirements for entrance to college. It was recommended that between one and one and one-half years be given to plane geometry and that it be taught simultaneously with algebra or preceded by at least one year of algebra.

In the treatment of exercises the committee recommended that careful thought be given to their distribution and gradation; it seemed to feel that the tendency had been to overemphasize difficult abstract applications of various theorems in the exercises. It, therefore, suggested concrete exercises along with "a judicious selection of a reasonable number of abstract originals." Material for exercises was to be found in other subject fields such as architecture, natural design, indirect measurement, and any other

[1] *Ibid.*, pp. 41–47.

Report of Committee XII of the International Commission, "Graduate Work in Mathematics in Universities and in Other Institutions of Like Grade in the United States" (U.S. Office of Education Bulletin 6, 1911), pp. 45–47.

[2] Committee of Fifteen, "Provisional Report on Geometry Syllabus," *School Science and Mathematics*, **11** (1911), 330.

source available to the individual teacher.   A great deal of emphasis was given to the nature and importance of the concept of locus.[1]

The National Committee on Mathematical Requirements.   In 1916 the National Committee on Mathematical Requirements was organized under the auspices of the Mathematical Association of America, Inc., "for the purpose of giving national expression to the movement for reform in the teaching of mathematics, which had gained considerable headway in various parts of the country, but which lacked the power that coordination and united effort alone could give."[2]

The committee was instructed to concern itself with making a comprehensive study of the whole problem of mathematical education on the secondary and collegiate levels.   One of the major problems was thus to make proper provision for the comparatively new, yet fairly well-established, junior and senior high school program of instruction.   In its final report the committee formulated the aims of mathematical instruction into three general classes: practical, disciplinary, and cultural.[3]   Instead of a detailed syllabus for the junior high school the committee proposed only a general outline by topics and stated that further experimentation was necessary before determining a standardized syllabus.   Although the committee refused to commit itself on the arrangement of topics, it did suggest five plans for distribution of this material, hoping that they might prove helpful in the organization of mathematics curricula for the junior high school.   It further recommended that the mathematics proposed for the grades of the junior high school be required of all pupils.[4]

The committee recommended that provision be made for the specific aims of the mathematics of the senior high school through a body of elective material which should be open to all pupils who had satisfactorily completed the required work of the junior high school.   Fully realizing that the method of organization of this material could be more elastic in nature than that for grades 7 to 9, and also being thoroughly cognizant of the fact that no one best plan had been determined, the committee suggested four different plans, any one of which might be used for the purpose of more efficiently organizing the instructional content of the mathematics of grades 10 to 12.

Additional electives such as elementary statistics, mathematics of investment, shop mathematics, surveying and navigation, and descriptive or projective geometry were suggested for schools where there was a need

[1] *Ibid.*, pp. 434–460, 509–531.

[2] The National Committee on Mathematical Requirements, "The Reorganization of Mathematics in Secondary Education" (Boston: Houghton Mifflin Company, 1923), p. vii.

[3] *Ibid.*, pp. 6–13.

[4] *Ibid.*, pp. 29–42.

for such work and where the conditions warranted their inclusion in the curriculum.   It was also recommended that extensive use be made of historical and biographical material in the entire teaching program to lend interest and significance to the subject matter studied.[1]

General Mathematics.   The arrangement of subject matter has always been a problem at least as difficult as the selection of subject matter.   The early tendency was simply to follow the compartment system of organization, and that has continued to be the familiar pattern of the traditional high school course.   The scheme has given way in part, however, to a plan that has gained considerable favor, particularly at the level of the junior high school.   The new plan for arrangement of material calls for a closer correlation of related subject matter and reduction of emphasis on formalism; the course so planned has become known as "general mathematics."   The philosophy of instruction underlying the new plan can be traced largely to the efforts of the Committee of Ten and the Committee on College Entrance Requirements during the latter part of the nineteenth century.   Although there had been a few scattered instances of such treatment of mathematical subject matter prior to that time, the reports of the two committees seem to carry the first evidence of any concentrated thought devoted to its consideration.   In an address before the National Education Association (1902), Newhall expressed the hope that a time would come when the secondary school course would comprise six years and mathematics would not be limited by artificial boundaries as was the case in the study of algebra, geometry, and trigonometry.[2]   Contemporaneous with this address, the influence of Klein in Germany, Tannery and Borel in France, Perry and Nunn in England, and Moore in America made the conditions more favorable for a fairly rapid growth of general mathematics.

However, the effort to present the mathematics of even the junior high school in a fused course has not been without its rather severe critics. There are those who feel that it is too much of a hodgepodge of superficialities that tends to general weakening of the subject content.   Some critics have felt that too much emphasis is given to fusion of subject matter and not enough attention is paid to the significance of the individuality of different topics.   Nevertheless, the fact that two of the fundamental services of the junior high school have been to provide for exploration and for contact with minimum essentials has helped to concentrate interest in general mathematics as an instructional unit in its curriculum.

The effort to evolve a functional mathematical program well adapted to the education of the masses has also brought about significant changes

[1] *Ibid.*, pp. 48–57.
[2] Charles W. Newhall, Correlation of Mathematical Studies in Secondary Schools, *Proceedings of the National Education Association* (1902), pp. 488–492.

in the content and instructional techniques of senior high school mathematics. The mathematical content for the later years of secondary instruction is more specialized in nature than that of the three previous years and, as a consequence, has not been so readily adapted to a fused method of organization.   One of the most difficult of the problems which confront the teachers of senior high school mathematics is that of so organizing and presenting subject content as to preserve its intrinsic characteristics and yet to introduce the desired continuity.

In the development of the mathematics curriculum of the junior college there are definite indications of a trend toward a more integrated pattern of content organization in these first two years of the college program. The best evidence of the truth of this statement is to be found in the many different types of integrated texts now in use and also in the recommendations from the Committee on the Undergraduate Mathematical Program (CUP) of the Mathematical Association of America.[1] Many teachers feel that students taking such a course get a deeper appreciation of the fundamental interrelations of mathematical material and consequently have a better idea of the real meaning of mathematics than do those who take the traditional compartmentalized type of course.   They also claim that such a student will attain just as satisfactory a degree of mastery of the fundamentals.

College Entrance Examination Board.   The problem of the curriculum of secondary mathematics has always been closely related to the question of college entrance requirements.   The entire program of the Latin grammar school was defined in terms of preparation for college.   The academy, however, early expanded its program to include not only preparation for college but also a terminal type of program for the non-college-bound pupil.   In meeting the demands of this new function of secondary education, the academy gradually encroached upon the educational program of the colleges.   The natural consequence of this was a material increase in college entrance requirements.

At the close of the eighteenth century the only mathematics required for admission to college was "a knowledge of the rules and processes of vulgar arithmetic."   The statutes of 1807 prescribed that the requirements for admission to Harvard should include the rules of arithmetic dealing with simple and compound notation, addition, subtraction, multiplication, division, reduction, and the single rule of three.   In 1820 these requirements were extended to include the algebra of simple equations, roots and powers, and arithmetical and geometrical progressions.   Columbia added algebra to her entrance requirements in 1821; Yale, in 1847; and Princeton, in 1848.   In 1844, candidates for admission to Harvard Col-

---

[1] Report of the Committee on the Undergraduate Mathematical Program, *American Mathematical Monthly*, **63** (1955), 511–520.

lege were examined in arithmetic, algebra, and geometry (up to the book on proportion). Geometry was made an entrance requirement at Yale in 1865; at Princeton, Michigan, and Cornell in 1868; and at Columbia in 1870. By 1870 the admission requirements at Harvard had been extended to include higher arithmetic, algebra through quadratic equations, logarithms, and the elements of plane geometry. Yale and Princeton specified only to quadratic equations in algebra. While Yale specified the first two books of Playfair's "Euclid" (or an acceptable equivalent), Princeton specified only the first book. Similar requirements existed at the other leading universities of that period.[1]

The National Committee on Mathematical Requirements in its 1923 report recognized the far-reaching influence of college entrance requirements upon the teaching of secondary mathematics. It criticized the prevailing type of examination as overemphasizing "the candidate's skill in formal manipulation." In an effort to make desirable modifications in the prevailing type of college entrance examination, members of the national committee met with members of a committee from the College Entrance Examination Board and drew up a list of recommendations which were incorporated in the 1923 report. While attention was paid to the problem of reducing the excessive "difficulty and complexity of the formal manipulative questions," two of the most significant recommendations were as follows:[2]

1. An effort should be made to devise [algebraic] questions which will fairly test the candidate's understanding of principles and his ability to apply them, while involving a minimum of manipulative complexity.

2. The examinations in geometry should be definitely constructed to test the candidate's ability to draw valid conclusions rather than his ability to memorize an argument.

Early in 1921 the College Entrance Examination Board appointed a commission to study the problem of college entrance requirements and make recommendations for desirable revisions in the definitions of requirements in elementary mathematics. In their reports[3] published in 1923 the commission eliminated from the list of requirements in algebra the extended and useless manipulation of polynomials, reduced factoring to three types, and simplified the requirements in fractions. Increased recognition was given to the formula and the graph, and two notable changes were made in the simplification of the material dealing with surds and in

---

[1] E. C. Broome, "A Historical and Critical Discussion of College Admission Requirements" (New York: The Macmillan Company, 1903), pp. 41–53.

[2] The National Committee on Mathematical Requirements, *op. cit.*, pp. 76–77.

[3] College Entrance Examination Board, *Documents* 107 and 108 (New York: College Entrance Examination Board, 1923).

the introduction of numerical trigonometry. For plane geometry only 89 theorems were included in the syllabus, and of these only 31 were starred to be used for purposes of proofs. In the case of the unstarred propositions the candidate was expected to be familiar with content so that he might answer questions related to substance or use the propositions in solving originals. Similar provisions were made for solid geometry. A new type of examination was one designed to take care of a one-year course in plane and solid geometry. The committee made the effort to reorganize the examination material in such a way that the demands on the candidate's memory would be lightened and increased opportunity for the development of geometrical understanding would be given. These examinations have functioned to set up more definite goals of instruction as well as provide a principal pattern of textbook construction. There are those who feel that the influences have been more detrimental than helpful because of the enforced curriculum, the restricted selection of materials and content, and the curbing of creative work on the part of teachers.[1] It is true, however, that the work of the board has helped to clarify the problem of entrance requirements and provide for better articulation between the work of the senior high school and that of the freshman year of college.

In 1935 the Commission on Examinations in Mathematics, a commission of the College Entrance Examination Board, completely revised the examinations in mathematics. In the new ones, known as alpha, beta, and gamma, the effort was made "to combine the advantages of the longer essay-type, multiple-step question with those of the single-step question."[2] Two of the significant differences between the new and the old form of entrance examinations were the increased objectivity in scoring and the reduced emphasis upon the traditional compartmentalized treatment of subject matter.

The commission postulated that "the examinations should be such as to determine: (a) the candidate's understanding and appreciation of the fundamental principles and characteristic modes of approach of mathematics; (b) his technical equipment and his knowledge of mathematical facts."[3] Furthermore, in recognition of the different interpretations of the meaning of "fitness for college," the commission attempted to provide examinations for the three following groups:[3]

---

[1] L. H. Whitcraft, "Mathematics and the College Entrance Examination Board," *Contributions to Education* 557 (New York: Bureau of Publications, Teachers College, Columbia University, 1933), pp. 104–106.

[2] College Entrance Examination Board, "Description of Examination Subjects" (New York: College Entrance Examination Board, 1940), pp. 34–37. An earlier draft of this document, later edited, was published in *Mathematics Teacher*, **28** (1935), 154–166.

[3] *Ibid.*

(α) Those who are not ready to carry on in college the study of mathematics or natural science, but who base their claim to be admitted to college in part upon the study of mathematics in the secondary schools

(β) Those who intend to fulfill at least the minimum college requirement in mathematics or natural science

(γ) Those who look forward to more advanced undergraduate work in mathematics and science

In presenting these new examinations the commission stated that while, in specifying the scope of the examinations, it desired to exercise sufficient definiteness to avoid uncertainty on the part of the teacher, it was "strongly influenced by the wish to leave teachers of mathematics in secondary schools free to guide the development of their pupils in such ways as seem to them most desirable."[1]

Soon after the introduction of these examinations there began to develop a rather general demand from schools that there be provided an examination suitable for candidates whose first two years had been devoted primarily to the study of algebra. In response to this demand the Committee of Examiners in Mathematics of the College Entrance Examination Board introduced in June, 1942, Mathematics 2A (Alternative Alpha).

After the discontinuance in 1943 of the alpha, beta, and gamma tests, the board went through five distinct but unsatisfactory phases of testing. Each phase represented a definite effort to work out a satisfactory combined use of the Scholastic Aptitude Test and various types of achievement tests in mathematics. The final plan, which was put into use in 1950, called for two distinct phases: (1) the Scholastic Aptitude Test, taken by mathematics candidates along with all candidates during the morning session, and (2) two 1-hour achievement tests in mathematics (Intermediate Mathematics and Advanced Mathematics) in the afternoon.

In 1955 the board assumed the responsibility for continuing the work on the advanced placement program, which originated in 1952 in the School and College Study of Admission with Advanced Standing, a project sponsored by the Fund for the Advancement of Education. The first administration of the program was held in May, 1956, and the program has since continued to be administered yearly by the Educational Testing Service. Advanced placement is defined[2] by the board to mean:

---

[1] *Ibid.*

[2] College Entrance Examination Board, "Fifty-third Annual Report of the Director" (New York: College Entrance Examination Board, 1955), p. 20.

(1) Exemption from prescribed courses and placement in an advanced college course instead of in an elementary course which would otherwise have been required, or

(2) the award of college credit in recognition of achievement in covering the work ordinarily required in a course of college level, or

(3) both advanced placement and college credit.

In 1955 another important action was taken by the board in the interest of improved instruction in mathematics. The Commission on Mathematics[1] was appointed

. . . (1) to study the present secondary school mathematics curriculum with a view toward the recommendation of a realignment of the entire secondary mathematics program to provide adequate preparation for the study of present-day college and advanced mathematics; and (2) . . . to investigate the Board's activities in the testing of mathematics and to recommend any possible improvement therein.

Believing that "the improvement of secondary school mathematics instruction . . . would be greatly facilitated and the colleges in nowise handicapped," the commission strongly recommended that the traditional requirements in elementary algebra, intermediate algebra, advanced algebra, plane and solid geometry, and trigonometry be replaced by a new formulation of entrance requirements in mathematics. The new program would designate the new requirements in terms of length of time spent in study. The titles suggested for courses to be given in four successive high school years were Elementary Mathematics I, Elementary Mathematics II, Intermediate Mathematics, and Advanced Mathematics. The commission then proceeded to define in rather specific detail the subject-matter content of each year's program.[2] In order to help implement its recommendations for revised and renewed emphases in the content of instruction, the commission published a separate volume of appendixes concurrent with its report.

The commission, recognizing the need for a "context of reference" for the proper interpretation of its recommendations, closed its report with the following brief summary[3] of all the commission's recommendations:

College preparatory mathematics should include topics selected from algebra, geometry (demonstrative and coordinate), and trigonometry—all broadly interpreted. The point of view should be in harmony with contemporary mathe-

[1] College Entrance Examination Board, "Fifty-fifth Annual Report of the Director" (New York: College Entrance Examination Board, 1957), p. 10. The report of the commission was published in April, 1959.

[2] "Report of Commission on Mathematics" (New York: College Entrance Examination Board, 1959), pp. 20–47.

[3] Ibid., pp. 60–61.

matical thought; emphasis should be placed upon basic concepts and skills and upon the principles of deductive reasoning regardless of the branch of mathematics from which the topic is chosen. In every case, the standard of substance and content should be commensurate with that of the courses outlined in Chapter 4 [on pages 20–47]. Courses designed for other purposes (e.g., consumer mathematics, business mathematics, shop mathematics) are not acceptable.

The commission did not overlook the importance of the well-prepared teacher; a considerable portion of the report is devoted to the discussion of both preservice and in-service training of both elementary school and secondary school teachers of mathematics.[1]

National Organizations. No discussion of the forces that have had significant influence in the evolution of the program in secondary mathematics would be complete without mention of the Mathematical Association of America, the National Council of Teachers of Mathematics, and the Central Association of Science and Mathematics Teachers.

The Mathematical Association of America. This group was organized at Columbus, Ohio, in December, 1915, and incorporated under the laws of the state of Illinois on September 8, 1920. In the interest of improved instruction in collegiate mathematics the association has sponsored the following:

1. The publication of the *American Mathematical Monthly,* a high-grade mathematical magazine devoted to the interests of collegiate mathematics.

2. The organization of a large number of sections in which papers in mathematical research are presented and instructional problems in collegiate mathematics are discussed.

3. The organization of many undergraduate clubs in colleges and universities. These clubs have been very effective in motivating interest in mathematics.

4. The appointment of many committees for the study of problems related to the content and methods of mathematical instruction and the better training of teachers of mathematics. Some of the committees have been independent committees of the association; others have been joint committees with representation from other interested groups.

Each year, in addition to the sectional meetings, the association holds two regular national meetings at which papers are read and instructional problems are discussed. Further evidences of the interest of the association in the promotion of mathematics are (1) annual subsidies paid to journals that are interested in the publication of mathematical research, (2) the publication in December, 1929, of the Rhind Mathematical Papyrus, (3) the publication of the *Carus Monograph Series,* (4) the awarding of the $100 Chauvenet Prize, the purpose of which is to stimu-

[1] *Ibid.,* pp. 48–58.

late expository contributions in mathematical journals, (5) the sponsoring of various committee studies of secondary school and college mathematics programs, (6) the sponsoring of competitive tests at the college and high school levels, and (7) the promotion, under grants from the National Science Foundation, of two programs of visiting lectures, one at the college level and one at the high school level.

The National Council of Teachers of Mathematics. This group was organized at Cleveland, Ohio, on February 24, 1920, and incorporated under the Illinois laws on April 28, 1928. The purpose of the council is to promote interest in mathematics, especially in the elementary and secondary fields, by the following means:

1. The holding of meetings for the presentation and discussion of papers. At present four such meetings are held each year, one in winter, one in spring, and two in summer. One of the summer meetings is held in conjunction with the summer meeting of the National Education Association, of which the council, while retaining its identity and independent status, became a department on July 8, 1950.

2. The publication of three journals and of books, papers, and reports for the purpose of vitalizing and coordinating the work of local organizations of teachers of mathematics and of bringing the interests of mathematics to the attention and consideration of the educational world. The official journal of the Council is the *Mathematics Teacher*, the only magazine in the United States whose interests are devoted entirely to the improvement of instruction in mathematics at the secondary level. In 1954 the council established the *Arithmetic Teacher*, the only magazine in the United States whose interests are devoted entirely to the improvement of instruction in arithmetic. The council also publishes the *Mathematics Student Journal*, which provides enrichment and recreational material for pupils in grades 7 to 12. A further significant contribution to the literature of better instruction in mathematics is the *Yearbook*, published at intervals since 1926 by the council, which is devoted to the discussion of important aspects of the teaching of elementary and secondary mathematics. There is a continuing Yearbook Planning Committee which gives a great deal of thought to the planning of the yearbook program.

A new venture in the interest of mathematics and its place in the modern educational program is the series of supplementary publications. The purpose of this series of publications is to enrich the instructional background of the teacher of elementary and secondary mathematics and to provide supplementary instructional aids and enrichment materials for students.

3. The promotion of the affiliation of local organizations of teachers of mathematics with the council and of close cooperation with other profes-

sional organizations.   Recently the council has become somewhat international in nature through such affiliation with groups from certain provinces of Canada.

4. The promotion of investigations for the purpose of improving the teaching of elementary school and secondary school mathematics.   This work has been carried on largely through the sponsoring of committees such as the Committee on Individual Differences,[1] the Committees on Geometry,[2] the Committee on Arithmetic,[3] the Joint Commission to Study the Place of Mathematics in Secondary Education, the Commission on Post-War Plans, a permanent Research Committee, the Elementary School Curriculum Committee, and the Secondary School Curriculum Committee.

The Central Association of Science and Mathematics Teachers.   Although it is a sectional organization, this group has exerted a national influence over the teaching of secondary school mathematics.   The Central Association was organized in April, 1903, and incorporated in July, 1928.   Since its organization, it has sponsored a very active program in the interest of improved teaching of science and mathematics in the secondary schools of our nation.   Its program has been carried forward through annual meetings and the publication of *School Science and Mathematics,* "a journal for all science and mathematics teachers."   The annual meetings, held during the Thanksgiving holiday season, are characterized by programs which are inspirational and informative as well as pedagogical in nature.

In this connection there should be mentioned also the *Mathematics Magazine,* published in Los Angeles, California.   This magazine devotes a portion of each issue to The Teaching of Mathematics, a section in which are discussed teaching problems as they are primarily related to the junior college.

The Joint Commission to Study the Place of Mathematics in Secondary Education.   In the fall of 1933 a Commission to Study the Place of Mathematics in Secondary Education was appointed by the Mathematical Association of America; later this commission was incorporated into a Joint Commission of the Mathematical Association and the

---

[1] Report of Committee on Individual Differences, *Mathematics Teacher,* **25** (1932), 420–426; **26** (1933), 350–365.

[2] The reports of the different committees on geometry may be found in *Mathematics Teacher,* **24** (1931), 298–302, 370–394; **25** (1932), 427–428; **26** (1933), 366–371; **28** (1935), 329–379, 401–450.

[3] The reports of the different major committees on arithmetic may be found in three *Yearbooks* of the National Council: *Tenth* (1938); *Sixteenth* (1941); and *Twenty-fifth* (1960).

National Council of Teachers of Mathematics. In its final report[1] the commission undertook to define the place of mathematics in the modern educational program and then organize a mathematical curriculum for grades 7 to 14 (secondary education was defined to include the junior college) in terms of the major mathematical fields which would provide for continuity of development and flexibility of administration.[2]

It is the opinion of this Commission that the obvious difficulty of providing for both continuity and flexibility has been the great stumbling block in the development of a nation-wide mathematical program of instruction. Accordingly, in this Report is described a program for mathematics in grades 7 to 14 that definitely aims to provide for continuity of development, and that at the same time respects the reasonable demands for flexibility on the part of school administrators and teachers.

The proposed program was based upon an assumed "normal mathematical equipment of the American pupil who has satisfactorily completed the work of the sixth grade," which was defined[3] as follows:

1. A familiarity with the basic concepts, the processes, and the vocabulary of arithmetic

2. Understanding of the significance of the different positions that a given digit may occupy in a number, including the case of a decimal fraction

3. A mastery of the basic number combinations in addition, subtraction, multiplication, and division

4. Reasonable skill in computing with integers, common fractions, and decimal fractions

5. An acquaintance with the principal units of measurement, and their use in every day life situations

6. The ability to solve simple problems involving computation and units of measurement

7. The ability to recognize, to name, and to sketch such common geometric figures as the rectangle, the square, the circle, the triangle, the rectangular solid, the sphere, the cylinder, and the cube

8. The habit of estimating and checking results

In recognition of existing differences in educational philosophies and practices and in an effort to make "a definite step toward educational harmony," the commission set up a tentative list of guiding principles to be followed in organizing the mathematical program for grades 7 to 12.

[1] Joint Commission of the Mathematical Association of America, Inc., and the National Council of Teachers of Mathematics, "The Place of Mathematics in Secondary Education," *Fifteenth Yearbook* (Washington, D.C.: National Council of Teachers of Mathematics, 1940). (Hereafter referred to as the Joint Commission.)

[2] *Ibid.*, p. 53.

[3] *Ibid.*, p. 54.

In the light of these principles two classifications of the materials of mathematical instruction were made.[1]

1. *The subdivision according to major subject fields*
   I. The field of numbers and computation
   II. The field of geometric form and space perception
   III. The field of graphic representation
   IV. The field of elementary analysis
   V. The field of logical (or "straight") thinking
   VI. The field of relational thinking
   VII. The field of symbolic representation and thinking
2. *The subdivision according to certain broad categories enumerated as follows:*
   I. Basic concepts, principles, and terms
   II. Fundamental processes
   III. Fundamental relations
   IV. Skills and techniques
   V. Applications

In Chaps. V and VI of the report the commission proposes and discusses in considerable detail two alternative curriculum plans. The two differ somewhat in detail and emphasis, but both give recognition to the guiding principles enumerated and are consonant with the foregoing dual classification of subject matter. For one of these plans a grade placement chart displays a suggested allocation and organization of the subject matter in each year for grades 7 to 12.[2]

The report contains suggestions for modification of the program to give flexibility to the curriculum, and it also contains a discussion of the problems of both retardation and acceleration in their bearing upon the program of mathematical instruction. In this connection there is presented a second grade placement chart, which gives a proposed selection and grade allocation of subject matter for slow students in grades 7 to 9.[3]

In the discussion of the mathematics program for grades 13 and 14 (the junior college) the commission points out that the preparatory type of student is in the minority and that the mathematical needs of this type of student are adequately provided for in the traditional courses. Accordingly, the discussion deals mainly with the problem of providing for the terminal type of student. Two programs, somewhat different in nature, are proposed as possible terminal courses for students who do not plan to pursue the study of mathematics further. These courses are based on the commission's belief that the junior college curriculum should make provision for a mathematical course of at least one year in extent for all students.

[1] *Ibid.*, p. 61.
[2] *Ibid.*, pp. 72–119, 246–251.
[3] *Ibid.*, pp. 120–148, 252–253.

The commission emphasizes that in no sense is this recommended program of mathematical instruction to be regarded "as a final unchanging yardstick inhibiting personal initiative and further experimentation." The intention is, rather, that this might prove to be a step forward in securing "for mathematics the place in education it so richly deserves" and a safe standard for comparison in this era of curriculum experimentation and change.

The Progressive Education Association Committee on the Function of Mathematics in General Education.   In 1932 the Executive Board of the Progressive Education Association established the Commission on Secondary School Curriculum.   This commission subsequently established several committees to explore the respective contributions of various subject fields to general education at the secondary level; among them was the Committee on the Function of Mathematics in General Education. The complete report of this committee was issued in tentative (mimeographed) form in 1938 and published in final form in 1940.[1]

The report is in four parts.   The first of these presents the educational philosophy which guided the committee in the formulation of the report. Central in this philosophy is the premise that mathematics, in order to justify its place in the secondary school curriculum, must contribute to the satisfaction of the needs of the students.   These needs are enumerated in terms of the following four "basic aspects of living":[2]

1. Personal living
2. Immediate personal-social relationships
3. Social-civic relationships
4. Economic relationships

This part of the report closes with a discussion of the role of mathematics in satisfying the needs of people with respect to these four aspects of living.

Part II is the most extensive section of the report.   It consists of an elaborate discussion of certain broad concepts or understandings which find application in problem solving, whether this be in situations that are peculiarly mathematical or not.   In the discussion of these concepts an effort is made to show applications to situations encountered in ordinary living as well as to strictly mathematical situations.   In other words, much emphasis is placed upon the *generality* of the concepts and

---

[1] Maurice Hartung and others, Commission on Secondary School Curriculum of the Progressive Education Association, "Mathematics in General Education," *Report of the Committee on the Function of Mathematics in General Education* (New York: Appleton-Century-Crofts, Inc., 1940).

[2] *Ibid.*, p. 20

upon various broad aspects involved in their understanding. Separate chapters are devoted to the consideration of the following major concepts:

Formulation and solution   Operations
Data   Proof
Approximation   Symbolism
Function

Part III is concerned with an explanation of the nature and development of mathematics.

Part IV considers the problem of understanding the student and stresses the need for considering not only overt behavior but also the various influences which have operated to shape the student's personality. It contains a section on implications for teaching. The report closes with a chapter on the evaluation of student achievement. This chapter discusses the purposes of evaluation and contains some interesting suggestions of new and unique means and devices for organizing an evaluation program in terms of instructional objectives previously set up.

This report confines itself mainly to the discussion of a program of mathematical education in terms of broad outlines and general principles and does not attempt to set forth any detailed organization of subject matter. It recognizes frankly that the formulation of a series of courses based upon the report's proposals would require years of experimentation and that such experimentation would probably eventually modify some of the suggestions made. It looks to the future instead of trying to set up a practical program for the immediate present.[1]

It is with respect to this point that the task undertaken by this Committee differed from that of the Joint Commission of the Mathematical Association of America and the National Council of Teachers of Mathematics. In preparing its report of *The Place of Mathematics in Secondary Education*, the Joint Commission, after discussing the general aims of education, sought to outline a program of the sort being offered at the moment by some schools in advance of the great majority. Most of its suggestions have been tested to some extent in practice, and the Joint Commission took a practical rather than experimental point of view.

The AAAS Co-operative Committee on the Teaching of Science and Mathematics. Concomitant with the great increase in size in the program of secondary education in the United States during the last three centuries there has been a vast expansion of purpose. Modern educational problems are rooted in the context of mass education, which seems to nurture extensive, and at times seemingly excessive, curriculum design. These problems will always remain complex; there is no way to simplify them. The only hope for an intelligent approach to their solution is

[1] *Ibid.*, p. 14.

through the cooperative effort of duly organized groups who are interested in the formulation and promotion of that program in our schools which will be most significant when evaluated in terms of the educational needs of a school population that is highly heterogeneous as to abilities, aptitudes, and interests.

An important step in this direction was made in 1941 when the representatives of several scientific societies created the Co-operative Committee on Science Teaching "to work on educational problems the solution of which can be attained better by co-operative action than by any single scientific group working alone." The Mathematical Association of America was one of the societies represented on the original committee before its reorganization, in 1944, as a committee of the American Association for the Advancement of Science (AAAS). As presently constituted, the committee consists of representatives from fourteen national scientific societies, two of which are the Mathematical Association of America and the National Council of Teachers of Mathematics.

Since its organization, the committee has given attention to the problem of the preparation of teachers of science and mathematics. In 1946 it published its recommendations relative to this important problem in a report on The Preparation of High School Science and Mathematics Teachers, in which the following proposals were made:[1]

(1) A policy of certification in closely related subjects within the broad area of the sciences and mathematics should be established and put into practice.

(2) Approximately one-half of the prospective teacher's four-year college program should be devoted to courses in the sciences.

(3) Certificates to teach general science at the 7th-, 8th-, or 9th-grade level should be granted on the basis of not less than 42 semester hours of college courses in the subjects covered in general science.

(4) Colleges and certification authorities should work toward a five-year program for the preparation of high-school teachers.

(5) Curriculum improvements in the small high school should go hand in hand with improvement in teacher preparation.

The Committee not only has directed its attention to many other problems and projects but also has projected a rather active future program of study and service.[2] Among the most important projects undertaken was the study of the effectiveness of the teaching of science and mathematics at all levels, which served as the basis for a report incor-

[1] Report of the AAAS Co-operative Committee on the Teaching of Science and Mathematics, The Preparation of High School Science and Mathematics Teachers, *School Science and Mathematics*, **46** (1946), 107–118.

[2] The Co-operative Committee on the Teaching of Science and Mathematics: Its Organization and Program, *Science*, **106** (July 11, 1947), 28–30.

porated as Appendix II of Volume 4 of the report on *Science and Public Policy* made by the President's Scientific Research Board.[1] In this study appraisals of the science and mathematics programs from grades 1 to 12 were made. These served as the basis for certain recommendations for improvement, among which were the following which pertained to mathematics:[2]

(1) A complete appraisal should be made of science and mathematics teaching in secondary schools. This should include a survey of curriculum offerings, student enrollments, available laboratory and demonstration equipment, methods of instruction, the workweek of the teachers, and the total preparation of teachers for their responsibilities.

(2) The secondary-school mathematics curriculum should be studied to determine the effectiveness of present offerings with regard to the general education needs of all students and the special needs of students talented in science and mathematics. New courses in mathematics should be designed wherever indicated by this study.

(3) The secondary-school science curriculum should be reorganized so as to permit . . . at least 3 years of science for students with special talents in science and mathematics. . . .

(4) . . .

(5) Studies should be made concerning the place, value, and effective use of biographical and historical materials relating to science and mathematics.

(6) Studies should be made of the various curricular and administrative arrangements employed in small and large communities to meet the needs of talented youth. Reports should be prepared to make more teachers acquainted with best practices.

(7) Studies should be made of the guidance procedures used in secondary schools. . . . Bulletins revealing effective materials and practices concerning science and mathematics should be prepared for and studied by secondary-school teachers and counselors.

(8) Studies should be made to determine the most effective ways to use demonstration, laboratory, project, shop, and field experiences and such facilities as library materials, audio-visual aids, etc., in the teaching of science and mathematics.

(9) A study should be made of the administrative devices which will encourage greater use of community resources in the teaching of science and mathematics.

(10) The work of science and mathematics supervisors, special consultants, visiting teachers, and other special advisory personnel should be studied with a view to making more prevalent the practices and techniques most effective in developing sound programs involving science and mathematics for general education, and in providing optimum opportunities for the development of students with special talents.

[1] "Science and Public Policy" (Washington, D.C.: President's Scientific Research Board, 1947), **4**, 47–149.

[2] *Ibid.*, pp. 93–94.

The report also included many very pertinent recommendations for the recruitment and training of teachers of science and mathematics in the elementary and secondary schools.[1]

The Emergency of World War II.   During the past quarter of a century, there has been an increasing amount of evidence which points to the inadequacy of the mathematics program in our schools.   This inadequacy became very conspicuous in the light of the deficiencies in mathematics discovered among the inductees into the war-training program of World War II.   To meet the emergency of the situation, the U.S. Office of Education in cooperation with the National Council of Teachers of Mathematics appointed two committees to give the problem careful study.   The first committee worked in close cooperation with the Army, Navy, and Civil Aeronautics Administration.   Its report[2] was based on a detailed analysis of approximately 50 unit courses used in the Federal-state program of Vocational Training for War Production Workers, 20 Navy training manuals, and 50 Army instructional manuals.   The committee gave attention to the entire program of secondary mathematics and made specific recommendations for a Special One-year Course and a Special One-semester Course designed as an emergency refresher course for high school pupils near graduation or induction but not studying mathematics.

The report[3] of the second committee served as an extension of that of the first committee in that it was designed to supplement the earlier report "by amplifying the suggestions offered for the *lower* levels of mathematics as represented in the Special One-year Course."   The procedure used by this committee consisted of conferences "with Army officers directly in charge of training enlisted men" and observation of "the basic training process itself during the first thirteen weeks of the inductee's Army life."   A rather detailed outline of minimum essentials was given along with a presentation of "general suggestions with respect to instruction."   Although this report was directed entirely to the wartime emergency, its summary[4] of the "minimum essentials" has definite implications for civilian needs.

Young men about to enter the Army must be taught . . . the ability to meet quantitative problems effectively, confidently, and sensibly.   They must be able (*a*) to identify the quantitative aspects of the situations which confront them, (*b*) to deal with these situations by approximation and estimation when computa-

[1] *Ibid.*, pp. 107–109.

[2] National Council of Teachers of Mathematics, Report on Pre-induction Courses in Mathematics, *Mathematics Teacher*, **36** (1943), 114–124.

[3] National Council of Teachers of Mathematics, Report of the Committee on Essential Mathematics for Minimum Army Needs, *Mathematics Teacher*, **36** (1943), 243–282.

[4] *Ibid.*, p. 246.

tion is not required, (c) to recognize and use the simpler symbolisms of mathematics, (d) to tell when and how mathematical symbolism, concepts, and processes are to be employed, and (e) to compute accurately, quickly, and intelligently when computation is called for.

These two reports are given special prominence because of their specific and important implications concerning the teaching of mathematics in the elementary and secondary schools. The War Preparedness Committee (appointed in 1940) and the War Policy Committee (appointed in 1943) were joint committees of the American Mathematical Society and the Mathematical Association of America. Their interests were primarily in the organization and direction of manpower in mathematical research for most efficient and effective service to the war effort. A similar committee was the National Committee of Physicists and Mathematicians, appointed in 1943. Some of the reports of these committees had significant import for mathematics at the secondary level.[1]

The Commission on Post-War Plans. At its annual meeting in February, 1944, the Board of Directors of the National Council of Teachers of Mathematics created the Commission on Post-War Plans for the purpose of planning for effective programs in secondary mathematics in the postwar period. As originally constituted the commission consisted of five members. This number was expanded later to include thirteen members from eleven widely scattered states. The commission found significant background for its thinking and planning in the work of the first two of the above-mentioned committees of the war period.

In its first report[2] the commission announced its plan of organization and solicited help from the interested public in these words: "We are asking discerning school people and thoughtful laymen for good ideas and definite suggestions from which a sensible report may later stem that will provide adequate training in mathematics for *all* students in our schools —each according to his needs." With the hope of helping to crystallize thinking and "in order to promote discussion . . . in workshops and professional courses" the commission proposed, and discussed briefly, the following five recommendations which it felt "should be carefully considered by many persons in planning our work for the postwar years:"

[1] William L. Hart, On Education for Service, *American Mathematical Monthly*, **48** (1941), 353–362. Also published in *Mathematics Teacher*, **34** (1941), 297–304.

Marston Morse and William L. Hart, Mathematics in the Defense Program, *Mathematics Teacher*, **34** (1941), 195–202.

William L. Hart et al., Universal Military Training in Peace Time, *Mathematics Teacher*, **39** (1946), 17–23.

[2] Commission on Post-War Plans, First Report, *Mathematics Teacher*, **37** (1944), 226–232.

1. The school should insure mathematical literacy to all who can possibly achieve it.

2. We should differentiate on the basis of needs, without stigmatizing any group, and we should provide new and better courses for a high fraction of the schools' population whose mathematical needs are not well met in the traditional sequential courses.

3. We need a completely new approach to the problem of the so-called slow learning student.

4. The teaching of arithmetic can be and should be improved.

5. The sequential courses should be greatly improved.

The commission's second report[1] contained its recommendations for the improvement of mathematics in grades 1 to 14. These recommendations were presented in the form of 34 theses. The first thesis stated that: "The school should guarantee functional competence in mathematics to all who can possibly achieve it." Realizing the desirability of being explicit as to the implications of "functional competence in mathematics," the commission proceeded to delineate its essentials in the form of a check list consisting of 28 items. This list was later expanded in the "Guidance Pamphlet"[2] to include 29 items. While full significance of the check list can be had only by reference to the questions listed in it, some idea can be obtained from the following list[3] of key ideas or concepts of each of the 29 items:

1. Computation	16. Drawings
2. Per cents	17. Vectors
3. Ratio	18. Metric system
4. Estimating	19. Conversion
5. Rounding numbers	20. Algebraic symbolism
6. Tables	21. Formulas
7. Graphs	22. Signed numbers
8. Statistics	23. Using the axioms
9. The nature of a measurement	24. Practical formulas
10. Use of measuring devices	25. Similar triangles and proportion
11. Square root	26. Trigonometry
12. Angles	27. First steps in business arithmetic
13. Geometric concepts	28. Stretching the dollar
14. The 3-4-5 relationship	29. Proceeding from hypothesis to conclusion
15. Constructions	

The remaining theses of the second report were presented according to the following outline:

[1] Commission on Post-War Plans, Second Report, *Mathematics Teacher*, **38** (1945), 195–221.

[2] Commission on Post-War Plans, Guidance Report, *Mathematics Teacher*, **40** (1947), 315–339. Later published as the "Guidance Pamphlet in Mathematics."

[3] *Ibid.*, pp. 318–319.

1. *Mathematics in grades* 1 *to* 6. Theses 2 to 8 give emphasis to the consideration of arithmetic as a content subject as well as a tool subject and as having both mathematical and social aims, the need for more careful attention to meanings and wiser use of drill, the realization of the importance of readiness and the futility of incidental teaching, and the desirability of more careful evaluation of learning.

2. *The mathematics of grades* 7 *to* 8. Theses 9 to 11 point out the uniqueness of the demands of the unified program for all students for these two grades.

3. *Mathematics in grade* 9. Theses 12 and 13 emphasize the need for a double-track program in mathematics and also for a careful consideration of the content of the algebra program in the ninth grade.

4. *Mathematics in grades* 10 *to* 12. Theses 14 to 20 treat of the main objectives and essential characteristics of the sequential courses of these three years in the high school program.

5. *Mathematics in the junior college.* Theses 21 to 23 call attention to the different demands likely to be made on the mathematics program of the junior college by three different groups of students: those with cultural interests only, those with prevocational needs, and those who have major interests in mathematics.

6. *The education of teachers of mathematics.* Theses 24 to 32 discuss in fairly full detail some of the significant problems of teacher preparation at the various levels of instruction.

7. *Multisensory aids in mathematics.* The last two theses of the report briefly emphasize the significance of multisensory aids in effective instruction in mathematics at all levels.

In 1942 the Consumer Education Study was organized with two chief purposes in mind: (1) to investigate what should be taught and how it could best be organized and objectively presented and (2) to facilitate the work of the schools by providing instructional materials. It was recognized that mathematics has an important contribution to make to consumer education, both in the elementary school and in the secondary school. The Commission on Post-War Plans was invited to make recommendations on what this contribution might and should be. In 1945, in conjunction with the Consumer Education Study, the Commission published a pamphlet entitled "The Rôle of Mathematics in Consumer Education."[1] In this report the commission first analyzed the nature and purposes of consumer education in general. It then proceeded to point out the relation of elementary school and secondary school mathematics to this total program and also to suggest to administrators and

---

[1] Commission on Post-War Plans, *The Rôle of Mathematics in Consumer Education* (Washington, D.C.: The Consumer Education Study, National Association of Secondary School Principals, 1945).

teachers a form for organization of materials as well as methods of instruction.

One of the recognized major problems in modern secondary education is that of intelligent guidance of pupils as they plan their school programs in the context of the actualities of the present and the horizons of the future. It is a well-established fact that in no subject-matter area have high school students suffered more from erratic and unwise guidance than in the field of mathematics. The Commission on Post-War Plans made a significant attempt to correct this unfortunate situation in the publication of the previously mentioned "Guidance Pamphlet," in the preparation of which they were aided materially by the counsel of representatives from the U.S. Office of Education, who were men of wide experience in the problems and techniques of educational guidance. The pamphlet was addressed to the high school student in the spirit suggested by this opening paragraph:

Why should I study mathematics? What good will mathematics be to me? Perhaps you have asked yourself these two questions. If so, you have a right to good answers, and you will find them in the following pages.

The commission then proceeded in simple style to present to the high school student significant information within the framework of the following carefully determined outline, from which it suggested that the reader should select only those areas in which he is interested:

    I. Mathematics for Personal Use
    II. Mathematics Used by Trained Workers
   III. Mathematics for College Preparation
   IV. Mathematics for Professional Workers
    V. Women in Mathematics
   VI. Mathematics Used by Civil Service Workers
  VII. Mathematical Organizations
 VIII. Graduate Schools Offering the Doctorate in Mathematics
   IX. Selected References on Mathematical Careers

This pamphlet, through subsequent revisions, has continued to render service in the guidance of young people as they seek to chart their educational course through the secondary school and college.

Mathematics in General Education. During the early 1950s, the demands of a program of "general education" began to make their imprint upon the curriculum from the elementary school through the junior college. This new emphasis in educational philosophy was in essence a reaction against the emphases of an age of specialism. The claim was made that the college graduate was educated in the sense that he had acquired competencies in some particular occupation, yet fell short of the demands of active citizenship in his community.[1] There were many who felt that the graduate of the secondary school could be characterized similarly. The trend toward specialization had led to the introduction of many courses and varied curricula in both the secondary school and the college. The net result of such emphases had been a decreasing opportunity on the part of the student to participate in a program from which he might derive an "integrated view of human experience." As an antidote to the trend toward specialization there evolved a plan of general education which emphasizes a program designed to develop the abilities, attitudes, understandings, and behavior patterns which should be the common experience of all educable men and women.

What contribution can mathematics make to such a program? There is a body of mathematical content that is of significance to every individual capable of intelligent participation in the educational program, whether it be at the level of the elementary school, secondary school, or college. It is the professional obligation of informed groups to determine what this content is, how it should be organized and presented, and what basic training is essential to prepare teachers to meet the challenge and responsibility of the program. This continues to constitute a major problem in mathematics instruction, the significance of which is discussed in the next chapter.

Other Activities. At its meeting in December, 1956, the Board of Directors of the National Council of Teachers of Mathematics appointed the Secondary School Curriculum Committee (SSCC) with the commission "to make a comprehensive and critical study of the curriculum and instruction in mathematics in secondary schools with relation to the needs of contemporary society." The membership of the committee was selected from secondary school and college teachers of mathematics, research workers in pure and applied mathematics, and personnel from business and industry. The committee work was carried out through the use of subcommittees appointed to make intensive studies in each of the following areas:[2]

1. The place of mathematics in a changing society and the implications of contemporary mathematics
2. The aims of mathematics education and the pedagogy of mathematics
3. The nature of mathematical thought in grades 7–12
4. How geometry should be introduced and developed
5. Content and organization of junior-high-school mathematics
6. Foreign mathematics programs

[1] "Higher Education for American Democracy," vol. I, "Establishing Goals" (Washington, D.C.: President's Commission on Higher Education, 1947), p. 48.

[2] The report of the Secondary School Curriculum Committee was published in the May, 1959, issue of *Mathematics Teacher*, pp. 389–417.

7. Adjustment of the mathematics program to pupils of average and below-average ability
8. Aids to teaching
9. The organization of the mathematics program
10. The administration of the mathematics program
11. Programs of instruction for the mathematically gifted pupil

The Committee on the Undergraduate Mathematical Program (CUP) of the Mathematical Association of America was appointed in January, 1953. This committee was directed "to consider the problems of making available in our society the values of modern mathematics" and "to attack the problem with broader scientific and cultural objectives than could be expressed through another mere study of curriculum revision." The committee proposed to write completely new materials for experimental tryouts with the hope that ultimately from these would evolve an undergraduate college program in mathematics which would retain from the traditional and introduce from the new that mathematical content of established significance. This significance was to be evaluated in the context of the extended mathematical needs of engineering, physical science, biological science, social science, and high-speed digital automata. Outlines have been published and some actual writing of materials has been accomplished for the first two years; the outlines for the third and fourth years are still in a somewhat nebulous stage.[1]

The American Association for the Advancement of Science, in 1955, inaugurated its Science Teaching Improvement Program (STIP). This was to be "an action program to increase the number of well-qualified science and mathematics teachers at the secondary-school level." In January, 1957, a plan for regional consultants in science and mathematics was inaugurated. The purpose of this plan was to stimulate regional efforts to recognize problems related to improved instruction and to initiate plans and programs designed to solve these problems on a regional basis. The program, made possible under a grant from the General Electric Educational and Charitable Fund, was in effect for 18 months and was instrumental in shaping the plans of the American Association for a continuing program in the interest of improved instruction in science and mathematics.

[1] Any interested person can obtain further information about the publications of CUP by writing to Prof. H. M. Gehman, Secretary, Mathematical Association of America, University of Buffalo, Buffalo 14, New York. The following source books have been published: First Course: 1. "Universal Mathematics"; 2. "Elementary Mathematics of Sets—with Applications." Second Course (designed chiefly for biology and social science majors): "Modern Mathematical Methods and Models"— M-4 Volume I ("Multicomponent Models"), M-4 Volume II ("Mathematical Models").

The National Science Foundation sponsors numerous summer institutes and a smaller number of year-long institutes throughout the nation. The programs of these institutes are designed to help elementary teachers, secondary teachers, and college teachers of science and mathematics to enrich their backgrounds in science and mathematics.

In the summer of 1958 the School Mathematics Study Group (SMSG), having received its initial support from the National Science Foundation, started its activities with a writing conference held at Yale University. The conference consisted of a group of 40 persons selected from among top-level research mathematicians and secondary school teachers. The first project of this group was directed at grades 7 to 12. The study "provides for a more extended view of mathematics education at all levels of instruction than has been possible in any of the other studies." A second writing session was held during the summer of 1959 at the University of Colorado. As a result, during the academic year of 1959–60, the School Mathematics Study Group sponsored tryouts of experimental material for grades 7 through 12 by approximately 600 teachers scattered throughout the country. Subsequent writing sessions and extended experimentation are planned.

Among the significant activities taking place in the interest of improved instruction in mathematics at the secondary level there are at least four experimental studies of such broad scope as to demand national attention. These four projects, which have received substantial grants and which give promise of significant results, are being carried on at the University of Illinois, the University of Maryland, Syracuse University, and Ball State Teachers College. Also, there are various scholarship programs and institutes sponsored by industrial concerns and conferences such as those sponsored by the American Association for the Advancement of Science, the American Association of School Administrators, the Council of Chief State School Officers, the National Association of Secondary School Principals, and the Scientific Manpower Commission in cooperation with the U.S. Office of Education.[1] The National Defense Education Act of 1958, which is administered by the U.S. Office of Education, provided funds to be used by the schools of the country in the purchase of equipment for aid in teaching science, mathematics, and foreign languages. The act also made provision for financial assistance to state departments of education in the employment of supervisors in these three areas of the school program.

This is indeed an era of revived and concerned interest in the real import of mathematics as an integral part of the American program of education from the early elementary grades on through the total program.

[1] "Mathematics and Science Education in U.S. Public Schools" (U.S. Office of Education, 1958).

It is the sincere hope of all concerned that the study now being given to the problem of improved instruction will be sufficiently intensive and extensive to produce a curriculum and a pattern of teaching that will offer to the boys and girls of our land unexcelled opportunities to become significantly informed in the field of mathematics.

EXERCISES

1. What have been some of the more important aspects of the evolving philosophy of education in the United States?

2. Cite evidences of the effect each of the points of view called for in exercise 1 has had on the mathematics curriculum.

3. What was the mathematics curriculum of the Latin grammar school?

4. How did the mathematics curriculum of the academy differ from that of the Latin grammar school?

5. At approximately what time did textbooks begin to be used extensively in mathematical instruction?

6. Name four important mathematics texts of the Latin grammar school period and also four of the academy period.

7. Briefly trace the influence of college entrance requirements in mathematics on the secondary school mathematics curriculum.

8. What were some of the more important causes of change in the mathematics program of the Latin grammar school and the academy?

9. What evidences are there of French and English influences on the instruction in mathematics during the early periods of American education?

10. In what way did the Pestalozzian movement affect the teaching of mathematics?

11. Name the early texts that most vividly reflected the Pestalozzian influence.

12. Name four texts that played a very important part in shaping the early instruction in algebra and geometry.

13. Name six influences that have been significant in the evolution of the mathematics curriculum of the secondary school. Give the major contribution of each.

14. What was the purpose and what were the main recommendations of the Committee of Fifteen on Geometry?

15. Briefly outline the recommendations for secondary mathematics made in the report, "The Reorganization of Mathematics in Secondary Education."

16. What classification of aims was given in the report, "The Reorganization of Mathematics in Secondary Education"?

17. Point out the distinguishing characteristics of each group of aims called for in exercise 16. Also, indicate the extent to which the groups overlap.

18. Briefly outline the recommendations of the Joint Commission concerning the program of secondary mathematics.

19. Contrast the recommendations of the Joint Commission with those of the National Committee on Mathematical Requirements.

20. What do you understand by the general-mathematics movement? By what other names has this movement been designated?

21. Compare the value of general mathematics in the senior high school with the value in the junior high school and in the junior college.

22. In what ways has the junior college movement affected the curriculum of secondary mathematics?

23. What is your evaluation of the Joint Commission's discussion of the role of mathematics in civilization and the place of mathematics in the educational program?

24. In what respects does the Progressive Education Association Committee's Report differ from the Report of the Joint Commission?

25. Compare the two reports cited in exercise 24 with respect to their recommendations on evaluation in mathematics.

26. What are some of the more significant aspects of the nature and work of the Commission on Mathematics of the College Entrance Examination Board?

27. Criticize or justify the statement that the quotation on page 29, from the Report of the Committee on Essential Mathematics for Minimum Army needs, has definite implications as to the minimum essentials in mathematics for civilian needs.

28. Briefly outline the work of the Commission on Post-War Plans.

29. Criticize or justify the check list of functional competence in mathematics as presented in the second report and "Guidance Pamphlet" of the Commission on Post-War Plans.

30. Briefly summarize the most important of the implications of the 34 theses of the second report of the Commission on Post-War Plans.

31. Point out significant uses that may be made of the "Guidance Pamphlet."

32. What are some of the more significant aspects of the Report of the Secondary School Curriculum Committee (SSCC)?

33. What are some of the more important recommendations of the Committee on Undergraduate Program (CUP)?

34. What are some of the more important activities of the School Mathematics Study Group (SMSG)?

BIBLIOGRAPHY

Beatley, Ralph: Coherence and Diversity in Secondary Mathematics, "Eighth Year-book" (Washington, D.C.: National Council of Teachers of Mathematics, 1933), pp. 165–215.

———: Secondary Mathematics and the College Entrance Examination Board, *Harvard Educational Review*, **7** (1937), 93–112.

Betz, William: Our Students Are Not Getting Enough Mathematics, *School and Community*, **32** (1946), 112.

———: Looking Again at the Mathematical Situation, *Mathematics Teacher*, **41** (1948), 372–381.

Breslich, E. R.: "The Technique of Teaching Mathematics in Secondary Schools" (Chicago: University of Chicago Press, 1930), pp. 189–236.

———: Curriculum Trends in High School Mathematics, *Education Digest*, **14** (1948), 14–18; also in *Mathematics Teacher*, **41** (1948), 60–69.

Brown, Kenneth E.: "General Mathematics in American Colleges," *Contributions to Education* 893 (New York: Bureau of Publications, Teachers College, Columbia University, 1943).

Cajori, F.: "The Teaching and History of Mathematics in the United States" (Washington, D.C.: Government Printing Office, 1890), pp. 9–10, 45–55, 106–127.

Commission on Mathematics, Report of: "Program for College Preparatory Mathematics" (New York: College Entrance Examination Board, 1959).

Commission on Post-War Plans: Second Report, *Mathematics Teacher*, **38** (1945), 195–221.

Commission on Secondary School Curriculum of the Progressive Education Association: "Mathematics in General Education: Report of the Committee on the Function of Mathematics in General Education." (New York: Appleton-Century-Crofts, Inc., 1940).

Court, Nathan Altshiller: Mathematics in the History of Civilization, *Mathematics Teacher*, **41** (1948), 104–111.

Douglass, H. R.: Current Trends in Secondary School Mathematics Curriculum, *National Association of Secondary School Principals*, **27** (February, 1943), 19–24.

Gager, William A.: "Terminal Business Mathematics in the Junior College," *Contribution to Education* 282 (Nashville, Tenn.: George Peabody College for Teachers, 1940).

Hannelly, R. J.: Mathematics in the Junior College, *American Mathematical Monthly*, **46** (1939), 581–585.

Hutchinson, C. A.: Mathematics Instruction for Purposes of General Education, *American Mathematical Monthly*, **48** (1941), 189–197.

Jackson, L. L.: "Sixteenth Century Arithmetic," *Contributions to Education* 8 (New York: Bureau of Publications, Teachers College, Columbia University, 1906).

Joint Commission of the Mathematical Association of America, Inc., and the National Council of Teachers of Mathematics: "The Place of Mathematics in Secondary Education," *Fifteenth Yearbook* (Washington, D.C.: National Council of Teachers of Mathematics, 1940).

Jones, Phillip S., Eileen K. Beckett, H. Vernon Price, and Virginia Terhune: A Report on Progress in Mathematics Education, *School Science and Mathematics*, **49** (1949), 465–474.

Kidd, Kenneth P.: "Objectives of Mathematical Training in the Public Junior College," *Contribution to Education* 394 (Nashville, Tenn.: George Peabody College for Teachers, 1947).

McCormick, Clarence: "The Teaching of General Mathematics in Secondary Schools," *Contributions to Education* 386 (New York: Bureau of Publications, Teachers College, Columbia University, 1929).

Mendenhall, Charles B.: "Mathematics in General Education," unpublished doctoral dissertation (Columbus, Ohio: The Ohio State University, 1939).

Monroe, W. S.: A Chapter in the Development of Arithmetic Teaching in the United States, *Elementary School Teacher*, **13** (1912–1913), 17–24.

———: Analysis of Colburn's Arithmetics, *Elementary School Teacher*, **13** (1912–1913) 239–246, 294–302.

Moore, E. H.: On the Foundations of Mathematics, "First Yearbook" (Washington, D.C.: National Council of Teachers of Mathematics, 1926), pp. 32–57.

National Committee on Mathematical Requirements: "The Reorganization of Mathematics in Secondary Education" (Boston: Houghton Mifflin Company, 1923).

Newsom, C. V.: A Course in College Mathematics for a Program of General Education, *Mathematics Teacher*, **42** (1949), 19–24.

Perry, John: The Teaching of Mathematics, *Educational Review*, **23** (1902), 158–181.

Pickard, Willis L.: "Evolution of Algebra as a Secondary School Subject," *Contribution to Education* 397 (Nashville, Tenn.: George Peabody College for Teachers, 1947).

Reeve, W. D.: Significant Trends in Secondary Mathematics, *School Science and Mathematics*, **49** (1949), 809–813.

Schorling, Raleigh: Trends in Junior High School Mathematics, *Mathematics Teacher*, **35** (1942), 339–343.

———: A Program for Improving the Teaching of Science and Mathematics, *American Mathematical Monthly*, **55** (1948), 221–237.

Schult, Veryl: Are We Giving Our Mathematics Students a Square Deal? *Mathematics Teacher*, **42** (1949), 143–148.

Secondary School Curriculum Committee of the National Council of Teachers of Mathematics, Report of: The Secondary Mathematics Curriculum, *Mathematics Teacher*, **52** (1959), 389–417.

Seybolt, R. F.: Notes on the Teaching of Elementary Mathematics in Colonial America, *Journal of Educational Research*, **11** (1925), 359–367.

Shuster, C. N.: A Call for Reform in High School Mathematics, *American Mathematical Monthly*, **55** (1948), 472–475.

Simons, L. G.: "Introduction of Algebra into American Schools in the Eighteenth Century" (U.S. Office of Education Bulletin 18, 1924).

Smith, D. E., and Jekuthiel Ginsburg: "A History of Mathematics in America before 1900," *Carus Monograph* 5, The Mathematical Association of America, Inc. (La Salle, Ill.: The Open Court Publishing Company, 1934).

Van Engen, H.: Why Teach Mathematics? *Mathematics Teacher*, **38** (1945), 51–55.

Wren, F. L., and H. B. McDonough: Development of Mathematics in the Secondary Schools of the United States, *Mathematics Teacher*, **27** (1934), 117–127, 190–198, 215–224, 281–295.

2

MATHEMATICS IN GENERAL EDUCATION

General education has been defined as that portion of the educational program which deals "mainly with preparation for life in the broad sense of completeness as a human being, rather than in the narrower sense of competence in a particular lot."[1] Thus, the total program of education is broadly considered as divided into two distinct, yet complementary, patterns, one for general education and one for special education. No onus of disrepute nor halo of respect is to be ascribed to the one in comparison with the other. Each program has its distinct function to perform and is to be evaluated only in the context of its determinate responsibility to the total educational program.

The large numbers of students at all levels of instruction, from the elementary school through the junior college, constitute part of the educational problem which confronts educators today. The other part of the problem, and equally as important, is the kind of education that is to be provided to prepare these students to live more effectively as responsible members of their social order. In such a total program, general education and special education are not to be distinguished from each other so much in subject matter as in point of view and method of treatment. At all levels, general education will attempt to develop those abilities, attitudes, understandings, and behavior patterns which should be within the common experience of all educable people. On the other hand, special education, at appropriate levels, will attempt to fashion programs leading to the development of competencies in special areas of interest and endeavor.

A Basic Philosophy of General Education. For some students the real responsibility of the educational program is to make provision for challenging their special interests and abilities and developing their individual competencies and understandings. For all students, however, there exists the potential of becoming rational, trustworthy, and useful individuals. The basic concern of general education is to help each

[1] Report of Harvard Committee, "General Education in a Free Society" (Cambridge, Mass.: Harvard University Press, 1945), p. 4.

student realize and accept the challenge of his individual potential and lay the foundation for successful pursuit of special interests and aptitudes so that he might develop to his full stature as a responsible citizen. The purposes of general education are thus fourfold: (1) to contribute to the preparation for life needs, not only those which the student realizes but also those he must be taught to realize, (2) to establish basic relevance between knowledge and everyday experience, (3) to provide a non-specialized type of training characterized by wide application, universal value, and great intellectual appeal, and (4) to lay the foundation of basic information essential to later intelligent pursuit of individual interests and special aptitudes.

The objectives of a program provided to meet such educational responsibilities should be designed to help the student (1) think effectively, (2) communicate thought, (3) discriminate among values, (4) make relevant judgments, (5) improve and maintain health, (6) do his part as an active and responsible citizen, (7) choose a vocation intelligently, (8) gain skill in adding to his previous knowledge, (9) find self-expression in and create an appreciation for things of beauty, (10) make sound emotional and social adjustments, (11) choose avocational interests wisely, (12) realize and appreciate his cultural heritage, and (13) understand his physical environment.

The program in mathematics can and must make significant contribution toward the attainment of these basic objectives of general education. It must make provision for:

1. Competence in the basic skills and understandings for dealing with number and form

2. Habits of effective thinking—a broad term involving analytical, critical, and postulational thinking, as well as reasoning by analogies and the development of intellectual curiosity

3. Communication of thought through symbolic expression and graphs

4. Development of the ability to make relevant judgments through the discrimination of values

5. Development of the ability to distinguish between relevant and irrelevant data

6. Development of intellectual independence

7. Development of aesthetic appreciation and expression

8. Development of cultural advancement through a realization of the significance of mathematics in its own right and in its relation to the total physical and social structure

It is in this context that there does exist a body of mathematical subject matter that is of significance to every educable individual at any and all levels of instruction.

The Junior High School.   It is true that the primary force back of the present-day demand for a program of general education has been a revolt against the elective system which has characterized for many years the instructional program of our colleges.   However, it is of interest to note that the basic philosophy of the evolving pattern for the contribution of mathematics to general education at the collegiate level of instruction is fundamentally the same as that expressed in 1923 by the National Committee on Mathematical Requirements as a guide for the general mathematics program of the junior high school.   As witness to the truth of this statement compare the above definition of general education, as given by the Harvard Committee,[1] and their implications for mathematics education with the following statement from the National Committee's report:[2]

The primary purposes of the teaching of mathematics should be to develop those powers of understanding and of analyzing relations of quantity and of space which are necessary to an insight into and a control over our environment and to an appreciation of the progress of civilization in its various aspects, and to develop those habits of thought and of action which will make these powers effective in the life of the individual.

To implement this stated purpose, the National Committee recommended that the program of study for grades 7 to 9 contain the fundamental ideas of arithmetic, algebra, intuitive geometry, numerical geometry, and an introduction to demonstrative geometry.   Furthermore, the report recommended that this body of mathematical subject matter be required of all pupils in these grades, since it was felt that its content included the mathematical knowledge and skills likely to be needed by every citizen.

The members of the committee seemed to have conceived of the program of mathematics in general education as performing two basic functions: (1) to give the students a broad view of the field of elementary mathematics in order to explore their interests and test their abilities and (2) to give the students the mathematical information and skills most likely to be useful to them in their vocational pursuits.

While no effort was made to recommend grade levels for the treatment of specific topics, several optional plans of organization which did have certain implications for grade placement were presented.   Basically, these recommended patterns of subject-matter organization have prevailed through the intervening years.   Support of the fundamental

---

[1] *Loc. cit.*

[2] National Committee on Mathematical Requirements, "The Reorganization of Mathematics in Secondary Education" (Boston: Houghton Mifflin Company, 1927), pp. 13–14.

philosophy and specific recommendations of grade content were included in the 1940 report of the Joint Commission of the Mathematical Association of America and the National Council of Teachers of Mathematics.[1] The major modification found in this second report consisted of a recommended two-track program in which the basic differentiation consisted of a possibility of two distinct patterns in grade 9: algebra for some and general mathematics for others. Both committees agreed in their recommendation that the mathematics program through grade 9 be required of all pupils. These recommendations were given further confirmation in the following theses of the 1945 report of the Commission on Post-War Plans:[2]

Thesis 9. The mathematical program of grades 7 and 8 should be essentially the same for all normal pupils.

Thesis 10. The mathematics for grades 7 and 8 should be planned as a unified program and should be built around a few broad categories.

Thesis 11. The mathematics program of grades 7 and 8 should be so organized as to enable the pupils to achieve mathematical maturity and power.

Thesis 12. The large (more than 200 pupils) high school should provide in grade 9 a double track in mathematics, algebra for some and general mathematics for the rest.

Thesis 13. In most schools first-year algebra should be evaluated in terms of good practice.

In support of thesis 13 the commission quotes a statement which was incorporated in the request for funds to underwrite the work of the National Committee on Mathematical Requirements. The statement is as follows:[3]

The situation that needs to be met may best be illustrated by the case of algebra. Our elementary algebra is, in theory and symbolism, substantially what it was in the seventeenth century. The present standards of drillwork, largely on nonessentials, were set up about fifty years ago. A considerable number of teachers, both in the secondary schools and the colleges, believe that the amount of time spent by pupils on abstract work in difficult problems in division, factoring, fractions, simultaneous equations, radicals, etc., is excessive; that such work leads to nothing important in the sciences and adds but little to facility in the manipulation of algebraic forms.

[1] Joint Commission of the Mathematical Association of America, Inc., and the National Council of Teachers of Mathematics, "The Place of Mathematics in Secondary Education," *Fifteenth Yearbook* (Washington, D.C.: National Council of Teachers of Mathematics, 1940).

[2] Commission on Post-War Plans, Second Report, *Mathematics Teacher*, **38** (1945), 204–207.

[3] *Ibid.*, p. 207.

Although this statement was written in about 1920, it sounds very much like statements that are read in current professional periodicals and are heard in various committee deliberations. It is to be hoped that significant improvements in the program are soon to take place and that we shall not have to wait another half century before instruction in mathematics will be oriented in the context of current thinking.

In the discussion of thesis 12 the commission states: "General mathematics for the ninth grade is here defined as a course that includes and emphasizes the elements of functional competence as outlined in the check list . . . of this report."[1] This definition of functional competence has been accepted rather generally as a satisfactory outline for general education at the junior high school level. The commission was very careful to emphasize "that the two parallel courses of the ninth grade are both tremendously worthwhile, but that they do have different goals and experiences for pupils with different interests and needs."[2]

While the items of the above-mentioned check list have served for several years as acceptable objectives for mathematics in a program of general education in the junior high school, it is quite true that they need to be subjected to close scrutiny in the context of the current thinking about the mathematics programs for our schools.

It has been a recognized fact for many years that a marked loss of interest in mathematics has been taking place in the post-elementary school days. While it is not too clear just what the causes are, there has been an expressed concern on the part of some that the program of the junior high school must assume a great deal of the blame. This accusation has not been completely justified, yet there are many who feel that the mathematics program of these grades is quite inadequate to meet the modern needs of the majority of the pupils in school. In particular, there seems to be a great deal of concern over the program for grade 8. It is important that careful consideration be given to the results of such experiments as those under way at this time at the Universities of Illinois, Syracuse, and Maryland. Also, careful attention must be given to the work of such groups as the Secondary School Curriculum Committee of the National Council of Teachers of Mathematics,[3] the Commission on Mathematics of the College Entrance Examination Board,[4] and the School Mathematics Study Group, which is concentrating its efforts on writing instructional materials for trial in the classroom.

[1] *Ibid.*, p. 206. The check list referred to is to be found on pages 197–198 of the report or, in condensed form, on page 31 of this text.

[2] *Loc. cit.*

[3] Secondary School Curriculum Committee, The Mathematics Curriculum, *Mathematics Teacher*, **52** (1959), 389–417.

[4] "Report of Commission on Mathematics," (New York: College Entrance Examination Board, 1959), pp. 18–19.

Some of the dissatisfaction with the junior high school mathematics program finds its origin in the feeling on the part of many that the selection and treatment of subject matter is not only inadequate but also, in many cases, quite inappropriate. For example, many people feel that in the eighth grade there is more emphasis on social applications than on the development of appropriate mathematical content and that in the ninth-grade algebra course there is more emphasis on mechanics than on appropriate considerations of basic structure. It might be added that for the ninth-grade general mathematics course there exists the same basic criticism as that expressed above for the present content of the eighth-grade mathematics course. Such topics as banking, taxation, stocks and bonds, and public utilities offer opportunities for pertinent applications of mathematical principles and skills, but they should not be used as the basic pattern for the organization and presentation of mathematical subject matter at any grade level. *It is the job of the mathematics teacher to teach mathematics, and this cannot be done incidentally.* The use of applications should be only for the purpose of guiding the immature thinker toward recognition of ways and means of putting his acquired mathematical knowledge to effective use. Pertinent applications sought from many different sources should be fashioned in the natural framework of problem situations, i.e., in variable patterns calling for realization of what the unknown elements are and what the problem situation is, discrimination between relevant and irrelevant data, determination of whether there is a need for any additional data, recognition of relationships between the data and between the known and unknown elements, selection of the most appropriate operations, and estimation of answers as a guide to reasonableness of results. This, however, should come only after the necessary mathematical concepts, principles, and skills have been developed. Only through the proper development of basic mathematical concepts, principles, and skills can the proper foundation be laid for true appreciation of mathematics as an important element of our culture and for the intelligent use of mathematics in solving many of the problems which occur in our daily lives.

Although the underlying philosophies calling for change in the report of the National Committee on Mathematical Requirements (1923) and making demands for modern reform are pretty much the same, there is one important difference, at least in implication. The basic emphasis on general mathematics (better said, mathematics in general education) of the 1923 report, the report of the Joint Commission (1940), and that of the Commission on Post-War Plans (1945) is reflected in this quotation from the Commission on Post-War Plans: " . . . general mathematics is *organized* differently, . . . it offers a greater *variety* of topics and . . .

it is related *more directly* with immediate application."[1] As has been stated previously, the basic emphasis of the modern demand for a program in general education is that general education and special education are not to be distinguished from each other so much in subject matter as in point of view and method of treatment. This implies that, while there may be differentiation in tracks, in the two-track program of the junior high school there will not be any differentiation in basic subject matter or basic preparation of teachers. The appropriate development of relevant basic mathematical skills, concepts, and principles will be the first responsibility of teachers regardless of track. The differentiation will come in the interpretation, supplementation, and enrichment of this development. For one track this aspect of the program will be oriented in the context of the user of mathematics; in the other it will assume the point of view of a forward look toward more advanced work in mathematics. There are some who are proposing still a third track to make provision for a still slower paced mathematics program for pupils of very low-level competence. Regardless of track, the teachers of mathematics in the junior high school will have to be equally well informed in mathematical subject matter, in the history of mathematics, in the psychology of individual differences, and in effective techniques of presentation of materials and evaluation of results.

The Senior High School.   The inception of the idea of dividing the six-year secondary education program of grades 7 to 12 into the junior high school and the senior high school dates from the early 1900s. Since that time, the primary function of the senior high school has been defined in terms of the provision of opportunities for the beginning of content specialization and the pursuance of one's aptitudes and special interests. While this has been generally accepted as the basic philosophy in the formulation of the senior high school program in mathematics, there have been those who have argued for the need to make provision for continuance of the general-education emphasis into the senior high school. It has been their contention that young people are graduating from high school with tragic inadequacies in the fundamentals of elementary mathematics.   From World War II to the present, emphasis on the reality of this situation has been increasing. It has come from military personnel, businessmen, and people in industry as well as from teachers of mathematics.   The accusations have been substantiated further by studies such as those by Beckmann, Brown, Davis, Ohlsen, and Renner, which are listed in the Bibliography for this chapter.

No program in mathematics for general education has as yet been designed for the senior high school. There have been a few efforts in

---

[1] Commission on Post-War Plans, *op. cit.* The italics are in the original and the comparisons are made with the algebra program of the ninth grade.

preparing texts which might provide content for a remedial program
of sorts at the eleventh- or twelfth-grade level.   The Secondary School
Curriculum Committee takes the position that it is desirable for all
graduates from the high school to have attained at least a certain minimum degree of mathematical competency and recommends that some
means should be provided to determine whether or not prospective
graduates have done so.   Further, it recommends that possibly grade 11
is the best place to subject the candidate to this check in order that a
required remedial program might be pursued in grade 12 by those who
fail to measure up to the requirements.[1]   It remains to be seen whether
the evidence of mathematical inadequacy and the public concern which
it has provoked will influence the groups engaged in the intensive restudy
of secondary mathematics to propose a program of mathematics for
general education specifically designed for the senior high school.   Here
again the pattern of individual differences can well call for a multiple-
track program.   If it is to have significance to the individual, the general
education program should be by no means degenerated into one of
remedial efforts.   Furthermore, the mathematically gifted should be
given the opportunity to work in an atmosphere of full challenge and
maximum interest.   There should be differentiation on the basis of need
and ability without "burdening with a stigma" or "investing with a
halo" any one group as compared with the other.   These basic facts
possibly create the necessity for a third track of instruction in the senior
high school as well as the junior high school.

   After an intensive study of the American high school, James Bryant
Conant recommends[2] a program of instruction structured in three categories, as follows:

First, there are the courses that should be *required* of *all* students, irrespective
of their academic ability or their vocational goals.   Then, there are two types
of elective programs—the nonacademic and the academic.
   The required program should occupy about half of every student's time.   It
should include four years of English, three or four years of social studies including
two of history, at least one year of mathematics and one year of science.   These
courses are intended to provide the groundwork for citizenship in a democracy. . . .
   The nature of the nonacademic elective program will depend almost entirely
on the community.   There may be a considerable number of parents who are
interested in having their children whose talents are nonacademic, take vocational
courses geared to employment opportunities in the community.   In that case,
such courses should be offered. . . .

   [1] Secondary School Curriculum Committee, *op. cit.*, p. 413.
   [2] James Bryant Conant, A Hard Look at Our High Schools, *Look*, **23** (Feb. 3, 1959),
31–32.

I am convinced . . . that, on a national basis, something like 15 per cent of the youth of high-school age have the ability to study effectively and rewardingly advanced mathematics, science, and a foreign language. And I think those academically talented students should be urged by the counselors to elect a minimum academic elective program that includes four years of mathematics, four years of *one* foreign language, and three years of a science.

These recommendations are directed toward 4-year high school programs, but they have important implications also for those programs which are on a 3-3 pattern of junior high school and senior high school.

The success of any such program of mathematics education will depend to a very great extent upon the preparation and experience of the teacher. Whether his instructional responsibilities are directed toward general education or toward the more specialized nonacademic and academic programs, he should be a person with a strong mathematical background, acquainted with the demands of individual differences, and informed on the relative merits of appropriate teaching techniques. These more highly specialized attributes of a good teacher should be supported by the cultural, disciplinary, and practical qualities of a sound program in general education.

The Junior College. The term "junior college" is here used to apply to grades 13 and 14, whether they are attached to the high school, organized as a separate two-year unit, or constitute the first two years of a four-year college program. At this level of instruction there exists, somewhat as at the junior high school level, the need to have concern for at least two large groups of students. There are those who, for various reasons, will desire to terminate their college program at the end of the two years, and there are those who will plan to go on to the more advanced work of later years. Also, from the point of view of mathematics, there are those who, even though they continue for four years or more of college and university work, do not have any special interest in and aptitude for mathematics. Recognition of this fact, and of the fact that in our modern technological society mathematics has a responsible contribution to make to the program of general education, has given concern to educators and mathematicians alike. What is the most effective contribution which mathematics can make to the program of general education at the college level? There is not as yet any real agreement on the answer. Committees have given, and still are giving, concentrated attention to the problem of finding the most appropriate answer. In particular, the work of the Committee on the Undergraduate Mathematical Program is to be noted.[1] The professional journals have also carried many articles expressing individual points of view on the content of such a program. Despite the wide differences

---

[1] Report of Committee on the Undergraduate Mathematical Program, *American Mathematical Monthly*, **63** (1955), 511–520.

of opinion, there seems to be universal agreement on one fundamental characteristic of the program, namely, *the content of the course must be mathematics and not just about mathematics.*

Texts that reflect different points of view are beginning to appear. The most generally accepted program seems to be developed around the broad areas of the basic notion of number, measurement, probability and statistics, function, and the nature of proof. The discussion of number seems to be concerned with the following: (1) the historical background of our number system, paying special attention to the concepts of one-to-one correspondence, place value, and order, (2) number systems with nondecimal bases, (3) the basic properties of real numbers, (4) extension of number systems from natural numbers to complex numbers, including the concepts of sets, groups, and fields, (5) congruences and modular number systems, (6) the number line, and (7) rectangular coordinates. The approximate nature of measurement is developed along with the concepts of precision and accuracy, significant digits and standard notation, linear, area, volume, and capacity measurements, direct and indirect measurement, and computation with approximate numbers. The introduction to probability and statistics is restricted to the basic patterns of probability and the simpler measures of central tendency and variability. There is some consideration of basic characteristics of a normal distribution and the product-moment correlation. Sets, relations, and functions form an important part of the language and the subject matter of this program. More precise definitions of constant, variable, and function are given. Simple algebraic and trigonometric functions are introduced, and appropriate techniques, including graphs, are used for deriving their properties. The study and use of the basic rules of logic and simple truth tables are introduced as a foundation for a clearer understanding of the nature of proof as it applies to various mathematical areas. The importance of intuition and the necessity of deduction are developed. Contrasts are drawn between the algebraic and the purely geometric types of proof, as well as between direct and indirect methods. Careful attention is also paid to the basic nature of postulates, with some extensions to Boolean algebra being made.

This not too carefully delineated outline of topics can be considered a rough indication of what might be thought of as a required program in mathematics for a general education program at the college level. An analysis of the outline will disclose an implementation of the generally accepted basic assumption upon which such courses are to be built, namely, the course must be mathematics, not just about mathematics.

There is no doubt that mathematical content for such a course can be developed in a very meaningful manner that is quite compatible with the scholastic aptitude of all college students. Just as in any instructional area, the final responsibility for the effectiveness and value of any such course is that of the teacher. No course designed for the program of general education should be relegated to the apprentice teacher or the graduate assistant. Teachers of such courses must be prepared specifically for the job. The teacher preparation program must provide learning experiences in advanced subject matter which will help the prospective teacher see more elementary content in the richer context of the more advanced and to interpret the more advanced in the language and understanding of the more elementary. It must help the prospective teacher see the profession of teaching as an opportunity to make a rich and valuable contribution to the field of mathematics, a contribution no less genuine than that which lies open to the person trained for research in pure or applied mathematics. Such a program of preparation must be carried out with advanced courses in mathematics and related areas which have been designed to develop basic interrelationships as well as specific properties, and it must emphasize the necessity to recognize the limitations of individual aptitudes as well as encourage the setting of high standards of endeavor. In the hands of a teacher so prepared the mathematics course in the general-education program can make a truly significant contribution to the intellectual growth of every educable individual.

EXERCISES

1. Distinguish between general education and special education.
2. What are the basic purposes of a program in general education?
3. What general abilities should a program in general education be designed to help students develop?
4. In what ways can the program in secondary mathematics contribute toward the attainment of the objectives of general education?
5. What should be the basic objectives in mathematics for a general-education program at the level of the junior high school? The senior high school? The junior college?
6. Contrast the implications for general education as contained in the Harvard Committee's definition (page 41) with those for junior high school mathematics as contained in the statement from the National Committee on Mathematical Requirements (page 43).
7. What are some basic changes which need to be made in the Commission for Post-War Plans' check list for functional competence in order to bring it in line with current thinking about the content of secondary mathematics?
8. What are some of the principal arguments for modification of the program in junior high school mathematics?
9. What are the arguments for and against the thesis that the relative order of emphasis in the teaching of mathematics at the junior high school level is (1) basic understandings of concepts, principles, and techniques of mathematics and (2) ability to apply acquired mathematical understandings and skills to the interpretation of social situations?
10. Discuss the thesis of exercise 9 for senior high school mathematics.

11. Discuss the thesis of exercise 9 for junior college mathematics.

12. Argue the merits of the following thesis as a fundamental principle upon which any sound program of mathematics for general education should be based: The content of the program must be mathematics and not just about mathematics.

13. Give some of the arguments both for and against placing emphasis on each of these content areas in a mathematics program for general education: the number concept, measurement, the nature of proof, functionality, statistics.

14. Are there other content areas than those listed in exercise 13 which should be included in a mathematics program for general education?

BIBLIOGRAPHY

Alberty, E. J.: Role of Mathematics in Core-program Development, *School Review*, **64** (1956), 300–306.

Beckmann, Milton W.: The Level of Mathematical Competency and Relative Gains in Competency of Pupils Enrolled in Algebra and General Mathematics, unpublished doctoral dissertation (Lincoln, Nebr.: University of Nebraska, 1951).

Bentz, Ralph B.: Critical Mathematical Requirements for the Program of the Community College, unpublished doctoral dissertation (Nashville, Tenn.: George Peabody College for Teachers, 1952).

Bevington, R. S.: Mathematics for Our Time, *Mathematics Teacher*, **47** (1954), 295–298.

Blank, L.: Mathematics for Life Adjustment, *Mathematics Teacher*, **47** (1954), 308–310.

Boyd, E. N.: Cultural Course in Mathematics for College Students, *Mathematics Teacher*, **47** (1954), 479–481.

Brown, Robert C.: Functional Competence in Mathematics of Louisiana High School Seniors, unpublished doctoral dissertation (Nashville, Tenn.: George Peabody College for Teachers, 1956).

Bryan, J. C.: Mathematics in General Education, *School Science and Mathematics*, **58** (1958), 249–255.

Burr, H.: Are We Providing for the Non-college Pupil in Mathematics? *California Journal of Secondary Education*, **30** (1955), 405–406.

Davis, David J.: A Comparative Study of Achievement Levels of Twelfth Grade Pupils on a Test Designed to Measure Functional Competence in Mathematics, unpublished doctoral dissertation (Ann Arbor, Mich.: University of Michigan, 1950).

Dixon, L. J.: Mathematics and General Education, *Mathematics Teacher*, **48** (1955), 204–208.

Fehr, Howard F.: Goal Is Mathematics for All, *School Science and Mathematics*, **56** (1956), 109–120.

Gager, William A.: Functional Mathematics—Grades Seven through Twelve, *Mathematics Teacher*, **44** (1951), 297–301.

Green, L. W.: From Knowledge into Power: A Philosophy of General Education, *Journal of General Education*, **11** (1958), 151–156.

Hannon, H. H.: Mastery of Certain Aspects of Mathematics for General Education, *Journal of Educational Research*, **50** (1957), 363–371.

Hartung, M. L.: What Mathematics Is Essential? *High School Journal*, **37** (1953), 83–87.

———: Mathematics in the Total School Program, *Mathematics Teacher*, **51** (1958), 336–343.

Harvard Committee, Report of: "General Education in a Free Society" (Cambridge: Harvard University Press, 1945).

"Higher Education for American Democracy," vol. I, "Establishing the Goals" (Washington, D.C.: President's Commission on Higher Education, 1947).

Kinsella, J. J.: Some Reflections on the General Mathematics Situation, *School Science and Mathematics*, **54** (1954), 431–438.

Layton, W. I.: Mathematics in General Education, *Mathematics Teacher*, **50** (1957), 493–497.

Leonhardy, A.: Mathematics Used in the Biological and Physical Science Areas in a College Program of General Education, *School Science and Mathematics*, **51** (1951), 265–274.

————: Mathematics Used in the Humanities, Social Science, and the Natural Science Areas in Program of General Education on the College Level, *Science Education*, **36** (1952), 252–253.

McFarland, Sister Mary F.: Mathematics, Our Common Heritage, *Journal of General Education*, **11** (1958), 170–181.

Mires, K. C.: General Mathematics for College Freshmen, *Mathematics Teacher*, **50** (1957), 513–516.

Moore, V. D.: General Mathematics in General Education at the College Level, *Teachers College Journal*, **23** (1952), 81–82.

Ohlsen, Merle M.: Control of Fundamental Mathematical Skills and Concepts by High School Students, *Mathematics Teacher*, **39** (1946), 365–371.

Progressive Education Association, Committee of: "Mathematics in General Education" (New York: Appleton-Century-Crofts, Inc., 1940).

Reeve, W. D.: General Mathematics in the Secondary School, *Mathematics Teacher*, **47** (1954), 73–80, 167–179.

Renner, John W.: Student Achievement of Functional Competence Three Years after Completing Algebra or General Mathematics, *Mathematics Teacher*, **50** (1957), 160–161.

Rowe, Jack L.: General Mathematics for Terminal Students in California Junior Colleges, *Mathematics Teacher*, **52** (1959), 105–106.

Simpson, T. M.: Mathematics in the College General Education Program, *Mathematics Teacher*, **50** (1957), 155–159.

Stone, D. R., and H. C. Bateman: Basic Elements in Defining General Education, *Junior College Journal*, **27** (1956), 90–92.

Sturm, H. E.: Development of a Junior College Mathematics Program for Non-science, Non-mathematics Majors, *School Science and Mathematics*, **50** (1950), 437–441.

Summerer, K. H.: College Mathematics for the Non-science, Non-mathematics Major, *School Science and Mathematics*, **56** (1956), 39–43.

Trimble, H. C.: Mathematics in General Education, *Mathematics Teacher*, **50** (1957), 2–5.

Trowbridge, H.: Forty Years of General Education, *Journal of General Education*, **11** (1958), 161–169.

Ullsvik, B. R.: Basic Learnings in Mathematics, *Educational Leadership*, **12** (1955), 199–204.

Wilson, J. D.: Mathematics in General Education at San Francisco State College, "Twenty-second Yearbook" (Washington, D.C.: National Council of Teachers of Mathematics, 1954), pp. 288–303.

Zant, J. H.: Critical Thinking as an Aim in Mathematics Courses for General Education, *Mathematics Teacher*, **45** (1952), 249–256.

3

THE IMPACT OF MODERN MATHEMATICS

Writing, in 1954, under the above title, MacLane[1] said:

My subject is vacuous; the lively modern development of mathematics has had no impact on the content or on the presentation of secondary-school mathematics. Algebra and geometry, as covered in schools, consist exclusively of ideas already well known two hundred years ago—many of them two thousand years ago. No matter how much better these particular ideas are taught to more and more pupils, their presentation leaves school mathematics in a state far more antiquarian than that of any other part of the curriculum. The pupils can conclude only that there is no such thing as a new mathematical idea.

Though regrettably pertinent when made, this accusation has since lost some of its sting of tragic truth. The concern of individuals, the activity of organizations, the deliberation of committees, and the inquisitiveness of experimentation, all have combined to create a turbulence of significant thinking directed toward the need for improvement of both the content and the methods of presentation of the mathematics courses in the nation's schools. The result has been the launching of a purposeful program to effect basic change in the mathematics programs of both the elementary school and the secondary school. Anchored in the clear recognition of the need for careful evaluation of the educational merits of both the traditional and the new in mathematics, the thought engineering this change has been essentially bifocal in nature. One point of view has focused attention on a redirection of emphasis in the treatment of the portion of traditional subject matter that has been accepted as having valid current educational value. This new emphasis pays greater attention to basic structure and less attention to mere operational facility. The other point of view seeks ways and means for employing more recently developed concepts and techniques to clarify, simplify, and enrich the presentation of the mathematical content of both the elementary and the secondary curriculum. Thus, modern mathematics may be

[1] Saunders MacLane, The Impact of Modern Mathematics, *Bulletin of the National Association of Secondary-School Principals*, **38** (1954), 66–70.

said to be characterized by both a new point of view and a new body of subject matter.

Modern Mathematics as a Point of View. The origin of what might be called the modern point of view in mathematics can be traced to the pioneering efforts of Gauss, Bolyai, Lobachevski, and Riemann in the creation of non-Euclidean geometries. By daring to challenge that which for two millennia had been accepted as absolute, they freed the intellect to reject the evidence of the senses for the sake of what the mind might produce. The modern postulational method of mathematics finds its source in the publication by Lobachevski (1830) and Bolyai (1832) of a consistent geometric system which contradicted the Euclidean fifth postulate of parallelism while keeping all other postulates intact. It was further enhanced through the publication by Riemann (1854) of still another consistent non-Euclidean geometry based upon a still different contradiction of the fifth postulate and the non-Euclideanism of "curvature of space." Subsequent refinements by Pasch, Peano, and Hilbert succeeded in establishing the purely hypothetico-deductive nature of geometry. In fact it has been said that Hilbert's work "firmly implanted the postulational method, not only in the field of geometry, but also in nearly every other branch of mathematics of the twentieth century."[1]

This new method no longer recognizes postulates (axioms) as "self-evident truths," but merely as "acceptable assumptions." They are individual creations of the investigator's mind, and are to be used as the basic hypotheses for some type of intellectual venture. The investigator may or may not be concerned about their material truth or falsity; he is concerned with their consistency and is curious about their implication. After he is convinced of the validity of his conclusions, he may become interested in the possibility of existence of physical or social situations which would provide a context of "truth" for his assumptions. In such cases the same aura of usefulness would encompass his conclusions. The validity and consistency of results rather than the practicality of results, however, are the major concerns of the mathematician.

The new method also places emphasis on the necessity for clear distinctions between that which is defined and that which must remain undefined. It is recognized that concepts and terms are defined through the use of other concepts and terms. Therefore, to avoid undesirable circuity of definition, the necessity for undefined, or irreducible, elements is created. The experience of the individual usually serves as the basic orientation for the specification of such undefined elements and the selection of fundamental postulates. Thus the modern point of view concern-

[1] Howard Eves and Carroll V. Newsom, "An Introduction to the Foundations and Fundamental Concepts of Mathematics" (New York: Rinehart and Company, Inc., 1958), p. 86.

ing geometry is that it is a creation of man's intellect, its distinctive
structure being delineated by the basic postulates, the undefined elements,
the dimensionality of the space of orientation, and the techniques of
investigation.

In essentially contemporaneous development with geometry, algebra
too was being freed from the shackles of authoritative tradition. The
English mathematician George Peacock was the first, in about 1835, to
think of algebra as a hypothetico-deductive system. This concept of
algebra as an abstract science was developed further, in England, by D. F.
Gregory and Augustus De Morgan and, in Germany, by Hermann Hankel.
The central thought of this development had its origin in the recognition
and abstraction of the fundamental properties which characterize the
algebra of positive integers (natural numbers). Such abstraction provided the symbolization which led to the realization that these same properties could very well characterize operations with elements other than
the positive integers. If the operations are addition and multiplication
and if a, b, and c represent positive integers, distinct or not, then the
properties may be stated as follows:

Closure: If a and b are positive integers, then $a + b$ and $a \times b$ are
positive integers.

Associative: $a + (b + c) = (a + b) + c$
$\qquad a \times (b \times c) = (a \times b) \times c$
Commutative: $a + b = b + a \qquad a \times b = b \times a$
Distributive: $a \times (b + c) = (a \times b) + (a \times c)$

Sir William Rowan Hamilton, a British mathematician, did for algebra
what Lobachevski and Bolyai did for geometry. In 1834 he made known
his new quaternion algebra, in which he had dared to contradict the commutative property of multiplication. Other noncommutative algebras
followed, notably Grassmann's (1844) classes of algebras of still greater
generality than Hamilton's quaternion algebra and Cayley's (1857) matrix
algebra. Of more recent date are the nonassociative algebras such as
those of Jordan and Lie.

From such considerations of algebraic structure there have evolved
postulate sets for fields, rings, integral domains, and groups, each of which
has great potential for significant contribution at the level of the secondary school to the better understanding of the essential nature of algebra
as a body of mathematical subject matter.

In any hypothetico-deductive system the question of consistency is
the problem of major concern. How can one be assured that, among
all the implications derivable from the basic postulates, there can never
occur conflicting statements? Consistency can be of two types: *relative*

and *absolute*. In the above statements concerning the consistency of Lobachevskian and Riemannian geometries, relative consistency is implied. This was established in rather brilliant fashion by E. Beltrami who, in 1868, demonstrated[1]

. . . that plane hyperbolic [Lobachevskian] geometry can be interpreted as that of the geodesics (curves of shortest length) on a surface of constant negative curvature [pseudosphere or tractoid], and likewise for spherical geometry [plane Riemannian geometry] and a surface of constant positive curvature [sphere]. Since pseudospheres and spheres are familiar surfaces in Euclidean space, it was felt that the consistency of the classical non-Euclidean geometries had been demonstrated.

Of course, the implication is merely that the geometries of Lobachevski and Riemann are just as consistent as is that of Euclid, no more and no less. Euclidean geometry merely serves as a mathematical model of the non-Euclidean geometries, since it was found possible to find unique representation in Euclidean geometry of the postulates and undefined terms of the non-Euclidean geometries. For example, the controversial fifth postulate of Euclid was represented in each non-Euclidean geometry by its respective substitute; point was identified with point and the straight lines of Euclidean geometry with the geodesics of non-Euclidean; two straight lines (geodesics) intersect in one point in Euclidean and Lobachevskian geometry but in two points in Riemannian geometry. (Arcs of great circles on the surface of a sphere intersect in the two poles.)

When a mathematical system contains an infinite number of primitive elements, no better than relative consistency can be established. This is not always as nebulous as it may seem. For example, since the points of Euclidean plane geometry can be identified with ordered pairs of real numbers and algebraic meanings can be assigned to the five primitive terms (point, line, on, between, and congruent), it follows that Euclidean geometry, and hence the non-Euclidean geometries mentioned above, are as consistent as the real-number system.[2] Similarly, the consistency of many mathematical systems can be checked against that of the real-number system.

When a mathematical system contains only a finite number of primitive elements, concrete representation can be found in the domain of reality and, thus, absolute consistency of the system can be established.[3]

[1] E. T. Bell, "The Development of Mathematics," 2d ed. (New York: McGraw-Hill Book Company, Inc., 1940), p. 307.

[2] Eves and Newsom, *op. cit.*, pp. 96–102.

[3] See, for example, Burton W. Jones, Miniature Number Systems, *Mathematics Teacher*, **51** (1958), 226–231, and Miniature Geometries, *ibid.*, **52** (1959), 66–71. Also see Eves and Newsom, *op. cit.*, pp. 158–161, 164.

Since finite postulational systems can be checked for consistency against the concrete expectations of reality, the basic problem of consistency of postulational systems is that of infinite systems and, therefore, primarily that of the consistency of the real-number system. Through the inspirational researches of Peano, Dedekind, and G. Cantor the consistency of the real-number system has in turn been related to that of the system of natural numbers, thus giving[1]

. . . the mathematician a considerable feeling of security concerning the consistency of most of mathematics. This attitude follows from the fact that the natural number system seems to have an intuitive simplicity lacking in most other mathematical systems, and the natural numbers have been very extensively handled over a long period of time without producing any known inner contradictions.

The basic substance of the modern point of view in mathematics is described effectively by Bell[2] in these words:

In precisely the same way that a novelist invents characters, dialogues, and situations of which he is both author and master, the mathematician devises at will the postulates upon which he bases his mathematical systems. Both the novelist and the mathematician may be conditioned by their environments in the choice and treatment of their material; but neither is compelled by any extra-human, eternal necessity to create certain characters or to invent certain systems.

Modern Mathematics as New Subject Matter. The new subject matter, like the modern point of view in mathematics, had its origin in the field of geometry. It has been said that analytic geometry "constitutes the greatest single step ever made in the progress of the exact sciences."[3] The analytic geometry of Fermat (1629) and Descartes (1637) in a very real sense remade geometry by removing the bane of Greek classicism and making modern geometry possible. Though it was, in essence, only a technique to be used in geometric investigations, Cartesian geometry became the key to unlock the floodgates through which flowed the stream of modern mathematics. With the publication in 1637 of Descartes' "Discours de la Méthode," *analysis* became the characterizing technique of modern mathematics as contrasted with the *synthesis* of the old. It opened up new vistas in the field of geometry, provided stimulus for the invention of the differential and integral calculus by Newton (1666, 1684) and Leibniz (1673, 1675), and served as an aid in clarifying concepts and simplifying techniques in algebra and arithmetic.

---

[1] Eves and Newsom, *op. cit.*, p. 195. The authors present a very interesting discussion on The Postulational Approach to the Real Number System, pp. 190–216.

[2] Bell, *op. cit.*, pp. 305–306.

[3] John Stuart Mill, "An Examination of Sir William Hamilton's Philosophy" (London: Longmans, Green, Reader, and Dyer, 1878), p. 617.

Fermat also combined his mathematical talents with Pascal to lay the foundation for the theory of probability in the joint solution of a game-of-chance problem proposed to Pascal by Chevalier de Méré. In this episode of 1654 the mathematics of chance had its beginning; since then it has continued to develop to such stature that it has become basic in many areas of modern living and scientific investigation. Something of its significance is implied by the fact that the Commission on Mathematics of the College Entrance Examination Board has published an experimental text for high school use entitled "Introductory Probability and Statistical Inference for Secondary Schools."

The seventeenth century is also marked by three other distinct developments in the field of mathematics. Desargues and Pascal made significant contributions toward the beginnings of synthetic projective geometry; Pascal foreshadowed the modern fabulous era of computing machines with his invention of the first adding machine; Leibniz improved on Pascal's adding machine by extending the operational possibilities to include multiplication and laid the foundations for modern symbolic logic in his efforts to "reduce all reasoning of whatever kind to a universal 'characteristic' or . . . a symbolic mathematical science."[1] His inspiration seemed to have come from Descartes' reduction of geometry to a universal method.

In contrast to the positive stimulation of Leibniz to new endeavors, the great significance of the Cartesian approach to the study of geometry so overshadowed the work of Desargues and Pascal that their new projective geometry was lost temporarily in an oblivion of pure metric geometry. There it remained until revived by the publications by Carnot (1803, 1806) and Poncelet (1822). Further impetus was given to this area of investigation through the announcement by Gergonne (1825–1827) of the principle of duality "which, with its generalizations, left as substantial a residue of new and useful methods in geometry, algebra, and analysis as any mathematical invention of the nineteenth century."[2]

In 1872 Felix Klein announced his famous Erlanger program. In the address announcing this program he incorporated a definition of geometry which served to restore order, as it were, to the confusion existing in geometry. He appealed to algebra to give him the concept needed and defined a geometry as "the system of definitions and theorems invariant under a *group* of transformations." While this synthesis of geometrical thinking no longer seemed adequate after the advent of the general relativity theory, it does still serve to provide an effective approach to the better understanding of the real significance of geometry at the level of the secondary school. Invariance is an extremely important property of

[1] Bell, *op. cit.*, p. 133.
[2] *Ibid.*, p. 316.

geometrical configurations which is of sufficiently simple structure to be comprehensible at the secondary level of instruction yet sufficiently abstract to open up new vistas of mathematical endeavor of challenging interest.

Probably the most significant and most basic of all the newer concepts of modern mathematics is that of *set*. An aggregate, ensemble, assemblage, class, or set is merely a collection of elements which are thought of as having some characteristic coherence. Some examples of sets are a set of dishes, a swarm of bees, a flock of sheep, a herd of cows, the fingers on one hand, the letters of the alphabet, all the positive integers, all the integers, the rational numbers, the real numbers, the points of a line, the points of a plane. The symbol used to indicate a set is illustrated by $A = \{a,b,c,d,e\}$, which is a set of five elements. A basic relation existing between sets is that of *equivalence*, or *one-to-one correspondence* between elements. For example, the set A, above, is equivalent to the set of fingers on a normally shaped hand because to each finger there corresponds one and only one element of the set A and, conversely, to each element of the set A there corresponds one and only one finger. This basic concept of equivalence of classes (sets) was recognized by Galileo. In 1638 he published a work in which he not only recognized this basic principle of equivalence of sets containing finite numbers of elements but also announced the fundamental distinguishing characteristic of infinite sets, namely, an infinite set is one whose elements can be placed in one-to-one correspondence with only a portion of the elements of the set. Stated in better language, an infinite set is a set which is equivalent to a *proper subset* of itself. The set B is a proper subset of the set C if every element of B is an element of C and there is at least one element of C which is not an element of B. Galileo exhibited a one-to-one correspondence between the set of all positive integers and the proper subset of positive integers which are perfect squares. Thus the set of all positive integers was exhibited as an infinite set.

In contrast, a finite set is a set for which a one-to-one correspondence cannot be established with any of its proper subsets. For example, the set S of all the letters of the English alphabet is a finite set. A bit of thought should make it evident that a one-to-one correspondence cannot be established between the set S and the set $A = \{a,b,c,d,e\}$ or any other proper subset of S.

The significance attached to the concepts of set and equivalence of sets was relatively incidental until toward the latter part of the nineteenth century. Although Bolzano (1850) had earlier postulated the basic distinction between finite and infinite sets and Boole (1847, 1854) had made an algebraic approach to the study of the theory of sets, it was G. Cantor (1895) who recognized the nonintuitive character of the concept of set and proceeded through the structure of a theory of sets of points to make significant contributions toward the modernization of the field of mathematical analysis.

Following in close sequence, Fréchet (1906) generalized the Riemannian (1854) point-set approach to the study of geometry through his introduction of a theory of abstract spaces.   Such a space consisted merely of a set of undefined elements, usually points, and a set of relations involving these elements.   The geometries which evolved as distinct theories of such spaces served to provide effective techniques for the development of Einstein's general relativity theory.   It was this type of geometry which did not adapt necessarily to effective classification under Klein's transformation theory.

Further evidence of the fundamental significance of set theory lies in the fact that it is possible to define natural numbers in terms of sets. Such a definition not only reduces the number of undefined terms necessary for the structure of mathematical systems but also relates the consistency of such systems to the problem of the possibility of the structure of the theory of sets as a consistent postulational system.

Although the principal orientation of the early development of the concept of set was in the field of mathematical analysis, there probably has been no other concept that has so thoroughly permeated the whole domain of mathematical thought.   The modern mathematical theory of sets has made significant contributions toward clarification, simplification, and abstraction of concepts and techniques in arithmetic, algebra, geometry, and analysis alike.   It has become a powerful instrument for interpreting and clarifying the significant of the old in mathematics as well as an effective vehicle for simplification and adaptation of the pertinent of the new.[1]

Nature of Deductive Methods.   One of the most significant of all the new emphases affecting the modern program in mathematics directs more explicit and careful attention to the basic postulational structure of mathematics.   From the point of view of logic, a fundamental criterion directing such considerations of structure is that the number of properties necessary to be assumed should be minimized, thus maximizing the number to be proved.   Pedagogically, however, it is desirable, at times, to relax this criterion in order to present an equivalent structure more readily comprehensible to the immature mind.

For example, a postulational basis for the natural numbers was first announced in 1889 by the Italian mathematician G. Peano.   This was a minimum set of postulates from which can be deduced all the proper-

---

[1] For an excellent discussion of some of the basic concepts of set theory see E. J. McShane, Operating with Sets, "Twenty-third Yearbook" (Washington, D.G.: National Council of Teachers of Mathematics, 1957), pp. 36–64.

ties not only of the natural numbers but also, through proper extensions, of all integers, the rational numbers, the real numbers, and the complex numbers. A less abstract, but equivalent, set of postulates which adapts itself to greater ease of comprehension by the immature student is the following:[1]

For our primitive, or undefined, terms take a set N of elements called *natural numbers*, together with two binary operations on the set, called *addition* and *multiplication* and denoted by $+$ and $\times$ [having the property of closure and] satisfying the following ten postulates.

$N1$. If a and b are in N, then $a + b = b + a$.

$N2$. If a and b are in N, then $a \times b = b \times a$.

$N3$. If a, b, c are in N, then $(a + b) + c = a + (b + c)$.

$N4$. If a, b, c are in N, then $(a \times b) \times c = a \times (b \times c)$.

$N5$. If a, b, c are in N, then $a \times (b + c) = (a \times b) + (a \times c)$.

$N6$. There exists a natural number 1 such that $a \times 1 = a$ for all a in N.

$N7$. If a, b, c are in N and if $c + a = c + b$, then $a = b$.

$N8$. If a, b, c are in N and if $c \times a = c \times b$, then $a = b$.

$N9$. For given a and b in N one and only one of the following holds: $a = b$, $a + x = b$, $a = b + y$, where x and y are in N.

$N10$. If M is a set of natural numbers such that (1) M contains the natural number 1 and (2) M contains the natural number $k + 1$ whenever it contains the natural number k, then M contains all the natural numbers.

In the statement of the above postulates the relation of *equality* was used. Such a relationship between two or more natural numbers is characterized by the following five basic properties:

$E1$. *Reflexive Property.* If a is in N, then $a = a$.

$E2$. *Symmetric Property.* If a, b are in N and $a = b$, then $b = a$.

$E3$. *Transitive Property.* If a, b, c are in N such that $a = b$ and $b = c$, then $a = c$.

$E4$. *Addition Property.* If a, b, c are in N and $a = b$, then $c + a = c + b$.

$E5$. *Multiplication Property.* If a, b, c are in N and $a = b$, then $ca = cb$.

These five properties are stated here as characterizing the relationship of equality between natural numbers. They also hold for equality between all numbers. The first three properties (reflexive, symmetric, and transitive) are the properties which characterize the more general *equivalence* relation. They hold for such relations as similarity and congruence of geometric figures, equality of areas, perimeters, and volumes, and equality of line segments and angles and many other types of relations both mathematical and nonmathematical in nature.

From the ten postulates of the system of natural numbers and the five characteristic properties of equality all the remaining properties of the

[1] Eves and Newsom, *op. cit.*, p. 195.

system of natural numbers can be deduced as theorems. Certain appropriate definitions of terms will facilitate such development. For example, postulate $N9$ states that there are three basic relationships between any two given natural numbers a and b. They are:

$$a = b \quad \text{(a relationship of equality)} \tag{1}$$
$$a + x = b \quad \text{for } x \text{ in } N \quad \text{(relationships of inequality} \tag{2}$$
$$a = b + y \quad \text{for } y \text{ in } N \quad \text{between } a \text{ and } b) \tag{3}$$

When the relation (2) holds, a is said to be less than b ($a < b$), and when relation (3) holds, a is said to be greater than b ($a > b$).

As an illustration of the use of the above set of postulates in the development of other basic properties of the system of natural numbers, consider the familiar property frequently stated as the axiom: If equals are added to equals, the sums are equal. This may now be stated and proved as follows:

Theorem. If a, b, c, and d are in N and if $a = b$ and $c = d$, then

$$a + c = b + d.$$

Proof

1. The sum of any two of the elements a, b, c, and d is in N.	1. Closure property.
2. $a = b$.	2. Hypothesis.
3. $a + c = c + a$.	3. $N1$.
4. $c + a = c + b$.	4. $E4$ and hypothesis.
5. $c + b = b + c$.	5. $N1$.
6. $c = d$.	6. Hypothesis.
7. $b + c = b + d$.	7. $E4$.
8. Therefore, $a + c = b + d$.	8. Steps 2, 3, 4, 7, and $E3$.

The fact that, through appropriate definitions and extensions, the properties of systems, other than the system of the natural numbers, can be developed from this basic list of postulates[1] caused the algebraists to become interested in the possibilities of further abstractions. They recognized that these same properties would be valid for any system consisting of a set of elements and two defined operations for which the system of postulates $N1$–10 held. The desire for further abstractions led to the consideration of still other postulational systems, the sets of elements and the operations upon the elements being defined only in terms of the restrictions specified by the basic postulates. The body of theorems and properties implied by logical deduction from such a postulational

---

[1] Eves and Newsom, *op. cit.*, pp. 194–216; Ivan Niven, The Concept of Number, "Twenty-third Yearbook" (Washington, D.C.: National Council of Teachers of Mathematics, 1957), pp. 7–35.

system thus becomes a mathematical model for the analysis of situations amenable to the fundamental postulates. Herein lies the basic concept of the significance of *mathematical structure*.

From the point of view of the secondary school, one of the most important of such postulational systems is an *integral domain*, defined as follows:

A set I of elements for which the operations of addition and multiplication are defined is called an *integral domain* if the following postulates are satisfied:

*I*1. *Closure.* If a and b are in I, then $a + b$ and $a \times b$ are in I.

*I*2. *Uniqueness.* For $a, b, c,$ and d in I, if $a = b$ and $c = d$, then $a + c = b + d$ and $a \times c = b \times d$.

*I*3. *Commutative Property.* If a and b are in I, then $a + b = b + a$ and $a \times b = b \times a$.

*I*4. *Associative Property.* If a, b, and c are in I, then

$$(a + b) + c = a + (b + c) \quad \text{and} \quad (a \times b) \times c = a \times (b \times c)$$

*I*5. *Distributive Property.* If a, b, and c are in I, then

$$a \times (b + c) = (a \times b) + (a \times c)$$

*I*6. *Zero.* I contains an element 0 such that, if a is in I, then $a + 0 = a$.

*I*7. *Unity.* I contains an element 1 $(\neq 0)$ such that if a is in I, then $a \times 1 = a$.

*I*8. *Additive Inverse.* If a is in I, then there is an element $-a$ (a inverse or negative a) in I such that $a + (-a) = 0$.

*I*9. *Cancellation Law.* For $a, b,$ and c ($c \neq 0$) in I if $ca = cb$, then $a = b$.

This postulational system derives its name from the fact that the most elementary set of elements meeting the conditions of the definition is the set J consisting of all integers (positive and negative and zero), with the operations being the customary processes of addition and multiplication. A less familiar example of an integral domain is defined as follows:

1. The set I consists of all irrational numbers of the form $a + b \sqrt{2}$, where a and b are elements of the set J.

2. Addition and multiplication are defined as ordinary binomial addition and multiplication. Namely, for all a, b, c, and d in J,

$$(a + b \sqrt{2}) + (c + d \sqrt{2}) = (a + c) + (b + d) \sqrt{2}$$
$$(a + b \sqrt{2}) \times (c + d \sqrt{2}) = (ac + 2bd) + (ad + bc) \sqrt{2}$$

where the form ac is used in the same sense as $a \times c$.

3. $a + b \sqrt{2} = c + d \sqrt{2}$ if, and only if, $a = c$ and $b = d$.

4. 0 is defined to be $0 + 0 \sqrt{2}$.

5. 1 is defined to be $1 + 0 \sqrt{2}$.

The reader should verify that the two systems described in the above paragraph do satisfy the conditions for an integral domain.

The concept of a field is one of the most important of all the concepts of algebra. A field is a postulational system satisfying the postulates $I1$–8 of an integral domain plus the additional postulate of a multiplicative inverse. The postulates of a field, thus, are:

$F1$–8 the same as $I1$–8, except that for identification purposes the set of elements will be referred to as F rather than I.

$F9$; multiplicative inverse.[1] If a is a nonzero element of F, then there is an element a^{-1} (a inverse) in F such that $a^{-1} \times a = 1$.

The system consisting of the set J of all integers and zero and the ordinary processes of addition and multiplication does not form a field, while the system consisting of the set R of all real numbers with addition and multiplication does constitute a field.   Why?

One or two simple illustrations will point up the basic significance of the concept of field.   In the field of complex numbers both

$$x^2 - y^2 = (x - y)(x + y)$$

and $x^2 + y^2 = (x - iy)(x + iy)$ are factorable, while in the field of real numbers only $x^2 - y^2$ is factorable.   The equation $x^2 + 1 = 0$ has no solution in the field of real numbers but has two solutions, $+i$ or $-i$, in the field of complex numbers.   In other words, in the field of real numbers the solution set for $x^2 + 1 = 0$ is the null set, while in the field of complex numbers it is $\{i, -i\}$.   The solution set for the equation

$$6x^2 + x - 2 = 0$$

is $\{\tfrac{1}{2}, -\tfrac{2}{3}\}$ in the field of rational numbers, the field of real numbers, or the field of complex numbers.   Why is this not a correct statement: the solution set for the equation $6x^2 + x - 2 = 0$ is $\{\tfrac{1}{2}\}$ in the field of positive rational numbers?   What is a correct statement describing the situation which would restrict the solution set of the equation to $\{\tfrac{1}{2}\}$?

One of the simplest of all significant algebraic structures is that of a *group*.   In a form suitable for the secondary school a group may be defined in either of two ways:

1. A *multiplicative group* is a closed system consisting of a set of elements G and the ordinary operation of multiplication satisfying the four postulates:

---

[1] With the postulate of the multiplicative inverse $F9$ the cancellation property $I9$ becomes an easily derived theorem.   For if a,b,c are in F and $c \neq 0$, then c^{-1} is also in F.   Then, if $ca = cb$, we have by equality property $E5$ that $c^{-1} \times (ca) = c^{-1} \times (cb)$. The associative property implies $(c^{-1} \times c) \times a = (c^{-1} \times c) \times b$, or, by $F9$, $1 \times a = 1 \times b$.   Whence, by $F7$ and $F3$, $a = b$.

$G1$. If a and b are in G, then $a \times b = b \times a$.
$G2$. If a, b, and c are in G, then $a \times (b \times c) = (a \times b) \times c$.
$G3$. There is an element 1 in G such that $a \times 1 = a$ for a in G.
$G4$. If a is in G, then there exists an element a^{-1} in G such that $a^{-1} \times a = 1$.

A familiar set of elements which form a multiplicative group is

$$\{1, -1, -i, i\},$$

where $i^2 = -1$. The multiplication table is as shown in the accompanying table. $G3$ is obviously satisfied. Since $-i \times i = i \times -i = 1$, $-i$ is the inverse of i and i is the inverse of $-i$. Similarly, 1 and -1 are each their own inverse. Thus $G4$ is satisfied. Since the table is sym-

$\times$	1	-1	$-i$	i
1	1	-1	$-i$	i
-1	-1	1	i	$-i$
$-i$	$-i$	i	-1	1
i	i	$-i$	1	-1

metric with respect to its principal diagonal, running from the upper left corner to the lower right corner, $G1$ is satisfied. As an example that $G2$ is satisfied, $-1 \times (i \times -i) = -1 \times (1) = -1$ and

$$(-1 \times i) \times -i = -i \times -i = i^2 = -1;$$

therefore, $-1 \times (i \times -1) = (-1 \times i) \times -i$.

2. An *additive group* is a closed system consisting of a set of elements G' and the ordinary operation of addition satisfying the four postulates:

$G'1$. If a and b are in G', then $a + b = b + a$.
$G'2$. If a, b, and c are in G', then $a + (b + c) = (a + b) + c$.
$G'3$. There is an element 0 in G' such that $a + 0 = a$ for a in G'.
$G'4$. If a is in G', then there exists an element $-a$ in G' such that $(-a) + a = 0$.

A simple illustration of such a group is the set $W = \{0,1,2,3,4,5,6\}$, with addition defined as ordinary addition modulo 7. Such addition simply means that we divide the sum of any two numbers by 7 and use the remainder to express the sum. For example, $4 + 6 = 3$, since $10 \div 7 = 1$ with a remainder of 3. A check of the accompanying table will establish the fact that the postulates $G'1$–4 are satisfied. For example, since the element 0 (which satisfies $G'3$) is in the set and since each number of the set occurs once and only once in each row, each element of

THE IMPACT OF MODERN MATHEMATICS

the set has an inverse element in the set.   Also, $G'1$ is satisfied, since the table is symmetric with respect to its principal diagonal.

+	0	1	2	3	4	5	6
0	0	1	2	3	4	5	6
1	1	2	3	4	5	6	0
2	2	3	4	5	6	0	1
3	3	4	5	6	0	1	2
4	4	5	6	0	1	2	3
5	5	6	0	1	2	3	4
6	6	0	1	2	3	4	5

The above illustration of an additive group may seem a bit artificial, but it is a mathematical model which can be used effectively in calendar reckoning.   This can be accomplished by labeling the days of the week as follows: Sunday, 0; Monday, 1; Tuesday, 2; Wednesday, 3; Thursday, 4; Friday, 5; and Saturday, 6.   Such questions as What day is 5 days from today? and What day was 4 days ago? are answered through simple arithmetic computation.   For example, if today is Saturday, or 6, the answer to the first question is Thursday, since $6 + 5 = 4$, and the answer to the second question is Tuesday, since $2 + 4 = 6$.

The groups, as defined and illustrated here, are *Abelian groups*.   If postulates $G1$ and $G'1$ were removed, the definitions would be those of non-Abelian groups.   The illustrations are of finite groups.   The set of all nonzero rational numbers with the operation of ordinary multiplication is an example of an infinite Abelian group.

An interesting example of a finite geometry as a postulational system which exhibits absolute consistency can be constructed in the following manner:[1]

1. Consider "point" and "line" as the undefined elements and "lies on" as the undefined relation.   Such concepts have meanings derived intuitively from concrete experiences of our daily life.

2. Use as the fundamental postulates of this sytem the following statements:

*FG*1. If P_1 and P_2 are distinct points, there is at least one line on which they both lie.

[1] O. Veblen and J. W. Young, "Projective Geometry" (Boston: Ginn & Company, 1910), vol. I, pp. 1–7.

*FG*2. If P_1 and P_2 are distinct points, there is not more than one line on which they both lie.

*FG*3. Any two lines have at least one point which lies on both lines.

*FG*4. There exists at least one line.

*FG*5. For every line there are at least three distinct points which lie on it.

*FG*6. All points do not lie on the same line.

*FG*7. No more than three distinct points lie on any one line.

Figure 3-1 exhibits a model satisfying all seven postulates, thus establishing the absolute consistency of the system. (*Note:* The three points P_2, P_4, and P_6 lie on the curved line.)

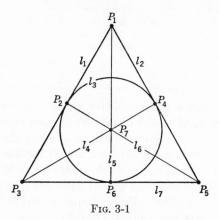

Fig. 3-1

By using these postulates, the following theorems can be proved:

Theorem 1. Any set of points satisfying the postulates *FG*1-7 contains at least seven points.

Theorem 2. For any two distinct points there exists one and only one line on which they both lie.

Theorem 3. There exist three points which do not all lie on the same line.

Theorem 4. For any two lines there is one and only one point which lies on both lines.

To illustrate the pattern of deduction, theorem 1 is proved.

Proof

1. There exists one line, call it l_1.   1. *FG*4.
2. There are exactly three points on l_1, say, P_1, P_2, and P_3.   2. *FG*5, 7.
3. There is at least one point not on l_1, say, P_4.   3. *FG*6.
4. Since P_4 is distinct from P_1, P_2, and P_3, there exist unique   4. *FG*1, 2, 3.
   and distinct lines $l_2(P_1P_4)$, $l_3(P_2P_4)$, and $l_4(P_3P_4)$.
5. There exists one and only one point on l_2 distinct from   5. *FG*5, 7.
   P_1 and P_4.

6. This point is also distinct from P_2 and P_3; call it P_5.

6. $FG1$, 2, and step 2.

7. Similarly, P_6 lies on l_3 and P_7 on l_4.

7. $FG1$, 2, 5, 7 and step 4.

8. P_1 now must lie on line P_6P_7 (call it l_5); P_2 on line P_5P_7 (call it l_6); and P_3 on line P_5P_6 (call it l_7).

8. $FG1, 2, 3, 5, 7$ and steps 2 and 4.

9. All postulates are now satisfied and there is a minimum of seven points, so the proof is complete.

The reader should provide proofs of the remaining three theorems.

While the above postulational system is oriented in the context of geometry, it can serve as a mathematical model for problems in distinctly different contexts.   Consider the following problem.

Example.   What is the minimum number of airplanes necessary to stage a demonstration designed to meet the following specifications?

1. There are to be formation patterns such that each two airplanes are to fly together in one and only one formation.

2. For any two formations there must be at least one airplane which flies in both formations.

3. There are to be exactly three airplanes which fly in each formation.

4. All airplanes cannot fly in the same formation.

If "airplane" is identified with "point," "formation" with "line," and "flies in" with "lies on," then it becomes evident that the specifications of this problem can be identified with postulates $FG1-7$.   Therefore, the answer to the question posed in the problem is this: A minimum of seven airplanes will be necessary to fly the specified formations.

Techniques of Deduction.   The new emphasis on the postulational structure of mathematical subject matter lends emphasis to the need for clearer understanding of the basic techniques used in valid patterns of deductive thinking.[1]   Such a pattern of argumentation is essentially one of combining statements, or propositions, into still other propositions.   There are four basic operations for making such combinations in order that they might lead to valid results.   They are *conjunction* ($\wedge$, read "and"), *disjunction* ($\vee$, read "either . . . or"), *implication* ($\rightarrow$, read "implies" or "if . . . then"), and equivalence ($\leftrightarrow$, read "is equivalent to" or "if and only if").   Rules for the use of these operations, known as truth tables, are given here.   The symbols p and q represent propositions, where by a "proposition" is meant a sentence so clearly stated that it can be declared unequivocally to be true or false.

---

[1] For an excellent discussion of such techniques see Carl B. Allendoerfer, Deductive Methods in Mathematics, "Twenty-third Yearbook" (Washington, D.C.: The National Council of Teachers of Mathematics, 1957), pp. 65–99.

The label T indicates that the proposition whose symbol is at the top of the column of any given table is to be considered as true, and F is the corresponding label for false.

Disjunction

Conjunction			Inclusive "or"			Exclusive "or"		
p	q	$p \wedge q$	p	q	$p \vee q$	p	q	$p \underline{\vee} q$
T	T	T	T	T	T	T	T	F
T	F	F	T	F	T	T	F	T
F	T	F	F	T	T	F	T	T
F	F	F	F	F	F	F	F	F

The conjunction of two propositions ($p \wedge q$) is considered true only if both propositions are true simultaneously.   The inclusive-"or" type of disjunction ($p \vee q$) is true if the label T can be applied to either one or both of the two propositions being combined.   The exclusive-"or" type of disjunction ($p \underline{\vee} q$) is considered true only when T is the label to be applied to one or the other *but not both* of the two propositions.   For example, consider the two propositions:

p: I shall go home.

q: I shall go to the show.

The conjunction $p \wedge q$ (I shall go home and I shall go to the show) is considered a true statement only if I go to both places.   The disjunction $p \vee q$ (I shall go either home or to the show) will be true if I go to either one or both places.   The disjunction $p \underline{\vee} q$ (at three o'clock either I shall go home or I shall go to the show) manifestly is true only if I am one place or the other; for I cannot be at both places at the same time.

Implication			Equivalence			Negation	
p	q	$p \to q$	p	q	$p \leftrightarrow q$	p	$\sim p$
T	T	T	T	T	T	T	F
T	F	F	T	F	F	F	T
F	T	T	F	T	F		
F	F	T	F	F	T		

The first two rows of the truth table for "implication" are quite acceptable from a purely intuitive point of view.   If we start with a true proposition and use a valid process of reasoning, it is quite natural to feel that we should arrive at a true conclusion.   That is the meaning to be derived from these first two lines.   A bit of reflection will convince one of the rationality and warn one of the danger pictured in the last two lines.   For example, consider the three following propositions concerning natural numbers:

p: $3 = 8$, which is false.

q_1: $11 = 11$, which is true.

q_2: $7 = 12$, which is false.

Let us now investigate the validity of these two theorems:

Theorem 1.   If $3 = 8$, then $11 = 11$ $(p \to q_1)$.

Theorem 2.   If $3 = 8$, then $7 = 12$ $(p \to q_2)$.

Theorem 1. $p \to q_1$.   *Theorem* 2. $p \to q_2$.

Proof

In each theorem we agree to accept p, though false, as the hypothesis.

1. $3 = 8$.   1. Hypothesis.   1. $3 = 8$.   1. Hypothesis.

2. $8 = 3$.   2. By $E2$ (p. 62).   2. $4 = 4$.   2. $E1$ (p. 62).

3. $11 = 11$.   3. Theorem (p. 63).   3. $7 = 12$.   3. Theorem (p. 63).

The law of the syllogism now justifies the conclusion:

4. $(3 = 8) \to (11 = 11)$, or $p \to q_1$.
A *false* hypothesis, through valid reasoning, has led to a *true* conclusion. This is the justification of line three of the truth table for "implication."

4. $(3 = 8) \to (7 = 12)$, or $p \to q_2$.
A *false* hypothesis, through valid reasoning, has led to a *false* conclusion. This is the justification of line four of the truth table for "implication."

Lines 3 and 4 of this truth table underscore the futility of reasoning from a false hypothesis.   Not only are the results questionable but the consequences dangerous.

The truth table for "equivalence" is to be interpreted as indicating that two statements are equivalent when and only when the same label applies to each, independently of context.   In the table, for example, in the rows where the statement $p \leftrightarrow q$ is labeled T, when p is true, so is q; when p is false, so is q; and conversely.

The table for "negation" is used simply to emphasize the statement made earlier that a proposition is a sentence that can be labeled as either true or false, in the sense of the exclusive "or."   Note that the symbol for the negation of a proposition p is $\sim p$, read "not p."

One of the most important principles of the process of deductive reasoning is the law of the syllogism, used above in the argument of theorems 1 and 2.   This law is of the form: If proposition p implies proposition q and proposition q implies proposition r, then it follows that proposition p implies proposition r.   This may be stated much more elegantly in symbolic form as $[(p \to q) \land (q \to r)] \to (p \to r)$.   Table 3-1, the truth table for this proposition of implication, illustrates a very important property of the law of the syllogism.   Columns 1, 2, and 3 display all the possible combinations of true and false of the three basic propositions p, q, and r. Columns 4 and 5 display the combinations of true and false for the two propositions whose conjunction is the hypothesis of the implication being investigated; column 6 records the analysis of the hypothesis; and column 7 records the analysis of the conclusion.   The final column exhibits the fact that the proposition being investigated is true regardless of the status of the original propositions p, q, and r as to truth or falsity.   A proposition formed by combining other propositions is a *tautology* if it is

Table 3-1
$$[(p \rightarrow q) \wedge (q \rightarrow r)] \rightarrow (p \rightarrow r)$$

1	2	3	4	5	6	7	8
p	q	r	$p \rightarrow q$	$q \rightarrow r$	$[(p \rightarrow q) \wedge (q \rightarrow r)]$	$p \rightarrow r$	$[(p \rightarrow q) \wedge (q \rightarrow r)] \rightarrow (p \rightarrow r)$
T	T	T	T	T	T	T	T
T	T	F	T	F	F	F	T
T	F	T	F	T	F	T	T
T	F	F	F	T	F	F	T
F	T	T	T	T	T	T	T
F	T	F	T	F	F	T	T
F	F	T	T	T	T	T	T
F	F	F	T	T	T	T	T

true independently of whether the component propositions are true or false.

One of the real trouble spots in the techniques of deductive reasoning is the proper use of related or derived implications; in particular this is true concerning the converse, inverse, and contrapositive propositions of a given implication.   If the given implication is $p \rightarrow q$, the *converse* is the implication $q \rightarrow p$, where hypothesis and conclusion have been interchanged; the *inverse* is $(\sim p) \rightarrow (\sim q)$, where both hypothesis and conclusion have been negated; the *contrapositive* is $(\sim q) \rightarrow (\sim p)$, where the hypothesis and conclusion have been both negated and interchanged. The truth table, Table 3-2, makes clear that *only* the contrapositive proposition is equivalent to the original proposition.   If one is true, so is the other; if one is false, so is the other.   This is not true for either the converse or the inverse.   For these two propositions separate investigations are necessary to determine whether they are true or false.

The following is a simple but interesting exercise.   First guess the answer to the question and then check your guess by the construction of the proper truth tables.

Table 3-2

p	q	$\sim p$	$\sim q$	Proposition, $p \to q$	Converse, $q \to p$	Inverse, $(\sim p) \to (\sim q)$	Contrapositive, $(\sim q) \to (\sim p)$
T	T	F	F	T	T	T	T
T	F	F	T	F	T	T	F
F	T	T	F	T	F	F	T
F	F	T	T	T	T	T	T

Example. Given the statement: If the sun shines, then the school will have a picnic $(p \to q)$. Which of the following is the negative of the given statement?

1. If the sun shines, then the school will not have a picnic $[p \to (\sim q)]$.

2. If the sun does not shine, then the school will have a picnic $[(\sim p) \to q]$.

3. The sun is shining and the school is not having a picnic $[p \wedge (\sim q)]$.

4. If the sun does not shine, then the school will not have a picnic $[(\sim p) \to (\sim q)]$.

5. The sun is not shining and the school will have a picnic $[(\sim p) \wedge q]$.

A great deal more can be said about the techniques of deduction; the effort here has been simply to point out some of the fundamental patterns and basic principles.

The Nature of Proof. Mathematics is primarily a deductive science in that propositions are proved by showing that they are implied by propositions that have been proved, definitions that have been stated, and postulates that have been accepted. The definitions of fundamental terms should be phrased to conform with experience, experiment, and common and universal usage. The principal characteristics of good definitions are clarity, simplicity, and brevity. In the last analysis there necessarily will be certain undefined terms which are accepted as established elements of common knowledge. For example, there is no clarification of concepts gained by setting up formal definitions of point, line, plane, and space in the approach to the study of geometry. Similarly, in any deductive science there necessarily will be a basic list of fundamental assumptions. It should be emphasized that these assumptions are merely statements accepted as true because of their conformity with common experience and sound judgment and that they are in no sense to be considered as "self-evident truths." From a pedagogical point of view the principal characteristics of such a body of assumptions are:

1. Consistency. There should be no contradictory statements in the list.

2. Simplicity of statement. The assumptions should be free from ambiguous statements and should be in a form that will permit ready deductions.

3. The assumptions should present no conflict with established knowledge or observable facts.

When a mathematical system has been clearly structured by the selection of the undefined elements, the definition of basic terms, and the acceptance of a fundamental set of assumptions, then the proving of theorems, i.e., derivable propositions, becomes the major concern. Every theorem has two characteristic properties, a hypothesis and a conclusion. The hypothesis is a statement, simple or compound, of the accepted relationships existing between elements of the given structure which are to be used in the search for the new relationships which are summed up in the conclusion, again a simple or compound statement. The *proof* of the theorem consists in the establishment of the truth of the conclusion through implications and inferences that find their original source of justification in the hypothesis. There are three distinct processes to be used in establishing the proof of any given theorem.

Synthetic Process. The synthetic process consists of the drawing of a series of necessary conclusions until the desired conclusion is reached. The hypothesis implies, as a necessary consequence, the hypothesis of some axiom, postulate, or previously established theorem; these hypotheses imply the conclusions associated with them, which in turn make further implications, and this chain of necessary deductions is pursued until the desired conclusion is reached. Although the simplicity, elegance, and rigor of this form of argument make it highly desirable, it is far from desirable as a sole procedure to be followed in deriving mathematical proofs. As a technique it makes no provision for the pupil to understand the reason for making significant constructions or applying auxiliary theorems. As a simple illustration let us consider a synthetic proof for the following theorem from geometry.

Theorem. If two sides of a triangle are equal, the angles opposite these sides are equal.

Fig. 3-2

Given. $\triangle ABC$, in which $AC = AB$.
To prove. $\angle B = \angle C$.

Proof

1. Draw AD bisecting $\angle BAC$ and meeting BC in D.
2. In $\triangle BAD$ and CAD, $AB = AC$.
3. $\angle BAD = \angle CAD$.
4. $AD = AD$.
5. $\therefore \triangle BAD \cong CAD$.

6. $\therefore \angle B = \angle C$.

1. To bisect a given angle.
2. By hypothesis.
3. By construction.
4. Common side.
5. Two triangles are congruent if two sides and the included angle of the one are respectively equal to two sides and the included angle of the other.
6. Corresponding angles of congruent $\triangle$.

The hypothesis of the given theorem, *through the auxiliary construction,* implies the conditions of the hypothesis of the congruence theorem (side, angle, side), which in turn implies through its conclusion the desired conclusion of the theorem, viz., the angles opposite the equal sides are equal. The inexperienced student, who has had no more insight into this theorem than that pictured here, is likely to become quite confused with the content of the very first step. Where did the author get the line AD? How did he know to draw it? Why not draw some other line? Many questions such as these are likely to arise, and they are certain indicators of a lack of understanding and self-confidence in the pursuit of geometric information. The neophyte in the techniques of deductive thinking needs more exercise of his intuition and opportunity for discovery than such a procedure provides.

Diagrammatically, the chain of reasoning may be written $H_1 \rightarrow H_2 \rightarrow C_2 \rightarrow C_1$, where the symbol $\rightarrow$ is to be read "implies" and H_i and C_i represent hypotheses and conclusions, respectively.

Analytic-Synthetic Process. The analytic-synthetic process is not only a principal research tool in the hands of the mature mathematician but also an effective technique for guiding the immature student in the ways of discovery and validation of results. The analysis is the process of discovery of ways and means of arriving at desired results. The investigator considers the desired conclusion and raises the question: What relation or property *is sufficient* to justify the use of this conclusion as a true statement? Once this relation or property is found, he analyzes it for the same purpose, with the hope in mind that ultimately he will arrive at the hypothesis of the theorem as the source of the chain of sufficient reasons. This process does not constitute a proof, however, until it has been established that the steps are reversible. The reverse argument is the *synthesis*.

The analytic approach to the theorem given above would be as follows:

1. By what methods can two angles be proved equal?

1. Among other methods, two angles can be proved equal if they can be shown to be corresponding angles of congruent ⚠.

2. Is it possible to introduce two congruent ⚠ into the figure?

2. Since $AB = AC$ by hypothesis, I see that by drawing the bisector of $\angle BAC$ I shall have the two congruent ⚠ BAD and CAD.

Analytic Process. In a sense the analytic process is a condensed form of the analytic-synthetic process. The investigator considers the desired conclusion and reasons that *it is implied* by the conclusion of some proposition. He follows such a chain of reasoning back to the hypothesis of the unproved theorem, thus closing the logical chain necessary to establish the validity of the desired conclusion. Diagrammatically, this type of proof may be written $C_1 \leftarrow C_2 \leftarrow H_2 \leftarrow H_1$, where the symbol $\leftarrow$ is read "is implied by."

Of course, the chain of implications can become much more complex than that indicated here, but the basic pattern remains the same regardless of the degree of complexity.

The two most important types of proof are *direct proof* and *indirect proof*. Direct argumentation takes place when we try to prove a truth as stated. The attempt is made to start with hypothesis and proceed through a chain of syllogistic reasoning to the implication of the desired conclusion. As has been pointed out above, it is frequently the case that a critical analysis of possible chains of sufficient conditions is *necessary* before an appropriate chain of necessary conclusions can be constructed.

Indirect reasoning (or indirect proof) is a method of reaching a desired conclusion through the process of investigation and elimination of *all other mutually exclusive possibilities.* Although teachers of mathematics have been inclined to neglect it, this form of argument is one of the most powerful and one of the most natural techniques of deduction. One prominent logician has estimated that about half of all our reasoned conclusions are arrived at through the method of indirect reasoning.[1] Another has said that "the process of *reductio ad absurdum* is of the greatest importance. It is the most prominent of all the methods by which men learn those truths of Nature that are unitedly known by the name of Science."[2]

[1] W. S. Jevons, "The Principles of Science" (London: Macmillan & Co., Ltd., 1920), p. 82.

[2] Alfred Milnes, "Elementary Notions of Logic" (London: W. Swan Sonnenschein and Co., 1884), p. 93.

A simple illustration of the technique of indirect reasoning is the following:

One evening Mr. Jones was reading when his light went out. He immediately set about to discover the source of the trouble. His first thought was that the current was out all over town, but a glance at his neighbor's house, where the lights were burning, eliminated that possible explanation. Next, he thought that the lights were out all over his house, but by trying a nearby lamp he found that it gave light, so another possibility was eliminated. By trying another lamp through the same floor plug, the light bulb of his lamp in another lamp, and his lamp with a light bulb known to be good, he finally eliminated all possibilities except the fact that there was something wrong with the wiring in the particular lamp he was using. Further investigation centered on the wiring of the lamp revealed the defect, which could then be corrected.

The characteristics of indirect reasoning that are put into play in the illustration are the use of contradictory possibilities and the gradual elimination of those which can be established as inconsistent with conditions which are known or can be shown to exist. First, Mr. Jones assumed (1) the current is out all over town or (2) the current is not out all over town. The error of the first of these assumptions was established by a glance at his neighbor's house, where the lights were burning. Second, he assumed (1) the lights are out all over the house or (2) the lights are not out all over the house. The fact that another lamp would light eliminated the first of these two possibilities. Similarly, in each succeeding case he was able to contrast two contradictory assumptions and test them for their validity until he was finally able to locate the source of the trouble definitely. Such pairs of contradictory propositions have the following characteristics:

1. They cannot both be true at the same time.
2. They cannot both be false at the same time.
3. If one of them is false, the other must be true.
4. If one of them is true, the other must be false.

If we wish, then, to prove one of two contradictory propositions true, it is sufficient to prove that the other one is false. This, in summary, is the essence of indirect proof in its simplest and most elemental form. It is based upon two fundamental and complementary laws or postulates of logic which, in turn, rest upon a third principle of logic for their application. These two laws are known as the law of contradiction and the law of the excluded middle. The law of contradiction asserts that a thing cannot both be and not be. The law of the excluded middle asserts that a thing must either be or not be. The above-mentioned characteristics of a pair of contradictory propositions are corollaries to these two postulates of logic and really give us our definition of contradictory propositions. This, of course, is to the effect that, if there exist two propositions having these characteristics, one of them must be true and the other one must be false.

The application of these two laws depends, as has been said, upon a third postulate of logic which asserts that there are only two ways in which a false conclusion may be reached. Either (1) the reasoning may be incorrect or (2) at least one of the assumptions upon which the reasoning is based may be false. If neither of these conditions exists in a given case, the conclusion which is reached must be correct. If either or both exist, the conclusion may be false. If, then, one reaches a false or inconsistent or contradictory conclusion and if he can be sure that he has reasoned correctly, it must follow that he must have started out with at least one false assumption.

There are at least two points of distinction to be noted between the method of indirect reasoning used by Mr. Jones in detecting the trouble with his floor lamp and the method of indirect proof as applied to propositions in mathematics. In the first place, propositions in mathematics are generally so stated that one knows at the outset the particular thing which he is required to establish, e.g., Prove that *under such and such conditions* so and so will be true. In the case of the lamp, as in many practical situations, it was not so simple as this at the outset. It was not a case of "prove that the trouble is in the lamp," but rather, a case of "find out in which of several possible places the trouble is located." In life situations the problems are generally not so strictly defined and delimited as they are in most propositions in mathematics. Moreover, it is generally easier in mathematical situations than in life situations to be sure that we have included all possibilities in our setup of the problem.

Secondly, the procedure is not identical in the two cases; it is usually more formal in mathematics. We set up our pair of contradictory statements, assume as true the one which we wish to prove untrue, and then set about showing, through a chain of logical reasoning, that this supposition necessarily leads to a contradiction or an inconsistency. This is the recognized and well-defined procedure. On the other hand, in a practical situation we rarely set down our possibilities in the manner of formal contradictory statements. We generally proceed more or less intuitively. But even if we should formalize the problem, our investigation of possibilities will often be more in the nature of open-minded experiment than by way of establishing a preconceived opinion by logical reasoning. For example, the light bulb was tested, not with the idea of proving logically that it was defective or with the idea of proving that it was good, but rather with the idea of *seeing whether or not* it was defective. Such experiment often requires less mental effort than the formal proof of the falsity of a mathematical proposition, so that, while indirect proof in mathematics is generally less complicated in its setup, this advantage is probably more than offset in many cases by the difficulty of the intellectual effort required in the investigation. This may explain why many people who have difficulty in using formal indirect proof in mathematics are able to apply more or less informal indirect reasoning in nonmathematical situations quite successfully.

The technique of indirect proof in mathematics may be conveniently analyzed into four very specific steps to be followed:

1. Set up a pair of contradictory propositions, one of which you desire to prove true. Select the latter at the outset.

2. Assume, for the time being, that the other of the two is true and test the consequences by deductive reasoning to see whether this assumption leads to a contradiction or an inconsistency.

3. If the assumption of step 2 does lead, by correct reasoning, to an inconsistency or a contradiction, conclude that it was a false hypothesis.

4. Under the conditions of step 3, conclude that the contradictory propositions selected in step 1, i.e., the one you want to prove true, is necessarily true, since the only alternative proposition has been shown to be false.

It should be noted that, when the proposition to be proved is in the form of an implication, the pattern of argumentation by indirect proof is essentially identical with that of argumentation by use of the contrapositive proposition.

Two other forms of proof, which are of limited significance, are the *existence proof* and the *enumeration proof*. The existence proof consists in setting up an example which establishes the truth of the proposition. For example, suppose the statement is that every quadratic equation with complex coefficients has two roots of the form $a + bi$, where a and b are real numbers. The general quadratic equation in its simplest form is $x^2 + px + q = 0$, with p and q both real. The two values $(-p + \sqrt{p^2 - 4q})/2$ and $(-p - \sqrt{p^2 - 4q})/2$ can be verified as solutions, and they are of the form $a + bi$. The enumeration proof, which has application in a situation involving only a small number of cases, consists in checking each case for the truth of a given proposition. For example, it would not be a very difficult job to verify that multiplication is commutative for the positive integers modulo four.

The mathematician frequently is involved in efforts to disprove a proposition rather than prove it. The use of *counterexamples* is an effective method for disproving statements. For example, the statement that $p = n^2 - n + 41$ will always produce a prime number can be disproved by the fact that, when $n = 41$, $p = (41)^2$, which is not prime. Unfortunately, this technique is of no value in the proof of the truth of a general statement. Another effective method for disproof is that of *contradiction*. This technique involves assuming the truth of some statement and then showing that a chain of logical deductions from this assumed truth leads to the contradiction of some previously established truth. This is, of course, quite similar to the method of indirect proof.

The Nature and Significance of Induction.[1]   Although the deductive process provides the technique for drawing valid conclusions and deriving necessary consequences, the inductive process provides the means for imaginative inquiry and daring discovery. The investigation of specific cases and the observation of characteristic behavior can lead to conjectured generalizations. Such induction has played a very significant role in the history of mathematical research. Euler is credited with having said:[2]

> The properties of the numbers known today have been mostly discovered by observation, and discovered long before their truth has been confirmed by rigid demonstration. There are even many properties of the numbers with which we are well acquainted, but which we are not yet able to prove; only observations have led us to this knowledge.

Two of the most famous illustrations of the lasting truth of the above statement are Fermat's last theorem, "The equation $a^n + b^n = c^n$ is not solvable in integers for any $n > 2$" and Goldbach's conjecture, "Every even number greater than 2 is the sum of two prime numbers." Neither of these statements has been either proved or disproved, but each has challenged many mathematicians to engage in significant research. The immature pupil needs guidance in learning how to profit from considered guesses and significant hunches. He needs to be taught to search experience and experimentation for basic information upon which to base pertinent inductions.

When a pupil measures the angles of several triangles and finds that in each case the sum of the angles closely approximates 180°, or when he cuts out these angles and fits them together and finds that they make a straight angle, he has the background for the induction that the sum of the interior angles of any triangle is 180°. If an individual had two containers, one conical in shape and the other cylindrical but of the same height and diameter, it would be a very simple experiment to show that the conical container held only one-third as much as the one which was cylindrical in shape. The induction might possibly follow for this individual that such

---

[1] For a very helpful and enlightening treatment on the significance of induction as a mathematical process see G. Pólya, "Mathematics and Plausible Reasoning" (Princeton, N.J.: Princeton University Press, 1954), vols. I and II.

[2] Pólya, *op. cit.*, vol. I, p. 3.

a relationship between the contents of a cone and a cylinder of the same dimensions would always hold. Such inductions are important in the discovery of mathematical truths regardless of the area of interest.

On the other hand, there are many dangers involved in making use of the inductive process. It is always dangerous to make generalizations from specific cases. In the case of the above-mentioned formula $p = n^2 - n + 41$, each of the values of n from 1 through 40 will produce a value for p which is a prime number. The one counterexample, however, when $n = 41$, is sufficient to destroy the generalization one might be tempted to make. Discoveries by induction are in the realm of probable truths. Thus by induction the pupil who experiments with the angles of a triangle or the relationship between a cone and cylinder of like dimensions can only say, in the respective cases, (1) It is probably true that the sum of the interior angles of any triangle is 180°; (2) the volume of a cone is probably equal to one-third the volume of a cylinder of the same dimensions.

Such experiments as these lay the foundations for inductive generalizations which in turn call for deductive demonstrations to establish validity and universality of application.

What of the Impact?   There is such a great amount of activity, both individual and group, directed toward curriculum revision in mathematics that it would be quite difficult, if not entirely impossible, to delineate the total, or even the most significant, impact which modern mathematics will have on the programs of the elementary and secondary schools.   The fact is that the impetus which has inspired the cooperative efforts now in process has the potential of providing the interest and stimulation which will foster a continuing concern that the mathematics program in our schools shall be live, stimulating, and challenging.   Whatever the final results may be, it is safe to say that some of the immediate effects will be a greatly increased emphasis on structure, a reconsideration and refinement of definitions, a clearer attention to the deductive process, a better balance in the treatment of equations and inequalities, a broadening of the concepts of algebra and geometry, a revised treatment of trigonometric functions and techniques, a more realistic treatment of techniques and principles of measurement, a fundamental treatment of probability and statistical inference, and a reevaluation of the significance of many of the manipulative procedures at all levels of instruction.

Teachers and curriculum workers alike must keep in mind that there is good and bad in both the old and the new in mathematics. The possible contributions of each to the mathematics program of our schools must be weighed in the scales of effective and efficient training in mathematics in an era when technological patterns are subject to rapid and drastic change. Such change can outmode in rapid and serious fashion mere manipulative procedures, but the basic structure of mathematical systems is anchored on the rocks of ageless endurance. This significant fact very possibly may serve as the keystone to all future curriculum planning in elementary and secondary mathematics. If this should be the case, then the result of the impact of modern mathematics on the program of the secondary school will be tremendous.

EXERCISES

1. Give two illustrations of "modern mathematics as a point of view."
2. Give two illustrations of "modern mathematics as new subject matter."
3. What is meant by the basic structure of arithmetic? Of algebra? Of geometry?
4. What are the basic postulates of Lobachevskian geometry? Of Riemannian geometry? Of Euclidean geometry?
5. What are the implications of this statement: One man's postulate may be another man's theorem?
6. What is meant by the consistency of a system of postulates?
7. What is meant by a mathematical model?
8. Distinguish between relative consistency and absolute consistency.
9. What is the principle of duality for two-space? For three-space?
10. State the plane dual of the following: (a) A triangle consists of three noncollinear points and their three lines of join. (b) The opposite sides of any simple hexagon whose vertices lie on a conic intersect (are joined) in three points which lie on a line.
11. State the space dual of the following: (a) A tetrahedron consists of four noncoplanar points, no three of which are collinear, and their six lines of join. (b) A triangle consists of three coplanar but noncollinear points and their three lines of join.
12. Why are triangles and tetrahedrons said to be self-dual figures?
13. Exhibit a method of setting up a one-to-one correspondence between the positive even integers and the natural numbers.
14. Why is the geometry exhibited on pages 67 to 69 called a finite geometry?
15. Establish that the relations of similarity and congruence of geometric figures are relations of equivalence.
16. Why are the relations "is less than" ($<$) and "is greater than" ($>$) called inequalities?
17. Which of the following relations are equivalence relations? (a) "Is as tall as," (b) "is shorter than," (c) "is less than or equal to" ($\leqq$), (d) "is the father of," (e) "is identical to," (f) "has the same area as."
18. Two complex numbers $a + bi$ and $c + di$ are said to be equal if and only if $a = c$ and $b = d$. Show that this relation between complex numbers satisfies the five properties of equality of numbers.
19. Show that numbers of the form $a + bi$ (with a and b real and with the usual definitions of equality, addition, and multiplication of complex numbers) constitute an integral domain.
20. Which of the following sets of numbers, with the usual definitions of addition and multiplication, constitute a field? (a) Positive integers, (b) all integers, including zero, (c) rational numbers, (d) real numbers, (e) complex numbers.
21. Do the positive integers with addition modulo 5 form a group? With modulo 6? With multiplication modulo 5? With modulo 6?

22. Construct the truth table in each case: (a) $[(p \to q) \land (q \to r)] \to (p \to r)$, (b) $[\sim(p \lor q)] \leftrightarrow [(\sim p) \land (\sim q)]$, (c) $[\sim(p \to q)] \leftrightarrow [p \land (\sim q)]$.

23. Which of the statements of exercise 22 are tautologies?

24. First express each of the following statements symbolically and then construct the truth table.

a. If Ann is informed and Sue is uninformed, then Ann will win the prize.

b. Ann will win the prize if and only if she is informed or Sue is uninformed.

c. If Sue is uninformed but Ann fails to win the prize, then Ann is uninformed.

d. It is not true that Ann is uninformed if and only if Sue is uninformed.

25. Which of the two following arguments is valid? Verify your answer symbolically.

a. If Ann is informed, then Sue is uninformed. Sue is informed only if Ann does not win the prize. Therefore, if Ann wins the prize, she is informed.

b. If Ann is informed, then Sue is uninformed. Ann will not win the prize only if Sue is informed. Therefore, if Ann does not win the prize, she must not be informed.

26. How many men will it take to form committees meeting the following conditions?

a. If M_1 and M_2 represent two different men, then there is one and only one committee on which both M_1 and M_2 serve.

b. Any two committees have at least one man in common.

c. There is at least one committee.

d. Not all men serve on the same committee.

e. Each committee consists of three and only three men.

27. What is the smallest number of committees that can be formed under the conditions of exercise 26?

28. What is meant by the deductive process?

29. Select an editorial, news item, or advertisement and analyze it for terms which need to be defined, assumptions which are made, and conclusions which are drawn. Evaluate the validity of these conclusions.

30. Distinguish between induction and deduction, synthesis and analysis.

31. Why, in a deductive science, must there be undefined terms and accepted assumptions?

32. Is there any significant difference in the logical and pedagogical implications of the fact that there must be undefined terms and accepted assumptions in a deductive science?

33. Distinguish between the implications of (a) a self-evident truth and (b) an accepted assumption.

34. Distinguish between direct proof and indirect proof.

BIBLIOGRAPHY

Allendoerfer, C. B., and C. O. Oakley: "Principles of Mathematics" (New York: McGraw-Hill Book Company, Inc., 1955).

Andree, Richard V.: Modern Trigonometry, *Mathematics Teacher*, **48** (1955), 82–83.

———: How Modern Mathematical Concepts Shed Light on Elementary Mathematics, *Mathematics Magazine*, **28** (1955), 173–176.

———: What Is a Geometric Tangent? *Mathematics Teacher*, **50** (1957), 498–501.

Banks, J. Houston: "Elements of Mathematics" (New York: Allyn and Bacon, Inc., 1956).

Beberman, Max, and Bruce E. Meserve: Graphing in Elementary Algebra, *Mathematics Teacher*, **49** (1956), 260–266.

Bennett, Albert A.: A Note on "Variable," *Mathematics Teacher*, **48** (1955), 464–468.

Boyer, C. B.: Descartes and the Geometrization of Algebra, *American Mathematical Monthly*, **66** (1959), 390–393.

Bradley, Spurgeon: Modern Mathematics and the High School, *Peabody Journal of Education*, **33** (1956), 334–336.

Bruck, R. H.: Recent Advances in the Foundations of Euclidean Plane Geometry, *American Mathematical Monthly*, **62** (August–September, II, 1955), 2–17.

Brumfiel, Charles: The Foundations of Algebra, *Mathematics Teacher*, **50** (1957), 488–492.

————: The Ball State Experimental Program in Geometry and Algebra, *American Mathematical Monthly*, **66** (1959), 228–233.

————, Robert Eicholz, and Merrill Shanks: The Ball State Experimental Program, *Mathematics Teacher*, **53** (1960), 75–84.

Brune, Irvin H.: Symbols and Functions, *Mathematics Teacher*, **51** (1958), 232–235.

Commission on Mathematics of College Entrance Examination Board: "Introduction to Algebra from the Point of View of Mathematical Structure" (Princeton, N.J.: Educational Testing Service, 1958). (Pamphlet.)

————: "Modernizing the Mathematics Curriculum" (Princeton, N.J.: Educational Testing Service, 1958). (Pamphlet.)

————: "Sets and Functions" (Princeton, N.J.: Educational Testing Service, 1958). (Pamphlet.)

Court, Nathan Altshiller: "Mathematics in Fun and in Earnest" (New York: The Dial Press, Inc., 1958).

Diamond, Louis E.: Some Elementary Properties of the Relation, Congruence, Modulo M, *Mathematics Magazine*, **28** (1955), 213–220.

Duren, W. L., Jr.: The Maneuvers in Set Thinking, *Mathematics Teacher*, **51** (1958), 322–335.

Eves, Howard, and Carroll V. Newsom: "An Introduction to the Foundations and Fundamental Concepts of Mathematics" (New York: Rinehart & Company, Inc., 1958).

Exner, Robert M., and Myron F. Rosskopf: "Logic in Elementary Mathematics" (New York: McGraw-Hill Book Company, Inc., 1959).

Fehr, Howard F.: "Secondary Mathematics" (Boston: D. C. Heath and Company, 1951).

Graves, Lawrence M.: The Postulates of Algebra, and Non-Archimedean Number Systems, *Mathematics Teacher*, **52** (1959), 72–77.

Jones, Burton W.: Miniature Number Systems, *Mathematics Teacher*, **51** (1958), 226–231.

————: Miniature Geometries, *Mathematics Teacher*, **52** (1959), 66–71.

Kennedy, Joe: Modern Mathematics in the Twelfth Grade, *Mathematics Teacher*, **52** (1959), 97–100.

Kenner, Morton R.: Helmholtz and the Nature of Geometrical Axioms: A Segment in the History of Mathematics, *Mathematics Teacher*, **50** (1957), 98–104.

Klimczak, W. J.: The Solution of Linear Equations and Inequalities, *Mathematics Teacher*, **48** (1955), 460–463.

Luce, R. D.: "*Studies in Mathematics*," vol. I, "Some Basic Mathematical Concepts" (New Haven, Conn.: School Mathematics Study Group, 1959).

MacLane, Saunders: The Impact of Modern Mathematics, *Bulletin of the National Association of Secondary-School Principals*, **38** (1954), 66–70.

May, Kenneth O.: What Does "If" Mean? *Mathematics Teacher*, **48** (1955), 10–12.

Meder, Albert E., Jr.: Modern Mathematics and Its Place in the Secondary School, *Mathematics Teacher*, **50** (1957), 418–424.

————: What Is Wrong with Euclid? *Mathematics Teacher*, **51** (1958), 578–584.

———— with the collaboration of Edward Begle, Julius Hlavaty, Cletus Oakley, Robert E. K. Rourke, and Max Sobel: "Teacher Education in Modern Mathematics" [five 16-mm sound motion pictures] (New York: McGraw-Hill Book Company, Inc., 1959). (These films, titled Patterns in Mathematics, Number Fields, Irrational Numbers, Concept of Function, and Sentences and Solution Sets, are suitable for acquisition and use by secondary schools under Title III of the National Defense Act of 1958 to strengthen instruction in mathematics.)

Menger, Karl: Why Johnny Hates Math, *Mathematics Teacher*, **49** (1956), 578–584.

Meserve, Bruce E.: Foundations of Algebra, *Mathematics Teacher*, **50** (1957), 356–360.

————: Implications for the Mathematics Curriculum, "Twenty-third Yearbook" (Washington, D.C.: National Council of Teachers of Mathematics, 1957), pp. 404–428.

National Council of Teachers of Mathematics: "Insights into Modern Mathematics," *Twenty-third Yearbook* (Washington, D.C.: National Council of Teachers of Mathematics, 1957).

————: "The Growth of Mathematical Ideas," *Twenty-fourth Yearbook* (Washington, D.C.: National Council of Teachers of Mathematics, 1959).

Northrop, E. P.: Modern Mathematics and the Secondary School Curriculum, *Mathematics Teacher*, **48** (1955), 386–393.

Olander, Clarence E.: Let's Teach Statistics, *Mathematics Teacher*, **51** (1958), 253–260.

Pólya, G.: "Mathematics and Plausible Reasoning" (Princeton, N.J.: Princeton University Press, 1954), vols. I and II.

————: Mathematics as a Subject for Learning Plausible Reasoning, *Mathematics Teacher*, **52** (1959), 7–9.

Richardson, Moses: "Fundamentals of Mathematics" (New York: The Macmillan Company, 1941).

Rippey, Robert M.: A Unit about Numbers, *Mathematics Teacher*, **52** (1959), 101–104.

Rosenberg, Herman: The Changing Concept of Trigonometry as a School Subject, *Mathematics Teacher*, **51** (1958), 246–252.

Rosskopf, Myron F., and Robert M. Exner: Some Concepts of Logic and Their Applications in Elementary Mathematics, *Mathematics Teacher*, **48** (1955), 293–297.

Rourke, Robert E. K.: Some Implications of the Twentieth Century Mathematics for High Schools, *Mathematics Teacher*, **51** (1958), 74–86.

———— and Myron F. Rosskopf: What Do We Mean? *Mathematics Teacher*, **49** (1956), 597–604.

Schumaker, John A.: The Algebra of Sets in the Teaching of Trigonometry, *Mathematics Teacher*, **52** (1959), 20–23.

Servais, W.: Equations and Geometric Loci: A Logical Synthesis, *Mathematics Teacher*, **50** (1957), 114–122.

Smart, J. R.: Algebra: A Modern Secondary School Subject, unpublished doctoral dissertation (Nashville, Tenn.: George Peabody College for Teachers, 1957).

Students of Algebra II, University High School, Florida State University: Symbolic Logic and Logical Circuitry in the High School: *Mathematics Teacher*, **50** (1957), 23–26.

Tierney, John A.: Trigonometric Functions of a Real Number, *Mathematics Teacher*, **50** (1957), 38–39.

University of Illinois Committee on School Mathematics: Words, 'Words,' "Words," *Mathematics Teacher*, **50** (1957), 194–198.

Wiseman, John D., Jr.: Complex Figures in Geometry, *Mathematics Teacher*, **52** (1959). 91–94.

4

MODERN CURRICULUM PROBLEMS
IN MATHEMATICS

The current interest in and demand for change in the mathematics program of the secondary school springs from three clearly defined sources: (1) the great hiatus existing between the content of the mathematics curriculum and the spirit and genius of modern mathematical thought, (2) the misdirected emphases in instructional patterns, and (3) the mathematical inadequacies of the high school graduate. Some have argued that, though mathematics is one of the fastest growing of all the sciences, it is being taught in our schools as though nothing new had happened in at least the last three centuries.[1] Others have felt that the program of instruction of recent years has tended to place too great emphasis on the manipulative aspects of mathematics, with entirely too little attention being paid to the basic structure and fundamental interrelationships.[2] Furthermore, frequent expressions of concern over the mathematical inadequacies of high school graduates have been published in newspapers and periodicals, and many of the complaints have been substantiated by reliable experimentation.[3]

[1] See George A. W. Boehm's two articles, The New Mathematics, *Fortune*, **57** (June, 1958), 141–145ff, and The New Uses of the Abstract, *ibid.*, **57** (July, 1958), 124–127, 152ff. See also Peter Drucker, Mathematics Even Parents Can Understand, *Harper's Magazine*, **216** (April, 1958), 73–75ff.

[2] Maurice L. Hartung, Trends in Secondary School Mathematics, *School Science and Mathematics*, **58** (1958), 25–26.

Albert E. Meder, Jr., Modern Mathematics and Its Place in the Secondary School, *Mathematics Teacher*, **50** (1957), 418–423, and What Is Wrong with Euclid? *ibid.*, **51** (1958), 578–584.

Karl Menger, New Approach to Teaching Intermediate Mathematics, *Science*, **127** (1957), 1320.

E. P. Northrop, Modern Mathematics and the Secondary School Curriculum, *Mathematics Teacher*, **48** (1955), 386–393.

Robert E. K. Rourke, Some Implications of the Twentieth Century Mathematics for High Schools, *Mathematics Teacher*, **51** (1958), 74–86.

[3] Katherine C. Mires, General Mathematics for College Freshman, *Mathematics Teacher*, **50** (1957), 513–516. Also see the reference to studies by Beckmann, Brown, Davis, Ohlsen, and Renner listed in the bibliography for Chap. 2.

The references listed here are but a sample of the many expressions of concern, from both laymen and professional people, over the mathematics program in our schools.   Further significance is given to this important current educational problem by the work of committees representing the thinking of prominent professional organizations,[1] and the experimentation being carried on for the purpose of discovery of pertinent modifications of curriculum content and instructional procedures.[2]

Although the mathematics program of the elementary school has received some attention amid all this professional activity,[3] the major portion of interest and concern of all groups has been directed toward the junior high school, the senior high school, and the junior college, with a particular concern being directed toward the formulation of a more realistic program for taking care of individual differences.

Grades Seven and Eight.   The mathematics program of grades 7 to 9 has been a problem of great concern for many years.   The varying patterns of administrative organization (6-3-3, 6-6, 7-5, and 8-4) contribute confusion to the basic educational philosophy which should underlie the program of the junior high school; distorted interpretations of educational values becloud the objectives of instruction; unrealistic standards of competency for promotion from lower grades tend to temper the challenge of instruction; and inadequate preparation of teachers restricts the depth of understanding in presentation of materials.   It is a well-known fact that, during these impressionistic years, many boys and girls lose interest in mathematics.   Some observers feel that this is due, in large measure, to the overemphasis on "socialized arithmetic" in the seventh and eighth grades.   The Secondary School Curriculum Committee states:[4]

In grades seven and eight much of the time is given to so-called social applications, some of which seem inappropriate at this level.   Few new mathematical ideas are introduced.   Teachers often report that the traditional courses at this

[1] See Bibliography listings as follows: Commission on Mathematics of the College Entrance Examination Board, Committee on the Undergraduate Mathematical Program, Joint Committee of the American Society for Engineering Education and the Mathematical Association of America, Midwest State College Conference on Science and Mathematics Teacher Education, National Council of Teachers of Mathematics, Secondary School Curriculum Committee, and Washington Conference of the Mathematical Association of America.

[2] For example, the experiments in process at the Universities of Illinois, Syracuse, and Maryland and the Ball State Teachers College.

[3] See "Twenty-fourth Yearbook" and "Twenty-fifth Yearbook" (Washington, D.C.: National Council of Teachers of Mathematics, 1959, 1960), the work of the Elementary School Curriculum Committee of the National Council and the School Mathematics Study Group, and the extended experimentation program of the University of Illinois Project.

[4] Secondary School Curriculum Committee, Report of, *Mathematics Teacher*, **52** (1959), 403.

level offer little challenge to the upper 50 per cent of the pupils, and that review and maintenance provided for the lower 50 per cent usually serve only to deaden their interest because emphasis usually is on drill, with little provision for bringing out deeper insight and understanding.

The Commission on Mathematics of the College Entrance Examination Board recommends a program for grades 7 and 8 which it feels the college-capable can cover in one and one-half years. The outline of this program is:[1]

(1) *Fundamental operations and numeration*—whole numbers and fractions (common and decimal), place value in the decimal system and other systems (particularly the binary), arithmetic mean, and a knowledge of square root including methods of approximating square roots of whole numbers. (2) *Ratio*—making comparisons and scale drawings, per cent with moderate treatment of applications. (3) *Measurement*—English and metric systems, geometric measurements, use of ruler and protractor, indirect measurement of lengths, areas, volumes, etc. (4) *Relationships among geometric elements*—parallel, perpendicular, intersecting, and oblique lines (in a plane and in space), various types of angles and triangles, Pythagorean relation, sums of interior angles of polygons, symmetry about a point and a line. (5) *Graphs and formulas*—reading and construction of bar graphs, line graphs, pictograms, circle graphs, and continuous line graphs, meaning of a scale, basic formulas.

The content and pattern of instruction in the eighth grade has created a problem of greater concern than has that of the seventh grade. There are many who feel rather strongly that, particularly in this grade, the mathematics program is impaired very seriously because of its incidental relationship to the analysis and solution of social problems which, at best, are of questionable interest and value to immature boys and girls. Mathematics cannot be taught effectively at any grade level when presented only in such incidental fashion. The programs of both grades 7 and 8 thus constitute a fundamental curriculum problem of current interest and significance. Scattered experimentation is investigating, for appropriateness of presentation and challenge, units from such areas as nondecimal numeration, factoring and primes, nonmetric geometry, techniques of deductive reasoning, averages, finite systems, measurement, approximations, and probability and statistics.[2]

Some feel that the first course in algebra should become the program for the eighth grade. Others would rather extend the instruction in this grade to more advanced properties of number and more general treatment of graphs. Many feel that, whatever the curriculum content of the math-

[1] "Report of Commission on Mathematics of the College Entrance Examination Board" (New York: College Entrance Examination Board, 1959), p. 19.

[2] School Mathematics Study Group, "Experimental Units for Grades Seven and Eight" (New Haven, Conn.: Yale University, 1959).

ematics program for grades 7 and 8 might be, it must be mathematics, with the emphasis on adaptation to social usage held incidental and used only as an instructional aid in the systematic development of the fundamental mathematical concepts and principles of pertinent concern.

The curriculum content and instructional techniques of grades 7 and 8 are thus seen to present many problems of current concern.   The problems are of such great educational consequence that they demand wide experimentation and intense investigation before intelligent proposals can be made for their significant solution.

Grade Nine.   The philosophy of the junior high school has been defined in terms of four fundamental principles: (1) better articulation between the elementary school and the secondary school, (2) exploration, revelation, and guidance, (3) interpretation of environment, and (4) motivation. Under the influence of this philosophy and inspiration of men like Felix Klein, of Germany, John Perry, of Scotland, and E. H. Moore, of America, there developed early in this century a demand for a noncompartmentalized form of organization of subject matter in the mathematics program of the secondary school.   Although there were a few scattered efforts during the early days of the movement toward such a pattern in grades 10 to 12, the ninth grade has been, until fairly recently, the only grade for which there has been any generally recognized acceptance of such a program as a basic plan for the organization of mathematical subject matter. The recommendations of the Committee on Mathematical Requirements (1923), the Joint Commission (1940), and the Commission on Post-War Plans (1945) gave support to the significance of such a program in general mathematics for grade 9.   The basic purposes of such a program, as designed by its original proponents, were to show the interrelationships between the fundamental structure and techniques of the major areas of mathematical endeavor and to build for the individual an understanding and competence in mathematics essential for intelligent living amid the quantitative demands of a technological environment.   It was thus designed as a second-track program for those pupils who had neither aptitude nor interest to justify their pursuing the course in first-year algebra.

While the two-track approach has continued to characterize the program of the ninth grade in most schools, it is unfortunately true that narrow interpretations of some of the implications of the pragmatism which has predominated in our educational philosophy of recent years succeeded in serious misdirection of the emphasis in presentation of the program in general mathematics.   This diversion of basic purpose has followed two patterns: (1) The mathematical content has been made incidental to the social situation and (2) the content has been allowed to degenerate in many areas into that of a refresher program of drill, trivial problem solving, and repetition of the mechanics of operation.   This fact has caused great concern among those interested in a bona fide program in mathematics which can be of distinct benefit to educable boys and girls of ninth-grade stature.

The consensus of committee reports, experimentation, and professional point of view seems, at present, to favor one program in algebra but with varying degrees of emphasis and levels of attainment. For example, the Secondary School Curriculum Committee states:[1]

All students may eventually study the same algebra, but not at the same depth of understanding, at the same time and rate, with the same application, nor necessarily in the same sequence. Thus, for example, in the ninth school year, one group may be doing a development of the number system from an axiomatic point of view, another group may be studying positive and negative numbers as usually presented in an inductive manner, while a third less able group may be making use of the basic concepts of algebra to help strengthen their understanding of arithmetic processes.

While the emphasis seems to be to make drastic modifications in the general-mathematics program of the ninth grade, the algebra program is also being subjected to rather critical survey. Here the principal emphasis is more in the direction of modernization of content and treatment. New concepts from the language of sets will be used for refinement of basic definitions and principles; relative importance of different areas of subject matter will be weighed and new concepts and techniques will be introduced; mechanical manipulation no longer will predominate the instructional pattern but will allow for attention to basic structure. The Commission on Mathematics makes this statement:[2]

In the proposed program, the mechanics or formal manipulations in algebra will be the same as hitherto taught, and the subject matter is largely the same. The difference is principally in concept, in terminology, in some symbolism, and in the introduction of a rather large segment of new work dealing with inequalities, treated both algebraically and graphically. Solution sets of inequalities involving two variables are also studied.

The new emphasis in the study of algebra is upon the understanding of the fundamental ideas and concepts of the subject, such as the nature of number systems and the basic laws for addition and multiplication (commutative, associative, distributive). The application of these laws in various number systems, with emphasis on the generality of the laws, the meanings of conditional equations and identities and inequalities is stressed. The nature of a function—in particular, the linear, the quadratic, exponential, and logarithmic functions—is also discussed.

There are many problems of curriculum content and instructional procedure in the revision of the mathematics program of grades 7 to 9. Only

[1] Secondary School Curriculum Committee, *op. cit.*, pp. 408–409.
[2] Commission on Mathematics, *op. cit.*, pp. 21–22.

through the considered deliberation and careful experimentation of interested and informed groups can effective solutions be found.

The Senior High School. One of the major criticisms directed against the mathematics program of the senior high school is that it has been largely a bag of unrelated specialties and manipulative procedures. Artificial barriers exist between arithmetic, algebra, geometry, and trigonometry. The needed extensions of our number system from the domain of positive numbers of the elementary school are made mostly by rule and rote rather than by discovery and understanding. Algebra still has the ring of the seventeenth-century pattern of learning the proper trick to perform to arrive at the solutions of problems, many of which are couched in language of social artificiality. Geometry, when compared with Euclid's "Elements" of 300 B.C., presents basically the same subject content but a psychologically thinned presentation, which too frequently has removed significant challenge rather than provided better learning conditions. Trigonometry continues to overemphasize the computation and triangle-solution techniques and not to pay sufficient attention to the analytic behavior of the circular functions.

The modern emphasis in mathematics points out that the true essence of mathematics is in logic, decision making, and in systematic search for the underlying structure of any given system or situation. Formerly, instruction in mathematics tended toward the search for various types of quantitative problems as they arose. There were some who even recommended the grouping of problems by types and adapting solution techniques to the individual characteristics of respective types. Now the emphasis is directed toward the search for underlying principles and basic structure as guides to fundamental generalizations and abstractions. "Technology is subject to rapid change. Training in specifics can, and may, soon become obsolete. On the other hand, a person with fundamental training in mathematics will have the background for making adaptations to applications, even to those not now foreseen."[1] This quotation might very well be considered the basic theme directing the thinking and activity of those interested in essential revision of the mathematics curriculum of the secondary school.

The content of algebra will no longer be defined largely in terms of manipulative skills; rather, it will emphasize a study of mathematical structure. Attention will be directed to the postulational structure of algebraic systems and to the use of deductive techniques in the development of the basic properties of such a system. Such concepts as group, integral domain, and field will be used to clarify and simplify algebraic language. The language of sets will be used also for clarification, simplification, and unification of concepts and techniques. For example, a *variable* may be defined as a symbol which represents any one of a set of elements.

[1] Secondary School Curriculum Committee, *op. cit.*, pp. 411–412.

The *set of elements* is called the domain of the variable. Similarly a *relation* may be defined as a set of ordered pairs (x,y) such that to each value of the first element x there corresponds at least one value for the second element. The domain of the first element is called the domain of the relation, and that of the second element, the range of the relation. If to each value of the first element there corresponds one and only one value of the second element, then the relation is called a *function*.

Equations and inequalities may be thought of as sentences which make statements about the variables included. These statements may be thought of as *set selectors*, in that they select values of the variables for which the sentence is true. Thus, if the *universal set*, the set from which all usable values are to be selected, is the set of all integers, the sentence $x + 1 = 5$ selects the value 4; the sentence $y = x^2$, when x is assigned arbitrary values, selects all integral squares. To each first element x there corresponds one and only one second element y. Thus $y = x^2$ defines a function, although there are two distinct first elements which produce the same second element. For example $(2,4)$ and $(-2,4)$ both make $y = x^2$ a true statement. The sentence $y > x^2$ also selects values of y for any given x, but in this case to each first element x there correspond infinitely many values of the second element y. For example, if $x = 2$, then y can be any integer greater than 4. Thus $y > x^2$ defines a relation and not a function.

Inequalities will receive the recognition they are due. Simultaneous systems involving both equations and inequalities will be treated, and careful attention will be given to the graphical solution of such systems. For example, in Fig. 4-1 the point $(-2,3)$ is the graph of the *solution set*, or truth set, of the system of equations

$$x + 2y = 4$$
$$3x - 2y = -12$$

Fig. 4-1

The shaded portion of Fig. 4-1 represents the graph of the infinite set which is the solution set of the system of inequalities

$$x + 2y > 4$$
$$3x - 2y > -12$$

The program in geometry has been of growing concern for many years. The basis for this concern has been sixfold in nature: (1) the recognition of the existence of logical defects in the Euclidean structure, (2) the failure to make appropriate adaptations of Cartesianism to simplify and enrich geometric study, (3) the failure to recognize the postulational nature of Euclidean geometry and the possibility of the existence of non-Euclidean geometries, (4) the failure to recognize the basic projective properties of geometric configurations, (5) the possible overemphasis on the restriction of geometric constructions to only those possible by straightedge and compass alone, and (6) the inadequate attention paid to three-dimensional geometry.

How to make corrections for these inadequacies in the high school geometry program has created a curriculum problem of no mean consequence. The Commission on Mathematics has proposed a year's program in geometry in their Elementary Mathematics II for grade 10.[1] This program is summarized in the following words:[2]

The program proposed by the Commission envisages an informal and intuitive introduction to geometric ideas, followed by an informal discussion of the nature of deductive reasoning. The course would then take up a short but important sequence of theorems, studied deductively, culminating in the Pythagorean Theorem. In the treatment of this sequence, both the geometric and the logical ideas previously introduced informally would be illustrated, consolidated, and confirmed by more formal study. Specific postulates, including in addition to the usual assumptions the congruence properties of triangles, would be introduced.

With the Pythagorean Theorem and theorems about similar triangles established, it is possible to proceed with coordinate geometry. The essential topics to cover are:

1. Location of points by coordinates
2. Length and slope of a line segment
3. Division of a segment in a given ratio
4. Equation of a line
5. Equation of a circle

The remainder of plane geometry can now be developed by using both synthetic and analytic methods. Emphasis should be placed on the development of skill in analyzing a situation and a valid proof of either kind.

[1] Commission on Mathematics, *op. cit.*, pp. 28–29. Also see report appendices 11, 12, and 14–16 for additional discussion of specific aspects of the proposal.

[2] *Ibid.*, pp. 27–28.

This summary fails to indicate that the proposed program is designed as "a course in plane and solid geometry." The outline includes suggestions concerning the drawing of three-dimensional figures and basic definitions, theorems, and formulas related to solid figures.

The Secondary School Curriculum Committee, in its report, supports a stronger emphasis on synthetic geometry than does the commission. It, too, recommends a combined treatment of solid geometry with the plane, the principal emphasis being directed to the configurations of the plane. Suggestions are made of "elements of geometry [which] are regarded as appropriate at the various grade levels." The point of view of the committee with reference to the total geometry program of the high school is summarized in these words:[1]

It is the considered opinion of this committee that elements of geometry should be taught throughout the secondary sequence (grades seven to twelve) and that one year should be devoted to synthetic geometry with particular emphasis on the geometry of the plane. This does not imply any desire to minimize the importance of co-ordinate geometry. Indeed the study of co-ordinate systems should permeate the entire secondary sequence beginning with the idea of one-to-one correspondence between numbers and points on a line in grade seven. The year devoted to synthetic geometry should be no exception. For example it is instructive to extend the study of loci to the co-ordinate plane. . . . It is also desirable to use analytic methods, on occasion, to provide alternative proofs for certain theorems which have been proved synthetically. Such proofs give pupils confidence in their ability to use analytic methods.

During the year course some teachers with superior classes may find it possible to include a considerable amount of solid geometry along with the plane geometry without sacrificing the essential values of the latter. Indeed some references to space geometry do much to enhance the pupils' understanding of relations which were first considered in the plane. The first consideration should be the presentation of a thorough course in plane geometry in which pupils receive intensive training in the solution of a large number of miscellaneous problems. In this situation the pupil needs time for contemplation, time for the formulation of conjectures, and time to test these conjectures for consistency with known facts. On the other hand, there is no point in pursuing an endless elaboration of originals which are confined to the plane. At some point during the year the good student will find it both natural and profitable to consider solid geometry in a systematic manner and not merely as counterpoint for plane geometry.

Both committees agree that a full half-year program in solid geometry is no longer justified. Also, both committees agree that it is highly desirable that more careful attention be given to deductive techniques and to the possibilities of other geometries than the metric geometry of the Euclidean plane.

[1] Secondary School Curriculum Committee, *op. cit.*, pp. 404–405.

The School Mathematics Study Group has expressed the opinion "that the traditional content of Euclidean geometry amply deserves the prominent place which it now holds in the high school curriculum." They have implemented this belief with the publication of a text (with teacher's supplement) in which solid geometry is introduced early and "is used as a foil to develop the students' space perception," and "geometry is connected with algebra at every reasonable opportunity."[1]

The course in trigonometry should be designed to fix and apply algebraic and geometry concepts. The definitions of trigonometric functions for the general angle, graphs and the periodic nature of the functions, inverse functions, and solutions of equations should be stressed, and less emphasis should be placed on the solution of triangles and the use of tables. While the logarithmic relation is important, logarithms as a means of computation have been outmoded to a very great extent by electronic computers. There is still value in the use of trigonometric techniques to acquaint the immature student with the basic characteristics of indirect measurement. The solution of triangles should continue to occupy a place of importance in trigonometry as a medium for introducing the procedures of indirect measurement and the more elementary techniques of computing with approximate data and the use of tables in such computation. The treatment of complex numbers as vectors, circular measure, and circular functions of real numbers (winding functions) are to receive important emphasis in the revision of the trigonometry program. The proper adaptations of the proposed modifications create important curriculum problems demanding careful study.

The program for the twelfth year offers almost limitless possibilities and poses many significant curriculum problems. The program for this year is more of an elective program than those of previous years. It is also true that the tight sequence of mathematical study begins to break down a bit at this level. These two facts make it both possible and desirable that the planning of the mathematics curriculum for grade 12 should provide for variation in interests and aptitudes for mathematically capable students. Furthermore, the twelfth grade should make provision for potential graduates who do not yet meet the minimum requirements in mathematics to have the opportunity to meet such requirements.[2]

The literature carries descriptions of experiments and suggestions for topics to be used as instructional units in the program for this grade. Possibly the most carefully considered and the most authoritative recom-

---

[1] School Mathematics Study Group, "Geometry" (New Haven, Conn.: Yale University, 1959). Also see their "Euclidean Geometry Based on Ruler and Protractor Axioms," Studies in Mathematics, vol. II (New Haven, Conn.: Yale University, 1959).

[2] Secondary School Curriculum Committee, *op. cit.*, p. 413.

mendation of a program for the mathematically capable is that given by
the Commission of Mathematics. Their recommendation is for "a course
to be called Elementary Functions," for the first semester, to be followed
by a second semester "devoted either to introductory probability with
statistical applications or to an introduction to modern algebra (fields and
groups).[1] They also state that there are other just as satisfactory possibilities. "Indeed, any serious mathematics, creatively and imaginatively
taught, would be appropriate."[2]

The Junior College. From one point of view at least, the program of the
junior college is analogous to that of the junior high school. For many
students the two years of the junior college become the final years of their
formal educational career. Many others, though they continue in college,
are not interested in further study in mathematics. These facts create a
tremendous curriculum problem.[3] Though the wise determination of
such a minimum curriculum in mathematics has been of major concern
for several years, it is but one of several critical problems which have
challenged the best thinking of professional groups interested in improved
instruction in mathematics. Also calling for careful study are the
demands for change in character of content and for increased intensity of
application of the mathematics prerequisite to the natural sciences and
engineering. Too, there are increasing demands for pertinent prerequisite training in mathematics from less technical areas such as the social
sciences and psychology, as well as from business and industry. Furthermore, there exists an urgent need for the establishment of a closer affinity
between the mathematics of these first two college years and that which
serves as the foundation of modern scientific research.

The Joint Committee of the American Society for Engineering Education and the Mathematical Association of America recommended that
colleges should raise standards for mathematics performance, pay more
attention to the fundamentals of probability and statistics, and provide
for preengineering students more course electives in mathematics as well
as a more intensive program of problem solving.[4]

While the Commission on Mathematics was interested in the college-
capable students of the high school and directed its report entirely in the
direction of such students, it did not overlook the fact that "the colleges
have contributed to the high school curriculum problem by their inertia."
The report further states that "the Commission sees no hope of effective

---

[1] Commission on Mathematics, *op. cit.*, pp. 30–33, 42–47.

[2] *Ibid.*

[3] This problem is discussed in Chap. 2.

[4] Joint Committee of the American Society for Engineering Education and the
Mathematical Association of America, Report of, *American Mathematical Monthly*,
62 (1955), 385–392.

curricular reform at the secondary level unless this reform is supplemented by a related effort at the college level."[1]

There have been scattered attempts to prepare materials for both the freshman and sophomore years.   At the freshman level these have taken the form of integrated texts in algebra and trigonometry, or algebra, trigonometry, and analytic geometry; texts attempting to give integrated treatments involving ideas from set theory and deductive methods; and, in some areas, texts extending the integration to include calculus.

The most concentrated effort toward the modification of the junior college program has been that of the Committee on the Undergraduate Program (CUP), a committee working under the auspices of the Mathematical Association of America.   In assessing the need for revision they not only called attention to the widespread dissatisfaction with existing programs but also pointed out that any program of revision must take into account the extending needs of science and engineering and also the rapidly increasing needs of econometrics, psychology, sociology, genetics, and the new field of numerical analysis.[2]   With these needs in mind the committee proceeded to design a program in Universal Mathematics for the freshman year to serve the purposes of all students regardless of their interests in mathematics.   The first semester emphasizes coordinate systems, the real-number system, scientific measurement, functions, limits, some of the more fundamental aspects of differential and integral calculus, and logarithmic and exponential functions.   The second semester treats of sets, the natural numbers, laws of counting, probability, mathematical systems, and algebraic structures.   The emphasis in this program varies with the basic interests of the students, being more intensive for those planning to go further in mathematics, sciences, or engineering.   For this group the second-year program is the classical calculus–analytic geometry course.   For this part of the program the committee, as yet, has not prepared any new materials.   For the biological and social science majors a new type of course has been prepared.   The title for this program is Modern Mathematical Methods and Models.   The first semester (Multi-component Methods) is divided into four units: Matrix Algebra, Calculus of Finite Differences, Multivariable Functions, and Optimization Problems.   The second semester (Mathematical Models) also has four units: Probability Theory, Order Relations, Markov Chains, and Models.[3]   The fact that the committee considers these volumes only as experimental editions and urges their trial in as many situations as possible points up the

[1] Commission on Mathematics, *op. cit.*, p. 62.

[2] Committee on the Undergraduate Mathematical Program, Report of, *American Mathematical Monthly*, **62** (1955), 511–520.

[3] Experimental editions of the first-year program and of the "Modern Mathematical Methods and Models" have been published.   See footnote p. 35.

immensity of the problem of curriculum revision in the mathematics program of the junior college.

Individual Differences. The recognition of and the making of proper provision for individual differences in learning potential and performance through the years has been, and will continue to be, a major curriculum problem in the shaping of the secondary school program in mathematics. It is a well-known fact that this problem intensifies at the level of the secondary school.   Here there are to be found wide variations in ability, ranging from the academically gifted to the very slow learner.   It is indeed a problem of serious concern which confronts teachers as they attempt to deal with individual pupils and with groups in accordance with their ability to learn.   The classification of pupils (slow learner, average, academically talented) should be the result of cooperative effort on the part of the administrator, the guidance personnel, the teacher, and the parents.   It should be based on information from a cumulative record begun in the elementary school and containing results from intelligence and achievement tests, interest and aptitude inventories, and other types of information pertinent to social adjustment and school progress.

There are certain distinguishing characteristics which should be helpful in recognizing the slow learner in mathematics and the mathematically gifted in contradistinction to each other and to the average group. Although there are many possible exceptions to any given pattern, the following[1] might be safely listed as characteristics of the slow learner:

1. Intelligence quotient below 90
2. Has little drive
3. Has short span of attention
4. Has weak association memory
5. Is a poor reader
6. Has difficulty with abstractions
7. Is not logical
8. Lacks imagination
9. Unable to detect his own errors
10. Has little power to transfer training
11. Is not creative in his thinking

In contrast the Secondary School Curriculum Committee gives the following lists of general and special characteristics which mark the mathematically gifted:[2]

---

[1] Mary Potter and Virgil Mallory, "Education in Mathematics for the Slow Learner" (Washington, D.C.: National Council of Teachers of Mathematics, 1958), pp. 11–12.

[2] Secondary School Curriculum Committee, *op. cit.*, p. 410.

1. General characteristics
   a. Makes associations readily and retains them indefinitely
   b. Recognizes similarities and differences quickly
   c. Has excellent memory, good vocabulary, broad attention span, and high reading ability
   d. Has a relatively mature sense of values
   e. Pursues interests with tremendous energy and drive
   f. Uses his spare time productively
2. Special characteristics
   a. Recognizes patterns readily and enjoys speculating on generalizations
   b. Prefers to think on higher levels of abstraction
   c. Classifies particular cases as special cases of more general situations with relative ease
   d. Follows a long chain of reasoning, frequently anticipating and contributing
   e. Frequently asks profound questions
   f. May be reading mathematics books years ahead of his class
   g. Is frequently impatient with drill and details that he thinks are not important

Though the identification of the relative-ability groups is a problem of tremendous responsibility, there remain other problems of just as great concern and difficulty. What mathematics program is the most significant for each of the three groups (slow learner, average, and mathematically gifted)? Is there a close similarity or a wide variation in the content of the program for each group? There seems to be rather general agreement that the basic content must be the same for all three groups but must vary in amount, pattern of organization, manner of presentation, and intensity of attention. For the slow learner the manner of presentation must emphasize the approach to abstractions through a large amount of concrete experience bolstered by frequent reviews and intensive practice. Furthermore, the abstractions must be kept in simple form. The minimum program must be carefully defined to protect the boys and girls against the demands of an age that is becoming more and more technological in nature.

From the point of view of greatest potential for service to our society, the academically talented students are the ones who place the most serious demand on curriculum designers for careful thinking and imaginative planning. The College Entrance Examination Board has taken cognizance of this fact in the report of its Commission on Mathematics[1] and in the sponsoring of the advanced placement program for admission to college with advanced standing.[2] Other groups have studied the problem

[1] Commission on Mathematics, *op. cit.*
[2] College Entrance Board, "Fifty-third Annual Report of the Director" (New York: College Entrance Examination Board, 1955), p. 20.

and made recommendations for solution.[1] The School Mathematics Study Group in its summer writing sessions has been preparing materials for experimental use in classrooms. These materials are designed primarily to interest and challenge the mathematically gifted. The University of Maryland Mathematics Project is using experimental materials for more significant instruction in mathematics for the gifted.

The Secondary School Curriculum Committee seems to have summarized and underscored the best thought on this extremely important problem in these words:[2]

All schools should provide opportunities for the gifted. Ability grouping is a widely acceptable and desirable practice, and special classes for the able are recommended where organizational and staff facilities permit. Honors classes, seminars, and special projects provide excellent means for challenging the gifted. A policy of acceleration is followed in some areas. Two basically different patterns are used: (1) A narrow type, or "mere speed-up" plan, in which pupils are allowed to "cover" the requirements of one year's program to get into that of the next year, for example: two years of algebra in one year; and (2) a broad type or "faster growth-in-depth" plan, where more mature understandings and procedures are expected sooner.

There is some question about the advisability of the "mere speed-up plan." A sophomore pupil, for example, who is undertaking senior mathematics could easily be a triple loser. He could be so completely out of step with the educational pattern that he would be confronted with unnecessary confusion in planning for the future; secondly, he could have lost material benefits by not having had the opportunity to make significant explorations below the surface of mere satisfactory accomplishment; and thirdly, he could have missed the inspiring challenge that can come from inquisitive search into the rationale of procedures, the foundations of concepts, and the implications of principles. On the other hand, a carefully planned acceleration program of the "faster-growth-in-depth" type can benefit the able pupil very materially through the provision of opportunities for deeper investigation of foundations, broader contact with related areas of cultural and utilitarian value, and more significant appreciation of basic interrelationships as well as advancement in grade-level accomplishment.

Any program of enrichment for the mathematically gifted not only should

[1] Joint Conference of the Cooperative Committee on the Teaching of Science and Mathematics of the American Association for the Advancement of Science and the United States Office of Education, Report of, "Education for the Talented in Mathematics and Science" (U.S. Office of Education, Bulletin 15, 1952, reprint 1953).

E. P. Vance (Editor), "Program Provisions for the Mathematically Gifted Student in the Secondary School" (Washington, D.C.: National Council of Teachers of Mathematics, reprint 1959).

Joint Conference of National Education Association and the National Council of Teachers of Mathematics, Report of, "Mathematics for the Academically Talented Student" (Washington, D.C.: National Council of Teachers of Mathematics, 1959).

[2] Secondary School Curriculum Committee, op. cit., pp. 410–411.

provide real challenge to excellent accomplishment but also should provide basic information essential to top-level performance in mathematics, both for the present and for the future.   This can be accomplished in better fashion by less emphasis on drill and on delineation of applications, in order to provide more opportunity for discovery of significant patterns and formulation of generalizations.   Under informed guidance such pupils should be encouraged to read widely, to investigate significant topics which offer them challenge, participate in competitive endeavors, and seek occasion to meet with other mathematically gifted pupils both within their own school and from other schools.

Since the purpose of ability grouping in mathematics is to increase the efficiency of learning, it behooves teachers to adjust their methods of teaching in order to take maximum advantage of homogeneity of the several groups and to gear instruction to the learning level of the students in each group.   Furthermore, administrators should strive (1) to develop in their staffs an understanding of the basic purposes of ability grouping and the desirability of taking advantage of it, (2) to adjust class size for optimum benefits from such grouping, and (3) to reduce non-teaching duties so that all teachers will have better opportunity for taking care of individual differences at all levels of instruction.

The Individual Classroom Teacher.   As is evident from the discussion of this chapter, many questions are being asked and many problems are being considered, all of which are pertinent to intelligent planning for the curriculum reforms so urgently needed in secondary mathematics.   What can the classroom teacher, as an individual, contribute as his part in the total effort toward curriculum revision?   The recommendations of committees and the verifications of experimentation all will be of no avail unless implemented by teachers in the classrooms of the nation.   Each teacher should consider it a personal challenge and a professional opportunity and obligation to evaluate recommended new ideas and procedures in the context of his particular situation and to make the most effective use of those which are found to be appropriate and pertinent.

The leaders in curriculum planning must strive to think clearly in the mixed perspective of ideal growth in mathematical insight and realistic restriction of unselected student personnel.   The classroom teacher must, in turn, strive to make maximum adaptations of approved curriculum content and instructional procedures within the limitations of local pupil potential and individual teaching proficiency.   Only through a closely coordinated program of such professional teamwork can the goal of effective curriculum revision in mathematics be accomplished.

EXERCISES

1. Summarize what you consider to be the major implications in the two articles by George A. W. Boehm in *Fortune* and the one article by Peter Drucker in *Harper's Magazine*. (See Bibliography.)

2. What do you consider to be the major implications of the six articles listed in footnote 2 of page 86?

3. What are the major recommendations for curriculum reform in mathematics made by the Commission on Mathematics of the College Entrance Examination Board?

4. What are the major recommendations for curriculum change in mathematics made by the Secondary School Curriculum Committee of the National Council of Teachers of Mathematics?

5. What is the advanced placement program sponsored by the College Entrance Examination Board?

6. What is the School Mathematics Study Group and what is its program for curriculum reform in mathematics?

7. What are the University of Illinois Mathematics Project and the University of Maryland Mathematics Project? What are the basic distinctions between these two experimental programs?

8. What are some of the major criticisms of the mathematics program of grades 7 and 8, and what are some of the more important recommendations for change?

9. What are some of the major criticisms of the general mathematics program of the ninth grade?

10. What are some of the more important recommendations for change of the algebra program in the secondary school?

11. What are some of the more important recommendations for change of the geometry program in the secondary school?

12. What are some of the principal recommendations for change in the trigonometry program of the high school? Of the junior college?

13. What are some of the more important trends which characterize the change taking place in the mathematics program of the junior college?

14. Summarize some of the arguments for and against this statement from the report of the Secondary School Curriculum Committee: The mathematics studied by all high school pupils must be the same in "structure and concepts, but varying in amount, in complexity, in depth and in manner of organization and presentation in order to be consistent with the pupil's ability and his past achievement."[1]

15. Assuming ample staff and facilities, what are some of the arguments for and against ability grouping of high school mathematics students?

16. What are some of the recommended patterns of instruction designed to present more significant challenge to the mathematically gifted students?

BIBLIOGRAPHY

Adkins, J. R.: College Preparatory Mathematics in Grades Nine through Twelve, *Mathematics Teacher*, **50** (1957), 209–213.

Albers, Mary E., and May V. Seagoe: Enrichment for Superior Students in Algebra Classes, *Journal of Educational Research*, **40** (1947), 481–495.

Allen, F. B.: Mathematics Tomorrow, *NEA Journal*, **46** (1957) 309–310.

Baum, J. D.: Mathematics, Self Taught, *American Mathematical Monthly*, **65** (1958) 701–705.

Baumgartner, R. A.: The Status of the Secondary Mathematics Program for the Talented, *Mathematics Teacher*, **49** (1956), 535–540.

[1] Secondary School Curriculum Committee, *op. cit.*, p. 408.

Beberman, Max: "An Emerging Program of Secondary Mathematics" (Cambridge, Mass.: Harvard University Press, 1958).

Benjamin, Harold R.: The Saber Tooth Tiger Returns, *Indiana Teacher*, April, 1950, 424, 425ff.

Bernhard, Ida M.: Materials Available for Counseling in Mathematics, *Mathematics Teacher*, 47 (1954), 279–280.

Boehm, G. A. W.: New Mathematics, *Fortune*, 57 (June, 1958), 140–145.

———: New Uses of the Abstract, *Fortune*, 57 (July, 1958), 124–127, 152ff.

Brinkmann, H. W.: Mathematics in the Secondary School for the Exceptional Student, *American Mathematical Monthly*, 61 (1954), 319–323.

Burington, Richard S.: Contemporary Applications of Mathematics, *Mathematics Teacher*, 49 (1956), 322–329.

Clark, N.: Challenge to the Gifted, *Mathematics Teacher*, 48 (1955), 434–435.

Cogan, E. J.: New Approach to High School Mathematics, *Mathematics Teacher*, 50 (1957), 347–349.

"Commission on Mathematics of the College Entrance Examination Board, Report of" (New York: College Entrance Examination Board, 1959). (This commission also published several helpful pamphlets.)

Committee on the Undergraduate Mathematical Program, Report of, *American Mathematical Monthly*, 62 (1955), 511–520.

Conant, James B.: "The American High School Today" (New York: McGraw-Hill Book Company, Inc., 1959).

Cooperative Committee of the American Association for the Advancement of Science and the U.S. Office of Education: "Education for the Talented in Mathematics and Science" (U.S. Office of Education Bulletin 15, 1952).

Drucker, Peter: Math Even Parents Can Understand, *Harper's Magazine*, 216 (April, 1958), 73–75ff.

Duren, W. L., Jr.: The Maneuvers in Set Thinking, *Mathematics Teacher*, 51 (1958), 322–335.

Elder, Florence L.: Providing for the Student with High Mathematical Potential, *Mathematics Teacher*, 50 (1957), 502–506.

Fehr, H. F.: Goal Is Mathematics for All, *School Science and Mathematics*, 56 (1956), 109–120.

———: Mathematics Curriculum for the High School of the Future, *Teachers' College Record*, 59 (1958), 258–267.

———: Breakthroughs in Mathematical Thought, *Mathematics Teacher*, 52 (1959), 15–19.

Ficken, F. A.: The Use of Films and Television in Mathematics Education, *American Mathematical Monthly*, 65 (1958), 393–403.

Hartung, Maurice: Mathematics in the Total School Program, *Mathematics Teacher*, 51 (1958), 336–343.

Ingham, Carolyn, and Joseph N. Payne: An Eighth Grade Unit on Number Systems, *Mathematics Teacher*, 51 (1958), 392–395.

Jackson, Harvey O.: The Superior Pupil in Mathematics, *Mathematics Teacher*, 52 (1959), 202–204.

Joint Committee of the American Society for Engineering Education and the Mathematical Association of America on Engineering Mathematics, Report of, *American Mathematical Monthly*, 62 (1955), 385–392.

Joint Commission on Atomic Energy: Can We Continue To Ignore These Warnings? *Mathematics Teacher*, 51 (1958), 240–245.

Jones, A. M.: Television Activity, Department of Mathematics, University of Alabama, *American Mathematical Monthly*, 65 (1958), 421–424.

Jones, P. S.: Notes on the Status and Future of Films and TV in Collegiate Mathematics Education, *American Mathematical Monthly*, **65** (1958), 403–415.

Kemeny, J. G.: Honors Mathematics at Dartmouth, *Mathematics Teacher*, **49** (1956), 455–457.

Kennedy, Joe: Modern Mathematics in the Twelfth Grade, *Mathematics Teacher*, **52** (1959), 143–165.

Kennedy, Joseph W., and John R. Mayor: Individual Differences and Mathematics, *Phi Delta Kappan*, **37** (1956), 222–224.

Kline, Morris: The Ancients Versus the Moderns: A New Battle of the Books, *Mathematics Teacher*, **51** (1958), 418–427.

MacDuffee, C. C.: Mathematics Curriculum in Perspective, *Mathematics Teacher*, **52** (1959), 265–267.

Meder, A. E., Jr.: Modern Mathematics and Its Place in the Secondary School, *Mathematics Teacher*, **50** (1957) 418–423.

————: The Ancients Versus the Moderns—A Reply, *Mathematics Teacher*, **51** (1958), 428–433.

————: What Is Wrong with Euclid? *Mathematics Teacher*, **51** (1958), 578–584.

———— with the collaboration of Edward Begle, Julius Hlavaty, Cletus Oakley, Robert E. K. Rourke, and Max Sobel: "Teacher Education in Modern Mathematics" [five 16-mm sound motion pictures] (New York: McGraw-Hill Book Company, Inc., 1959). (These films, titled Patterns in Mathematics, Number Fields, Irrational Numbers, Concept of Function, and Sentences and Solution Sets, are suitable for acquisition and use by secondary schools under Title III of the National Defense Education Act of 1958 to strengthen instruction in mathematics.)

Menger, Karl: New Approach to Teaching Intermediate Mathematics, *Science*, **127** (1957), 1320.

Midwest Regional State College Conference on Science and Mathematics Teacher Education, Report of: Promising Practices in Mathematics, *School Science and Mathematics*, **58** (1958), 25–40.

National Council of Teachers of Mathematics: "Insights into Modern Mathematics," *Twenty-third Yearbook* (Washington, D.C.: National Council of Teachers of Mathematics, 1957).

————: "The Growth of Mathematical Ideas," *Twenty-fourth Yearbook* (Washington, D.C.: National Council of Teachers of Mathematics, 1959).

————: Report of the Secondary School Curriculum Committee, *Mathematics Teacher*, **52** (1959), 389–417. (This committee also published helpful pamphlets.)

"New Developments in Secondary School Mathematics," reprinted from the Bulletin of the National Association of Secondary-school Principals, No. 247, May, 1959, (Washington, D. C.: National Council of Teachers of Mathematics, 1959).

Newsom, Carroll V.: The Place of Mathematics in Modern Education, *Scripta Mathematica*, **17** (1951), 161–172.

Northrop, E. P.: Modern Mathematics and the Secondary School Curriculum, *Mathematics Teacher*, **48** (1955), 386–393.

Norton, M. S.: Enrichment as a Provision for the Gifted in Mathematics, *School Science and Mathematics*, **57** (1957), 339–345.

Payne, Joseph: Self-instruction Topics for Bright Pupils in High School Algebra, *Mathematics Teacher*, **51** (1958), 113–117.

Renner, John W.: Student Achievement of Functional Competency Three Years after Completing Algebra or General Mathematics, *Mathematics Teacher*, **50** (1957), 160–161.

Rosenberg, Herman: The Role of Statistics in General Mathematics Courses for College Freshmen, *Mathematics Teacher*, **50** (1957), 343–346.

Rosskopf, Myron: What Algebra for Seventh and Eighth Grades? *Mathematics Teacher*, **51** (1958), 377–379.

Rourke, Robert E. K.: Some Implications of the Twentieth Century Mathematics for High Schools, *Mathematics Teacher*, **51** (1958), 74–86.

Seibert, W. F.: Teaching Calculus by Closed-circuit Television, *American Mathematical Monthly*, **65** (1958), 430–439.

Smith, Rolland R.: Provisions for Individual Differences, "Twenty-first Yearbook," (Washington, D.C.: National Council of Teachers of Mathematics, 1953), pp. 271–302.

Vance, E. P., et al.: "Program Provisions for the Mathematically Gifted Student in the Secondary School" (Washington, D.C.: National Council of Teachers of Mathematics, 1958).

Washington Conference of the Mathematical Association of America, Report of, *American Mathematical Monthly*, **65** (1958), 575–586.

Wilks, S. S.: New Fields and Organizations in the Mathematical Sciences, *Mathematics Teacher*, **51** (1958), 2–9.

————: Teaching Statistical Inference in Elementary Mathematics Courses, *American Mathematical Monthly*, **65** (1958), 143–153.

Yates, R. C.: The Trigonometric Functions, *Mathematics Teacher*, **51** (1958), 191–193.

5

STIMULATING AND MAINTAINING INTEREST IN MATHEMATICS

It may be taken as axiomatic that students will work most diligently and most effectively at tasks in which they are genuinely interested. To create and maintain interest becomes, therefore, one of the most important tasks of the teacher of secondary school mathematics. It is also one of the most difficult problems which the teacher encounters. The interest of students of secondary school age is capricious. It is easily caught by any new thing, but it is as easily distracted to other new things. Ordinarily it cannot be depended upon to maintain itself for any great length of time unless the work has been carefully and deliberately planned to that end, and even then it usually needs occasional stimulation. Thus the motivation of the work in mathematics has two aspects, viz., that of creating or arousing interest and that of maintaining the interest after the novelty of the work in hand has worn off.

As a rule, students readily *become interested* in things which are new or exciting, in things for which they can perceive practical values or applications to situations and fields of study in which they are already interested, and in things which involve puzzle elements or elements of mystery. Other things being equal, the possession of a background of related information tends to intensify interest in new work, but this is neither a necessary condition nor a sufficient guarantee for the awakening of interest. Novelty is sometimes more compelling than familiarity. The elements of novelty, usefulness, and sheer intellectual curiosity are the primary stimuli for the awakening of interest.

It is easier to interest students in their work than it is to keep them interested after the work has got under way and the novelty has worn off. In this connection it is worthwhile to observe that students tend to *remain interested* in those things which they can do most successfully and which they understand most completely. Inability to understand or to perform satisfactorily usually begets a condition of listlessness, inattention, and general loss of interest which not infrequently ripens into open disaffection. This is not to say that the work should be made flabby and diluted and that it should never present difficulties to the students.   Nothing can cause interest to flag more quickly than this, and nothing could be more undesirable from an educational standpoint.   The work should present a continual challenge, but it should be a challenge in a real sense and not mere drudgery at tasks devoid of meaning or inexcusably difficult.   Consequently, it is of the greatest importance that work in mathematics be so organized and conducted as to emphasize the values and the inherent intellectual challenge of the subject and to ensure understanding and a reasonable degree of competence by keeping the subject matter and the activities at a level of difficulty appropriate to the intellectual maturity of the students.   Within these conditions are to be found the motives basic to hard and effective work in mathematics.   Interest in the subject can be effectively augmented by numerous special devices and activities, some of which can be used in connection with class instruction while others, such as mathematics clubs and special programs, are essentially coordinate and supplementary activities.[1]

Hartung's Analysis of the Problem of Motivating Learning in Mathematics. In what is probably the most penetrating and thorough published analysis of motivation as related to the learning of mathematics, Hartung[2] distinguishes between motives and incentives.   In making this distinction, motives are considered to be states or conditions or "drives" residing within the student, while incentives are external impelling factors.   Both can lead to purposeful activity and perhaps toward the same goal.   *Interests* are described as motives which serve as important influences in producing both activities and attitudes that are favorable to learning.   A strong interest in mathematics then would tend to produce a favorable attitude toward the subject, and such an attitude would in turn probably lead to or enhance the desire to study mathematics in a serious and productive way.   Thus the development and stimulation of interest in mathematics becomes an important concern of the teacher:[3]

Interests are motives that almost all teachers try to use to promote learning. The literature on mathematical education contains numerous references to the importance of arousing the interests of students, and dozens of suggestions as to means of doing so.   Unfortunately, many of these suggestions seem to stem from a relatively narrow conception of the nature of interest in mathematics.

[1] Walter H. Carnahan, Maintenance of Interest in Mathematics, *Bulletin of the National Association of Secondary-School Principals*, **38** (1954), 110–116.   See also Margaret Joseph, The Factor of Interest in the Teaching of Mathematics, *School Science and Mathematics*, **40** (1940), 201–207.

[2] Maurice L. Hartung, Motivation for Education in Mathematics, "Twenty-first Yearbook" (Washington, D.C.: National Council of Teachers of Mathematics, 1953), pp. 42–67.

[3] *Ibid.*, pp. 51, 52.

Genuine interest in mathematics probably depends basically upon the problem solving aspect of the subject. Problems, once recognized or sensed, leave an individual in a state of perplexity, uneasiness, or tension until they are solved. When a solution has been found, tension-reduction and satisfaction results. If mathematics is properly taught, it presents the student with an abundance of problems, and it also provides him with certain general modes of thought and a supply of techniques which enable him to attack these problems successfully. With each successful solution he receives a dividend of satisfaction—he feels good when he gets the answer. As a result, he seeks more experiences of the same kind, and displays other desirable types of behavior which were described earlier in defining interest.

As the student grows in mathematical maturity, he obtains satisfaction also from contemplation of the power of his methods and the sharpness and beauty of his tools. The term "appreciation" is often used in this connection. The behavior is relevant to interest, however, because it leads the student to seek more experiences with mathematics, to discuss it favorably with other people, and to value it for what it does for him personally.

A good many of the devices recommended for arousing interest seem to be based on the assumption that mathematics itself is uninteresting and hence learning must be encouraged by extraneous elements such as the mystery of a puzzle or the competition of a game. When, however, the subject preferences of children are investigated by objective methods, mathematics is often found to rank high on the list. . . .

No mere summary can do full justice to this excellent analysis of the problem of motivating learning in mathematics, but since it cannot be reproduced in full here, it seems desirable to mention at least a few additional observations and conclusions given therein.

Incentives may serve to build motive or "inner drive" and thus to promote genuine interest in mathematical work, but the use of incentives cannot guarantee this. Incentives are only means to an end; they should not be regarded as ends in themselves, and they should not be used indiscriminately or thoughtlessly. Unless they are used judiciously, some incentives such as marks and rewards of various kinds may, indeed, even produce undesirable attitudes. Whether they produce desirable motivation or not depends on the kinds of incentives used and the ways in which they are used.

Most of the suggestions discussed in the literature on mathematics education deal with devices which are essentially thought of as incentives. Among these are such things as mathematical games and contests; tricks, puzzles, and other recreations; films and multisensory aids of various kinds; laboratory projects; applications; information about the need for and the uses of mathematics in certain vocations and professions; historical material; and mathematics clubs. All of these can be useful if presented in proper perspective and with proper concern for the real objective.   Some of them, e.g., games, puzzles, and recreations, may fail to contribute much beyond transient attention getting unless care is taken to emphasize the mathematical aspects.   They can serve as interesting settings for mathematical principles, but they should not be allowed to obscure those principles.   Hartung says:[1]

If tricks and puzzles are overemphasized, the students are likely to get a distorted idea of the nature of mathematics.   They think that mathematics consists largely of a bunch of tricks. . . . If a theoretical explanation of a trick or puzzle is accessible to the student, the discovery of it may, of course, become a genuine problem.   Investigating whether a trick which works for a particular set of numbers will work for others, or in general, may be much more interesting than many practical problems.   It is to be noted, however, that in this case the interest is derived not from the trick as a trick, but from the more general mathematical or problem-solving behavior that is evoked.

Mathematics clubs constitute one form of special activity which is always desirable.   They provide extra avenues of interest for students who are already well motivated, and even if the programs are largely concerned with puzzles and special problems not related to the regular classwork, nothing is lost.   The students who belong to mathematics clubs nearly always do so voluntarily, and they are usually among the better students.

Multisensory aids and laboratory and field experiences in mathematics are often regarded as means for motivation, and it is proper that they should be so regarded.   They are, however, more than mere motivating devices; they are indeed avenues through which important learning can and should take place.

The most powerful and enduring motivation for learning mathematics comes from genuine understanding of the subject itself.   The more fully students understand mathematics, the more they want to learn about it. Lack of understanding leads to continued frustration and to negative attitudes, but understanding and successful experience contribute powerfully toward the development of self-confidence, pride in accomplishment, and desirable attitudes toward the work.

The following check list from Hartung[2] is proposed as suggesting kinds of questions which teachers might well have in mind in deciding upon or evaluating motivational procedures or devices.

1. Is the proposed procedure likely to be effective?
    a. Does it draw upon motives actually present in the learner?
    b. Is it designed to utilize a combination of several motives in the learner?
    c. Is it appropriate for the age level of the learner?

[1] *Ibid.,* p. 53.
[2] *Ibid.,* pp. 65–66.

   d. Is it based upon recognition of a goal by the learner, and does the learner believe he can achieve his goal?
   e. Does it motivate many students or just a few?
   f. How long is the motivation likely to persist?
2. Is the motivation of a desirable type?
   a. Does it lead the student to value the learning experience itself rather than external rewards?
   b. Will it widen and deepen the interests of the learner?
   c. Does it tend to develop desirable attitudes toward the content or skill and toward the teacher?
   d. Are the goals which are set actually attainable?
   e. Does the motivation tend to strengthen attitudes necessary for democratic citizenship?
   f. Is the motivation consistent with the promotion of good social relations between students?
3. Is the procedure practicable?
   a. Is the required expenditure of time and money within the means of the school?
   b. How well can the procedure be controlled in practice?
   c. Does the teacher know how to administer the procedure?

In concluding his article,[1] Hartung distills the essence of the problem of motivation as follows:

We may reflect that the interests and attitudes of most children when they enter school are favorable to learning mathematics. Some of them learn to *like* it. Others learn to *dislike* it. To change an unfavorable attitude once formed into a favorable one is a difficult assignment. Efforts on the part of teachers to arrange conditions so that unfavorable attitudes are not learned will, in the long run, probably pay generous dividends.

Motivation through Application to Other Fields of Study. The relation of mathematics to other fields of study often provides an important means of stimulating interest. At all levels of secondary education from the junior high school to the junior college the contribution which mathematics has made and can make to the more adequate development and understanding of many subjects is coming to be recognized more fully than ever before, and teachers should not fail to stress its importance from this standpoint. There is no lack of material bearing upon this matter. Many articles discussing the relation of mathematics to other fields of study can be found in such magazines as the *Mathematics Teacher* and *School Science and Mathematics* and in some of the yearbooks of the National Council of Teachers of Mathematics, as well as in other publications.

The basic importance of mathematics in relation to other fields of study

[1] *Ibid.,* p. 66.

has been nowhere more emphatically or more strikingly portrayed than in the mural entitled "The Tree of Knowledge" which was displayed in the Hall of Science at the Century of Progress Exposition in Chicago in 1933 (see Fig. 5-1). In this picture mathematics is represented as the main root of the tree, and springing from it are the other roots, stems, and branches representing the various basic and applied sciences. Copies of this painting can be secured at a nominal charge,[1] either in color or black and white, and in a size suitable for framing to hang on the walls of mathematics classrooms or in a small size suitable for pasting in the front of individual textbooks. This affords an excellent means of keeping before the students a continual reminder of the contribution which mathematics makes to these other subjects and fields of study.

The dependence of physics, chemistry, and astronomy upon mathematics is so manifest that it is hardly necessary to dwell upon it here. Mathematics is literally indispensable in the study of these subjects, and no informed person would question its instrumental value in this connection. It has only been in comparatively recent years that biologists have begun to realize the vast possibilities arising out of the application of mathematics to their science. The work of Quételet, Galton, and Pearson and their followers has opened up new avenues of approach and innumerable possibilities for systematizing and expanding this science and for the investigation and interpretation of biological phenomena through the formulation of precise mathematical expressions of the relationships and changes involved. Remarkable advances have been made through the application of mathematical procedures to advanced studies in genetics, heredity, nutrition, growth and maturation, senescence, metabolism, fatigue, the effects of various stimuli on organisms, and many other special phases of biological and physiological study. Indeed, it is hardly too much to say that it is no longer possible to pursue the study of biological phenomena very far beyond the early descriptive stages without the aid of mathematical analysis and treatment.

The social sciences are also beginning to draw heavily upon mathematics, particularly statistical and graphic methods, for the investigation and interpretation of social phenomena. Much of the mathematics used in connection with these subjects is so simple and so enlightening that it can be incorporated easily and very appropriately even in junior high school courses in which are studied such matters as public health, safety campaigns, thrift, population trends, expenditure of public moneys, and other topics which deal in simple fashion with social and economic phenomena. Economics and sociology deal essentially with mass phenomena, and there is a widespread feeling that the only mathematics which is used in connec-

[1] Inquiries and orders should be mailed to the Business Manager of the Museum of Science and Industry, Jackson Park, Chicago, Ill.

Tree of knowledge

Forestry and agronomy

Public health and hygiene

Pharmacology

Medicine

Economics

Sociology

Education

Animal Husbandry

Marine and military engineering

Aeronautic engineering

Electrical engineering

Mining engineering

Architectural engineering

Mechanical engineering

Physiology

Anthropology

Psychology

Bacteriology

Zoology

Astronomy

Physics

Chemistry

Geology

Botany

Mathematics

Basic and applied sciences

FIG. 5-1. Adaptation of "A Century of Progress," mural by John Norton, 1933. (Copyright Museum of Science and Industry, Chicago; adapted by special permission of Museum of Science and Industry, Chicago.)

tion with these subjects is statistics.   It is quite true that statistics, including graphics, is more extensively and more obviously used than other mathematical procedures in the elementary work in these fields, but in some of the more advanced work, especially in theoretical studies related to social and economic phenomena, there are to be found important applications of mathematics such as high-speed computation, stochastic processes, linear programming, and game theory, which are non-statistical in nature.[1]

In one way or another mathematics leaves its imprint upon the foundations of many of the school subjects.   Its applications are more manifest in some than in others, but seldom, indeed if ever, are they lacking altogether.   We have seen that they are not limited to the physical sciences but have important bearings upon the biological and social sciences as well.   The industrial arts require mathematics.   Psychology is finding more uses for it all the time.   Even English, the foreign languages, and the fine arts are enriched by an understanding of the mathematical principles of form and number, of symmetry and order, upon which they are based.   By continually impressing upon the students the relationships and applications of mathematics to other school subjects, teachers can stimulate interest in the study of mathematics and can at the same time give the students a more comprehensive and complete idea of the nature of the other subjects.

Motivation through Showing the Application of Mathematics to Business, Industry, and the Professional Fields.[2]   Another important means of stimulating interest in mathematics is through pointing out the applications of mathematics to fields of work through which people gain their livelihood.   Students are interested in this not only from an academic standpoint but for practical reasons as well.   All boys and many girls must look forward to the intensely practical problem of selecting an occupation and earning a living, and they are generally interested in learning something about the opportunities and requirements in different fields. The extent to which mathematics enters into the upper levels of many lines of work is not realized by most people.   Many articles can be found, however, which discuss the applications of mathematics in various vocational fields, and there are even numerous textbooks with titles such as "Business Mathematics," "Mathematics of Finance," "Shop Mathe-

---

[1] See the following listings in the Bibliography, under General: Commission on Post-War Plans (in *Mathematics Teacher*), J. G. Kemeny et al., O. M. Rasmussen, P. H. Daus and W. M. Whyburn, M. Rees, D. E. Scates, R. C. Seber, H. Winthrop, and S. S. Wilks.

[2] The articles by the following authors, which are listed in the Bibliography under General, are suggested for supplementary reading: C. J. Carlton, R. Elias, A. P. Fugill and others, A. Luff, and E. C. Stephenson.

matics," "Mathematics for Printers," "Mathematics for Electricians," and "Mathematics for Agriculture." By pointing out these applications, teachers can perform valuable service in the way of guidance to the students and at the same time stimulate their interest in mathematics itself.

It should be emphasized that professional work in a number of fields requires extensive training in and, indeed, continual use of mathematics. In a preceding section the application of mathematics to the natural and social sciences has been discussed, and it is obvious that individuals desiring to take up professional work in teaching or research in these sciences will be either entirely prevented from doing so or greatly handicapped in their work unless their interest and aptitude for such work is implemented by the ability to adapt mathematical techniques to the circumstances and problems peculiar to their particular lines of study. In this connection the attention of students should be called to the fact that mathematics is now coming to be recognized as a necessary part of the professional equipment in such fields as anatomy, physiology, psychology, psychiatry, and medicine.

Students scarcely need to be told that mathematics is the foundation of engineering. While mechanical devices such as the integraph and handbooks of tables and formulas have reduced the need for the actual applications of calculus and differential equations in much routine engineering work, there will inevitably arise from time to time situations to which no ready-made formula will apply. In such cases the engineer needs to be able to size up the situation and detect the principles and relationships involved and express and investigate them by means of mathematics. A good working knowledge of college algebra, trigonometry, analytic and descriptive geometry, and calculus and a considerable familiarity with differential equations are generally regarded as essential for carrying on or directing engineering work.

Industry and commerce have made less extensive demands upon individuals for mathematical training than have the fields which have just been discussed. However, it will stimulate the students to a sense of the usefulness of mathematics, even in the field of business, if they are impressed with the fact that executive positions generally require the ability to analyze and interpret complex statistical data and that the businessman who has been trained in statistical methods and the mathematics of large-scale finance has a notable advantage over the man who lacks such training. Also, the recent, sudden, and almost explosive impact upon large-scale business and industry of the electronic computer with its allied field of programming offers another important avenue for stimulating students' interest in mathematics. The coding and programming of data for these computers represents a new, interesting, and highly remunerative field in which it now appears that the demand for mathematically trained personnel is destined to exceed the available supply for many years to come.

Calling attention to these matters is both a legitimate and an important way of stimulating students to an interest in their present courses in mathematics as necessary steps in the hierarchy of courses leading to work of professional stature in these fields.   It will probably provide a greater stimulus to the more capable students than to those with less ability.   Such information is not only important as background for proper guidance of the individual students but in the public interest as well.

Motivation through Emphasis on Cultural and Educational Values.   While the practical motive for the study of mathematics is a powerful one, teachers should not neglect to point out the cultural and general educational values.   It should be the responsibility of the teachers to emphasize continually that it is an essential part of culture and education to understand the background and the nature of the developments which are going on in the world.   It is no easy task, however, to keep oneself informed in these matters in a world in which social, economic, and especially scientific changes are taking place with the rapidity characteristic of the present time.   Students should be impressed with the fact that many of these important developments which directly affect our daily lives cannot be adequately understood except through an understanding of scientific principles whose development, expression, and interpretation depend, in turn, upon mathematical principles.   They should be led to see that mathematics will aid them even in such matters as interpreting social and economic phenomena and that it is indispensable to the understanding and development of scientific theory.

Students will sometimes argue that it is not necessary to understand these things, that one can operate an automobile effectively without knowing the adiabatic formula or can turn on a radio and enjoy the program without knowing even of the existence of Maxwell's equations.   All of which, of course, is true.   The thing which students so often fail to realize, however, and which should be impressed upon them continually, is that to limit their interest in such things to the bare utilitarian aspect is to miss the real thrill and wonder of them as well as to run the risk of setting up a barrier to subsequent intelligent study of their characteristics. It is not necessary to be able to solve difficult differential equations in order to be able to *appreciate* the role which mathematics plays in the development of modern science, but such appreciation can hardly be attained without some considerable study of mathematics beyond that which is needed to compute the area of a field or keep oneself from being shortchanged.   Indeed, without such a background it is impossible to read understandingly not only a great many scientific articles of general interest but also a rather large number which are written for popular consumption:[1]

Mathematics provides an outlook, and a means of understanding. There are important aspects of the world which only mathematics can interpret to the citizen. Mathematics affords one a mode of thinking about many aspects of life, and a very general kind of language. A liberal view of education regards such matters as genuine needs of even the ordinary citizen. It rejects the thought of being satisfied with such a minimum working equipment as would enable him to exist as nothing more than "a hewer of wood and a drawer of water."

Aside from the technical aspects of the subject, the *postulational method* of mathematics has a major contribution to make to the cultural education of the individual. If students are kept aware of the nature and the universal applicability of this method, it will be found to provide an exceedingly strong motive for the study of mathematics, not only from the standpoint of its cultural significance but also because of its intrinsic interest. An appreciation of the significance of the "if-then" type of reasoning is one of the most important potential educational and cultural values of the study of mathematics. When once attained, it in turn not only makes mathematics infinitely more meaningful but infuses a keener interest into the study and provides one of the most powerful motives for the continued pursuit of work in this field.

In one important sense of the word, the cultural values of mathematics may be likened to what we think of as the cultural values of fine music or art or literature. They constitute something which derives from the medium in question and gives enduring intellectual satisfaction colored with esthetic and even emotional overtones, and which at the same time deepens the appreciation and refines the taste. This is a very important facet of the cultural value of mathematics, but one of which people have been too little aware. The reason for this is probably that mathematics is so seldom taught in such a way as to reveal its beauty, its delicacy, its universality, its vagaries, its surprises, even its little jokes. To teach it in such a manner requires rich background and high artistry, but the dividends in intellectual and esthetic satisfaction are tremendously worthwhile. Probably no better or more delightful essay on this aspect of the cultural value of mathematics can be found than that given by Clifton Fadiman in his commentary on a set of books, to which reference is made elsewhere in this chapter, and it seems appropriate to conclude this section with some excerpts from his article.[2]

[1] Joint Commission of the Mathematical Association of America, Inc., and the National Council of Teachers of Mathematics, The Place of Mathematics in Secondary Education, "Fifteenth Yearbook" (Washington, D.C.: National Council of Teachers of Mathematics, 1940), p. 210.

[2] Clifton Fadiman, Party of One, *Holiday*, **21** (January, 1957), 8.

In the mysterious metaphors we have agreed to call mathematics all creation is involved, from the symbol-happy logician down to those cunning geometers, the bees.   When I trust myself to a ladder I lean upon an equation.   Every baby is a formula baby, for when we say that its growth is a function of its nourishment, what are we citing but a case of the calculus?   The toddler, gratified to discover a correspondence between the toes of his right foot and those of his left, has taken his first steps in number theory. . . .

The mass of us who quail before the word mathematics are often merely suffering from a bad persistent case of early pedagogy.   We were poisoned in our youth by the notion that mathematics is identical with problem-solving.   But in truth it is no more equivalent to problem-solving than is music to counterpoint.

As Scott Buchanan puts it in his wonderful little book *Poetry and Mathematics:* "The structures with which mathematics deals are more like lace, the leaves of trees, and the play of light and shadow on a meadow or a human face."   The fact is (I quote from G. H. Hardy's *A Mathematician's Apology*) " . . . most people have some appreciation of mathematics just as most people can enjoy a pleasant tune." . . .

James Newman has edited a four-volume collection of mathematical writings called *The World of Mathematics.*   His title is just: mathematics is not a subject, it is a world.   Within his 2500 pages you will, it is true, encounter a few Greek letters and a few eccentric symbols.   But you will also meet soap bubbles, calculating prodigies, chess playing machines, the mathematics of golf, the astonishing mind of a superman named Gauss, birds who count, the laws that govern poker, a professional teataster, Bernard Shaw on the vice of gambling and the virtues of insurance, assorted infinities, a one-sided strip of paper, and even some fiction, odd or brilliant, involving mathematics. . . .

Being incapable, I cannot talk about mathematics itself.   But I can talk about the charm of reading about and around mathematics, for I have sensed that charm as vividly as one may sense the charm, without ever being quite able to define it, of a lovely face or voice or piece of architecture. . . .

It is a curious circumstance that, though mathematics is but a set of marks on paper, it should have such numberless connections with what is called the real world.   This airy structure, shimmering like a heat haze in the minds of a few men, is also a kind of hub of the universe from which radiate the spokes of a hundred arts and sciences.   Or it is like a circular window opening on 360° of thought.   It points toward everything else, from a Bach fugue to the propulsion of a spitball, from soap films to diplomacy.   Study the myriad spirals of nature and at once you meet the logarithm.   Look into D'Arcy Thompson's *On Growth and Form,* and see how mathematics enters into the growth of wild goats' horns, the architecture of a snowflake, the shape of eggs.   The mathematical concept of symmetry is tied up not alone with music but with women's veils, flower petals, and the activities of bees.   Mathematics is part and parcel of modern war, not merely in the gross concerns of ballistics but in the subtler ones of strategy and tactics.   There are few human concerns on which it does not throw some light. . . . It is this marvelous connectivity of mathematics, its bewildering universal-jointedness, that leads the shallowest student to echo Einstein's wonderment: "How can it be that mathematics, being after all a product of human thought independent of experience, is so admirably adapted to the objects of reality?"

Motivation through Mathematical Recreations and Clubs. In the minds of a good many people the concept of motivation has become identified with, and in some cases limited to, the idea of games, puzzles, plays, anecdotes, and other interesting, but sometimes more or less trivial and unrelated, matters often referred to under the generic title of mathematical recreations. It is unfortunate that this should be the case, because motivation implies a much broader and more significant connotation than this and takes place through various avenues. At the same time such mathematical recreations and peripheral activities, if kept within proper perspective, can be valuable and legitimate in relieving the tedium of necessary routine work and in presenting an aspect of mathematics the existence of which is at times not even suspected. It is a rare individual, especially child, who is not interested in games or in things which are unusual or unsuspected and which contain elements of surprise or mystery. While mathematical puzzles, contests, and games cannot be permitted to pre-empt too much of the time allotted to regular classwork, there is abundant evidence that the moderate and appropriate employment of such devices does add much of interest and zest to the courses.[1]

Mathematics clubs provide an excellent means of stimulating and fostering mathematical study. Membership in these clubs is usually voluntary, and for this reason the clubs are composed mainly of students who have a real interest in mathematics and who desire to obtain a view of the subject which is somewhat different from that gained in the classroom. Such clubs offer excellent opportunities for free consideration of matters of special interest to the members without the necessity of having the programs follow any particular organic sequence of topics such as is generally necessary in regular class instruction. Secondary school pupils, like all others, are dependent upon each other in their mental, physical, social, domestic, and other relationships. They listen to ideas expressed by others and add their own; they criticize and are criticized. The fact that they do not always agree stimulates interest and motivates discussion. A mathematics club offers an ideal place for a free exchange of mathematical ideas and for frank and helpful criticism of these ideas. The club also makes possible an informality and a social atmosphere which the classroom can hardly provide. The club should be an organization of, by, and for the students, the teacher being a sympathetic counselor whose main function is to foster a continuance of interest and to cooperate in guiding the activities of the club along appropriate lines.

The principles of organization of a mathematics club should be neither

---

[1] Louis Grant Brandes, Why We Use Recreational Mathematics in Our Secondary School Mathematics Classes, *School Science and Mathematics*, **54** (1954), 289–293.

Arthur J. Hall, Using Mathematical Recreations in the Junior High School, *Mathematics Teacher*, **48** (1955), 484–487.

numerous nor involved. The objectives should be clearly stated and understood by all the members. Emphasis should be on active participation of the members. There should be a faculty sponsor who should be inconspicuous but ready to advise and help when needed. In general, any criticisms that he might have to make concerning programs should be given in private to the individual students concerned. It is desirable that each club limit its membership to such size that there will be opportunity for all to participate, and that all meetings be held at regularly scheduled times.[1]

The programs of mathematics clubs may cover a wide range of topics, many of which have been listed and discussed in numerous books and in articles in such periodicals as the *Mathematics Teacher*, *School Science and Mathematics*, the *Pentagon*, and the *Mathematics Student Journal*. These will include topics drawn from the history of mathematics, including biographical sketches and interesting anecdotes; the evolution and development of certain aspects of present-day mathematics; topics from algebra, geometry, arithmetic, or trigonometry; games and contests; and applications to other subjects and fields of activity. Discussion of some elementary aspects of modern mathematics may well rate some priority in club programs. The nature of the programs and topics to be discussed will of necessity depend considerably upon the age and advancement of the members of the club. Some subjects which could be discussed with interest and profit by students in the junior college or in the upper years of the senior high school would not be appropriate for junior high school clubs, whereas certain activities in which these clubs could well engage would be too elementary to hold much interest for the older students. The membership of the mathematics club should be, so far as possible, fairly homogeneous as regards age and grade level in order that programs which will be of interest to all the members may be arranged.

There is now an extensive and rapidly growing literature on mathematical recreations, clubs, and books and articles of popular interest. Indeed, it is growing so fast that a bibliography is likely to be somewhat incomplete even by the time it is published. Several such bibliographies and a great many individual articles and books of popular interest have been published in the past quarter century, but they are quite scattered, and the task of assembling them is not easy. In order to facilitate reference to these sources, a composite list, classified under four headings and fairly complete up to the time of this edition, is presented in the Bibliography under Mathematical Recreations and Clubs.

Several of the sources listed contain rather extensive bibliographies or

---

[1] Annie John Williams, Organizing a Mathematics Club, *Mathematics Teacher*, **49** (1956), 149–150.

lists of references on mathematical recreations, clubs, and books or articles of popular interest on mathematical topics.

In addition to these bibliographies it will be worthwhile to note some continuing sources of ideas for motivation in mathematics teaching. Some of them appear currently, or have appeared, as regular departments in certain journals. Among them those listed in the Bibliography under Mathematical Recreations and Clubs, Continuing Sources, can be helpful.

Two other subsections of the Bibliography, under the major division Mathematical Recreations and Clubs, bring together a considerable number of detailed references which will be found helpful in locating materials dealing with mathematical recreations or suitable for use in connection with mathematics clubs or programs. These references will be found under the two headings Books and Periodical References. The book list includes some books which were cited in the earlier editions of this work. On the other hand, the periodical references, with very few exceptions, are to articles which have appeared since the publication of the second edition of this book in 1951. For earlier references the reader should consult the first or second editions of this book or some of the other lists given above.

Motivation through Intellectual Curiosity. Many teachers and textbook writers have never recognized the power of sheer intellectual curiosity as a motive for the highest type of work in mathematics, and as a consequence they have failed to organize and present the work in a manner designed to stimulate the student's interest through a challenge to his curiosity. A notable instance of this is to be found in the fact that practically all theorems of demonstrative geometry are set up as exercises in establishing certain prestated conclusions rather than as exercises for free exploration and investigation of the consequences of certain hypotheses. Thus the element of discovery of the central fact or relationship in each theorem is removed at the outset, whereas this element of discovery could in many cases be retained and used to quicken the interest of the students. For example, the statement Prove that an inscribed angle is measured by half of its intercepted arc sets forth a task to be performed, while the question What relation, if any, exists between the number of degrees in an inscribed angle and the number of degrees of arc in its intercepted arc? is designed to whet the curiosity of the student instead of satisfying it at the outset.

As a rule, secondary school students are not intellectually lazy. That they may often appear to be so is due in large measure to the fact that their work is so largely set up for them as tasks to be done rather than as situations to be investigated, and they simply become bored and indifferent. Most students in the secondary school are persistently curious individuals, and they will work, and work hard, at things that interest them.

They do not hate mathematics, as some seem to think; they hate only drudgery and boredom and frustration.   Teachers need to remind themselves continuously that to bring out the best in their students they must appeal to interest motives that are strong and that intellectual curiosity is one of the strongest, as well as the most desirable, of these motives. The range of the potential intellectual interests of these students is practically unlimited.   The writers of modern detective fiction have recognized this and have capitalized on it.   The enormous popular response which has brought this type of fiction to the front rank in sales and library withdrawals can be attributed only to the general reader's insatiate curiosity in the development and denouement of a problem situation.

Evidence that mathematics is not devoid of strong appeal to the curiosity and interest of people can be found in the appearance and widespread sale, over the past few years, of a large number of books on mathematical recreations and popular mathematics for the general reader.   Even the more serious among these books are attaining sales records far beyond expectation.   Indeed, in one instance an expensive four-volume set of books on mathematics[1] achieved a record of sales so impressive that it evoked a lengthy article and commentary by a distinguished writer in a widely distributed popular magazine.   In it he comments as follows: "Perhaps the most extraordinary thing about it is its commercial career, which bears out my feeling that large numbers of us ordinary people are repressed mathematicians. . . . I know of no matching phenomenon in the entire history of publishing."[2]

Mathematical situations lack, of course, the lurid human interest of the ordinary mystery novel, but they do not lack the essential curiosity-provoking possibilities.   "Think-of-a-number" games are popular at parties, even among people who anticipate or recall the study of algebra with dread, yet the games are nothing except algebra somewhat obscured, perhaps, by a screen of mysticism which only serves to stimulate curiosity. People are interested in seeing how numbers behave, and algebra is essentially the science of the behavior of numbers.   Puzzle problems in mathematics have often been criticized as being unreal or having no genuine application to life situations.   A little experience in teaching algebra, however, will soon convince the most skeptical critic that problems which purport to represent "real" situations may not be interesting to students and that, on the other hand, problems may be quite interesting without being "real."   As a matter of fact, it is quite possible that the presence

[1] James R. Newman: "The World of Mathematics" (New York: Simon and Schuster, Inc., 1956).   Even before publication, the entire planned first printing was far oversubscribed at a prepublication price of $14.95.   Within seventeen days after publication more than 105,000 sets had been sold.

[2] Clifton Fadiman, *op. cit.*, p. 8.

of the puzzle element in problems is often a greater stimulus to *interest* than those elements of so-called reality which authors of textbooks try so hard to incorporate in problems.[1]

Obviously there must be system and organization in mathematics. Arithmetic and algebra cannot and should not consist entirely of number games and puzzles, nor demonstrative geometry of incidental and undirected investigations. These are sequential subjects and must be developed in sequential form. Haphazard or piecemeal work will achieve nothing of value. But within the framework of the systematic organization of a course in mathematics at any level of secondary instruction there are many opportunities for motivating the work by deliberate stimulation of the curiosity of the students along the lines indicated. The greater the extent to which this is done, the greater will be the interest, understanding, and assiduity with which the students will work and the more meaningful and worthwhile will the work become to them.

Motivation through the Use of Multisensory Aids and Devices. Most people gain new impressions more readily and more vividly through sensory experiences than they do through reading or abstract reasoning. The remarkable growth and public acceptance of motion pictures, radio, and television leaves no doubt of the interest-getting power of these audio-visual media. Advertisements in newspapers and magazines and on billboards and television commercials are found to be more effective when they have eye appeal than when they are confined to mere statements in words, even though the connection between the picture and the subject may be pretty farfetched. Thus, a pleasant wooded lake or an attractive young lady seem to be standard adjuncts in advertising almost anything from soap, cigarettes, and beer to refrigerators, automobiles, and waterfront lots.

Teachers of mathematics have been slower than their colleagues in English, geography, science, history, and the social studies to take advantage of this eye-and-ear appeal as a means of stimulating interest among their students. This has been partly due to the nature of the subject, which is essentially one of ideas rather than things. That, in turn, accounts in large measure for the fact that not very many really good pictorial or physical representations of mathematical topics have been commonly available. Commercially, such devices have been limited mainly to a few good sound films and filmstrips and a number of not-so-good ones and to certain rather expensive models and mechanical devices for illustrating theorems in geometry. These aids and devices, for one reason or another, have not been very widely used, though as they are improved, it can be expected that their use will increase.

[1] In this connection see Hartung, *op. cit.*, p. 53.

Multisensory aids, however, are not limited to motion pictures and filmstrips, and in the past decade increasing attention has been given to the employment of other sensory devices both for motivation and for instruction. Evidence of this is found, for example, in the efforts to improve the effectiveness of textbooks through more and better diagrams and illustrations, the improvement of type face and format, and the liberal use of color. It is also seen in the increasing number of suggestions in textbooks and elsewhere for stimulating interest in mathematics through projects involving the use of instruments and the construction and use of visual or mechanical devices for illustrating mathematical concepts, facts, and principles. Activities of this kind are commonly called laboratory work in mathematics. Part of the next chapter will be devoted to discussion of such work as an important avenue to learning. Its importance, however, even from the standpoint of motivation alone, is so great that it must not be overlooked in this connection.

A selected list of references on this subject is given in the Bibliography under Multisensory Aids. Some of the references are given in the second edition of this book; others have become available since the publication of the second edition. The list is offered in the hope that it may provide a convenient and helpful source of reference and so promote the use of multisensory aids and devices to stimulate interest in the work.

A Final Word. The means and devices which have been discussed in the foregoing pages will be found helpful in stimulating and maintaining interest in mathematics. In themselves, however, they cannot be regarded as panaceas or guarantees. In the last analysis the first and greatest factor in creating interest is a sympathetic, well-informed, competent, and inspiring teacher. Not all the devices in the world can bear the fruit of a continuing and enthusiastic student interest if they are grafted upon the dead stump of instruction in the hands of an incompetent or uninterested teacher. The truly inspiring teacher must first of all be thoroughly grounded in the subject matter of mathematics, well beyond the level of any material which he is expected to teach, in order that he may inspire the confidence and respect of his students. He must have a sympathetic understanding of student difficulties and must be always ready and willing to offer proper guidance and stimulation. Finally, he must have an enthusiastic interest in his subject and in teaching it. He must believe in its values and its contribution to the educational well-being of the students. Enthusiasm is contagious, and sane enthusiasm backed by sympathetic and enlightened competence is the only real guarantee of the effective maintenance of student interest. Devices are helpful, but they are not sufficient unto the task. The inspiring teacher is the real *sine qua non*.

EXERCISES

1. Prepare an outline and summary of the "Guidance Pamphlet" published by the National Council of Teachers of Mathematics. Explain in some detail how this pamphlet could be useful as a means of motivation.

2. Various large industrial companies publish and distribute pamphlets or brochures for the purpose of stimulating interest in mathematics. Try to obtain some of them and evaluate them from the standpoint of motivation.

3. Recent issues of mathematical and technical journals have carried many paid advertisements indicating the rapidly growing need for mathematicians in industry and the remunerative opportunities in this field. Consult various sources and prepare a composite list of such advertisements to place in the hands of high school students.

4. In the *Mathematics Teacher*, January, 1958, there is a brief article entitled "Things and Un-Things." Read it. Does the idea around which it is built seem promising as a means of motivation? Discuss this.

5. Take some contemporary textbook on shop mathematics and for each of the following describe two situations or problems in which it is required: (a) operations with fractions, (b) evaluation of formulas, (c) algebraic solution of formulas or equations, (d) application of geometry, (e) application of trigonometry.

6. The article "Sebastian and the 'Wolf'," in the *Mathematics Teacher*, February. 1955, is concerned with an interesting relation between mathematics and music, Read this article and discuss it with the class. See if you can find other articles about applications of mathematics to music.

7. Read the articles on "Geometric Drawing," "Curve Stitching," and "Window Transparencies" in the "Eighteenth Yearbook of the National Council of Teachers of Mathematics." Report on them and discuss any mathematical principles involved in these designs.

8. Give some examples of applications of mathematics to economics, home economics, biology, and agriculture.

9. Construct a piece of demonstration apparatus to illustrate the principle that all angles inscribed in a given segment of a circle are equal.

10. A good deal is being said these days about the use of motion pictures, filmstrips, and television for stimulating interest in mathematics. Try to find some articles on this subject. Discuss the potential advantages and also the limitations of these media, considered as means of motivation.

11. The launching of the first Russian satellite produced immediate and great concern on the part of the public with school mathematics. To what extent do you think the coming of the space age has motivated or will motivate student interest in mathematics?

12. Make a slide rule for addition and subtraction and show how it works.

13. Prepare at least two recreations, in the form of mathematical fallacies, for presentation.

14. In the *Mathematics Teacher*, April, 1955, there is an article, entitled Tricks that Click, on the use of puzzles in teaching mathematics. Study this article and report it to the class, including the references listed in the bibliography at the end of the article.

15. Most children are interested in simple probability and the laws of chance. Make up some simple experiments in drawing numbers from prearranged sets, so that the probabilities can be tested experimentally by the students. Try out these experiments on your classmates.

16. From books on mathematical recreations select ten which you think would be

good to use (*a*) with junior high school students and (*b*) with senior high school students.   Present one or more of these to the class.

17. Make a device to show that it is possible to have a surface which is curved at every point even though it is made up entirely of straight lines.

18. Assume that you have been asked to present a 20-minute talk to a ninth-grade mathematics club.   Select an appropriate topic, outline your talk, and be prepared to give it orally.

19. Assume that you are to have as an audience a club made up of high school seniors all of whom are superior students and are taking their fourth year of high school mathematics and prepare a talk as in exercise 18.

20. Assume that you are to have as an audience a club made up of average and better-than-average seventh-grade students and prepare a talk as in exercise 18.

21. Examine several recent issues of the *Pentagon* and note the lists of topics suggested there as being appropriate for mathematics clubs made up of college students. Which, if any, of these topics do you think would be suitable for presentation to a high school mathematics club?

22. Discuss both the possibilities and the limitations of mathematics contests as means of stimulating and maintaining interest in mathematics.   Consult the article entitled "The National Status of Mathematics Contests" in the *Mathematics Teacher,* October, 1956.

23. What suggestions do you find in S. I. Jones' "Mathematical Clubs and Recreations" that would be helpful to you in organizing or sponsoring a mathematics club of high school students?   (See Bibliography under Books.)

24. Summarize the article on mathematics exhibits found on pages 104–108 in the "Eighteenth Yearbook of the National Council of Teachers of Mathematics."

25. Consult the "Nineteenth Yearbook of the National Council of Teachers of Mathematics" and prepare a talk on the development and uses of early surveying instruments.

26. Consult the "Seventeenth Yearbook of the National Council of Teachers of Mathematics" and note the application of mathematics to art (pages 183–187).   Also, examine recent issues of *Scripta Mathematica* and report on any striking designs that have their bases in mathematics.

27. Construct a design that has some mathematical basis as well as esthetic appeal. Explain the mathematics involved.

28. Read completely the article "Party of One" (see footnote, p. 116) and try to get the esthetic feeling for mathematics which the author endeavors to convey.   Report on your success, or lack of it.

29. The assertion has been made that, if high school students could really be made to see what algebra is about, the problem of lack of interest would largely disappear. Discuss this assertion.

30. Explain how various simple numbers would be written in a system of notation using five as the base.   Also, show how to add and multiply numbers in this system.

31. Repeat exercise 30 by using a binary notation whose only numerals are 1 and 0.

32. Without using arabic numerals, find the sum of CDXXXVII, XLVI, and CCXIX.   Check by writing the numbers in arabic numerals and finding the sum.   In a similar way, find and check the product of XLIX and IV.   (This exercise affords a good opportunity to point out some of the advantages of our own decimal system of notation.)

33. Devise numerical exercises to illustrate the following algebraic identities: $(a + b)(c + d) = ac + ad + bc + bd$; $(a + b)^2 = a^2 + 2ab + b^2$.

34. Give geometric illustrations of the identities of exercise 33.   Do you think such

illustrations would be very helpful in stimulating students' interest through giving them better insight into the meanings of the identities?

35. What part of secondary mathematics, in your opinion, requires the least special effort for the creation and maintenance of interest? In what part of the work is such effort most needed? Give reasons for your answers.

36. Discuss the value of such devices as progress charts or records as means of stimulating and maintaining interest in mathematical work.

37. Discuss the advantages and disadvantages of using grades as incentives.

38. Genuine insight into the meaning of the subject matter and into the nature of mathematics itself gives probably the most enduring and powerful motivation of all. To what extent do you think the failure of teachers to develop such insight in their students is due to their own lack of it?

BIBLIOGRAPHY

General

Amir-Moez, Ali R.: Creating Interest for Gifted Students, *Pentagon*, **16** (1957), 88–90.

Association of Assistant Masters in Secondary Schools, "The Teaching of Mathematics" (London: Cambridge University Press, 1957), pp. 54–59, 128–133, 179–193.

Barnes, H. M.: Technical Training Applications, *School Science and Mathematics*, **54** (1954), 377–380.

Baumgartner, Reuben A.: A Mathematics Curriculum for the Gifted, *School Science and Mathematics*, **53** (1953), 207–213.

Berger, Emil J., and Donovan A. Johnson: "A Guide to the Use and Procurement of Teaching Aids for Mathematics" (Washington, D.C.: National Council of Teachers of Mathematics, 1959).

Billig, Albert L.: Student Attitude as a Factor in the Mastery of Commercial Arithmetic, *Mathematics Teacher*, **37** (1944), 170–172.

Blank, Laura: Teaching Mathematics in Technicolor, *Mathematics Teacher*, **41** (1948), 229–231.

Blumenthal, Leonard M.: The Relativity of Mathematics, *Pentagon*, **11** (1951), 3–12.

Boehm, George A. W., and the editors of *Fortune*: "The New World of Mathematics" (New York: The Dial Press, Inc., 1959).

Boyd, James R.: A Mathematics Club for the Able, *Mathematics Teacher*, **46** (1953), 43–45.

Brandes, Louis Grant: Why Use Recreational Mathematics in Our Secondary School Mathematics Classes? *School Science and Mathematics*, **54** (1954), 289–293.

———: Recreational Mathematics as It May Be Used with Secondary School Pupils, *School Science and Mathematics*, **54** (1954), 383–393.

———: Recreational Mathematics for the Mathematical Classrooms of Our Secondary Schools, *School Science and Mathematics*, **54** (1954), 617–627.

———: Cross-number Puzzles: A Teaching Aid for Classes of General Mathematics, *Mathematics Teacher*, **50** (1957), 567–569.

Brock, Paul: Mathematicians and Automata, *Mathematics Teacher*, **47** (1954), 514–519.

Brown, Claude H.: "The Teaching of Secondary Mathematics" (New York: Harper & Brothers, 1953), pp. 319–320.

Brune, Irvin H.: Vocational Opportunities in Mathematics, *Bulletin of the National Association of Secondary-School Principals*, **38** (1954), 20–31.

Buck, R. Creighton: A Look at Mathematical Competitions, *American Mathematical Monthly*, **66** (1959), 201–212.

Carlton, Carl J.: Mathematics in the Skilled Trades, *Mathematics Teacher*, **46** (1953), 8–13, 27.

Carnahan, Walter H.: Enrichment of Mathematics Teaching, *Mathematics Teacher*, **42** (1949), 14–18.

———: Maintenance of Interest in Mathematics, *Bulletin of the National Association of Secondary-School Principals*, **38** (1954), 110–116.

———: "Mathematics Clubs in High Schools" (Washington, D.C.: National Council of Teachers of Mathematics, 1957).

Commission on Post-War Plans: "Guidance Pamphlet in Mathematics for High School Students" (Washington, D.C.: National Council of Teachers of Mathematics, 1947).

———: Guidance Report, *Mathematics Teacher*, **40** (1947), 315–339.

Daus, Paul H., and William M. Whyburn: "Introduction to Mathematical Analysis with Applications to Problems of Economics" (Reading, Mass.: Addison-Wesley Publishing Company, Inc., 1958).

Davis, David R.: "The Teaching of Mathematics" (Reading, Mass.: Addison-Wesley Publishing Company, Inc., 1951), pp. 66–87.

Duodecimal Bulletin, The. (Periodical publication of the Duodecimal Society of America, 20 Carlton Place, Staten Island, New York.)

Dutton, Wilbur H.: Attitudes of Prospective Teachers toward Arithmetic, *Elementary School Journal*, **52** (1951), 84–90.

Eales, John R.: A Job Survey as Class Motivation in General Mathematics, *Mathematics Teacher*, **43** (1950), 318–320.

Elias, Robert: Mathematics at Work in the Paper Industry, *Mathematics Teacher*, **46** (1953), 529–536.

Enterline, H. G., et al.: "Blueprint for Tomorrow" (New York: Educational Division, Institute of Life Insurance, 1956).

Fadiman, Clifton: Party of One, *Holiday*, **21** (January, 1957), 6, 8, 11, 14, 113.

Fehr, Howard F.: Teaching for Appreciation in Mathematics, *School Science and Mathematics*, **52** (1952), 19–24.

Feltges, Edna M.: Planning a Mathematics Tournament, *Mathematics Teacher*, **43** (1950), 268–270.

Fish, D.: Individual Projects Create Interest in Mathematics, *Ohio Schools*, **34** (1956), 18–19.

Fugill, A. P., W. H. Hulswit, and C. V. Winder: The Need for Mathematics in Business and Industry, *Mathematics Teacher*, **46** (1953), 23–27.

Gisonté, Frank: The Most Important Objective in the Teaching of Mathematics, *Mathematics Magazine*, **27** (1953), 37–38.

Goins, William F., Jr.: Putting More Meaning in the Teaching of Measurement, *School Science and Mathematics*, **50** (1950), 745–749.

Gouss, Harold A.: Come to the Fair, *New Jersey Mathematics Teacher*, **8** (1951), 12–14.

Grove, Ethel L., Anne M. Mullikin, and Ewart L. Grove: Mathematics and America's Future, *American Book Company Bulletin*, **111** (1956), 1–5.

Grubbs, Ethel Harris: Stimulating Interest in Junior High School Mathematics, *Mathematics Teacher*, **48** (1955), 147–152.

Hach, Alice: A High School Mathematics Club, *Mathematics Teacher*, **45** (1952), 457–461.

Hahn, Hans: Geometry and Intuition, *Scientific American*, **190** (1954), 84–91.

Hall, Arthur J.: Using Mathematical Recreations in the Junior High School, *Mathematics Teacher*, **48** (1955), 484–487.

Hartung, Maurice L.: Motivation for Education in Mathematics, "Twenty-first Yearbook," (Washington, D.C.: National Council of Teachers of Mathematics, 1953), pp. 42–68.

Heard, Ida Mae: Using Special Interests to Stimulate the Study of Mathematics, *Mathematics Teacher*, **41** (1948), 309–310.

Hicks, Charles R.: Two Problems Illustrating the Use of Mathematics in Modern Industry, *Mathematics Teacher*, **48** (1955), 130–132.

Hodor, Mary Lou, and Nan Hutchings: A Step Forward, *Pentagon*, **10** (1951), 11–16.

Hofeditz, Paul H.: Sequoia Junior High School Mathematics Team, *Mathematics Teacher*, **49** (1956), 473–474.

Johnson, Donovan A.: Attitudes in the Mathematics Classroom, *School Science and Mathematics*, **57** (1957), 113–120.

————: Mathematical Games Build Skills, *Mathematics Teacher*, **50** (1957), 292–294.

Jones, Phillip S.: Tangible Arithmetic, *Mathematics Teacher*, **47** (1954), 482–487, 535–542; **48** (1955), 91–95, 153–157.

Kemeny, John G., et al.: "Introduction to Finite Mathematics" (Englewood Cliffs, N.J.: Prentice-Hall, Inc., 1957).

Kidd, Kenneth P.: Improving the Learning of Mathematics, *Mathematics Teacher*, **47** (1954), 393–400.

Kinney, Lucien Blair, and C. Richard Purdy: "Teaching Mathematics in the Secondary School" (New York: Rinehart & Company, Inc., 1952), pp. 352–369.

Klotz, C. E.: Mathematics Clubs for High Schools, *School Activities*, **21** (1949), 59–61.

Ladd, Carl: Mathematics as a Sport, *Mathematics Teacher*, **52** (1959), 140–142.

Lankford, Francis J., Jr.: Practical Mathematics Is Challenging to Students, *Mathematics Teacher*, **48** (1955), 401–405.

Levy, Norton: Toward Discovery and Creativity, *Mathematics Teacher*, **50** (1957), 19–22.

Luff, Andrew: The Growing Emphasis on Science and Mathematics in Industry, *School Science and Mathematics*, **56** (1956), 240–244.

MacLane, Saunders: The Impact of Modern Mathematics, *Bulletin of the National Association of Secondary-School Principals*, **38** (1954), 66–71.

Malone, W. H., and E. L. Freel: A Preliminary Study of the Group Attitudes of Junior and Senior High School Students towards Mathematics, *Journal of Educational Research*, **47** (1954), 599–608.

Manheimer, Wallace: A Club Project in a Modern Use of Mathematics, *Mathematics Teacher*, **50** (1957), 350–355.

"Math Problems from Industry" (Detroit, Mich.: Educational Services, Department of Public Relations, Chrysler Corporation, 1956).

Mathematics Student Journal. (Published four times a year by National Council of Teachers of Mathematics, 1201 Sixteenth Street, N.W., Washington 6, D.C.)

Meder, Albert E., Jr., with the collaboration of Edward Begle, Julius Hlavaty, Cletus Oakley, Robert E. K. Rourke, and Max Sobel: "Teacher Education in Modern Mathematics" [five 16-mm sound motion pictures] (New York: McGraw-Hill Book Company, Inc., 1959). (These films, titled Patterns in Mathematics, Number Fields, Irrational Numbers, Concept of Function, and Sentences and Solution Sets, are suitable for acquisition and use by secondary schools under Title III of the National Defense Education Act of 1958 to strengthen instruction in mathematics.)

Minnick, J. H.: "Teaching Mathematics in the Secondary Schools" (Englewood Cliffs, N.J.: Prentice-Hall, Inc., 1939), pp. 307–326.

National Council of Teachers of Mathematics: "Multi-sensory Aids in the Teaching of Mathematics," *Eighteenth Yearbook* (Washington, D.C.: National Council of Teachers of Mathematics, 1945).

National High School and Junior College Mathematics Club (M A Th), *Mathematics Teacher*, **50** (1957), 372–373.

Norton, Monte S.: Enrichment as a Provision for the Gifted in Mathematics, *School Science and Mathematics*, **57** (1957), 339–345.

Oliver, Robert J.: Mathematics Bulletin Board Displays, *Mathematics Teacher*, **47** (1954), 91–92.

Palmer, B. W.: School Situations That Vitalize Mathematics, *Mathematics Teacher*, **37** (1944), 373–374.

Parker, Jean: The Use of Puzzles in Teaching Mathematics [with bibliography], *Mathematics Teacher*, **48** (1955), 218–227.

Porges, Irwin: Mathematics Motivated through Science Fiction, *School Science and Mathematics*, **56** (1956), 1–4.

Ranucci, Ernest R.: Mathematics and the Assembly Program, *New Jersey Mathematics Teacher*, **8** (1952), 4–6.

Rasmussen, Otho M.: Mathematics Used in Courses in Various Departments in a University, *Mathematics Teacher*, **48** (1955), 237–242.

Rees, Mina: The Impact of the Computer, *Mathematics Teacher*, **51** (1958), 162–168.

Reeve, William David: "Mathematics for the Secondary School" (New York: Henry Holt and Company, Inc., 1954), pp. 486–509.

Reynolds, Neil B.: Mathematics and the Needs of Industry, *Bulletin of the National Association of Secondary-School Principals*, **38** (1954), 31–35.

Riley, Geraldine: Mathematics Puzzle Box, *New Jersey Mathematics Teacher*, **12** (1956), 4–5.

Sawin, E. I.: Motivation in Mathematics: Its Theoretical Basis, Measurement, and Relationships with Other Factors, *Mathematics Teacher*, **44** (1951), 471–478.

Scates, Douglas E.: Statistics—The Mathematics for Social Problems, *Mathematics Teacher*, **36** (1943), 68–78.

Schaaf, William L.: References for Mathematics Teachers [bibliography of plays and assembly and club programs], *Mathematics Teacher*, **44** (1951), 526–528.

————: The High School Mathematics Library [selected bibliography], *Mathematics Teacher*, **47** (1954), 121–125, 199–203.

————: Scales of Notation [bibliography], *Mathematics Teacher*, **47** (1954), 415–417.

————: "Recreational Mathematics" (Washington, D.C.: National Council of Teachers of Mathematics, 1958). (Extensive bibliography, revised and classified.)

Schiff, Herbert J.: A Proposed Trip—A Teaching Device, *School Science and Mathematics*, **55** (1955), 393–394.

Schutter, Charles H.: Improving the Quality of Instruction in Mathematics, *School Science and Mathematics*, **47** (1947), 404–408.

Seber, Robert C.: "Mathematics for Non-Physical Science Students" (Iowa City, Iowa: University Bookstore, The State University of Iowa, 1955). (Mimeographed.)

Smith, D. E., and W. D. Reeve: "The Teaching of Junior High School Mathematics" (Boston: Ginn & Company, 1927), pp. 359–406.

Spitzer, Herbert F.: "Practical Procedures for the Enrichment of Arithmetic" (St. Louis, Mo.: Webster Publishing Company, 1956).

Stephens, Harold W.: A Mathematics Club for Future Mathematicians, *School Science and Mathematics*, **54** (1954), 715–718.

Stephenson, E. C.: Mathematics in a Retail Business, *Mathematics Teacher*, **46** (1953), 18–22.

Stubblefield, Ethel: A Community Approach to General Mathematics, *Mathematics Teacher*, **49** (1956), 195–199.

Students of Algebra II, University High School, Florida State University: Symbolic Logic and Logical Circuitry in the High School, *Mathematics Teacher*, **50** (1957), 23–26.

Totten, W. Fred: Words as a Basic Factor in Understanding Algebra, *School Science and Mathematics*, **56** (1956), 230–233.

Trump, Paul: The Enrichment of Mathematics Instruction, *Mathematics Teacher*, **40** (1947), 363–369.

Turner, C. T.: Motivating Junior High School Mathematics, *Elementary School Journal*, **36** (1936), 371–372.

Urbancek, Joseph J.: New Teaching Aids, *Chicago Schools Journal*, **30** (1949), 307.

Walch, J. Weston: "Colorful Teaching of Mathematics" (Portland, Maine: published by the author, 1955).

Wilks, S. S.: New Fields and Organizations in the Mathematical Sciences, *Mathematics Teacher*, **51** (1958), 2.

Willerding, Margaret F.: Review of the Fundamental Processes—The Cross-number Puzzle, *School Science and Mathematics*, **54** (1954), 51–52.

————: Stimulating Interest in Junior High Mathematics, *Mathematics Teacher*, **52** (1959), 197–201.

Williams, Annie John: Organizing a Mathematics Club, *Mathematics Teacher*, **49** (1956), 149–150.

Winthrop, Henry: Mathematics in the Social Sciences, *School Science and Mathematics*, **57** (1957), 9–15.

Wirszup, Izaak: Some Remarks on Enrichment, *Mathematics Teacher*, **49** (1956), 519–527.

Young, J. W. A.: "The Teaching of Mathematics" (New York: Longmans, Green & Co., Inc., 1924), pp. 163–169.

Mathematical Recreations and Clubs: Bibliography Listings

Andree, Richard V.: Cryptography as a Branch of Mathematics, *Mathematics Teacher*, **45** (1952), 503–509.

Bauer, Marie L.: Projects for Plane Geometry, *Mathematics Teacher*, **44** (1951), 235–239.

Brandes, Louis Grant: Why Use Recreational Mathematics in Our Secondary School Mathematics Classes, *School Science and Mathematics*, **54** (1954), 289–293.

Breslich, E. R.: "The Technique of Teaching Mathematics in Secondary Schools" (Chicago: University of Chicago Press, 1930), pp. 63–65, 69–71, 72, 75, 77–78, 82, 85–86.

Brueckner, Leo J., F. E. Grossnickle, and John Reckzeh: "Developing Mathematical Understanding in the Upper Grades" (Philadelphia: John C. Winston Company, 1957), pp. 549–551.

Davis, David R.: "The Teaching of Mathematics" (Reading, Mass.: Addison-Wesley Publishing Company, Inc., 1951), pp. 395–403.

Deason, Hilary J.: Traveling High School Science Libraries, *Science*, **124** (Nov. 23, 1956), 1–4.

Gloden, A.: Additions to Schaaf's "List of Works on Mathematical Recreations," *Scripta Mathematica*, **13** (1947), 26–27.

Johnson, Donovan A., and Henry W. Syer: A Bibliography of Mathematics Films and Filmstrips, *School Science and Mathematics*, **49** (1949), 650–657.

Kinney, Lucien Blair, and C. Richard Purdy: "Teaching Mathematics in the Secondary School" (New York: Rinehart & Company, Inc., 1952), pp. 368–369.

Lloyd, Daniel B.: Bibliography of Popular Mathematics, *School Science and Mathematics*, **38** (1938), 186–193.

———: A Golden Decade of Popular Mathematics, *Mathematics Teacher*, **41** (1948), 210–217.

———: Use of the Library, *Bulletin of the National Association of Secondary-School Principals*, **38** (1954), 144–151.

Minnick, J. H.: "Teaching Mathematics in the Secondary Schools" (Englewood Cliffs, N.J.: Prentice-Hall, Inc., 1939), pp. 323–325.

Moulton, Elton J.: A Selected List of Mathematical Books for Colleges, *American Mathematical Monthly*, **48** (1941), 600–609.

National Council of Teachers of Mathematics: "Fifteenth Yearbook" (Washington, D.C.: National Council of Teachers of Mathematics, 1940), pp. 242–245.

———: "Seventeenth Yearbook" (Washington, D.C.: National Council of Teachers of Mathematics, 1942).

———: "Eighteenth Yearbook" (Washington, D.C.: National Council of Teachers of Mathematics, 1945), pp. 100–103, 195–203, 223–225, 407–455.

Parker, Jean: The Use of Puzzles in Teaching Mathematics, *Mathematics Teacher*, **48** (1955), 218–227.

Schaaf, William L.: List of Works on Mathematical Recreations, *Scripta Mathematica*, **10** (1944), 192–200.

———: References for Mathematics Teachers [plays and programs], *Mathematics Teacher*, **44** (1951), 526–528.

———: The Theorem of Pythagoras, *Mathematics Teacher*, **44** (1951), 585–588.

———: The High School Mathematics Library, *Mathematics Teacher*, **47** (1954), 121–125, 199–203.

———: Paperback Mathematics, *Mathematics Teacher*, **50** (1957), 388–389.

———: "Recreational Mathematics" (Washington, D.C.: National Council of Teachers of Mathematics, 1958). [Extensive bibliography.]

Schorling, Raleigh: "The Teaching of Mathematics" (Ann Arbor, Mich.: The Ann Arbor Press, 1936), pp. 224–240.

Smith, D. E., and W. D. Reeve: "The Teaching of Junior High School Mathematics" (Boston: Ginn & Company, 1927), pp. 359–403.

Starr, David W.: Enrichment Materials for First Year Algebra, *Mathematics Teacher*, **32** (1939), 68–77.

Topics for Chapter Programs: Plays [for mathematics clubs], *Pentagon*, **11** (1951), 32–34.

Ullsvik, B. R.: New Materials and Equipment in the Teaching of Mathematics, *School Science and Mathematics*, **39** (1939), 432–442.

Urbancek, Joseph J.: Mathematical Teaching Aids, *Chicago Schools Journal*, **35** (supplement, November–December, 1953, January–February, 1954).

Continuing Sources

Applications, *Mathematics Teacher*. (Briefly presents special applications of elementary mathematical principles, mainly to physical problems.)

Clubs and Allied Activities, *American Mathematical Monthly*. (Some issues contain accounts of programs and activities of mathematics clubs in various colleges.)

Curiosa, *Scripta Mathematica*. (Descriptive accounts of mathematical curiosities.)

Devices for a Mathematics Laboratory, *Mathematics Teacher*. (Short, pointed suggestions for interesting physical devices useful in teaching certain topics in secondary school mathematics.)

Elementary Problems and Solutions, *American Mathematical Monthly*. (Special problems and solutions appear in every issue.   These problems presuppose two years of college mathematics.)

Historically Speaking, *Mathematics Teacher*.   (Articles of historical interest with respect to various mathematical concepts and topics.)

Mathematical Recreations, *Mathematics Teacher*.   (Interesting and nontrivial recreations suitable for use with capable high school students.)

Mathematical Scrapbook, *Pentagon*.   (A section made up of mathematical curiosa and miscellanea.)

Mathematics Student Journal.   (Published quarterly.   Contains challenging problems, recreations, and enrichment material for mathematics in grades 7–12.)

Miscellanea—Mathematical, Historical, Pedagogical, *Mathematics Teacher*.   (A "swapping post" for all kinds of notes which add interest to mathematics teaching.)

Notes on the History of Mathematics, *Mathematics Teacher*.   (Brief articles and anecdotes from the history of mathematics, suitable for use in secondary school classes.)

The Problem Corner, *Pentagon*.   (A section given over to special problems and solutions at the college level.)

The Problem Department, *School Science and Mathematics*.   (Special problems and solutions appear regularly.   An important source of interest for students and teachers of high school mathematics.)

Problems and Questions, *Mathematics Magazine*.   (College level.   Special problems, questions, and solutions appear regularly.)

Recreational Mathematics, *Scripta Mathematica*.   (Descriptive accounts of mathematical games, puzzles, and other mathematical recreations.)

Topics for Chapter Programs, *Pentagon*.   (Suggestions of topics for programs of mathematics clubs, with bibliographies on some topics.)

Books

Abbott, E. A.: "Flatland: A Romance in Many Dimensions" (New York: Dover Publications, 1952).

Abraham, R. M.: "Winter Nights Entertainment" (New York: E. P. Dutton & Co., Inc., 1933).

————: "Diversions and Pastimes" (New York: E. P. Dutton & Co., Inc., 1935).

Adler, Irving: "Magic House of Numbers" (New York: Signet Key Books, 1958).

————: "The New Mathematics" (New York: The John Day Company, Inc., 1958).

Allendoerfer, C. B., and C. O. Oakley: "Principles of Mathematics" (New York: McGraw-Hill Book Company, Inc., 1955).

————: "Fundamentals of Freshman Mathematics," (New York: McGraw-Hill Book Company, Inc., 1959).

Alliston, Norman: "Mathematical Snack Bar" (Cambridge, England: W. Heffer & Sons, Ltd., 1936).   (Now distributed by the Chemical Publishing Company, Inc., Brooklyn, N.Y.)

Anderson, Raymond W.: "Romping through Mathematics" (New York: Alfred A. Knopf, Inc., 1947).

Andrews, W. S.: "Magic Squares and Cubes" (La Salle, Ill.: The Open Court Publishing Company, 1908).

Axelrod, Aaron: "Machine-shop Mathematics," 2d. ed. (New York: McGraw-Hill Book Company, Inc., 1951).

Bakst, Aaron: "Mathematics—Its Magic and Mastery" (Princeton, N.J.: D. Van Nostrand Company, Inc., 1952).

Ball, W. W. Rouse: "String Figures: An Amusement for Everybody" (Cambridge, England: W. Heffer & Sons, Ltd., 1921).

————: "Mathematical Recreations and Essays" (New York: The Macmillan Company, 1947).

———— and H. S. M. Coxeter: "Mathematical Recreations and Essays," 11th ed. (London: Macmillan & Co., Ltd., 1956).

Banks, J. Houston: "Elements of Mathematics" (New York: Allyn and Bacon, 1956).

Bell, Eric T.: "Numerology" (Baltimore: The Williams & Wilkins Company, 1933).

————: "Men of Mathematics" (New York: Simon and Schuster, Inc., 1937).

————: "The Development of Mathematics," 2d ed. (New York: McGraw-Hill Book Company, Inc., 1945).

————: "The Magic of Numbers" (New York: McGraw-Hill Book Company, Inc., 1946).

————: "Mathematics, Queen and Servant of Science" (New York: McGraw-Hill Book Company, Inc., 1951).

Bellafiore, Ignatius: "Pharmaceutical Arithmetic," 3d ed. (St. Louis: The C. V. Mosby Company, 1953).

Blanche, Ernst E.: "You Can't Win: Facts and Fallacies about Gambling" (Washington, D.C.: Public Affairs Press, 1949).   (Pamphlet.)

Boehm, George A. W., and the editors of Fortune: "The New World of Math" (New York: The Dial Press, Inc., 1959).

Boon, F. C.: "A Companion to Elementary School Mathematics" (New York: Longmans, Green & Co., Inc., 1924).

Boyer, Lee Emerson: "An Introduction to Mathematics for Teachers" (New York: Henry Holt and Company, Inc., 1945).

————: "Mathematics: An Historical Development" (New York: Henry Holt and Company, Inc., 1955).

Bradley, A. Day: "Mathematics of Air and Marine Navigation" (New York: American Book Company, 1942).

Bragdon, Claude F.: "The Beautiful Necessity" (New York: Alfred A. Knopf, Inc., 1922).

————: "The Frozen Fountain" (New York: Alfred A. Knopf, Inc., 1932).

Brandes, Louis G.: "Math Can Be Fun" (Alameda, Calif.: published by the author, 1950).

————: "A Collection of Cross-number Puzzles" (Portland, Maine: J. Weston Walch, Publisher, 1957).

Breslich, E. R.: "Excursion in Mathematics" (Chicago: The Orthovis Company, 1938).

————: "Algebra: An Interesting Language" (New York: Newson and Company, 1939).

Brown, J. C.: "Easy Tricks with Numbers" (Pelham, N.Y.: Pelham Public Schools, 1943).

Burnett, Major J. C.: "Easy Methods for the Construction of Magic Squares" (London: Rider and Company, Publishers, 1936).

Cell, John W.: "Engineering Problems Illustrating Mathematics" (New York: McGraw-Hill Book Company, Inc., 1943).

Chamberlin, L. S.: "Related Mathematics for Carpenters" (Chicago: American Technical Society, 1952).

Collins, A. Frederick: "Fun with Figures" (New York: Appleton-Century-Crofts, Inc., 1928).

Cooley, Hollis R., et al.: "Introduction to Mathematics," 2d ed. (Boston: Houghton Mifflin Company, 1949).

Corbman, Bernard: "Mathematics of Retail Merchandising" (New York: The Ronald Press Company, 1952).

Courant, Richard, and Herbert Robbins: "What Is Mathematics?" (New York: Oxford University Press, 1941).

Cundy, H. M.: "Mathematical Models" (New York: Oxford University Press, 1958).

Cuthbert, W. R.: "Days for Dates" (Alhambra, Calif.: published by the author, 1953).

De Grazia, Joseph: "Math Is Fun" (New York: Emerson Books, Inc., 1954).

De Morgan, Augustus: "A Budget of Paradoxes" (New York: Dover Publications, 1954).

Dickason, Alfred: "The Calculation of Sheet Metal Work" (New York: Pitman Publishing Corporation, 1950).

Dubisch, Roy: "The Nature of Number" (New York: The Ronald Press Company, 1952).

Dudeney, Henry E.: "Amusements in Mathematics" (New York: Thomas Nelson & Sons, 1921).

————: "Modern Puzzles" (Philadelphia: Frederick A. Stokes Company, 1926).

————: "Puzzles and Curious Problems" (New York: Thomas Nelson & Sons, 1940).

————: "The Canterbury Puzzles" (New York: Thomas Nelson & Sons, 1949).

Edwards, William H.: "Precision Shop Mathematics" (Boston: D. C. Heath and Company, 1947).

"Fascinating Figure Puzzles" (Detroit: Burroughs Adding Machine Company, 1933).

Fehr, Howard F.: "Secondary Mathematics: A Functional Approach for Teachers" (Boston: D. C. Heath and Company, 1951).

Freeman, Mae, and Ira Freeman: "Fun with Figures" (New York: Random House, Inc., 1946).

Freund, John E.: "A Modern Introduction to Mathematics" (Englewood Cliffs, N.J.: Prentice-Hall, Inc., 1956).

Gamow, George: "One, Two, Three . . . Infinity" (New York: The Viking Press, Inc., 1954).

———— and Marvin Stern: "Puzzle-Math" (New York: The Viking Press, Inc., 1958).

Gardner, Martin: "The Scientific American Book of Mathematical Puzzles and Diversions" (New York: Simon and Schuster, Inc., 1959).

Gardner, Randolph: "Instruments for the Enrichment of Secondary School Mathematics" (Ann Arbor, Mich.: J. W. Edwards, Publisher, Inc., 1951).

Ghyka, Matila: "The Geometry of Art and Life" (New York: Sheed & Ward, Inc., 1946).

Gibson, W. B.: "Brain Tests" (Boston: L. C. Page & Company, 1930).

Gilles, William F.: "The Magic and Oddities of Numbers" (New York: Vantage Press, Inc., 1953).

Greenhood, David: "Down to Earth: Mapping for Everybody" (New York: Holiday House, Inc., 1951).

Hardy, G. H.: "A Mathematician's Apology" (New York: Cambridge University Press, 1940).

Heath, Royal Vale: "Mathemagic" (New York: Dover Publications, 1953).

Hill, T. H. Ward: "Mathematics for the Layman" (New York: Philosophical Library, Inc., 1958).

Hogben, Lancelot: "Mathematics for the Million" (New York: W. W. Norton & Company, Inc., 1937).

————: "The Wonderful World of Mathematics" (New York: Garden City Books, 1955).

Hooper, A.: "The River Mathematics" (New York: Henry Holt and Company, Inc., 1945).

——: "Makers of Mathematics" (New York: Random House, Inc., 1948).

Hudson, Hilda P.: "Ruler and Compasses" (New York: Longmans, Green & Co., Inc., 1916).

Huff, Darrell, and Irving Geis: "How to Lie with Statistics" (New York: W. W. Norton & Company, Inc., 1954).

Infeld, Leopold: "Whom the Gods Love: The Story of Evariste Galois" (New York: McGraw-Hill Book Company, Inc., 1948).

Johnson, Lee H.: "The Slide Rule" (Princeton, N.J.: D. Van Nostrand Company, Inc., 1949).

Jones, Burton W.: "Elementary Concepts of Mathematics" (New York: The Macmillan Company, 1947).

Jones, S. I.: "Mathematical Wrinkles" (Nashville, Tenn.: published by the author, 1929).

——: "Mathematical Nuts" (Nashville, Tenn.: published by the author, 1936).

——: "Mathematical Clubs and Recreations" (Nashville, Tenn.: published by the author, 1940).

Kafka, F.: "Statistics without Numbers: A Visual Explanation" (New York: Lifetime Editions, 1950).

Kasner, Edward, and James Newman: "Mathematics and the Imagination" (New York: Simon and Schuster, Inc., 1940).

Keal, H. M., and C. J. Leonard: "Essential Mathematics for Skilled Workers" (New York: John Wiley & Sons, Inc., 1942).

Kemeny, John G., J. Laurie Snell, and Gerald L. Thompson: "Introduction to Finite Mathematics" (Englewood Cliffs, N.J.: Prentice-Hall, Inc., 1957).

Kinnaird, Clarke (Editor): "Encyclopedia of Puzzles and Pastimes" (New York: Grosset & Dunlap, Inc., 1946).

Kline, Morris: "Mathematics in Western Culture" (New York: Oxford University Press, 1953).

Kokomoor, F. W.: "Mathematics in Human Affairs" (Englewood Cliffs, N.J.: Prentice-Hall, Inc., 1942).

Kraitchik, M.: "Mathematical Recreations," rev. ed., (New York: Dover Publications, 1953).

Kramer, Edna: "The Main Stream of Mathematics" (New York: Oxford University Press, 1951).

Kuehn, Martin H.: "Mathematics for Electricians," 3d ed. (New York: McGraw-Hill Book Company, Inc., 1949).

Lee, W. W.: "Math Miracles" (Durham, N.C.: published by the author, 1950).

Leeming, Joseph: "Fun with Puzzles" (Philadelphia: J. B. Lippincott, Comet Books Edition, 1958).

Levinson, Horace C.: "The Science of Chance: From Probability to Statistics" (New York: Rinehart & Company, Inc., 1950).

Licks, H. E.: "Recreations in Mathematics" (Princeton, N.J.: D. Van Nostrand Company, Inc., 1916).

Lieber, Lillian R., and Hugh Gray Lieber: "The Education of T. C. Mits" (New York: W. W. Norton & Company, Inc., 1944).

—— and ——: "Mits, Wits, and Logic" (New York: W. W. Norton & Company, Inc., 1947).

Loflin, Z. L., and Ida Mae Heard: "Just for Fun" (Lafayette, La.: published by the authors, 1948).

Logsdon, Marie Irwin: "A Mathematician Explains" (Chicago: University of Chicago Press, 1947).

Loomis, E. S.: "The Pythagorean Proposition," 2d ed. (Ann Arbor, Mich.: J. W. Edwards, Publisher, Inc., 1940).

MacHuisdean, Hamish: "Yesterday's Impossibilities" (Glasgow: Fraser, Edward, and Company, 1943).

MacMahon, P. A.: "New Mathematical Pastimes" (New York: Cambridge University Press, 1930).

Maedel, George F.: "Basic Mathematics for Radio" (Englewood Cliffs, N.J.: Prentice-Hall, Inc., 1948).

Manning, H. P.: "The Fourth Dimension Simply Explained" (New York: Munn and Company, 1910).

Mansfield, John: "Everyday Arithmetic for Printers" (New York: McGraw-Hill Book Company, Inc., 1940).

"Math Problems from Industry" (Detroit, Mich.: Educational Services, Department of Public Relations, Chrysler Corporation, 1956).

McKay, Herbert: "Odd Numbers, or Arithmetic Revisited" (New York: The Macmillan Company, 1940).

Mergendahl, C. H., and L. R. Foster: "One Hundred Problems in Consumer Credit," *Pollak Pamphlet* 35 (New Hampshire: Pollak Foundation for Economic Research, 1948).

Merrill, Helen A.: "Mathematical Excursions" (New York: Dover Publications, 1933).

Meyer, Jerome S.: "Fun with Mathematics" (Cleveland: The World Publishing Company, 1952).

Miller, Denning: "Popular Mathematics" (New York: Coward-McCann, Inc., 1942).

Minnick, J. H.: "Teaching Mathematics in the Secondary Schools" (Englewood Cliffs, N.J.: Prentice-Hall, Inc., 1939).

Modley, Rudolph, et al.: "Pictographs and Graphs" (New York: Harper & Brothers, 1952).

Moore, J. H., and J. A. Mira: "The Gist of Mathematics" (Englewood Cliffs, N.J.: Prentice-Hall, Inc., 1942).

Mott-Smith, Geoffrey: "Mathematical Puzzles for Beginners and Enthusiasts," 2d ed. (New York: Dover Publications, 1954).

Nadler, Maurice: "Modern Agricultural Mathematics" (New York: Orange Judd Publishing Company, Inc., 1947).

National Council of Teachers of Mathematics: "First Yearbook" (Washington, D.C.: National Council of Teachers of Mathematics, 1926).

———: "Third Yearbook" (Washington, D.C.: National Council of Teachers of Mathematics, 1928).

———: "Eighth Yearbook" (Washington, D.C.: National Council of Teachers of Mathematics, 1933).

———: "Seventeenth Yearbook" (Washington, D.C.: National Council of Teachers of Mathematics, 1942).

———: "Eighteenth Yearbook" (Washington, D.C.: National Council of Teachers of Mathematics, 1945).

———: "Nineteenth Yearbook" (Washington, D.C.: National Council of Teachers of Mathematics, 1947).

———: "Twentieth Yearbook" (Washington, D.C.: National Council of Teachers of Mathematics, 1948).

Newman, James R.: "The World of Mathematics" (New York: Simon and Schuster, Inc., 1956), vols. I–IV.

Northrup, E. P.: "Riddles in Mathematics—A Book of Paradoxes" (Princeton, N.J.: D. Van Nostrand Company, Inc., 1944).

Ogilvy, C. Stanley: "Through the Mathescope" (New York: Oxford University Press, 1956).

Öre, Oystein: "Cardano, the Gambler-Scholar" (Princeton, N.J.: Princeton University Press, 1953).

Phillips, Hubert: "Brush Up Your Wits" (New York: David McKay Company, Inc., 1936).

———: "Question Time: An Omnibus of Problems for a Brainy Day" (New York: Rinehart & Company, Inc., 1938).

——— et al.: "Caliban's Problem Book" (London: T. de la Rue and Company, 1933).

Pollock, Saul: "Mathematical Paradoxes and Recreations" (Los Angeles: American Association for the Advancement of Visual Instruction in Mathematics, 1937).

Pólya, G.: "How to Solve It" (Princeton, N.J.: Princeton University Press, 1945, 1957).

Proskauer, J.: "Puzzles for Everyone" (New York: Harper & Brothers, 1944).

Ransom, William R.: "Geometry Growing" (Washington, D.C.: National Council of Teachers of Mathematics, 1958).

Read, A. H.: "A Signpost to Mathematics," Thrift Books No. 8 (London: C. A. Watts & Co., Ltd., 1951).

Richardson, Moses: "Fundamentals of Mathematics" (New York: The Macmillan Company, 1958).

Row, T. Sundara: "Geometric Exercises in Paper Folding" (La Salle, Ill.: The Open Court Publishing Company, 1941).

Rulon, P. J.: "Brain Teasers" (Boston: L. C. Page & Company, 1932).

Rupert, William W.: "Famous Geometrical Theorems and Problems" (Boston: D. C. Heath and Company, 1900), parts I–IV.

Sanford, Vera: "A Short History of Mathematics" (Boston: Houghton Mifflin Company, 1930).

Sawyer, W. W.: "Mathematician's Delight" (Baltimore: Penguin Books, Inc., 1943).

——— and L. G. Srawley: "Designing and Making" (New York: Oxford University Press, 1952).

Schaaf, William L. (Editor): "Mathematics—Our Great Heritage" (New York: Harper & Brothers, 1948).

Schorling, Raleigh: "The Teaching of Mathematics" (Ann Arbor, Mich.: The Ann Arbor Press, 1936).

Schubert, H.: "Mathematical Essays and Recreations" (La Salle, Ill.: The Open Court Publishing Company, 1917).

Shackle, G. L. S.: "Mathematics at the Fireside" (New York: Cambridge University Press, 1952).

Shuster, Carl N., and Fred L. Bedford: "Field Work in Mathematics" (New York: American Book Company, 1935). (Distributed by Yoder Instruments, East Palestine, Ohio.)

Sloane, T. O.: "Rapid Arithmetic" (Princeton, N.J.: D. Van Nostrand Company, Inc., 1922).

———, J. E. Thompson, and H. E. Licks: "Speed and Fun with Figures" (Princeton, N.J.: D. Van Nostrand Company, Inc., 1939).

Smith, D. E.: "Number Stories of Long Ago" (Washington, D.C.: National Council of Teachers of Mathematics, 1919).

—————— and Jekuthiel Ginsberg: "Numbers and Numerals" (Washington, D.C.: National Council of Teachers of Mathematics, 1937).

Smith, N. S.: "Designing with Wild Flowers" (Milwaukee: The Bruce Publishing Company, 1927).

Steinhaus, H.: "Mathematical Snapshots" (New York: Oxford University Press, 1950).

Storme, P., and P. Stryfe: "How to Torture Your Friends" (New York: Simon and Schuster, Inc., 1941).

Sykes, Mabel: "Source Problems in Geometry" (Boston: Allyn and Bacon, Inc., 1912).

"The Pursuit of Accuracy" (Lancaster, Pa.: Hamilton Watch Company, undated).

Travers, James: "Puzzling Posers" (London: George Allen & Unwin, Ltd., 1952).

Van Horn, C. E.: "A Preface to Mathematics" (Boston: Chapman & Grimes, Inc., 1938).

Weeks, Raymond: "The Boys' Own Arithmetic" (New York: E. P. Dutton & Co., Inc., 1931).

White, William F.: "A Scrapbook of Elementary Mathematics" (La Salle, Ill.: The Open Court Publishing Company, 1908).

Whitehead, Alfred North: "An Introduction to Mathematics" (New York: Oxford University Press, 1948).

Williams, W. T., and G. H. Savage: "The Penguin Problems Book" (Baltimore: Penguin Books, Inc., 1940).

—————— and ——————: "The Second Penguin Problems Book" (Baltimore: Penguin Books, Inc., 1944).

Wolfe, H. E.: "Introduction to Non-Euclidean Geometry" (New York: The Dryden Press, Inc., 1945).

Wolfe, J. H., W. F. Mueller, and S. D. Mullikin: "Industrial Algebra and Trigonometry with Geometrical Applications" (New York: McGraw-Hill Book Company, Inc., 1945).

—————— and E. R. Phelps: "Practical Shop Mathematics," vol. I, "Elementary," vol. II, "Advanced" (New York: McGraw-Hill Book Company, Inc., 1948, 1949).

World Calendar. (Booklets and information about the proposed world calendar will be provided free upon request to the World Calendar Association, Inc., New York.)

Yates, Robert C.: "The Trisection Problem" (Baton Rouge, La.: The Franklin Press, 1941).

Periodical References and Pamphlets

"The Amazing Story of Measurement" (Saginaw, Mich.: The Lufkin Rule Company, 1957). (Pamphlet.)

Andree, Richard V.: Cryptanalysis [with bibliography], Scripta Mathematica, 18 (1952), 5–15.

——————: Cryptography as a Branch of Mathematics [with bibliography], Mathematics Teacher, 45 (1952) 503–509.

——————: A Simple but Fruitful Arithmetic, Mathematics Teacher, 50 (1957), 58.

Anning, Norman: Four Squares, Pentagon, 10 (1951), 67–70.

Arnold, C. J.: An Answer to "Arguments against Universal Adoption of the Metric System," School Science and Mathematics, 51 (1951), 310–315.

Artin, Emil: The Theory of Braids, Mathematics Teacher, 52 (1959), 328–333.

Atkins, Robert A.: Mathematics in Elementary Photography, School Science and Mathematics, 55 (1955), 175–178.

Aude, H. T. R.: A Class of Integral Triangles, Pentagon, 11 (1951), 23–24.

————: Chains of Integral Triangles, *Pentagon*, **12** (1953), 78–82.

————: A Project in Trigonometry, *Pentagon*, **13** (1954), 98–99.

Bakst, Aaron: Evaluation of Determinants, *Mathematics Teacher*, **45** (1952), 183–186.

Bankoff, Leon: The Golden Arbelof, *Scripta Mathematica*, **21** (1955), 70–76.

————: Regular Polygons of 2, 3, 4, and 6 Sides Inscribed in Circles of Unit Radius, *Scripta Mathematica*, **21** (1955), 252.

Baravalle, H. von: The Number π, *Mathematics Teacher*, **45** (1952), 340–348.

Barnes, George: An Easily Constructed Chart for Finding the Roots of Quadratic Equations, *Mathematics Teacher*, **50** (1957), 40–42.

Beard, Colonel Robert S.: Tessellated Polygons, *Scripta Mathematica*, **17** (1951), 125–131.

Betts, Barbara B.: Cutting Stars and Regular Polygons for Decorations, *School Science and Mathematics*, **50** (1950), 645–649.

Block, Daniel: Kraitchik's Tables of Squares, *Scripta Mathematica*, **20** (1954), 99–101.

Bogen, Isidore: Mathematics in Life [assembly program], *High Points*, **31** (1949), 73–79.

Brandes, Louis Grant: Optical Illusions: A Presentation for High School Mathematics Students, *School Science and Mathematics*, **54** (1954), 557–566.

————: Constructing the Common Cross Number Puzzle, *School Science and Mathematics*, **57** (1957), 89–97.

———— and Darrell Dickey: Why Not Use Cross Number Puzzles as a Teaching Aid with Your General Mathematics Classes? *School Science and Mathematics*, **57** (1957), 647–664.

Braverman, Benjamin: The Quiz in a Mathematics Assembly Program, *High Points*, **29** (1947), 64–69.

Buchman, Aaron: Mnemonics Giving Approximate Values of Pi, *School Science and Mathematics*, **53** (1953), 106.

Burtchart, J. H., and Leo Moser: No Calculation Please [playlet in the form of a dialogue], *Scripta Mathematica*, **18** (1952), 221–236.

Carnahan, Walter H.: Einstein's Proof of $E = mc^2$, *School Science and Mathematics*, **50** (1950), 104–106.

————: Methods for Systematically Seeking Factors of Numbers, *School Science and Mathematics*, **52** (1952), 429–435.

————: Pi and Probability, *Mathematics Teacher*, **46** (1953), 65–66, 70.

————: Prime Numbers in Sequences, *School Science and Mathematics*, **54** (1954), 313–315.

Cell, John W.: Imaginary Numbers, *Mathematics Teacher*, **43** (1950), 394–396.

Chipman, Hope: A Mathematics Quiz Program, *Mathematics Teacher*, **46** (1953), 537–540.

Clair, Harry S.: The Theorem of the Mean and Its Application to Problems of Maxima and Minima, *School Science and Mathematics*, **57** (1957), 468–472.

Corliss, Carlton J.: "The Day of Two Noons" (Washington, D.C.: Association of American Railroads, ca. 1953).   (Pamphlet.)

Coxeter, H. S. M.: The Four-color Map Problem, 1840–1890, *Mathematics Teacher*, **52** (1959), 283–289.

Dagobert, E. Bonavent: Analysis of an Ancient Method of Computation, *Mathematics Teacher*, **48** (1955), 557–559.

Denbow, Carl H.: An Algebra Slide Rule, *School Science and Mathematics*, **55** (1955), 395–396.

Diamond, Louis E.: Irrational Numbers, *Mathematics Magazine*, **29** (1955), 89–99.

Drake, Odessa: Geometry Football, *Mathematics Teacher*, **45** (1952), 461, 470.

Drew, J. William: Product of Two Numbers Each Ending in Five, *School Science and Mathematics*, **50** (1950), 64–65.

Eagle, Edwin A.: Construct Any Angle with a Steel Tape, *Mathematics Teacher*, **48** (1955), 563–564.

Eaves, J. C.: Pythagoras, His Theorem, and Some Gadgets, *Mathematics Magazine*, **27** (1954), 161–167.

————: The Pythagorean Theorem—Proof Number One Thousand, *Mathematics Teacher*, **47** (1954), 346–347.

Enos, Judith Cretcher: Methods of Extracting Square Roots, *Pentagon*, **14** (1954), 3–15.

Esmond, Robert V.: Magic Letters—TV—and Magic Squares, *Mathematics Teacher*, **48** (1955), 26–29.

Eveland, Kenneth C.: Alligation—A Mathematical Relic, *Mathematics Teacher*, **48** (1955), 339–341.

Fadiman, Clifton: Party of One, *Holiday*, **21** (January, 1957), 6, 8, 11, 14, 113.

Fleming, Robert E.: A Family of Numbers, *School Science and Mathematics*, **54** (1954), 410–413.

Freitag, Herta Taussig: Relationships for Radii of Circles Associated with the Triangle, *Mathematics Teacher*, **45** (1952), 357–360.

Gager, William A.: Newton and His "Principia Mathematica," *School Science and Mathematics*, **52** (1952), 258–262.

Gardner, Martin: Mathematical Tricks with Common Objects, *Scripta Mathematica*, **15** (1949), 17–25.

————: Topology and Magic, *Scripta Mathematica*, **17** (1951), 75–83.

————: Mathematical Tricks with Special Equipment, *Scripta Mathematica*, **18** (1952), 237–249.

Gattegno, C.: Notes on Pythagoras' Theorem, *Mathematics Teacher*, **45** (1952), 6–9.

"General Electric's Answer to *Three Whys*" (Schenectady, N.Y.: Educational Relations, Dept. 2-119, General Electric Company, ca. 1958).

Getty, G. A.: Uncle Ed Juggles Figures, *Mathematics Teacher*, **48** (1955), 143–146.

Gillespie, Raymond H.: Solution of the Quadratic Equation, *Pentagon*, **9** (1950), 59–84.

Goldberg, Michael: The Squaring of Developable Surfaces, *Scripta Mathematica*, **18** (1952), 17–24.

————: Central Tessellations, *Scripta Mathematica*, **21** (1955), 253–260.

Gosselink, John G.: The Proof by Nine, *School Science and Mathematics*, **55** (1955), 190–198.

Graesser, R. F.: The Date of Easter, *School Science and Mathematics*, **52** (1952), 371–372.

————: The Most Economical Tin Can, *School Science and Mathematics*, **56** (1956), 317–318.

————: A Curious Problem in Probability, *School Science and Mathematics*, **57** (1957), 72–73.

Gray, Mrs. James T.: Historically Speaking [playlet], *School Science and Mathematics*, **52** (1952), 345–355.

Grove, Ethel, and others: A Dial-A-Factor, *School Science and Mathematics*, **50** (1950), 741–742.

Gruber, Joseph: The Pill Box Slide Rule, *New Jersey Mathematics Teacher*, **12** (1956), 5.

Hallerberg, Arthur E.: The Geometry of the Fixed Compass, *Mathematics Teacher*, **52** (1959), 230–244.

Harmon, Mildred Marie: All in One Day [playlet], *School Science and Mathematics*, **55** (1955), 15–23.

Hart, Phillip J.: Pythagorean Numbers, *Mathematics Teacher*, **47** (1954), 16–21.

"Heedless Horsepower" (Hartford, Conn.: Travelers Insurance Companies, 1957). (Pamphlet.)

Herold, Don: "How to Choose a Pocket Slide Rule" (Detroit, Mich.: Keuffel & Esser Company, 1940). (Pamphlet.)

————: "How to Choose a Slide Rule" (Detroit, Mich.: Keuffel & Esser Company, 1940). (Pamphlet.)

"Household Finance Corporation: Money Management Booklets" (Chicago: Household Finance Corporation, 1959). (Pamphlets.)

Hilton, Wallace A.: Lissajous Figures, *School Science and Mathematics*, **57** (1957), 7–8.

Holder, Lorena W.: A Place Value Game, *Arithmetic Teacher*, **3** (1956), 248–249.

Hopkins, Mildred: The Envelope of a Line Moving between Two Concentric Circles, *Mathematics Teacher*, **43** (1950), 264–268.

Horner, Walter W.: Addition-Multiplication Magic Squares, *Scripta Mathematica*, **18** (1952), 300–303.

————: Addition-Multiplication Magic Squares of Order 8, *Scripta Mathematica*, **21** (1955), 23–27.

Iyer, R. V.: The Hindu Abacus, *Scripta Mathematica*, **20** (1954), 58–63.

Jackson, William N.: The Interpretation of Data with Applications in Elementary Algebra, *School Science and Mathematics*, **56** (1956), 181–184.

Johnson, Donovan A.: How to Draw an Addition and Subtraction Nomograph, *Mathematics Teacher*, **49** (1956), 281.

———— and Clarence Olander: Mathematical Games Build Skills, *Mathematics Teacher*, **50** (1957), 292–294.

Jones, Phillip S.: The Oldest American Slide Rule, *Mathematics Teacher*, **46** (1953), 500–502.

Karner, Dorothy: Geometric Inversion, *Pentagon*, **10** (1951), 3–10.

Kays, George: An Integraph, *Mathematics Teacher*, **48** (1955), 158–161.

Kempe, A. B.: How to Draw a Straight Line: A Lecture on Linkages, *Pentagon*, **11** (1952), 67–100.

Kidd, Kenneth P.: How Much?   A Mathematics Playlet, *School Science and Mathematics*, **54** (1954), 628–634.

Kingston, J. Maurice: Mosaics by Reflection, *Mathematics Teacher*, **50** (1957), 280–286.

Kirkpatrick, Paul: Probability Theory of a Simple Card Game, *Mathematics Teacher*, **47** (1954), 245–248.

Kraitchik, Maurice: On the Factorization of $2^n \pm 1$, *Scripta Mathematica*, **18** (1952), 39–52.

Lange, Lester: In Mathematics Too: Linger and Learn, *School Science and Mathematics*, **53** (1953), 478–483.

————: More Mathematical Lingering: A Maximum Theorem, *School Science and Mathematics*, **54** (1954), 478–483.

Langman, Harry: A Problem in Checkers, *Scripta Mathematica*, **20** (1954), 206–208.

Laposky, B. F., and Rutherford Boyd: Mathematical Patterns in Design, *Scripta Mathematica*, **17** (1951), 132–141.   See also several subsequent issues.

Larsen, Harold D.: On Divisibility by Seven, *School Science and Mathematics*, **51** (1951), 315–317.

————: An Application of Duodecimals, *School Science and Mathematics*, **55** (1955), 422.

————: Pseudo logarithms. *Mathematics Teacher*, **52** (1959), 2–6.

Lausmann, R. F.: Fun With Figures.   (Syndicated column published in various daily newspapers and distributed through the Register and Tribune Syndicate of Des Moines, Iowa.)

Law, Bernadine: Some Mathematical Considerations of Dynamic Symmetry Underlying Visual Art, *Pentagon*, **13** (1953), 7–17.

Law, Carol: Arithmetical Congruences with Practical Applications, *Pentagon*, **17** (1957), 16–21.

Lenchner, George: "Mathletes," *Mathematics Teacher*, **52** (1959), 113–114.

Lloyd, Daniel B.: In Quest of Truth [pageant], *School Science and Mathematics*, **51** (1951), 275–285.

Manheimer, Wallace: A Club Project in a Modern Use of Mathematics, *Mathematics Teacher*, **50** (1957), 350–355.

"Math at General Electric" (Schenectady, N.Y.: Educational Relations, Dept. 2-119, General Electric Company, ca. 1955).

Mathematical Classes of Julia Diggins: A Mathematical Dr. I Quiz-'em Program, *Mathematics Teacher*, **45** (1952), 30–33.

Mathematical Pie. (A small magazine of mathematical recreations published three times a year. Editorial offices, 97 Chequer Road, Doncaster, England.)

"Mathematics and Perspective" (Yonkers-on-Hudson, N.Y.: World Book Company, ca. 1957). (Pamphlet.)

Mathematics Department of Deering High School: Math About Us [tableau], *Mathematics Teacher*, **46** (1953), 253–259.

Mathematics Staff of the College, University of Chicago: Three Algebraic Questions Connected with Pythagoras' Theorem, *Mathematics Teacher*, **49** (1956), 250–259.

————: A Problem on the Cutting of Squares, *Mathematics Teacher*, **49** (1956), 332–343.

————: More on the Cutting of Squares, *Mathematics Teacher*, **49** (1956), 442–454.

————: Still More on the Cutting of Squares, *Mathematics Teacher*, **49** (1956), 585–596.

————: New Exercises in Plane Geometry, *Mathematics Teacher*, **50** (1957), 125–135.

————: More New Exercises in Plane Geometry, *Mathematics Teacher*, **50** (1957), 330–339.

Mayer, Haverly O.: Testing with a Tangram, *Mathematics Teacher*, **48** (1955), 525–527.

Mazkewitsch, D.: Coefficients in Expansions of Polynomials, *School Science and Mathematics*, **58** (1958), 703–709.

Meserve, B. E.: Let's Teach Angle Trisection, *Mathematics Teacher*, **44** (1951), 547–550.

————: Topology for Secondary Schools, *Mathematics Teacher*, **46** (1953), 465–474.

Miksa, Francis L.: A Table of Integral Solutions of $a^2 + b^2 + c^2 = r^2$, *Mathematics Teacher*, **48** (1955), 251–254.

————: Integral Squares with Square Sum, *Mathematics Teacher*, **48** (1955), 481–483.

Miller, William G.: Tangent Circles and Conic Sections, *Mathematics Teacher*, **46** (1953), 78–81.

Mind, Nev. R.: Geometrical Magic, *Scripta Mathematica*, **19** (1953), 198–200.

————: Running Around in Circles, *Scripta Mathematica*, **20** (1954), 92–95.

————: Too Many? *Scripta Mathematica*, **21** (1955), 296–298.

Mitchell, Donald V.: Endless Numbers (Repetends), *School Science and Mathematics*, **55** (1955), 509–515.

Mock, Alex J.: Trisecting Any Angle, *Mathematics Teacher*, **52** (1959), 245–246.

Moessner, Alfred: Consequences of $A^2 + B^2 = C^2$, *Pentagon*, **16** (1957), 76–77.

"Moneys of the World" (New York: Chase Manhattan Bank, ca. 1955). (Pamphlet.)

Morrison, Theron V.: A Short Method of Long Division, *School Science and Mathematics*, **52** (1952), 684–686.

National High School and Junior College Mathematics Club (M A Th), *Mathematics Teacher*, **50** (1957), 372–373.

Olander, Clarence: An Electric Matching Device, *Mathematics Teacher*, **49** (1956), 278–279.

O'Leary, Vincent C.: Calendar Progress, *School Science and Mathematics*, **51** (1951), 22–26.

Oliver, Mina: Flying Saucers—A Project in Circles, *Mathematics Teacher*, **44** (1951), 455–457.

Perisho, Clarence R.: A Non-commutative Algebra, *School Science and Mathematics*, **58** (1958), 727–730.

Phelps, Clyde William: "Using Instalment Credit," *Studies in Consumer Credit*, No. 4 (Baltimore, Md.: Educational Division, Commercial Credit Company, 1956). (Pamphlet.)

Phillips, Jo McKeeby: Motivating the Study of Solid Geometry through the Use of Mineral Crystals, *School Science and Mathematics*, **52** (1952), 743–748; **53** (1953), 134–138.

Ponder, Wanda: Angle Trisection, *Pentagon*, **11** (1951), 13–18.

Pratt, Gertrude V.: Algebra Today and Yesterday, *Pentagon*, **11** (1951), 25–31.

Ransom, William R.: A Six-sided Hexagon, *School Science and Mathematics*, **52** (1952), 94.

————: Some Mirror Trigonometry, *School Science and Mathematics*, **55** (1955), 599–600.

————: Room Enough for You? *School Science and Mathematics*, **56** (1956), 319–320.

————: Divisibility Tests, *School Science and Mathematics*, **57** (1957), 208.

Read, Cecil B.: Arguments against the Universal Adoption of the Metric System, *School Science and Mathematics*, **50** (1950), 297–306.

————: An Interesting Paradox, *Mathematics Teacher*, **47** (1954), 265–267.

Reves, George E.: Outline of the History of Algebra, *School Science and Mathematics*, **52** (1952), 61–69.

————: Outline of the History of Geometry, *School Science and Mathematics*, **52** (1952), 299–309.

————: Outline of the History of Trigonometry, *School Science and Mathematics*, **53** (1953), 139–145.

Rosskopf, Myron F., and Gaylord C. Montgomery: A Department of Mathematics Prepares an Exhibit, *Mathematics Teacher*, **42** (1949), 187–191.

Rising, Gerald R.: A Geometric Approach to Field Goal Kicking, *Mathematics Teacher*, **47** (1954), 463–466.

————: Some Comments on a Simple Puzzle, *Mathematics Teacher*, **49** (1956), 267–269.

Ruderman, Harry D.: The Game of Tic-Tac-Toe, *Mathematics Teacher*, **44** (1951), 344–347.

Sabo, Joseph P.: Plato Shows in the Eighth at Guilford, *Mathematics Teacher*, **50** (1957), 225–228.

Sackman, Bertram S.: The Tomahawk, *Mathematics Teacher*, **49** (1956), 280–281.

Satterly, John: Meet Mr. Tau, *School Science and Mathematics*, **56** (1956), 731–741.

————: Meet Mr. Tau Again, *School Science and Mathematics*, **57** (1957), 150–151.

Sawyer, W. W.: Things and un-Things, *Mathematics Teacher*, **51** (1958), 14–15.

Schaaf, William L.: Mathematics and Art, *Mathematics Teacher*, **43** (1950), 423–426.

————: The Magic of Compound Interest, *Mathematics Teacher*, **48** (1955), 488–489.

Scheid, Francis: Feed it Back, *Mathematics Teacher*, **52** (1959), 226–229.

Schor, Harry: A Mathematics Assembly Program, *Mathematics Teacher*, **47** (1954), 476–478.

Schub, Pincus: A Mnemonical Hexagon, *Scripta Mathematica*, **20** (1954), 217.

Sesskin, S. H.: An Introduction to Cryptanalysis: Two Ciphers, *Pentagon*, **14** (1954), 16–26.

——: Elements of Cryptanalysis: The Simple Substitution Cryptogram, *Pentagon*, **13** (1954), 80–86.

Shoemaker, Richard W.: The Construction and Measurement of Angles with a Steel Tape: Surveyor's Method, *Mathematics Teacher*, **49** (1956), 550.

Shuster, Carl N.: The Calculation of Logarithms in the High School, *Mathematics Teacher*, **48** (1955), 322–323.

Sinkhorn, Richard, and Cecil B. Read: Mathematical Bingo, *School Science and Mathematics*, **54** (1954), 232–233.

Sister Marie Stephen: The Mysterious Number P H I, *Mathematics Teacher*, **49** (1956), 200–204.

Sleight, Norma: Com(n)ics, *School Science and Mathematics*, **50** (1950), 525–526.

Sornito, Juan E.: Squaring a Circle, *Mathematics Teacher*, **50** (1957), 51–52.

"So You're Going to Buy a Home" (Chicago: The Chicago Bar Association, 1953). (Pamphlet.)

Spence, John L.: Equations of Some Common Geometric Figures, *School Science and Mathematics*, **58** (1958), 674–676.

Steinbeck, Peggy: Paradox Lost—Paradox Regained, *Pentagon*, **16** (1957), 78–83.

Struyk, Adrian: Theme Paper, a Ruler, and the Central Conics, *Mathematics Teacher*, **47** (1954), 189–193.

——: Two Notes on the Binomial Coefficients, *Mathematics Teacher*, **49** (1956), 192–194.

Swallow, Kenneth P.: The Factorgram, *Mathematics Teacher*, **48** (1955), 11–17.

Tabler, E. A.: Products of Numbers Ending in 5, *School Science and Mathematics*, **53** (1953), 15–16.

Thébault, Victor: The Area of a Triangle as a Function of its Sides, *Scripta Mathematica*, **18** (1952), 151–161.

——: On Numbers Which Terminate Perfect Squares, *Mathematics Teacher*, **47** (1954), 348–349.

——: Geodesics, *Scripta Mathematica*, **21** (1955), 146–158.

——: On Certain Cases of Congruence in Triangles, *Mathematics Teacher*, **48** (1955), 341–343.

Tierney, John A.: Elementary Techniques in Maxima and Minima, *Mathematics Teacher*, **46** (1953), 484–486.

Trigg, C. W.: A Proof of the Law of Cosines, *School Science and Mathematics*, **54** (1954), 370.

——: Geometry of Paper Folding, I: Geometric and Trigonometric Properties of a Drinking Cup, *School Science and Mathematics*, **54** (1954), 453–455.

——: Unorthodox Ways to Trisect a Line Segment, *School Science and Mathematics*, **54** (1954), 525–528.

——: Holiday Greetings from Thirty Scrambled Mathematicians, *School Science and Mathematics*, **54** (1954), 679.

——: Geometry of Paper Folding, II: Tetrahedral Models, *School Science and Mathematics*, **54** (1954), 683–689.

——: Configurations Generated by Folding a Square, *Scripta Mathematica*, **21** (1955), 77–80.

Turner, Ethel M.: The Mathematical News, *Mathematics Teacher*, **47** (1954), 249–253.

Utz, W. R.: Maxima and Minima without the Calculus, *School Science and Mathematics*, **57** (1957), 263–266.

Wallin, Don: Similar Polygons and a Puzzle, *Mathematics Teacher*, **52** (1959), 372–373.

Wells, Franklin B.: Mathematical Figures, *School Science and Mathematics*, **54** (1954), 695–698.

"What Can Happen when You Buy on 'Time,' " (Chicago: The Chicago Bar Association, 1953).

Whitlock, W. P., Jr.: Nests of Pythagorean Triangles, *Scripta Mathematica*, **19** (1953), 66–68.

Wiener, L. M.: Take a Number, *Mathematics Teacher*, **48** (1955), 203.

Willerding, Margaret: Models of Solids of Known Parallel Cross Section, *School Science and Mathematics*, **51** (1951), 617.

Woodby, Lauren: The Angle Mirror: A Teaching Device for Plane Geometry, *Mathematics Teacher*, **47** (1954), 71–72.

Yates, Robert C.: Euclidean Constructions, *Mathematics Teacher*, **47** (1954), 231–233.

———: Sums of Powers of Integers, *Mathematics Teacher*, **52** (1959), 268–271.

Yen Yi-YÜN: The Chinese Abacus, *Mathematics Teacher*, **43** (1950), 402–404.

Zulauf, Zelia: From Greek to Gershwin: The Mathematical Basis of Music, *Pentagon*, **12** (1953), 70–74.

Multisensory Aids

Ahrendt, M. H.: Report of the Committee on Mathematics Kits, *Mathematics Teacher*, **42** (1949), 330.

Andrews, George R.: Teaching the Slide Rule by Television, *Mathematics Teacher*, **43** (1950), 272–274.

Archer, Allene, Miles C. Hartley, and Veryl Schult: "Plane Geometry Experiments" (Princeton, N.J.: D. Van Nostrand Company, Inc., 1949).

Baravalle, H. V.: Demonstrations of Conic Sections and Skew Curves with String Models, *Mathematics Teacher*, **39** (1946), 284–287.

———: A Model for Demonstrating the Pythagorean Theorem, *Scripta Mathematica*, **16** (1950), 203–207.

Barnes, George: An Easily Constructed Chart for Finding the Roots of Quadratic Equations, *Mathematics Teacher*, **50** (1957), 40–42.

Berger, Emil J.: A Model for Visualizing the Pythagorean Theorem, *Mathematics Teacher*, **48** (1955), 246–247.

——— (Editor): Devices for a Mathematics Laboratory, *Mathematics Teacher*, **44** (1951) and subsequent volumes.   (A series of short descriptive articles, usually with diagrams, on physical or mechanical devices for use as instruments for motivation and learning through laboratory work in mathematics.)

——— and Donovan A. Johnson: "A Guide to the Use and Procurement of Teaching Aids for Mathematics" (Washington, D.C.: National Council of Teachers of Mathematics, 1959).

Blank, Laura: Teaching Mathematics in Technicolor, *Mathematics Teacher*, **41** (1948), 229–231.

Bloss, E.: The Audio-Visual Way to Number Learnings, *Educational Screen*, **27** (December, 1948), 494–495.

Burns, Frances M.: The Use of Models in the Teaching of Plane Geometry, *Mathematics Teacher*, **37** (1944), 272–277.

Dale, Edgar: "Audio-Visual Methods in Teaching" (New York: The Dryden Press, Inc., 1946), pp. 316–336.

Davis, O. L.: Arithmetic at the School Camp, *Arithmetic Teacher*, **3** (1956), 157–161.

Drake, Richard, and Donovan Johnson: Vitalizing Geometry with Visual Aids, *Mathematics Teacher*, **33** (1940), 56–59.

Eagle, Edwin: Note on "Model for Visualizing the Pythagorean Theorem," *Mathematics Teacher*, **48** (1955), 475–476.

———: An Improved Trigtractor, *Mathematics Teacher*, **49** (1956), 28–29.

Eves, Howard: A Graphometer, *Mathematics Teacher*, **41** (1948), 311–313.

Exton, William: "Audio-Visual Aids to Instruction" (New York: McGraw-Hill Book Company, Inc., 1947).

Fehr, Howard F.: The Place of Multisensory Aids in the Teacher Training Program, *Mathematics Teacher*, **40** (1947), 212–216.

———: The Use of Hand-operated Calculating Machines in Learning Arithmetic (Orange, N.J.: Monroe Calculating Machine Company, Inc., 1956), pp. 2–15. (Pamphlet.)

Fuhrmann, Hans H.: Plane Truths Made Visible, *California Mathematics Council Bulletin*, **7** (1949), 6–8.

Gardner, Randolph: "Instruments for the Enrichment of Secondary School Mathematics" (Ann Arbor, Mich.: J. W. Edwards, Publisher, Inc., 1951).

Goins, William F., Jr.: Putting More Meaning in the Teaching of Measurement, *School Science and Mathematics*, **50** (1950), 745–749.

Graesser, R. F.: Models for the Regular Polyhedrons, *Mathematics Teacher*, **38** (1945), 368–369.

Grove, Ethel L.: Models for Introducing Parallelograms, *School Science and Mathematics*, **50** (1950), 551–552.

———: Model for Circles and Straight Lines, *School Science and Mathematics*, **50** (1950), 743–744.

———: Alternate Model for Arc and Angle Measurement, *School Science and Mathematics*, **51** (1951), 13–15.

———: Model for Illustrating Proportions; Model for Introducing Motion Problems, *School Science and Mathematics*, **51** (1951), 121–124.

———: Model Showing Derivation of the Formula for the Area of a Trapezoid, *School Science and Mathematics*, **51** (1951), 298–299.

———: Model for Introducing Congruent Triangles; Model for Introducing Overlapping Triangles, *School Science and Mathematics*, **51** (1951), 386–387, 454–455.

——— and others: Models for Introducing Special Products, *School Science and Mathematics*, **50** (1950), 662–664.

——— and others: Posters on Fractions, *School Science and Mathematics*, **51** (1951), 11–13.

——— and others: Model for Introducing Trigonometry on Ninth Grade Level, *School Science and Mathematics*, **51** (1951), 296–297.

——— and others: Substitute Devices for Illustrating Equations; Number Scale for Illustrating All Four Fundamental Processes with Directed Numbers, *School Science and Mathematics*, **51** (1951), 388–389, 456–460.

Haas, Kenneth B., and Harry A. Packer: "Preparation and Use of Visual Aids" (Englewood Cliffs, N.J.: Prentice-Hall, Inc., 1946).

Hartley, Miles C.: Models in Solid Geometry, *Mathematics Teacher*, **35** (1942), 5–7.

———: "Patterns of Polyhedrons" (Ann Arbor, Mich.: J. W. Edwards, Publisher, Inc., 1948).

Hartung, Maurice L.: Multi-sensory Aids in the Teaching of Mathematics, *School Review*, **54** (1946), 191–193.

Hawthorne, Frank: Making an Abacus, *School Science and Mathematics*, **51** (1951), 227–228.

———: A Model for the Conic Sections, *School Science and Mathematics*, **51** (1951), 299–300.

————: Frequency Distributions with Shot, *School Science and Mathematics*, **51** (1951), 394–395.

————: A Model of the Five Regular Polyhedra, *School Science and Mathematics*, **52** (1952), 125–126.

Hoag, Jessie May: Visual Aids in Teaching Geometry, *National Mathematics Magazine*, **14** (1939), 153–159.

Hoisington, Robert C.: Semi-permanent Chalk for Teaching, *Mathematics Teacher*, **47** (1954), 407.

Jackson, Humphrey: Better Bulletin Boards, *Mathematics Teacher*, **48** (1955), 358–359.

Jacobs, Edwin E.: A Home-made Clinometer, *School Science and Mathematics*, **43** (1943), 664–665.

Janes, W. C.: The Steel Square, *Bulletin of the Kansas Association of Teachers of Mathematics*, **17** (1943), 39–44.

Janicki, George: Mathematics Made Meaningful in Teaching Graphs, *Mathematics Teacher*, **48** (1955), 277–278.

Jenkins, Jen: Teaching the Concept of Cubic Measure through the Use of Manipulative Aids, *Mathematics Teacher*, **49** (1956), 489–490.

Johnson, Donovan A.: Vitalizing Geometry by the Use of Pictures, *School Science and Mathematics*, **38** (1938), 1032–1034.

————: Are Films and Filmstrips Effective in Teaching Geometry? *School Science and Mathematics*, **50** (1950), 570–574.

————: A Multi-model Demonstration Board, *Mathematics Teacher*, **49** (1956), 121–122.

————: How to Draw an Addition and Subtraction Nomograph, *Mathematics Teacher*, **49** (1956), 281.

———— and James F. Nickerson: The Future of Visual Aids in Mathematics, *Mathematics Teacher*, **40** (1947), 180–181.

———— and C. E. Olander: "How to Use Your Bulletin Board" (Washington, D.C.: National Council of Teachers of Mathematics, 1959).

———— and Henry W. Syer: A Bibliography of Mathematics Films and Filmstrips, *School Science and Mathematics*, **49** (1949), 650–657.

Jones, Phillip S.: Multi-sensory Aids Based on Applications of Mathematics, *Mathematics Teacher*, **40** (1947), 285–293.

Kafka, F.: "Statistics without Numbers: A Visual Explanation" (New York: Lifetime Editions, 1950).

Keppers, George, and Perry A. Chapdelaine: The Slide Rule Made Meaningful, *Mathematics Teacher*, **44** (1951), 392–394.

Kidd, Kenneth P.: "Instructional Materials for Mathematics Classes" (Gainesville, Fla.: College of Education, University of Florida, 1958).

Koenen, William: Using the Tower of Hanoi to Present Mathematical Induction, *Mathematics Teacher*, **48** (1955), 330–331.

Lewis, Eunice: The Role of Sensory Materials in Meaningful Learning, *Mathematics Teacher*, **49** (1956), 274–277.

Mathematics Teaching. (A semiannual magazine devoted to teaching aids for mathematics, with editorial offices at 97 Chequer Road, Doncaster, England, published by the Association for Teaching Aids in Mathematics.)

McCurdy, Sylvia E.: Colored Chalk Techniques for Basic Mathematics, *Mathematics Teacher*, **41** (1948), 369–371.

Meserve, Bruce E.: Linkages as Visual Aids, *Mathematics Teacher*, **39** (1946), 372–379.

Mewborn, Margaret E.: The Use of Audio-Visual Aids in Teaching Plane Geometry, *New Jersey Mathematics Teacher*, **7** (1950), 16–22.

Moore, Ethel L.: The Carpenter's Rule: An Aid in Teaching Geometry, *Mathematics Teacher,* **46** (1953), 478.

Myers, Sheldon, and others: Making Concrete Several Kinds of Variation in Algebra, *School Science and Mathematics,* **48** (1948), 639–646.

National Council of Teachers of Mathematics: "Multi-sensory Aids in the Teaching of Mathematics," *Eighteenth Yearbook* (Washington, D.C.: National Council of Teachers of Mathematics, 1945).

National Society for the Study of Education: "Audio-visual Materials of Instruction," *Forty-eighth Yearbook,* part I (Chicago: National Society for the Study of Education, 1949).

Neal, Offa: Use of Figures in Solving Problems in Algebra and Geometry, *Mathematics Teacher,* **33** (1940), 210–212.

Nyberg, Joseph: Models for Certain Pyramids, *Mathematics Teacher,* **39** (1946), 84–85.

Olander, Clarence: A Model for Visualizing the Formula for the Area of a Circle, *Mathematics Teacher,* **48** (1955), 246–247.

Oliver, Robert J.: Mathematics Bulletin Board Displays, *Mathematics Teacher,* **47** (1954), 91–92.

Reeve, William David: Multi-sensory Aids in the Teaching of Mathematics, *Teachers College Record,* **46** (1945), 420–427.

———: "Mathematics for the Secondary School" (New York: Henry Holt and Company, Inc., 1954), pp. 486–509.

Rosskopf, Myron C., and Gaylord C. Montgomery: A Department of Mathematics Prepares an Exhibit, *Mathematics Teacher,* **42** (1949), 187–191.

Saupe, Ethel: Simple Paper Models for the Conic Sections, *Mathematics Teacher,* **48** (1955), 42–44.

———: A Paper Model for Solid Geometry, *Mathematics Teacher,* **49** (1956), 185–186.

Schaaf, William L.: Laboratory Mathematics [bibliography], *Mathematics Teacher,* **44** (1951), 422–425, 428.

Schacht, John: Models of Loci, *Mathematics Teacher,* **47** (1954), 556.

——— and John J. Kinsella: Dynamic Geometry, *Mathematics Teacher,* **40** (1947), 151–157.

Schorling, Raleigh: A Laboratory Course for Making Visual Aids for Mathematics Classes, *Mathematics Teacher,* **44** (1951), 97–99.

Scientific Film Association: A First List of Films for Mathematics, *Mathematical Gazette,* **31** (May, 1947), 98–101.

Shuster, Carl N., and Fred L. Bedford: "Field Work in Mathematics" (New York: American Book Company, 1935). (Now distributed by Yoder Instruments, East Palestine, Ohio.)

Sokol, Irwin N.: The Eyes Have It, *School Science and Mathematics,* **53** (1953), 544–546.

Stern, Catherine: Concrete Representation of Geometric Progression, *Mathematics Teacher,* **44** (1951), 170–176.

Struyk, Adrian: Drawing with Ruler and Paper, *School Science and Mathematics,* **45** (1945), 211–214.

Syer, Henry W., and Peter J. Ingeneri: Multi-sensory Aids in Mathematics, *School Science and Mathematics,* **49** (1949), 134–140.

——— and Donovan A. Johnson: Aids to Teaching, *The Mathematics Teacher,* **41** (1948) and subsequent volumes. (A series of discussions of booklets, charts, pictures, films, filmstrips, models, instruments, equipment, and other teaching aids for mathematics. The discussions contain descriptions, reviews, appraisals, and source references of the aids.)

Tice, Charles B.: Multi-sensory Aids in Teaching Mathematics, *Bulletin of the Kansas Association of Teachers of Mathematics*, **21** (1947), 43–45.

Tripp, Hilliard C.: Making "Pi" Meaningful, *Mathematics Teacher*, **44** (1951), 230–232.

Uth, Carl: Teaching Aid for Developing $(a + b)(a - b)$, *Mathematics Teacher*, **48** (1955), 247–249.

Wenaas, Sigurd B.: Exploratory Development of Mathematics Kits, *Mathematics Teacher*, **46** (1953), 42–43.

Woodby, Lauren: The Angle Mirror—A Teaching Device for Plane Geometry, *Mathematics Teacher*, **47** (1954), 71–72.

Yates, Robert C.: "Geometrical Tools—A Mathematics Sketch and Model Book" (St. Louis, Mo.: Educational Publishers, 1949).

————: The Ladder Problem, *School Science and Mathematics*, **51** (1951), 400–401.

6

MEANS TO EFFECTIVE INSTRUCTION
AND GUIDED LEARNING

Schools exist for the primary purpose of promoting learning, and teachers of mathematics have as their primary objective the promotion of learning in mathematics. This is not a simple or routine task. The things that are to be learned and the maturity of the students vary from grade to grade, and learning has varied aspects and can take place through many avenues. The students may not all learn things in the same ways, or at the same speed, or with the same facility and completeness. Yet the teacher has the dual task of setting appropriate objectives with respect to the things to be learned and of planning kinds of learning activities which in his judgment give promise of providing his students with the kinds of experiences that can bring them to the attainment of the objectives. To this end, it is necessary that the teacher have a good understanding not only of the desirable mathematical objectives themselves but also of the ways in which children learn mathematics. Moreover, he must remember that there are phases, or stages, in learning as well as degrees of learning and that initial understanding or mastery of skills can deteriorate through disuse or lack of review or application. Such considerations should impel him to consider carefully the instructional means and devices which he plans to use and to adapt them for optimum effectiveness in enabling the students to attain the desired objectives.

Considerations with Respect to the Learning of Mathematics. As has been said, the problem of instruction is the problem of promoting learning. Since the learning must be done by the student, the problem of instruction becomes the problem of guiding the activities of the student in such ways that proper learning will take place. This cannot be stereotyped. The teacher who gives thought to ways in which children learn mathematics will be more likely to attain effective results than the one who does not. It seems reasonable, therefore, that some important considerations with respect to how mathematics is learned should be set forth at the outset. It would be difficult to give a better statement of such considerations than that given in the following quotation from a thought-provoking chapter in the "Twenty-first Yearbook" of the National Council of Teachers of Mathematics:"[1]

Children do not grow and develop in mathematical knowledge in a vacuum of such knowledge. Quantitative thinking is acquired in active mental dealing with quantitative situations. The quantitative aspects of a situation can go unnoticed unless they are deliberately brought to the sphere of attention of the student. . . . The child grows and develops in a numerical and geometric environment in which he changes his behavior to ever more complex organized patterns.

But progress is not made along a straight line from the fundamentals to the generalized theorems. This is the way the final learning can be organized, and is frequently so organized in texts, but it is not the way most students grow in wisdom. Our initial learnings in algebra are not Peano's axioms, nor is our initial learning in geometry Hilbert's postulates. Rather, the initial learning is in an area in which exploration first takes place. We count, measure, draw, and make preliminary statements which are refined downward toward the foundations and upward toward more abstract, complex, and generalized relations. After a while we discard many particular theorems for one more generalized theorem, and in advanced states of learning only is the area of exploration reorganized as a straight line mathematical development.

The growth in mathematical knowledge by each individual student thus calls for direction by a skillful teacher who has a balanced emphasis on the various phases of learning. He uses the heuristic method only so far as pupils need directed questions in the quest of their learning. He has an experimental attitude that allows freedom of approach in learning to the degree that the experiment is headed toward a desired concept, or relationship, and directs the experiment back to fruitful approaches when the student is adrift. He recognizes that drill can be dangerous and boring as well as good habit formation procedure. He balances each step from concrete experience to semiconcrete representations, to words and symbols, to generalized abstract theorems through proper evaluation and by appropriate attainable challenges. He recognizes also that not all learning begins in concrete material objects, but that much new learning may start in already learned abstractions. Thus algebraic fractions are referred back to the abstractions learned in the study of arithmetic fractions and not back to parts of concrete objects. Geometry is related to geometrical drawings, trigonometry is related back to geometry and algebra.

It is just because of this sequential aspect of mathematical knowledge that proper balance becomes the all important aspect in its learning. Unless a clearly and correctly formed mathematical concept emerges from a learning situation and it is related to other phases of already learned mathematics through sufficient practice to gain skill in the use of the concept, the learning of all later mathematics dependent upon this concept is seriously (and sometimes totally) impaired. The lack of correct concepts in arithmetic may be one of the great reasons for

[1] John R. Clark and Howard F. Fehr: Learning Theory and the Improvement of Instruction: A Balanced Program, "Twenty-first Yearbook" (Washington, D.C.: National Council of Teachers of Mathematics, 1953), pp. 346–348.

the difficulty algebra presents to so many of our students.   It is this balance that is indirectly referred to in every chapter in this text (*sic*): a mathematical problem within the comprehension of the student, but still a problem as the start of learning; motivation, sufficient to send him on toward the solution; the challenge to abstract, to generalize, to form concepts; the proper use of sensory aids, of drill, of appropriate language; not doing too much nor failing to do enough; and adapting these measures to the various individual differences in learning.   To gain such balance is to become a master teacher—the goal of all professionally minded educators.

Learning is an active process.   It is achieved not in any single way but through a variety of activities and is approached through a variety of avenues: reading, listening, asking questions, working with material objects, writing, drawing, comparing, analyzing, interpreting, computing, etc.   The one thing which all these activities need to involve is thinking. These activities need to be so planned that they will bring the learner along the path toward understanding and mastery of the subject at his level of advancement.   Each is important and each should contribute toward the attainment of some aspect of mastery.

Effective instruction cannot be guaranteed by any single simple formula. It goes without saying that, if instruction is to be really effective, the subject matter must be selected and organized in such a way as to make it appropriate and suited to the age and intellectual development of the students.   Further than this, it must be presented in an understandable and interesting way, and there must be provision for ample practice. Skills and concepts once developed must be maintained through reapplication and not allowed to deteriorate through disuse.   Since students do not learn with equal facility or at equal rates, there must be provision for individual differences.   If the instruction is to attain a maximum of usefulness, it must be carried on with the deliberate purpose of securing a maximum of transfer and in such a way that the relation of mathematics to other fields of learning and activity is made manifest.   These considerations involve careful planning and adequate testing of outcomes.

Three Fundamental Problems of Instruction in Mathematics.   Mathematics is a cumulative and a continuously expanding subject both in its theory and its applications.   At every stage the teacher of mathematics is confronted with three basic problems, viz., (1) helping the students to develop understanding and mastery of new concepts, principles, relationships, and skills, (2) helping them to maintain understandings and skills already attained, and (3) helping them to secure maximum transfer of learning to their physical and social environment.   These three phases of teaching should be interwoven as far as possible into a unified instructional program, but their implications are essentially distinct and supplemental rather than identical.   The teaching of new material necessarily draws upon the already established background as a frame of reference and to this extent serves as a means of maintenance, but such maintenance is relatively incidental to the mastery of the new material and must be so regarded.   Adequate maintenance and maximum transfer, especially of skills, cannot be assured by incidental contacts but require an instructional program designed especially for their attainment.

TEACHING FOR UNDERSTANDING: DEVELOPMENTAL TEACHING

As generally conceived, the foremost problem of direct instruction in secondary school mathematics is the teaching of new material.   It is this phase of instruction that makes the heaviest demand upon the skill and artistry of the teacher.   The primary jobs are to explain, to make clear, to challenge, to guide to discovery, to develop understanding.   In order to meet these responsibilities, the teacher must not only consider the logical relationships involved in the unit or topic but also be keenly aware of the relation of the new concepts to the experiential background of the students.   He must be able to anticipate probable difficulties and detect and clear up actual difficulties as they occur in the course of the development.   He must be able and continually willing to view the unfolding and (to the students) unfamiliar subject matter not merely through his own experienced eyes but from the standpoint of immature students to whom it is all new and strange.

Inventory and Preview.   Effective instruction requires that time shall not be wasted and that interest shall be stimulated and conserved. When new work is taken up with a class, the assumption is generally tacitly made that the students are all entirely unfamiliar with the new materials which they are to study, but this is not always so.   It not infrequently happens, especially in some of the junior high school work, that the students will already have acquired some acquaintance with certain parts of the material presented in the textbooks.   In some cases they will be found to have a fair degree of mastery of the supposedly new concepts and procedures.   It is both wasteful of time and deleterious to the maintenance of interest to go through the motions of teaching students things with which they are already familiar.   They become restless and impatient.   Attention wanders, disciplinary difficulties are likely to be created, and the whole atmosphere of the class situation is rendered unfavorable to effective learning.

Therefore, before planning the work of a new course or a new unit, it is desirable that the teacher find out as much as he can about the students' background with reference to such abilities and information as will be required in the new work.   This may sometimes be done by means of oral questioning and discussion, while in other cases suitable written inventory tests will be more satisfactory.[1]   Such tests are discussed and illustrated in Chap. 8.   By means of a preliminary investigation of this nature the teacher will be in a position to proceed intelligently in building up necessary backgrounds and in presenting the new work to the class in an effective manner.

In presenting a new unit of work, it is important that the students be given a preview of the unit as a whole in order that they may get a perspective of the major ideas, issues, and principles in the unit and the relations of these to each other, to the unit as a whole, and to the previous parts of the work.   A preview of this sort not only gives meaning and relevance to the larger ideas of the unit but also gives significance and motive to the detailed study which must make up a major part of the students' work in the mastery of the unit.   Teachers of mathematics have generally failed to recognize the importance of the preview as a part of instructional procedure.   All too often new work is taken up detail by detail, just as it appears in the textbook, with little thought of relating the details to the structure of the unit as a whole.   It is safe to say that this is partly responsible for much of the current dissatisfaction with the mathematics courses in our schools.

The preview should generally be given in the form of a well-organized talk by the teacher.   It should not be a long talk, because the span of concentrated attention for most students of secondary school age is not great.   Moreover, the purpose for which it is given does not require a lengthy discussion and would, in fact, be defeated by too much attention to detail, since this would tend to obscure the larger principles. The teacher should present the ideas that he wishes to emphasize in a consecutive account in which clear, concise statements are embellished by supplementary discussion only in so far as it will aid in making the statements definite and understandable to the students.   During this preview, the students should be mainly in the role of listeners. Interruptions and questions should not be prohibited, of course, but for the most part students should be urged to defer their questions until the conclusion of the teacher's discussion in order to avoid interrupting the continuity of thought, which is a most important feature of this phase of instruction.   The preview offers great possibilities for stimulating curiosity and interest and helping the students to cultivate the art of being good listeners.   It should generally be followed by a brief test to determine how effective the presentation has been and whether there is need for rediscussion of the outline before the class proceeds to a detailed study of the unit.

[1] E. R. Breslich, "The Technique of Teaching Mathematics in Secondary Schools" (Chicago: University of Chicago Press, 1930), pp. 4–11.

Teaching New Material.   No mere lecture procedure such as is commonly used in college classes will suffice for the job of teaching secondary school mathematics.   It is a common fault of teachers to employ too extensively the method of "telling" or of giving a coherent discussion of a topic and then proceeding as if on the assumption that the discussion has been followed and completely understood by the students.   This assumption is almost never justified.   Secondary school students are seldom able to assimilate adequately and immediately any lengthy one-sided teacher-given discussion of unfamiliar subject matter.   Points of difficulty will inevitably arise, and unless they are cleared up promptly, they will fail to register with the students; failure to get these points cleared up may easily result in blocking the understanding of the subsequent parts of the discussion.

This does not mean that telling is always and entirely out of place.   On the contrary, there are many times when judicious telling or explanation may be not only proper and valuable but absolutely necessary, as, for example, in making clear the meaning of new terms and concepts.   Such use of the telling, or lecture, method in secondary school mathematics, however, should generally take the form of explanations or illustrations, and these should not be protracted longer than necessary.   Moreover, the discussion should not be one-sided; it should be interspersed with frequent questions by the teacher, who should also strive to elicit questions and contributions from the class.

It is not always easy to get students to raise questions, because all too often the difficulties which arise in their minds are not well enough defined to enable them to put them into words.   Many students are quite sensitive about appearing slow of perception or "dumb" in the eyes of their classmates, and rather than run the risk of embarrassment, they commonly let these matters pass in silence.   For no better reasons than these, students will frequently allow statements to go unchallenged even though they do not understand them.   Such barriers to freedom of inquiry on the part of the students can be broken down only by tact and sympathetic encouragement.   The teacher should never resent an interruption of discussion when it is caused by the raising of a legitimate question or inquiry.   On the contrary, students should be given every encouragement to raise such questions at any time that they are unable to follow the discussion clearly.

At best, however, students cannot be depended upon to bring up all points which may need special attention in the course of a discussion or explanation.   The teacher must anticipate these as far as possible and be always alert to detect them as they become apparent.   This can often be done by noting that the students wear puzzled expressions even though they may not actually raise questions.   Always at such times, and frequently in any case, the teacher should check the understanding of the discussion by means of questions addressed to members of the class, and at the completion of the discussion of any new topic a check test of some sort should be given before passing on to other activities.   Merely to present a finished discussion, closing with some such general question as Is that clear to all of you? or Are there any questions? is entirely inadequate.   The silence with which such a question is generally received is absolutely no assurance that the class has followed the discussion at all, though as a rule this interpretation is wrongfully placed upon it.   It may simply mean that the students have not followed the discussion even well enough to be able to ask intelligent questions about it.

On the other hand, when by well-chosen questions students can be led to discover facts or relationships for themselves, the advantage is manifest. This makes the student a more active participant in the learning process. It provides a spur to quicken his interest, since it casts him in the role of at least a quasi investigator rather than a mere passive recipient of information.   That he has been guided toward his discoveries by the helpful and stimulating questioning of the teacher should not detract from his justifiable pride in his achievement.

Laboratory Work in Mathematics.   The use of multisensory aids, when well coordinated with the other classroom learning activities, can serve a double purpose: it not only serves to stimulate interest but provides a most effective means of clarifying many mathematical concepts and relations through the experience of associating them directly with physical things.   Thus it serves as a highly important avenue for organic learning as well as for motivation.   Such practice is often referred to as "laboratory work in mathematics."   The title is just, for the activities which do, or could, take place in the mathematics laboratory bear much the same relation to the mathematics courses as their counterpart activities in the physics or biology laboratories bear to those courses.   It is true that the idea of the mathematics laboratory has not yet received the same general acceptance as the science laboratory has, but this may well be because mathematics teachers have not themselves recognized and insisted upon its importance as the science teachers have.   Actually, most mathematics teachers have been very passive in this respect.   Teachers of science, art, music, home economics, and other subjects do not hesitate to ask for space and equipment for this type of work, and they get it.   But most mathematics teachers do not even ask for it, though to do so would be both reasonable and proper.

In spite of this, however, laboratory work in mathematics is receiving increasing attention.   New classrooms are being designed with this as one of the primary considerations.   Textbooks, teachers' manuals, and professional journals for teachers are giving more suggestions for such work than they ever have before.   Special courses are being given to equip teachers and prospective teachers for such work, and the mathematics laboratory has become almost a standard adjunct of institutes and professional meetings for mathematics teachers.   Its importance in the learning of mathematics may be compared to the importance of laboratory work in the learning of physics, chemistry, and biology and that of field work in biology and geography.   In view of the significant contribution which it can make and the fact that teachers have only begun to exploit its possibilities, it must be given more than passing mention here.

As the name implies, the underlying idea of the mathematics laboratory is that students will develop new concepts and understandings particularly well through experimental activities dealing with concrete situations such as measuring and drawing; counting, weighing, averaging, and estimating; taking readings from instruments; recording, comparing, analyzing, classifying, and checking data; and obtaining original data or impressions from concrete physical situations and working with such data.   Most work of this nature will involve the use of various kinds of physical equipment and will entail such activities as those listed here.   Some of this work can be done in the classroom that is suitably arranged and equipped; some can take the form of elementary field work such as determination of angles and distances and the mapping of small areas.   Most students find such work highly interesting, and it is doubtless true that through it they can develop many mathematical concepts and insights with an interest and a clarity often not attained through a strictly intellectual approach. It is also likely that these concepts and principles become more enduring and more functional and meaningful when they are seen in relation to actual applications.

There is, of course, some danger that, unless proper precautions are taken, laboratory work in mathematics may degenerate into more or less aimless playing with instruments, models, and gadgets.   Activities which are mere busywork and which contribute nothing toward understanding are practically worthless and a waste of time.   To be productive of learning, the activities must be carefully planned, closely supervised, and guided toward definite ends.   Responsibility for the effectiveness of whatever laboratory-type work is done rests squarely with the teacher, and the discharge of that responsibility depends upon adequate planning and supervision of the activities.

The activities involved in laboratory-type work in mathematics fall broadly into two classes which, though not mutually exclusive, may be called respectively demonstrations and experimental activities.   By the term "demonstration" we have in mind the illustration and explanation to the teacher or to the class of some mathematical concept or relation by a method in which some physical equipment or device is used to illustrate and help clarify the explanation. Thus the term is used here in the sense in which it is commonly used in connection with classes in physics or chemistry. For example, various physical devices have been used for the following purposes: to illustrate operations with positive and negative numbers, or the manner in which the trigonometric functions vary; to confirm the identification of the center of gravity of a flat triangular solid with the geometrical centroid of a triangle of the same shape and size; and to verify the geometric description of the locus of the vertex of an angle whose sides pass through two fixed points.[1] Demonstration activities therefore are associated with the "giving out" or transmitting to others of information and ideas already acquired by the demonstrator. The demonstrator may be either the teacher or a student; or perhaps a small group of students may cooperate in giving a demonstration. Any demonstration which is well planned and effectively carried out involves a real learning experience. Although it is ostensibly aimed at the receiving audience, every experienced teacher knows that the students giving the demonstration will probably learn even more through the deeper and clearer insight engendered by the activity itself.

The equipment or mechanical devices used in such demonstrations should be simple but not shoddy. They should be well made and sufficiently precise to do *well* what they are supposed to do. There is much to be said for student-made demonstration aids if they are well made, but a well-made device, even if produced by the teacher, is to be preferred to a poorly made device constructed by a student. The same thing is true with respect to homemade and commercially produced devices.

The following suggestions by a pioneer in this field[2] should be studied with care.

Demonstrations in mathematics that call for the use of equipment differ somewhat from the usual conception of demonstrations as carried on in the natural and physical sciences. For one thing there is less equipment available and very often a particular device can only be operated by the person who produced it. Then also those concepts which lend themselves to a demonstration at all are often not very easy to construct in the first place. Another difference is that the equipment used in a mathematical experiment is generally some home-made or adapted contrivance, as is certainly true with the type of aids discussed here, and so its structure must be fairly well understood before it can be used at all. Finally there are few organized laboratory outlines available for mathematics demonstrations so one must rely largely on his own ingenuity in preparing for

[1] A device to illustrate this locus was reported by the Mathematics Laboratory, Monroe High School, St. Paul, Minnesota. See *Mathematics Teacher*, **45** (1952), 595–596.

[2] Emil J. Berger, Principles Guiding the use of Teacher- and Pupil-made Learning Aids, "Twenty-second Yearbook" (Washington, D.C.: National Council of Teachers of Mathematics, 1954), pp. 160–161.

lessons of this type.   Because demonstrations in mathematics, relatively speaking at least, are still somewhat of a pioneering idea, the following suggestions on procedure may be found helpful:

1. To insure the workability of a demonstration it should be planned in advance and rehearsed if possible.   Demonstrating concepts with the aid of concrete materials is not the usual mode of approach to some of the topics of mathematics; hence familiarization with the plan of procedure may help one avoid the feeling of being "all thumbs."

2. If a demonstration is to be successful, students must understand what is going to be attempted.   The habit of writing leading questions on the board will be found helpful.

3. Do not attempt too much.   Many devices can be used to illustrate a whole series of related concepts, but yielding to the temptation to do so may not only becloud a student's understanding of the main concept being pursued but even destroy what meager insight he may have acquired initially.   Also, the person in charge of the demonstration must not allow himself to be led too far afield by one or two alert students who wish to examine some remote detail of the main concept.   The demonstration should be performed for the whole class at least the first time through.

4. Keeping up a running summary as the demonstration proceeds will help the slower student keep the details of the work in mind.

5. Repeat the demonstration for the slower student if it appears that such repetition will help him organize his thinking.

6. When the demonstration proper has been completed, opportunity should be provided for the members of the class to manipulate the demonstration device individually if they desire.   Occasionally a student is able to clear up some detail for himself in this way even when he is unable to formulate a question concerning his particular difficulty.   Handling a device by oneself is quite different from observing someone else perform a demonstration with it.

7. Finally follow up the demonstration with shrewd questioning, or possibly even a short quiz, to insure that the concepts demonstrated were actually communicated.

In speaking of experimental activities we shall have in mind any kind of activity which (1) is carried on individually or by small groups working together and (2) is aimed primarily at helping the experimenters themselves to clearer understandings.   This sort of activity can take many forms.   A student who has obtained timed temperature readings in a physics class in an experiment on the cooling rate of a liquid may, by working with these data in tabular and graphic forms, be helped to a clear understanding of the law of cooling and its mathematical representation.   Checking the solutions of simultaneous equations by accurately made large-scale graphs can serve to clarify and deepen the interpretation of graphs as well as make the algebraic solutions seem concrete and realistic.   By estimating and then measuring distances or angles, students clarify their concepts of a yard, a rod, 100 feet, or an angle of elevation of

15° or 45°.   Real appreciation of how many things make 1,000 will be sharpened by outlining on a piece of cross-section paper a rectangle containing 1,000 squares and then drawing a little ring in each one.   The axioms for solving linear equations can be given point and meaning by the use of a pair of balances.   A model cut from a large potato can be used to point up the proof that the volume of a triangular pyramid is one-third that of the prism in which it is inscribed.   Indeed, the illustration of many theorems of plane and solid geometry by means of physical devices adds a satisfying tangibility to the formal proofs.   In the junior high school the properties of geometric figures and concepts of distances, angles, weights, areas, volumes, and loci can be given more vivid impact through work of this experimental nature than through any other means.   With respect to this kind of work we read again:[1]

The use of this [experimental] procedure is time consuming but it is also one of the most direct methods that can be employed to assist students in experiencing the feel of what it means to make a genuine discovery.   The main problem encountered in using this technique is organizational.   What preparations must be made in advance?   How shall a lesson be motivated?   Can the plan be employed in the typical classroom?   Answers to these and similar questions are incorporated in the following suggestions:

1. Of necessity every student must be equipped with some simple tools, and as a measure for avoiding confusion, each student's materials should be stored individually somewhere in the classroom.   If individual drawer space is not available, then shoe boxes—or some other sort of boxes that are uniform in size and shape—should be used.   Uniform size and shape makes storage easy.   Each student's laboratory kit should contain such simple tools and materials as a pair of scissors, paper punch, razor blade, ruler, compasses, map pins, push pins, corkboard or Celotex square, mucilage, elastic, protractor, color crayons, pick-up sticks, fruit-jar covers, dress patterns, road maps, Scotch tape, and whatever else the teacher thinks may be useful.

2. Select only tools and materials that everyone can use, and that can be stored in the container selected.   Students should equip their own kits if this is feasible.

3. Raw materials such as construction paper, squared cross-section paper, and precut items such as cardboard strips should be distributed to students only as needed.

4. For best results the classroom should be equipped with tables—preferably two-chair tables.   Desks with large tops are superior for this type of work to lecture room armchairs.

5. If exercises attempted involve more than two or three steps, an outline of key steps should be duplicated or placed on the blackboard.

6. If the activity calls for building a model, mimeographed pattern sheets with instructions will be found helpful.

[1] *Ibid.*, pp. 162, 163.

7. Do not attempt too much.

8. A problem can be set up by posing questions whose answers suggest activity to the student. For example suppose students are given a set of precut cardboard strips and are asked to decide which sets of three each may be combined to form triangles. As another example, suppose students are directed to place two map pins on their Celotex squares three inches apart, and are then asked to locate all points that are two inches from each pin.

9. Resist the temptation to tell more than is absolutely necessary to motivate a student to action.

Space limitations make it impossible in this book to extend the discussion of laboratory work in mathematics, though a great deal more could be said about it. Fortunately, there are now available a number of excellent references dealing with this subject in many of its detailed aspects. For convenience some of them are brought together in the Bibliography under Selected References on Laboratory Work in Mathematics.

Developmental Teaching. Just as there is no single method through which new concepts are learned, so there is no single method of teaching which fits all learning situations. In order to develop new material successfully, the teacher must adapt his procedure to the situation as he finds it and modify his procedure in accordance with the changing requirements of the situation. Developmental teaching is an art. It can be neither standardized nor stereotyped. Procedures which are used successfully by one teacher may prove to be unsuccessful when tried by another, or perhaps even by the same teacher under different circumstances. Much depends upon the personality of the teacher, upon his enthusiasm, tact, understanding of children, and upon his ability to sense intuitively the procedures which will serve best to capitalize the psychological classroom situation of the moment or modify it in such a way that it may be made to contribute most powerfully in the drive toward the objective which has been set. That teacher will be most successful in developmental work who has at his command *various* methods of procedure and who uses them in such a way as to make them supplement each other most advantageously as occasion may indicate.

One of the greatest mistakes which many teachers make is to try to cover too much ground in a given period of time or to try to cover a given amount of material in too short a period of time. This nearly always results in superficial learning or in no learning at all. Particularly in the developmental teaching of new material, the teacher should avoid forcing the process too rapidly. The development of new concepts and principles is a slow process, and it always requires a certain amount of discussion. Sometimes it will be necessary for the teacher to carry the burden of the discussion in building up and coordinating the necessary background and in giving a first presentation of the new material, but this should be done in such a way as to avoid lecturing so far as possible. When it is feasible to guide students into exploratory activities through appropriate questioning or laboratory exercises so that they may discover things for themselves, it should be done. When it is necessary for the teacher to give direct information, it should be given briefly and concisely and should be checked by pointed and searching questioning. New understandings, as they are developed, should be given permanence, clarity, and interest by means of adequate illustration and application.

Developmental work is not the job of the teacher alone. In order to be successful, it requires the continuous interaction of the students' best efforts with those of the teacher. The aim at all times is to develop in the students a broadening background of mathematical understanding and foster a continuing interest in the subject to the end that the students will gain added appreciation of its nature and usefulness and will acquire increasing ability to do independent thinking in the field. The teacher must plan and direct the activities of the class toward these goals. He must strive to secure the highest possible degree of cooperative effort on the part of the students. He must be tactful and sympathetic, helping when necessary, encouraging, guiding, checking, and always stimulating the students to put forth their own best efforts. Such a program of developmental teaching may be expected to yield highly satisfactory results not only in developing mastery of the new subject matter immediately in hand but also in building up an added appreciation of mathematics and its contributions, in developing an increasing ability to do independent mathematical thinking, and in stimulating interest in the pursuit of further mathematical study.

TEACHING FOR ASSIMILATION: DIRECTED STUDY

The preceding sections of this chapter have dealt with the *development* of new material, i.e., with methods of presenting new material to the students, of discussing it with them, and of giving them their first basic understandings of it. It is well to reemphasize here that many of the difficulties which students encounter in mathematics can be traced to the inadequacy of the developmental work which precedes the period of independent study. Obviously, students will not be able to make much independent progress toward the assimilation of concepts, principles, and relationships of which they have not even gained a basic understanding. Adequate developmental teaching is an absolute prerequisite to successful assimilative study in mathematics. The teacher who neglects to assure himself that his developmental work has been reasonably effective is likely to find his students groping helplessly for light on matters of which they have gained but an imperfect understanding.   It is therefore of the utmost importance that, before the students are set to independent study of new material, measures be taken to test their understanding of the ideas which the teacher has tried to develop with them as a preliminary basis for their work during the assimilation period.   The results of such a test will often be extremely illuminating to the teacher by revealing points where further developmental work is needed.   Any such points should be cleared up immediately by thorough reteaching.

This, however, is only one step toward real and adequate mastery. Concepts are not ultimately mastered without many illustrations in varied contexts, nor principles without repeated application, nor processes without extensive practice, nor any of these without protracted and sustained intellectual effort on the part of the students themselves. The purpose of developmental teaching is to give the students adequate bases of understanding and appreciation and motive upon which to build, but the process of mastery can by no means be thought of as ending with this step.   On the contrary, this is merely a beginning which must be followed by an extensive period in which the student must devote himself to the task of assimilation and fixation of the ideas, principles, and processes which have been brought out in the developmental work.

Lest the foregoing statement be misunderstood, we do not mean that the activities of the assimilation work will necessarily be divorced from discussion, illustration, demonstration, experiment, and other kinds of work usually associated with developmental work.   Assimilation can take place through many avenues, although the principal one is individual directed study.   Let it be emphasized too that the term "directed study" as used here refers to a type of classroom activity rather than a method of teaching; it is to be thought of as a *phase* of teaching rather than a method. There is no reason why part of a class period cannot be devoted to developmental work on new concepts or processes and part of the same period be given to assimilation work on this or previously developed ideas.   The assimilation period need not, and probably should not, be an unbroken succession of class periods devoted wholly to study and devoid of everything else.   The thing to be noted especially is that the fundamental objective here is different from that in developmental teaching.   In the developmental phase of the work the principal aim is to produce threshold *understanding* of new material.   In the assimilative phase the aim is to produce fuller and deeper insights, greater familiarity, and improved facility; in short, the aim is to produce real mastery and a comfortable sense of feeling at home and at ease with the material.   The objectives, of course, will imply the methods or activities through which they can best

be attained, and we shall see that the activities of the assimilative phase
will, in general, differ somewhat from those of the developmental phase.

The teacher necessarily has a somewhat active role in at least some parts
of the developmental work. In the assimilative stage, however, the
situation is different. From this point on, the teacher's role, while no less
important than before, is much less obvious. The students and their
activities now occupy the center of the stage, while the teacher serves as a
sort of prompter and director operating from the wings. Of course there
will need to be some general discussion from time to time for purposes of
motivation and for clearing up points which offer persistent difficulties,
but such discussions should, for the most part, be incidental to the
directed study which is the characterizing activity in this part of the
work. In the process of assimilation through directed study the students
themselves are the main participants so far as overt activity is concerned.
The task of the teacher now should be that of guiding and directing
their work, stimulating them, encouraging them, helping them over
hard spots, evaluating their progress, and in every way possible striving
to get them to put forth their best efforts to achieve a permanent and
functional mastery of the material upon which they are working.

Directed Study in Mathematics. Under the recitation and homework
plan of teaching mathematics, the students are often compelled to do
their studying under conditions both physically and psychologically
unfavorable to effective work. Many homes are not so arranged that it
is possible for the children to have suitable desks in quiet rooms where
they can study to advantage. The whole atmosphere of such homes is
redolent of other things, and distracting elements are the rule rather
than the exception. Most schools maintain some form of study hall
during school hours; as a rule, the study halls provide conditions which
are more favorable for study than those which students find at home.
They are at least normally quiet, and the fact that they are conducted
during school hours eliminates certain psychological handicaps to effective
study which are likely to operate outside school hours. The well-
conducted general study period cannot, however, ordinarily provide
conditions which are as well adapted for most students to do really
effective work as those made possible under a well-ordered plan of directed
study. Nearly all students need help at times, but in many cases the
teachers who are in charge of study periods have had so little training in
mathematics that they are unable to be of any assistance in helping
students over difficulties or in directing their work in this field. The one
person who is best qualified to do so is the mathematics teacher himself.
The time and the place where it can be done to best advantage is directly
in the mathematics class. There the student can address himself completely to his mathematical work, and there he can receive such assistance

as he may need from the teacher who is in charge of this work and who is therefore in a better position than anyone else to give him the proper attention, assistance, and direction.

The aim in the foregoing paragraph has not been to deprecate the value of homework nor to discredit its significance in the effective study of mathematics. Rather, it has been to emphasize the importance of directed study in the total program of guiding students in the formation of such study habits that they may be able to work efficiently in their pursuit of mathematical knowledge, whether they study individually or in groups, at home or at school.

Suggestions for Conducting Directed Study in Mathematics. At first thought it may appear that directed study in mathematics makes little or no demand upon the teacher. It is true that the teacher's role is much less prominent than it is in developmental teaching, but it is hardly less important. Directed study does not reduce teaching to an entirely individual basis, but it does attempt to combine the main advantages of individual instruction for those students who need it with the economy of time and other advantages generally recognized as accruing to group instruction. Directing study involves much more than maintaining order. If it is to be really effective, the teacher must be continually in touch with the work of each individual student. This requires repeated inspection and quick sizing up of the difficulties and needs of the various students. The teacher must be adept, not only at spotting key difficulties and in helping the students to clear them up, but also in discriminating between students who are experiencing real difficulties and those who are merely disinclined to work for themselves.

Many teachers make the mistake of rushing to the assistance of students at the first sign of difficulty and virtually doing their work for them. This is bad practice for two reasons. In the first place it does the students little or no good. Mastery can come only through individual effort, and it is not likely to be gained by the student who is unwilling to assume substantial personal responsibility for results and who relies to an excessive extent upon the teacher's assistance. There will always be such students, and if the directed study program is to be effective, the teacher must be able to detect them. He should decline to extend them assistance unless he is convinced that they are seriously in need of it, and he should make every effort to get them to modify their attitude so that they will be willing to take a larger share of responsibility upon themselves and rely less upon assistance from him.

In the second place, if the teacher allows students to impose unduly upon his willingness to help them, he will soon find himself so swamped with demands of this nature that he will be unable to take care of them all in a satisfactory manner. If he allows himself to be so hurried that he has to rush from student to student, not only will many students waste time waiting for him, but inevitably he will tend to give direct information instead of helping students to think their own way through their problems; therefore, such ostensible assistance as he can give under such circumstances will largely defeat its own purpose. In addition to this, the pressure and stress will almost certainly leave him physically tired, mentally and emotionally disorganized, and generally unfitted for effective work. The only way in which these evil effects can be avoided is for the teacher to confine his assistance to those students who, in his opinion, really need it, and even then to the key difficulties which they encounter. Perhaps the mere explanation of a word will be sufficient. In any case, it is extremely important that the teacher be able to lead the student to disclose just what is causing his difficulty so that it may be cleared up without allowing extraneous matters to befog the issue and without unnecessary waste of time.

On the other hand, the teacher must not be niggardly with assistance when it is really needed. It is a fine art to determine just who really needs help, just what and how much assistance is needed, and in what manner it should be given. It can be done successfully only by a teacher who has a sympathetic understanding of the attitudes and abilities of his students, who has a good knowledge of the difficulties to be expected and the errors commonly made in the work underway, and who possesses a trained insight which will enable him to get directly at the root or key of the student's difficulty, even though the student himself may not know precisely what it is that is causing him trouble.

The following suggestions have been found helpful to teachers in conducting directed study in mathematics:[1]

1. Be sure that the preliminary developmental work has been clearly understood by the students before allowing them to begin their study. This work provides the basic foundation and framework with reference to which the subsequent assimilative study is oriented. That is, it provides the initial understandings which are to be assimilated, amplified, organized, and made permanent through subsequent study. Directed study can play its part in this process only if these preliminary understandings have been satisfactorily developed.

2. Be sure that the assignment of the work to be done is made clear to all the students, so that each one will know precisely what is expected of him.

3. Be sure that each student has the equipment which he will need for his work. The practice of borrowing breeds carelessness, wastes

[1] The list presented here includes adaptations of the excellent suggestions given by Breslich, *op. cit.*, pp. 41-44.

time, and causes disturbance. The teacher, however, should keep on hand a limited amount of equipment with which to provide against emergencies. If it becomes absolutely necessary for a student to borrow any equipment, it is better for him to borrow from the teacher than from a fellow student.

4. Soon after the directed study period has begun, make a rapid inspection of the work of all the students and note which students seem to be most in need of help. Ordinarily it is best not to interrupt this survey for the purpose of answering questions or giving assistance to individuals. Students in need of assistance can receive it later. The purposes of the survey are to ascertain whether there is a need for immediate reteaching of any parts of the work and to see what students, if any, seem unable to get started with their work.

5. If the survey shows that a considerable number of the students are having trouble in getting started, it may be advisable to stop the study work and do some general reteaching of any points which may appear not to have been developed clearly. If such reteaching is needed, it should be done immediately with the class as a whole. The study period can then be resumed.

6. If the survey shows that no *general* reteaching is needed, the teacher may then properly give attention to the difficulties of individuals. In doing this, the teacher should pass quietly about the room again, stopping this time to give individual attention to those students who have not been able to get started with their work or who are having serious difficulties. This amounts to individual instruction. As in the general developmental work, it should aim to enlist the student's fullest participation in the intellectual task—to guide his thinking rather than to give him ready-made procedures. He should be given only such direct information as may be indispensable in helping him to clear up the concepts, principles, or relationships involved, or in giving him some cue which will enable him to proceed under his own power. In most cases the heuristic method[1] should be used. It takes more time than it does to give information directly, but it is a method which fosters self-reliance and independent thinking, whereas the habitual giving of direct information may actually inhibit the development of these desirable characteristics.

7. Spend no more time than is necessary with a student. On the other hand, do not allow yourself to be rushed through a conference with one student by the importunities of others.

8. Establish with your students the understanding that in general the teacher should determine who needs help and when, and that, instead of asking for assistance and then idly waiting for it to come, they

[1] By this we mean a method which aims to lead the student, through well-chosen questions, to discover facts, information, relationships, and principles for himself.

should persistently continue their efforts to help themselves until such time as you can determine whether they need help or not.

9. Train yourself to detect quickly the key logs in students' mathematical log jams. Not only will this save much time both for the teacher and the students, but it will do much to increase both the interest and the independence with which the students will work. Often the difficulty can be traced to a careless reading of problems or instructions. At other times mistakes in computation or in fundamental algebraic mechanics may be responsible for the student's confusion. Such difficulties are relatively easy to correct. Often it is not necessary to do more than point out to the student the nature of his difficulty. These cases are very different from those which involve a lack of understanding, and the teacher should be able to determine readily into which class a given case falls. In cases of the latter type it will generally be necessary to do a careful job of reteaching with the individual student.

10. At all times, and above all other considerations, an atmosphere conducive to study should be maintained in the room. Comparative quiet should prevail. While students should not be prohibited from conferring with one another at times about their work, this should not represent the pattern for the conduct of the directed study period. Each student should be impressed with his personal responsibility in this direction and with the principle that he can best discharge this responsibility by keeping steadfastly at his own work.

Directing study along the lines which have been suggested here is a most illuminating and valuable experience for the teacher. It not only keeps him in touch with the work of all the students but often reveals unsuspected omissions or inadequacies in his teaching, and it is one of the most effective means of keeping his viewpoint adjusted to that of the less mature students. If he is observant, he will learn much concerning their study habits. This should enable him in many cases to help them eliminate unprofitable methods and substitute for them more effective procedures.

Some Suggestions to the Students on Studying Mathematics. There is abundant evidence that students often employ wasteful and inefficient procedures in studying mathematics. Sometimes they do not know how to begin their work; they waste time in aimlessly trying one thing after another. They fail to form the habit of depending upon themselves. They are unsystematic and do not take time for deliberate reflection before starting their work. They allow their attention to be distracted and their work interrupted. They are careless in their reading, in their listening, and in their written work. Many times they do not recognize that the specific procedures involved in the study of some parts of mathematics are not necessarily the same as those involved in the study of other parts of the subject, and they do not analyze their assignments to determine what particular procedures will contribute most effectively to the mastery of the work in hand.   If the students are to acquire the ability to do effective independent study, they need specific instruction in methods and habits of study, and it seems clear that one of the most important tasks of the mathematics teacher is to help them to a knowledge and acquisition of general habits which are conducive to the improvement of study in general and specific procedures which are involved in studying particular parts or aspects of the work.

The following list of suggestions will be helpful to students and teachers in this connection:

1. Form the habit of studying your mathematics at a regular time.

2. Form the habit of studying your mathematics in a regular place.

3. Form the habit of getting down to work *at once*.   Do not dally.

4. Form the habit of paying *concentrated and sustained attention* to your work after you start.

5. Do not allow avoidable interruptions after you start.

6. Work as rapidly as you can after you start.

7. Work by yourself for the most part.

8. As a preparatory step, get the assignment clearly in mind.   Recall the teacher's explanation, and, if necessary, study again the sample exercises and the explanations in your text.

9. Plan your work for the work period before you start.

10. Read the problems and exercises carefully.   In each case be sure you understand clearly what is given and exactly what you are expected to do, find, or prove.   Keep these things clearly in mind while you are working.

11. If you are to copy an exercise or a problem, be sure that you copy it correctly.

12. Take plenty of time to think.   Do not start to solve a problem or to make a proof until you have clearly in mind exactly what is given and exactly what is required or until you have developed a plan for doing what is wanted.

13. If you do not know how to begin, consult your textbook and try to recall the explanations which your teacher has given.

14. Try to write out the questions that bother you, making them very clear and specific.   Often the answer will then suggest itself.

15. Do not give up.   At least try to find out just where and what your difficulty is.

16. Form the habit of listing all new words and concepts and learning them at once.   Use the dictionary and your text.

17. Form the habit of using the index and the reference tables in your books as sources of information about new words, formulas, numerical values, etc.

18. Memorize important rules, formulas, and facts, but be sure you understand their meanings and can use them correctly.

19. It is easier and better to memorize statements and formulas as wholes than to memorize them by parts.

20. In memorizing formulas it helps to read them aloud.

21. Mnemonic devices are often helpful in memorizing.

22. Work carefully. It is easier to avoid mistakes than it is to find and correct them after they are made.

23. Write neatly. Put down figures in neat rows and columns. Small, round, vertical writing is most legible.

24. Never use scrappy, dog-eared paper. Use scratch paper as little as possible.

25. Remember that every symbol has a definite *meaning*. Always read meanings into the symbols you use.

26. Read thoughtfully, and reflect as you read. Superficial reading in mathematics is generally just a waste of time.

27. Form the habit of expressing verbal statements in symbols.

28. An exercise is frequently made up of a series of steps. Do one step at a time.

29. Compare exercises in algebra with similar types of exercises in arithmetic. Sometimes this will give a cue or suggestion that will be helpful.

30. Check your work and your answers.

31. In order to fix rules and formulas in your mind, use them as soon as possible after you have learned them.

32. Sketch diagrams or graphs when you can. This often makes it easier to understand problems.

33. In numerical problems form the habit of making a preliminary estimate to serve as a rough check on your work.

34. In preparing for a recitation spend some time in organizing the lesson in a logical form in your mind.

35. Replace large numbers by approximations in planning the solutions of problems.

36. When listening to discussion in class, listen with your whole attention. Do not have books opened or pencils in hand unless specifically asked to do so.

37. Be mentally alert, active, and aggressive.

38. Enjoy overcoming hard mathematical obstacles.

39. In studying material to be understood and digested (e.g., a proof in geometry), plan out the proof or the attack first; then go over it rapidly and sketchily to get it all in mind; next, take it section by section, writing out the details; and finally, review it and check it rapidly.

40. Be critical of all statements made, whether by yourself or by someone else. Be especially critical of statements that are not adequately supported by reasons.

By careful training in the systematic use of such a list of study suggestions the students may acquire both the habit and technique of analyzing and improving *their own* study habits. This is the goal toward which we should strive. Too much, of course, must not be expected from this or any other list of study suggestions.[1] It would be utterly misleading to suggest that any such list could be regarded as a panacea or as a guarantee

---

[1] A number of references that contain valuable suggestions for studying mathematics are collected in the Bibliography under Study Suggestions.

of efficiency.   On the other hand, it may confidently be expected that deliberate, organized, and systematic attention to the improvement of study habits will in fact return very substantial and gratifying dividends.

TEACHING FOR PERMANENCE: DRILL, REVIEW, AND MAINTENANCE

The developmental and assimilative phases of instruction represent essentially the stages during which actual learning of new material takes place.   Any subject matter, however, is likely to be forgotten, no matter how well it has been initially mastered, unless it is maintained by repeated application and practice.   This is particularly true of mathematical skills and relationships.   Skills need to be perfected and maintained through systematic drill, and concepts and relationships must be reviewed and applied at frequently recurring intervals.   The instructional effort which is directed toward these ends may well be called *teaching for permanence*. While it generally involves material that has already been learned rather than new material, its importance as a means of strengthening and maintaining learnings is commensurate with the importance of the developmental and assimilative phases of instruction as means of *acquiring* new learnings.   Its avenues are drill, review, and application.

The Function of Drill.   In his excellent article on drill, Sueltz[1] points out that the meaning attached to the word "drill" has changed and broadened during the past quarter century.   He uses the term to include all kinds of situations which involve recurring experiences, and hence his discussion of drill touches upon all three of the aspects of teaching for permanence of learning, as indicated in the title of this section.   There is some advantage in thus broadening the meaning of the word, but there is also some advantage in discussing the different aspects separately.   In this book we shall use the word "drill" in a somewhat more restricted sense than that suggested by Sueltz, and we shall discuss the other aspects of recurring experience under their separate headings "review" and "maintenance."

The place of drill in mathematics has been a much discussed issue in recent years.   The reaction against excessive use of abstract rote drill, which came along with the reorganization movement and with the increased emphasis on concepts and meanings, was certainly justified and doubtless overdue.   However, it caused many educators to go to the other extreme and inveigh against all drill as being futile and without value. The old pedagogy undoubtedly laid too much emphasis upon memorization and mechanical learning and to a considerable extent neglected meanings.   In such a scheme mechanical drill played an important part because it afforded a convenient and fairly efficient medium for the rapid

[1] Ben A. Sueltz, Drill–Practice–Recurring Experience, "Twenty-first Yearbook" (Washington, D.C.: National Council of Teachers of Mathematics, 1953), pp. 192–204.

memorization of details and the automatization of processes. The fact that these do not necessarily imply understanding, and that proficiency acquired without understanding is not likely to endure very long, was apparently not recognized, since it did not seem to cause much concern. Eventually, however, a strong reaction set in, with the extremists taking the position that meanings alone have value, that the development of new concepts and understandings is all that matters, and that drill, in its restricted sense, has no place in the educational process. This point of view overlooks the important element of fixation, without which it would be manifestly impossible to organize and relate concepts or to carry on any process at a reasonable level of efficiency.

An enlightened present-day view of mathematical instruction must reject both of these extreme positions as untenable. Drill must be recognized as an essential means of attaining some of the desired controls, just as a strong emphasis upon concepts and meanings must be regarded as essential for understanding. Both are necessary and neither alone is sufficient. Many of the operations of mathematics need to be performed not only correctly but with considerable facility and speed if they are to be very useful. Some of them need to be actually automatized. The acquisition of facility in such operations can be secured only through systematic and repeated practice, i.e., through drill.

If instruction is to be valuable, however, understanding must go hand in hand with operational facility. With a few possible exceptions children should not be drilled on procedures which they do not first understand. Drill under such circumstances lacks both significance and motive. It may indeed produce temporary facility, but facility will be without value unless it is associated with meaning. If understanding and motive are lacking, drill becomes little more than drudgery.

Principles of Drill. Educational psychology in recent years has done much to provide us with well-established principles whereby drill may be made interesting and effective, and authors and publishers have combined to make available materials specially designed to facilitate the application of these principles. In the following paragraphs some important considerations relating to drill in mathematics will be enumerated and briefly discussed.

Drill, to be most effective, must be well motivated. The attitude with which students approach the problem of mastering material has an important bearing upon both the rate and extent of mastery which they achieve. If the material contains no intrinsic interest and they can see no value in it, their work will be without interest. However, if they are working on something which they recognize as important or interesting in itself, they will work with enthusiasm and with concentrated attention, and their work will be correspondingly more effective. Witness, for example, the willingness with which the members of a football squad engage in charging and tackling drills.   The activity in and of itself is tiring and sometimes painful, but it is well motivated because the end toward which it is directed is clear and seems desirable.   Most students are not lazy.   They are willing to work hard at things which interest them, and when they appear to be lazy it is likely that they are only bored.   Contests between selected teams, improvement charts, and games involving the materials to be mastered are examples of the numerous devices which have been developed for motivating drill work in mathematics.

Drill exercises should be conducted in such a manner that students can work at differing rates and at different levels according to their abilities. The certainty of individual differences within a group makes it clear that the individuals, even though they may all need drill on the same things, will not perform at the same rate or at the same level of difficulty.   It is uneconomical to have those who have attained substantial mastery continue drilling on tasks which no longer challenge them.   It is equally wasteful to have them do nothing while waiting for the others to catch up. In order to avoid situations of this sort, drill exercises should contain enough material to keep all the students profitably occupied throughout the drill period and also sufficiently diversified material to provide worthwhile and stimulating practice for students of different attainments and capacities.

Drill periods should generally be rather short.   The attention span of children is not great, and long periods of continuous drill become tiresome and ineffective.   In general it may be said that no drill period should extend for more than 20 minutes and that in most cases drill periods of not more than half that length are preferable.   This does not mean that a given skill can be mastered to a desired point of proficiency in 5, or 10, or even 20 minutes.   Rather, it means that more time, if it is required, should be distributed in relatively small amounts at recurring intervals which should become more widely spaced as time goes on.   This principle of spaced learning, as contrasted with the idea of complete immediate mastery, is exceedingly important and is coming to be widely recognized in the organization of textbooks and instructional materials.

In order to be most effective, drill must be specific.   By this is meant that it should be concentrated upon particular skills or even on particular details of operation.   The students should, of course, be aware of the relation of any detail to the whole situation of which it is a part.   But for purposes of fixation, which is the object of all drill, the particular detail or skill should for the moment be dissociated from its setting and context and drilled upon per se.   When the desired proficiency in them has been attained, the details should be progressively reintegrated into the entire process or situation of which they are components.

When drill is begun on any process or skill, correctness should be insisted upon as the prime consideration, and for the time being speed should be regarded as of secondary importance. Every effort should be made to detect mistakes in students' work and eliminate them at the outset. Failure to do so will inevitably have unfortunate consequences, because a wrong habit is fixed as readily as a right one, and it is much harder to eliminate a wrong habit that has become established and replace it by a correct one than it is to establish the correct one in the first place. Thus it is of extreme importance to supervise *closely* the initial work of the students on any new process. The insistence upon *right practice* from the start cannot be too greatly emphasized. Teachers often overlook this important principle when they assign homework involving procedures which have not been previously mastered in class. When they do so, the students are likely to make mistakes that could have been avoided by a small amount of carefully supervised drill.

There are few things which cause students to take a keener interest in their work or apply themselves with more verve and intensity than the satisfaction of knowing immediately whether their work is right or not. In much of the work of secondary mathematics it is desirable to have students apply mathematical tests or checks to ascertain the correctness of their own work. The checking of work in this manner is a real educational exercise, in many cases fully as valuable as the original work itself. This method of applying mathematical checks can be used in connection with drill work just as it can with problem work. It has, however, the disadvantage of slowing up the drill and diverting time and attention to procedures other than those for which the drill was originally planned.

Some teachers dislike to provide students with answers to verbal problems or materials assigned for home study on the theory that the students may easily misuse the answers. It is quite conceivable that this argument may have some justification as regards the kind of work mentioned, but in drill work conducted in the classroom the situation is different. It is, in fact, a definite stimulus to the student to know *immediately* whether his responses are correct or not. If they are, he secures an immediate satisfaction; if they are not, he is challenged to correct his work before his attention has shifted to other things. For these reasons answers should be provided for selected problems and exercises, and when answers are not provided, specific and efficient checking techniques should have been developed previously. Students should be required to check all results with care. When answers are provided, mere agreement is a sufficient check. Otherwise, independent work must be carried out and results must agree. There are times when variety of experience is the major desideratum of the drill and time is at a premium. On such occasions answers should be provided for all exercises. The question of dishonesty is minimized. The fact that the student realizes that he is being trusted to play fair operates as a definite incentive to him to do just that. Experience has shown that it actually works out in this way and that it affords a real training in honesty and self-responsibility, besides adding zest to the work itself.

Whenever possible, drill materials should also be provided with some means whereby the student can *score* his own work and compare his performance not only with that of the other members of the class but also with established standards and with his own performance on previous occasions. Here again, experience has shown that students are greatly interested in noting their own progress, and no finer incentive than this could be devised. The most valuable of the published drill materials are those for which standards of comparison are available and which are provided with record sheets or charts on which each student can keep a continuous running record of his own achievement.

Finally, the students should be kept aware that drill work is only part of their mathematical training, but that without it they would be handicapped in their pursuit of understandings, appreciations, and generalizations. Without speed and correctness in the fundamental skills they would be under a handicap similar to that of a student of a foreign language whose vocabulary is deficient, or a person trying to play a Liszt rhapsody without having acquired a good technique of fingering the piano keyboard. The student who lacks mastery of the mechanical skills of mathematics will find it difficult to free his mind of those skills so that he can give full attention to interpretation and analysis of mathematical theorems or problems. Nobody can read Shakespeare or Tennyson or even a contemporary short story with much appreciation if he has to stop and spell out the words.

Most of the principles of drill discussed in these pages are embodied or suggested in the excellent summary given by Sueltz in the article to which reference has already been made. Despite the fact that this summary[1] is based on a somewhat broader interpretation of the term than we have used, it is presented here for convenient reference.

1. The learner should both understand what he is practicing and appreciate its significance to him as an individual.

2. The learner should have sufficient propaedeutic experience so that the *newness* in what he is practicing does not create a mental block for him.

3. The learner should be an active participant both in setting his goals and in the thinking-striving aspects of learning. He should not merely repeat "parrot-fashion" from a teacher or textbook.

4. Drill should follow the developmental and discovery stages of learning and be used to reinforce and extend basic learning.

[1] Sueltz, *op. cit.*, pp. 196, 197.

5. Drill should be varied so that procedures do not become monotonous and so that different pupils have types of drill perhaps better suited to them.

6. Drill should be spaced so that (a) time is not wasted in excessive overlearning in initial stages and (b) previous learnings are kept fresh and useful.

7. Drill should be an integral part of various phases of learning but should not be used to hasten the achievement of results at the sacrifice of meaning and understanding.

8. Drill policy should recognize different rates and modes of learning with different pupils and not try to fit all into a common mold.

9. In general, it is better to provide for drill upon whole processes rather than parts thereof, unless some particular part, such as, for example, subtraction in a long division exercise, causes trouble and needs teaching and practice for reinforcing.

10. Drill should be done with correct processes lest a child practice errors which need to be remedied later.

11. Drill should be based upon or involve thinking and insight so that it never becomes a mere mechanical repetition.

12. Drill should be used when and where needed. It should not be used as a punishment nor should things already well learned be assigned for more practice.

13. There should be some sense of organization of drill so that (a) pupils see the sense and relationships of what they are doing and (b) important elements are not overlooked.

14. It seems that pupils of lower mental abilities require more drill than the more able, but this may be due to other related factors such as attention, insight, and other such causes.

Review. Review is sometimes identified with drill because they are both characterized by repetition and because they both aim at the fixation of reactions, concepts, or relationships. As the terms are used in this book, however, a distinction is made between drill and review. Drill is aimed mainly at the automatization of relatively detailed processes and reactions. Review, on the other hand, aims not only at the fixation and retention of details but also at the thoughtful organization of the important things in a chapter or unit into a coherent whole in order that the relationship of the various parts to each other and to the whole unit may be clearly understood. As Reeve[1] puts it:

In a review lesson one should seek to accomplish two major purposes:

1. He should make certain that the students are keeping in mind the basal features already acquired; and

2. He should lead them to look, as from a hilltop, over the route which has been traveled, thus enabling them to obtain a much broader view than they had when walking along the lower road.

[1] William David Reeve, "Mathematics for the Secondary School" (New York: Henry Holt and Company, Inc., 1954), p. 134.

Review should usually be concerned with more or less comprehensive units of subject matter.   One of its functions is indeed to make recall more certain and more effective, but it aims to achieve this through the deliberate processes of organizing, systematizing, and relating elements to each other through giving, indeed, a "re-view" or a new look at the unit which has been studied, rather than through reducing reactions to the plane of automatic responses.   It emphasizes thought and meaning rather than habit formation.   Thus while drill and review have some things in common, they also have certain differences.   Each has its proper function and each is highly important in the study of mathematics.

Review work may be incidental in the sense that it may be integrated with the other work of the course, or it may be specialized by making it the primary feature and objective of particular assignments.   Both of these types of review are necessary to the most effective teaching. Review of the incidental type is especially valuable for the gradual building up and clarification of concepts through repeated reference and through continual reapplication in those situations in which they play component parts.   Concepts and principles are generalized through being met with in many situations which vary in other particulars and from which the concepts and principles are gradually dissociated and abstracted. Perhaps this process may not be recognized as review at all if it is systematically made an integral part of the regular work, but it is review in a very real and important sense.   One of the strong arguments for a continuous program of integrated mathematics is that this sort of incidental or integrated review would necessarily run systematically throughout the entire program, giving strength and coherence to the entire structure through continual interassociation of the components.

At the same time there is need of special review work to supplement the incidental review which has been described.   The functions of the special review are to help the student organize more or less comprehensive bodies of material with reference to their logical relationships, to assist him in classifying their important ideas, and to give him a sense of the unity of the whole which might otherwise be lacking.   The review lesson, which should be planned with this idea dominant, will generally follow the assimilative study of a unit.   In preparing for a review lesson, the student should be expected to summarize the outstanding ideas which have been considered in the unit and to make an outline from which he can give a brief but coherent and systematic discussion of the material in the unit or division.   The preparation of such an outline will make it necessary for the student to review the unit in the fullest sense of the term.   Through making the necessary association of the ideas in the unit, he will be aided not only in remembering them but in understanding them and appreciating their interrelations.

On the whole, most teachers do a better job of conducting drill work than they do of conducting review work of this type. This is probably due in part to their failure to recognize the main function of review as different from that of drill. Students need to be taught how to review material just as they need to be taught how to study. They cannot review effectively without definite instructions. Yet all too commonly the only instructions they receive are something like, Review chapters seven and eight for tomorrow. The task of helping students plan their review work is a responsibility which every teacher should take seriously.

Maintenance. A planned program of cumulative drill and review work is aptly designated a maintenance program. The importance of such a program is implied in the discussion in the foregoing paragraphs. The fundamental requirement of a satisfactory maintenance program is that it shall operate to prevent the forgetting of facts, concepts, and relationships and forestall the disintegration of skills. To this end it must provide for systematic application of the important elements of the instructional program and for appropriate or needed practice on these elements even after current attention and emphasis have passed on to other matters. Therefore the planning of a really adequate maintenance program must be built upon the following principles:

1. The materials to be included should be selected from the point of view of relative values. The program should not be cluttered up with trivial things. Only significant skills, concepts, relationships, principles, and problem situations should be included.

2. In accordance with established principles of drill and review, the items should be distributed throughout the program in such a way that practice upon any particular element will not be too greatly concentrated but will recur at increasing intervals and in decreasing amounts.

3. The maintenance program should be diagnostic, preferably self-diagnostic, so that each student may be able to discover his own weaknesses. To this end some means should be provided whereby each student may systematically keep and study his own achievements in detail.

4. There should be provided supplementary practice material for remedial work on the various particular elements included in the maintenance program. This supplementary material can be used most effectively if it is keyed with the diagnostic record. In this way each student will be able not only to determine those things upon which he most needs practice but to carry on his own remedial work with a minimum of direction.

5. The different sets of exercises in the maintenance program should be comparable in terms of some uniform scoring or rating schedule so that each student may keep a record of his general achievement and his progress. This will be of great value in stimulating pride, effort, and genuine

interest in maintaining skills and principles after the original interest due to their newness has worn off.

Numerous textbooks published in recent years recognize the need for systematic maintenance work and make provision for it through sets of drill exercises, diagnostic inventory tests, cumulative reviews, and the like placed at strategic points in the texts.   In some cases these exercises have evidently been prepared hastily and with little attention to their validity or suitability.   In other cases their organization and arrangement have been based upon extensive and painstaking study and upon well-established principles of the psychology of learning.   These same comments are equally applicable to the multitude of drill books and workbooks and sets of practice exercises which are now commercially available to supplement textbooks.   They are not all equally good, but the better ones are valuable aids to the teacher in carrying on an adequate maintenance program.   Many teachers lack both the experience and the time needed to prepare thoroughly suitable materials for regular maintenance work.   Prepared materials which are scientifically planned and for which standards of attainment are available serve at least three useful purposes: (1) they make for economy of time and labor and therefore for efficiency in instruction; (2) they provide a strong motive to achievement, since they foster the students' continued study of their own performances, and (3) they provide the best possible insurance against forgetting and against the deterioration of skills and understandings.

TEACHING FOR TRANSFER

The Transfer of Training.   When people speak about "transfer of training," it is not always clear just what they have in mind.   The idea and the term stem from the old theory of formal discipline, which held that the mind is made up of several "faculties," such as memory and reasoning, and that these can be strengthened in a general sense by exercise, much as a muscle can.   Thus it once was held that, since mathematics is largely concerned with reasoning, the study of mathematics would automatically strengthen the "logical faculty" as a whole, and that this faculty would then inevitably operate more effectively than before in every kind of situation.   This was a comfortable theory, but the early studies of William James, Thorndike, Woodworth, and others cast grave doubt upon its validity as a theory of learning, and it has long been discredited.   That is to say, with respect to the teaching of mathematics, reputable psychologists no longer hold that the study of mathematics will guarantee improved reasoning in other fields such as religion or politics or the affairs of daily life.

This is not to say, however, that the learning of mathematics has no effect on the learner beyond the immediate things learned. On the contrary, evidence indicates that considerable carry-over, or transfer, is possible and in fact is often attained. In other words, the effects produced upon one in learning mathematics may materially influence his reactions to situations other than the immediate one. This is transfer in a more limited and less definite sense, since usually it is incomplete and may take any of a large variety of forms. Although a few people still identify the term "transfer" with the old concept and doctrine of mental discipline, most people now use the term in this more restricted sense. It is usually taken to denote the functioning, in a second or new situation, of certain aspects or structures or relations which were learned in an original situation.

Much remains to be done in ascertaining the manner in which transfer takes place and the circumstances upon which it is conditioned, but competent psychologists are now agreed that under favorable conditions transfer can and does occur. On the other hand, there is abundant evidence that it is neither automatic nor inevitable. Various theories have been proposed to account for the fact and the nature of its occurrence and to determine ways of bringing it about.[1] It is evidently a very complex phenomenon. Probably each of the theories (except the doctrine of formal discipline) explains certain aspects of it and has some implications for teaching, and probably none of the theories gives the complete explanation. But while there may not be complete agreement on just how transfer takes place, the most competent observers do agree that, to achieve the transfer values for any subject, it is important to teach the subject with that end in view. As Rosskopf says,[2]

To secure maximum transfer, in the sense of applying "an integrated knowledge [a whole principle] . . . to all tasks involving the same principle," teachers of mathematics must teach in such a way that demonstration exercises (or tasks) serve as examples of the application of that principle.

Teaching or directing learning in mathematics in such a way as to achieve the transfer values of the subject must therefore be recognized as a major objective. The problem of how to attain that objective gives rise at once to the following questions:

(1) What are those elements of mathematical training the transfer of which to other situations is desirable?

(2) By what methods of teaching can the transfer of these elements be fostered and promoted most effectively?

---

[1] Myron F. Rosskopf, Transfer of Training, "Twenty-first Yearbook" (Washington, D.C.: National Council of Teachers of Mathematics, 1953), pp. 203–227.

[2] *Ibid.*, p. 217.

The Objects of Transfer.   The first of the questions in the preceding paragraph can be answered with definiteness.   In the first place, it is desirable that all those elements of mathematical training which most people have occasion to *use* shall be taught in such a manner that they *can* be used whenever occasion demands.   This category includes such things as the fundamental combinations, skills, operations, and concepts of arithmetic; the laws and formulas involved in mensuration of the common geometrical figures; the interpretation of commonly used statistical conventions and devices; the construction and interpretation of straight-line, circle, and bar graphs; the ability to read pictographs intelligently; the fundamental meaning of a formula; the ability to evaluate formulas; in a word, practically all the understandings and abilities, other than those of formal algebra, which are commonly included in the mathematics of the junior high school.   These things are fairly specific and are needed by practically everybody.   Since they cannot be directly taught in all the specific situations to which they have potential application, it is desirable that the generality of their application be emphasized so that the student will not be at a loss when occasion requires their use in new situations.

In the second place, the fundamental concepts, formulas, and skills of elementary algebra are desirable objects of transfer.   Too often these are taught with specific reference only to the immediate algebraic situations in which they occur in the textbook and with little or no reference to the generality of their meanings or applications.   To this group of algebraic understandings and skills should be added the knowledge and understanding of certain of the more important facts and relationships that are developed in plane and solid geometry.   Of course, every proposition constitutes a link in the immediate chain of development, and to this extent the very consciousness of its relation to the preceding and subsequent parts of the development involves a measure of transfer.   Also, some of the propositions constitute extremely important generalizations which have wide application not only in the field of demonstrative geometry itself but also in subsequent mathematical courses and in other fields of study such as engineering and certain parts of the physical sciences.   Substantially the same observation may be made with reference to the concepts, skills, and relationships of numerical trigonometry.   Such important and pervasive generalizations as the Pythagorean theorem, the angle-sum relationship, the proportionality of line lengths in similar figures, the sine and cosine laws, the metric properties of circles, and various area formulas are cases in point.

The foregoing list of objects of transfer may be grouped for convenience into two categories, viz., things to know and understand and things to be able to do.   The detailed items which would be included under either of these lists are reasonably specific.

A second type of objects of transfer is represented by broader and more abstract concepts. These are well illustrated by the headings of Chapters IV to X of the 1940 Report of the Committee on Mathematics of the Progressive Education Association[1] which are as follows:

Formulation and solution	Operations
Data	Proof
Approximation	Symbolism
Function	

From reading these seven chapters it seems clear that the intention is to emphasize the proposition that the study of mathematics should aim to bring about a consciousness of the general nature of these concepts and their applicability to specific situations. In other words, the aim, expressed or implied, is to emphasize the importance of developing these broad and abstract concepts with a view to realizing their transfer possibilities.

Finally, there is a third object of transfer which has received much emphasis in writings on mathematical education but not so much in actual teaching. This is the acquisition of a mathematical manner of thinking. It is implied in the statement of the "disciplinary aims" listed in the Report of the National Committee on Mathematical Requirements: "the acquisition of mental habits and attitudes which will make [mathematical] training effective in the life of the individual."[2] It is precisely the thing all mathematics teachers hope for but which, for lack of a methodology, has usually been anticipated as a by-product of mathematical instruction rather than a definite outcome to be worked for through definite procedures.

Under this broad interpretation the desirable transfer values of mathematical study may be thought of as involving potentially such values as awareness of and insistence upon precision; facility and confidence in the use of fundamental skills; the establishment of self-reliance and the self-imposition of responsibility for information, procedure, and results; persistence in the face of difficulty; habitual insistence upon the precise use of language and upon clarity and precision in definition and statement; the ability to discriminate between a mere assertion and an inference; the habitual testing of inferences for consistency with known or given conditions; the ability to discriminate between sound and specious argument

[1] Commission on Secondary School Curriculum of the Progressive Education Association, "Mathematics in General Education," *Report of the Committee on the Function of Mathematics in General Education* (New York: Appleton-Century-Crofts, Inc., 1940).

[2] National Committee on Mathematical Requirements, "The Reorganization of Mathematics in Secondary Education" (Boston: Houghton Mifflin Company, 1923), p. 12.

and between valid inferences and unwarranted inferences; awareness of the nature of postulational reasoning, the arbitrary nature of hypothesis and definition, and the inevitable but contingent nature of conclusion; the ability to build a consistent argument; the ability to generalize relationships and apply generalizations; and the ability to eliminate emotional or prejudicial factors from an argument.

In particular, the ability to generalize meanings, symbols, relationships, and processes and apply such generalizations to new situations represents transfer of the most genuine and vital sort.   In fact, this is precisely what is implied by the expression "functional" mathematics, which has come into use to express the dominant idea for the courses in general mathematics as well as for the more formal sequential courses.   Indeed, this aspect of transfer would seem to lie at the very root of all really functional education.   It is implied in every application and every interpretation of any concept or circumstance; for correct interpretation must form the basis for any intelligent application, whether to a problem in physics or geometry or to a business or social situation.

How Shall We Teach to Secure Transfer?   As has already been pointed out, students of modern educational psychology are agreed that transfer is possible but is neither automatic nor inevitable in its desirable forms. Furthermore, the theories on how it takes place seem to be drawing somewhat closer together.   There seems to be some agreement now that meaning plays a most important role in the process and that the theories of generalization and the structuring of knowledge probably represent substantially the avenues through which positive transfer of higher mental functions takes place.   Generalization does not deny the importance of the identical or similar "elements" which formed the basis of one of the early theories of transfer.   Indeed it implies their necessity but denies their sufficiency to account for the phenomenon.   It says, in effect, that if a principle is to transfer to (or be applied intelligently in) a particular situation, the situation must of course contain elements or relationships analogous to those found in the principle, but this is not enough.   These similarities must not only exist but also *be recognized by the learner* before significant positive transfer can take place.   It is this act of recognition of similar elements which really constitutes transfer at the higher levels and which, indeed, alone characterizes all functional and relational thinking and sets it apart from mere specific identification and mechanical rule-of-thumb procedure.

The problem of teaching for transfer would seem to resolve itself, then, into the problem of teaching children not only to recognize similarities between new situations and other situations with which they are already familiar but also to form the habit of consciously being on the lookout for these similarities.   When confronted by a new and unfamiliar situation, the student must learn to ask himself, in effect, "Does this situation fit into the pattern of any other experiences or situations with which I am already familiar? What elements of similarity are there, and how can I use these elements that are familiar to me in interpreting this new situation and in bringing it under my control?"

A typical illustration of lack of transfer is found in the inability of many students to apply the principles and operations of algebra to problems in physics. The physics teachers usually complain that the students have not mastered the mathematical principles involved, but in most cases it is more likely that they simply fail to recognize in the concrete physical problem relationships which are perhaps quite familiar to them when seen in the abstract or symbolic mathematical setting in which they have been encountered previously. Innumerable examples illustrating this point could be given; they occur many times even within a particular branch of mathematics itself. Thus students who will readily factor $a^2 - b^2$ may fail to recognize such expressions as $t^2 - 36$ or $x^2 - 2xy + y^2 - 9z^4$ as being of precisely the same type and so may be unable to factor the latter expressions. Similarly, in connection with verbal problems, which bear the reputation of being the hardest part of elementary algebra, the difficulty is almost never in solving the equations to which the problems give rise but rather in translating the verbal problems into symbolic form. This is mainly due to failure to recognize the essential identity of the abstract and generalized symbols, formulas, and equations of formalized algebra with the concrete and specific conditions and relationships set forth in the verbal statements of the problems.

In some cases, of course, the similarities or identities in different situations are simple and obvious, and in such cases transfer is fairly well assured, especially among students of superior intelligence. In many cases, however, the similarities are obscured by other, more prominent elements and, in such cases, it is often necessary to make careful analyses in order to disclose them. Children will not learn to make these analyses unless they are systematically trained to do so. They need to be shown how to make them, and they must have much practice under carefully supervised conditions in order to master the technique. But even this is not enough. If this practice is to become really functional in their mathematical training, the students should become impressed with the advantage of *habitually* making this approach to any problem. They should form the habit of deliberately instituting a search for elements or relationships in the problem in hand which are similar to corresponding elements or relationships in other situations with which they have already had experience, whenever such similarities are not apparent at the outset. To the extent that such a procedure is consistently followed, the transfer of mathematical processes and techniques will be facilitated and this essentially mathematical mode of thought will become a really functional contributor to the effectiveness of rational thinking in general.

EXERCISES

1. What is meant by developmental teaching? Why should it be regarded as a phase or aspect of teaching rather than as a method of teaching?

2. Make a clear contrast between the fundamental aims of (1) developmental teaching, (2) teaching for assimilation and for permanence, and (3) teaching for transfer.

3. Explain why all the aspects or phases of teaching listed in exercise 2 are complementary and necessary parts of the whole process of learning mathematics.

4. Point out the effects that would result from neglecting any of the kinds of teaching listed in exercise 2. Illustrate from your own experience if you can.

5. In your opinion which of the phases of the teaching-learning process listed in exercise 2 is most neglected? Give reasons for your answer.

6. Discuss the function of the inventory and the preview. Why is each important?

7. Compare the function of laboratory or field work in mathematics with the function of laboratory work or field work in the sciences. What are the principal advantages of laboratory or field work in mathematics?

8. In view of its apparent advantages, why has laboratory work in mathematics not played a more prominent part in mathematical instruction?

9. In what grades or in what mathematical courses is laboratory work likely to be most effective? Give reasons for your answer.

10. Describe several activities or projects which could be carried on profitably as laboratory work in mathematics. For each one tell quite specifically what things (understandings or skills) you would expect the students to gain from carrying out the project or activity.

11. List some of the items of equipment and supplies which you think would be most helpful for laboratory work in mathematics.

12. In this chapter a distinction is made between demonstration activities and experimental activities in connection with laboratory work in mathematics. Explain the distinction and make clear the principal aim and method of each type of activity.

13. Consult several of the short articles in the section Devices for a Mathematics Laboratory in the *Mathematics Teacher* and report descriptions of some of these devices to the class.

14. Give some examples of items of equipment for laboratory-type work in mathematics which could be made by students at little expense. Make and demonstrate one such item of equipment, explaining what it will be used for and why you think it would be helpful.

15. Why is laboratory work in mathematics properly considered to be a form or part of developmental teaching? Does (or can) it contribute to the other phases or aspects of teaching? Discuss this, giving illustrations if you can.

16. When you were in junior or senior high school, did you in your classes in mathematics have any work that could be regarded as laboratory-type work? If so, describe some of the things you did.

17. Discuss at some length the need for careful planning of laboratory work in mathematics, especially the experimental type, to prevent it from becoming desultory and aimless.

18. Enumerate the advantages claimed for directed study as an integral part of the teaching-learning program in secondary school mathematics.

19. What are some of the more important dangers which must be guarded against in any program of directed study?

20. How do you account for the fact that superior students seem to profit less from directed study in mathematics than do slower students?

21. What might be done to make directed study more profitable to superior students?

22. In what specific ways do you think the list of suggestions on studying mathematics, given in this chapter, could be helpful to students? In what ways could it be helpful to teachers?

23. What is a valid function of drill, and why is drill necessary? Give some examples to illustrate or back up your statement and your argument.

24. In what way does the interpretation of drill as discussed in this book differ from that used by Sueltz in the article to which reference has been made? Which interpretation comes nearest to your idea of drill?

25. Enumerate some of the important principles of drill procedure. Illustrate each.

26. In what respects are drill and review, as discussed here, alike? In what respects do they differ?

27. What is a valid function of review? Why is review important?

28. Explain clearly and illustrate what is meant by "incidental" review as discussed in this chapter.

29. Show why incidental review needs to be supplemented by special reviews at various times.

30. What is meant by a maintenance program, as the term is used in this chapter? Explain how you would go about setting up such a program, e.g., in ninth-grade algebra.

31. Compare several recent textbooks in ninth-grade algebra with respect to the adequacy with which they provide for systematic maintenance work.

32. Examine several workbooks in arithmetic, algebra, geometry, or general mathematics and try to decide which would be the most helpful in the kind of maintenance program you would like to use.

33. Summarize the discussion of the question, How shall we teach for transfer?, bringing out the main points in the discussion.

34. Describe how the transfer of "a mathematical manner of thinking" was accomplished in the experiment reported in the "Thirteenth Yearbook of the National Council of Teachers of Mathematics."

35. Give illustrations, selected from algebra and geometry, of the fact that transfer takes place whenever a student recognizes a particular problem situation as being a special case of a previously generalized relationship and applies the generalized principle to the particular case in question.

36. Justify or criticize the assertion that the traditional difficulty which students have with verbal problems in arithmetic and algebra is mainly due to lack of transfer.

37. Describe some fundamental mathematical process or concept which you did not have well mastered when you finished high school. Try to account for this lack of mastery, and tell how proper teaching in high school might have remedied this deficiency.

BIBLIOGRAPHY

General

Anderson, W. E.: An Attempt through the Use of Experimental Techniques to Determine the Effect of Home Assignments upon Scholastic Success, *Journal of Educational Research*, **40** (1946), 141–143.

Archer, Allene: "How to Use Your Library in Mathematics" (Washington, D.C.: National Council of Teachers of Mathematics, 1958).

Association of Assistant Masters in Secondary Schools: "The Teaching of Mathematics" (London: Cambridge University Press, 1957), pp. 179–193.

Bartnick, Lawrence P.: "Designing the Mathematics Classroom" (Washington, D.C.: National Council of Teachers of Mathematics, 1956).

Baum, John D.: Mathematics, Self-taught, *American Mathematical Monthly*, **65** (1958), 701–705.

Bayles, E. E.: Purposes and Procedures in Teaching Junior High School Mathematics, *Bulletin of the Kansas Association of Teachers of Mathematics*, **22** (1948), 36–42.

Beatley, Ralph: Reason and Rule in Arithmetic and Algebra, *Mathematics Teacher*, **47** (1954), 234–244.

Berger, Emil J.: Using Concrete Materials as Teaching Aids, *Bulletin of the National Association of Secondary-School Principals*, **38** (1954), 127–138.

——— and Donovan A. Johnson: "A Guide to the Use and Procurement of Teaching Aids for Mathematics" (Washington, D.C.: National Council of Teachers of Mathematics, 1959).

Bernstein, Allen: A Study of Remedial Arithmetic Conducted with Ninth-grade Students, *School Science and Mathematics*, **56** (1956), 25–31, 429–437.

Betz, William: The Teaching and Learning Processes in Mathematics, *Mathematics Teacher*, **42** (1949), 49–55.

Birnbaum, S., and K. Ommidvar: The Group Method, *Mathematics Magazine*, **28** (1955), 277–279.

Bold, Benjamin: Developmental Mathematics in Secondary Schools, *Mathematics Teacher*, **48** (1955), 87–88.

Breslich, E. R.: "The Technique of Teaching Mathematics in Secondary Schools" (Chicago: University of Chicago Press, 1930), pp. 1–61, 87–115.

———: "Problems in Teaching Secondary School Mathematics" (Chicago: University of Chicago Press, 1933), pp. 82–106.

———: Teaching Mathematics as a System of Understandings, *Mathematics Teacher*, **42** (1949), 61–66.

Brown, Claude H.: "The Teaching of Secondary Mathematics" (New York: Harper & Brothers, 1953), pp. 289–322.

Brown, G. W.: Textbook Series and Learning Theory, *Mathematics Teacher*, **48** (1955), 162–164.

Buzetti, Beatrice: An Experiment in Teaching, *Mathematics Teacher*, **48** (1955), 360–365.

Christofferson, H. C.: Creative Teaching in Mathematics, *Bulletin of the National Association of Secondary-School Principals*, **38** (1954), 117–123.

Commonwealth of Pennsylvania, Department of Public Instruction: "A Course of Study in Mathematics for Secondary Schools," *Bulletin Number 360*, (Harrisburg, Pa.: Department of Public Instruction, 1952), pp. 40–44, 59–63.

Davis, David R.: "The Teaching of Mathematics" (Reading, Mass.: Addison-Wesley Publishing Company, 1951), pp. 27–65, 88–106.

Dodes, Irving Allen: The Science of Teaching Mathematics, *Mathematics Teacher*, **46** (1953), 157–166.

Douglass, Harl R.: Remedial Work in Junior High School Mathematics, *Mathematics Teacher*, **48** (1955), 344–346.

Dunfee, Maxine: Developing Understanding in Junior High School Arithmetic, *School Science and Mathematics*, **48** (1948), 734–740.

Eagle, Edwin: The Relationship of Certain Reading Abilities to Success in Mathematics, *Mathematics Teacher*, **41** (1948), 175–179.

Elder, Florence L.: Providing for the Student with High Mathematical Potential, *Mathematics Teacher*, **50** (1957), 502–506.

Fawcett, Harold: The Nature of Proof, "Thirteenth Yearbook" (Washington, D.C.: National Council of Teachers of Mathematics, 1938).

Fehr, Howard F.: The Role of Insight in the Learning of Mathematics, *Mathematics Teacher*, **47** (1954), 393–400.

———: Psychology of Learning in the Junior High School, *Mathematics Teacher*, **49** (1956), 235–240.

Georges, J. S.: Teaching Functional Thinking in Mathematics, *School Science and Mathematics*, **46** (1946), 733–748.

———: Learning to Solve Problems Intelligently, *School Science and Mathematics*, **57** (1957), 701–707.

Goins, William F., Jr.: Putting More Meaning in the Teaching of Measurement, *School Science and Mathematics*, **50** (1950), 745–749.

Griff, Ernest R.: The Comparative Effectiveness of One-level and Three-level Assignments in Plane Geometry, *Mathematics Teacher*, **50** (1957), 214–216.

Hamilton, Jean: Remedial Arithmetic in the Regular Classroom, *School Science and Mathematics*, **56** (1956), 197–209.

Hassler, J. O., and R. R. Smith: "The Teaching of Secondary Mathematics" (New York: The Macmillan Company, 1930), pp. 131–195.

Henderson, Kenneth B.: Anent the Discovery Method, *Mathematics Teacher*, **50** (1957), 287–291.

Hines, Vynce A.: Homework and Achievement in Plane Geometry, *Mathematics Teacher*, **50** (1957), 27–29.

Jackson, Humphrey: Techniques for Drill in Arithmetic Fundamentals, *Mathematics Teacher*, **49** (1956), 47–48.

Johnson, Donovan A.: A Multi-model Demonstration Board, *Mathematics Teacher*, **49** (1956), 121–122.

———: Attitudes in the Mathematics Classroom, *School Science and Mathematics*, **57** (1957), 113–120.

——— and C. E. Olander: "How to Use Your Bulletin Board" (Washington, D.C.: National Council of Teachers of Mathematics, 1958).

———, Dirk Ten Brink, and Lauren Woodby: "How to Use Field Trips in Mathematics" (Washington, D.C.: National Council of Teachers of Mathematics, 1958).

Karstens, Harry: Effective Guidance in Problem Solving, *Mathematics Teacher*, **39** (1946), 172–175.

Kidd, Kenneth P.: Improving the Learning of Mathematics, *Mathematics Teacher*, **47** (1954), 393–400.

Kimball, Roland B.: Improvement of Science and Mathematics Instruction in New Hampshire, *School Science and Mathematics*, **57** (1957), 529–535.

Kinney, Lucien Blair, and C. Richard Purdy: "Teaching Mathematics in the Secondary School" (New York: Rinehart & Company, Inc., 1952), pp. 41–58.

Klein, Rose: Self-directed Homework, *Mathematics Teacher*, **44** (1951), 463–465.

Lankford, Francis G., Jr.: Helping Pupils to Make Discoveries in Mathematics, *Mathematics Teacher*, **48** (1955), 45–47.

Lazar, Nathan: A Technique for Giving Meaning to Elementary Mathematical Operations, *Mathematics Teacher*, **42** (1949), 67–68.

Lee, William: Provision for Individual Differences in High School Mathematics Courses, *Mathematics Teacher*, **40** (1947), 294–297.

Lewis, Eunice: The Pupil Discovers Algebra, *Mathematics Teacher*, **47** (1954), 81–85.

———: The Role of Sensory Materials in Meaningful Learning, *Mathematics Teacher*, **49** (1956), 274–277.

Lloyd, Daniel B.: The Laboratory Method in Mathematics Education, "Twenty-second Yearbook" (Washington, D.C.: National Council of Teachers of Mathematics, 1954), pp. 210–222.

Mallory, Virgil S.: Meaning in the Junior High School, *Mathematics Teacher*, **41** (1948), 251–259.

Mehl, William G.: Novel Drill Material for Signed Numbers, *Mathematics Teacher*, **52** (1959), 247–249.

Menger, Karl: Why Johnny Hates Math, *Mathematics Teacher*, **49** (1956), 578–584.

Minnick, J. H.: "Teaching Mathematics in the Secondary Schools" (Englewood Cliffs, N.J.: Prentice-Hall, Inc., 1939), pp. 16–33.

Morton, R. L.: The Review *versus* the Telescoped Reteaching of the Work of the Preceding Grades, *Mathematics Teacher*, **39** (1946), 225–228.

Mossman, Edith L.: What Shall It Be: Mechanical Drill or Development in Under-standing All the "Whys"? *Mathematics Teacher*, **38** (1945), 103–107.

Norton, Monte S.: Enrichment as Provision for the Gifted in Mathematics, *School Science and Mathematics*, **57** (1957), 339–345.

Olander, Clarence E.: The Use of a Readiness Test in Teaching a Unit on Signed Numbers, *School Science and Mathematics*, **57** (1957), 131–138.

Payne, Joseph N.: Teaching Mathematics to Bright Pupils, *University of Michigan School of Education Bulletin*, **29** (1958) pp. 97–106.

————: Self-instructive Enrichment Topics for Bright Pupils in High School Algebra, *Mathematics Teacher*, **51** (1958), 113–117.

Reeve, William David: The Play of Imagination in Mathematics, *School Science and Mathematics*, **54** (1954), 463–470.

————: "Mathematics for the Secondary School" (New York: Henry Holt and Company, Inc., 1954), pp. 59–62, 130–135, 140–149, 364–365.

Rosskopf, Myron F.: Transfer of Training, "Twenty-first Yearbook" (Washington, D.C.: National Council of Teachers of Mathematics, 1953), pp. 205–227.

Sawyer, W. W.: The Concrete Basis for the Abstract, *Mathematics Teacher*, **52** (1959), 272–277.

Schaaf, Oscar: Student Discovery of Algebraic Principles as a Means of Developing Ability to Generalize, *Mathematics Teacher*, **48** (1955), 324–327.

Schaaf, William L.: Psychology of Learning Mathematics [bibliography], *Mathematics Teacher*, **45** (1952), 60–63.

Schiff, Herbert J.: Let Them Measure, *School Science and Mathematics*, **57** (1957), 291–292.

Schmidt, Edward H.: "Ten Teaching Aids You Can Make for the Mathematics Classroom" (Baltimore: Schmidt Teaching Aids, 1957).

Schorling, Raleigh: "The Teaching of Mathematics" (Ann Arbor, Mich.: The Ann Arbor Press, 1936), pp. 29–34, 77–80, 123–132.

Schultz, Margaret, and M. M. Ohlsen: A Comparison of Traditional Teaching and Personalized Teaching in Ninth Grade Algebra, *Mathematics Teacher*, **42** (1949), 91–96.

Schultze, Arthur: "The Teaching of Mathematics in Secondary Schools" (New York: The Macmillan Company, 1927), pp. 30–49.

Schutter, Charles H.: Improving the Quality of Instruction in Mathematics, *School Science and Mathematics*, **47** (1947), 404–408.

Secondary School Curriculum Committee of the National Council of Teachers of Mathematics, Report of: The Secondary Mathematics Curriculum, *Mathematics Teacher*, **52** (1959), 389–417.

Sims, Weldon, and Albert Oliver: The Laboratory Approach to Mathematics, *School Science and Mathematics*, **50** (1950), 621–627.

Sister Mary Corona: Seminars—An Integrating Force in a Program of Concentration, *Mathematics Teacher*, **48** (1955), 209–213.

Skolnik, David: Let's Forget Mental Transfer, *Mathematics Teacher*, **45** (1952), 161–167.

Smith, D. E., and W. D. Reeve: "The Teaching of Junior High School Mathematics" (Boston: Ginn & Company, 1927), pp. 276–300.

Snader, Daniel W.: A Program for Individualizing Instruction in Mathematics, *Mathematics Teacher*, **38** (1945), 116–119.

Stein, Harry L.: How to Make Arithmetic Meaningful in the Junior High School, *School Science and Mathematics*, **53** (1953), 680–684.

Sueltz, Ben A.: Drill—Practice—Recurring Experience, "Twenty-first Yearbook" (Washington, D.C.: National Council of Teachers of Mathematics, 1953), pp. 192–201.

Swain, Henry: "How to Study Mathematics" (Washington, D.C.: National Council of Teachers of Mathematics, 1956).

Syer, Henry W., and Peter J. Ingeneri: Multi-sensory Aids in Mathematics, *School Science and Mathematics*, **49** (1949), 134–140.

"Teaching Rapid and Slow Learners in High Schools," (U.S. Office of Education Bulletin 5, 1954) pp. 42–49.

Totten, W. Fred: Words as a Basic Factor in Understanding Algebra, *School Science and Mathematics*, **56** (1956), 230–233.

Vance, E. P., Julius H. Hlavaty, Richard S. Pieters, and Leroy Sachs: "Program Provisions for the Mathematically Gifted Student in the Secondary School" (Washington, D.C.: National Council of Teachers of Mathematics, 1957).

Van Engen, Henry: The Child's Introduction to Arithmetic Reasoning, *School Science and Mathematics*, **55** (1955), 358–363.

————: Multitrack Programs, *Mathematics Teacher*, **52** (1959), 205–206.

Vaughn, William D.: Some Drill Techniques for Arithmetic, *Mathematics Teacher*, **50** (1957), 436–437.

Vollmar, Robert, and Philip Peak: "How to Use Films and Filmstrips in Mathematics Classes (Washington, D.C.: National Council of Teachers of Mathematics, 1958).

Willerding, Margaret E.: The Challenge of Practical Applications, *School Science and Mathematics*, **57** (1957), 437–446.

Wirszup, Izaak: Some Remarks on Enrichment, *Mathematics Teacher*, **49** (1956), 519–527.

Selected References on Laboratory Work

Berger, Emil J.: Using Concrete Materials as Teaching Aids, *Bulletin of the National Association of Secondary-School Principals*, **38** (1954), 127–138.

———— (Editor): Devices for a Mathematics Laboratory, *Mathematics Teacher*. (A regular department that contains many interesting ideas, illustrations of devices, and suggestions for laboratory work in mathematics.)

Commonwealth of Pennsylvania, Department of Public Instruction: "A Course of Study in Mathematics," *Bulletin* 360 (Harrisburg, Pa.: Department of Public Instruction, 1952), pp. 45–49.

Johnson, Donovan A.: A Design for a Modern Mathematics Classroom, *Bulletin of the National Association of Secondary-School Principals*, **38** (1954), 151–159.

Kinney, Lucien Blair, and C. Richard Purdy: "Teaching Mathematics in the Secondary School" (New York: Rinehart & Company, Inc., 1952), pp. 241–249, 298–303.

National Council of Teachers of Mathematics: "A Source Book of Mathematical Applications," *Seventeenth Yearbook* (Washington, D.C.: National Council of Teachers of Mathematics, 1942).   (Many of the applications in this book contain illustrations of or suggestions for physical devices which could be used in laboratory or field work to illustrate various mathematical facts, concepts, relations, and theorems.)

———: "Multi-sensory Aids in the Teaching of Mathematics," *Eighteenth Yearbook* (Washington, D.C.: National Council of Teachers of Mathematics, 1945).   (This entire book has bearing on laboratory work in mathematics.   Divisions of the book, each containing two or more articles, are as follows: Multi-sensory Aids; Drawing and Design; Demonstrations and Exhibits; Models and Devices; Instruments and Tools; Materials for the Construction of Models; History of Models and Devices; Slides, Films, Three-dimensional Projection and Equipment; Appendix (containing a long bibliography of early writings on mathematics laboratory work and equipment).   Two of the articles may be especially noted here: Grace R. Carroll, A Mathematics Classroom Becomes a Laboratory, pp. 16–29; Miles C. Hartley, A Laboratory Approach to Solid Geometry, pp. 42–63.)

———: "The Learning of Mathematics: Its Theory and Practice," *Twenty-first Yearbook* (Washington, D.C.: The National Council of Teachers of Mathematics, 1953).   (The following article in this book contains excellent suggestions for laboratory work and the use of multi-sensory aids in learning mathematics: Henry W. Syer, Sensory Learning Applied to Mathematics, pp. 99–155.)

———: "Emerging Practices in Mathematics Education," *Twenty-second Yearbook* (Washington, D.C.: The National Council of Teachers of Mathematics, 1954). (In this yearbook the following articles have special bearing on laboratory work in mathematics: Allene Archer, Aids for Junior High Mathematics, pp. 134–142; Emil J. Berger, Principles Guiding the Use of Teacher- and Pupil-made Learning Aids, pp. 158–172; Frances M. Burns, Illustrative Aids for the Senior High School, pp. 142–151; Daniel B. Lloyd, The Laboratory Method in Mathematics Education, pp. 210–222; Sheldon S. Myers, Laboratory Techniques with Specific Practices, pp. 102–108; Lauren G. Woodby, Suggestions for Making Slides, pp. 151–158.)

Reeve, William David: "Mathematics for the Secondary School" (New York: Henry Holt and Company, Inc., 1954), pp. 504–508.

Schaaf, William L. (Editor): Laboratory Mathematics, *Mathematics Teacher*, **44** (1951), 422–425, 428.   (An excellent bibliography of periodical references bearing on laboratory work in mathematics that is classified by subjects and is a rich source of help.)

Shuster, Carl N., and Fred L. Bedford: "Field Work in Mathematics" (New York: American Book Company, 1935).   (Now distributed by Yoder Instruments, East Palestine, Ohio.)

Study Suggestions

Arnold, W. C.: How to Study Mathematics, *American Mathematical Monthly*, **47** (1940), 704–707.

Breslich, E. R.: "The Technique of Teaching Mathematics in Secondary Schools" (Chicago: University of Chicago Press, 1930) pp. 87–115.

———: "Administration of Mathematics in Secondary Schools" (Chicago: University of Chicago Press, 1933), pp. 349–357.

Dadourian, D. A.: "How to Study—How to Solve" (Reading, Mass.: Addison-Wesley Publishing Company, 1949).

Hendrick, Ethel M.: How to Study Geometry, *School Science and Mathematics*, **30** (1930), 1068–1072.

Pólya, G.: "How to Solve It" (Princeton, N.J.: Princeton University Press, 1945).

Reese, Esther M.: How to Study Algebra, *School Science and Mathematics*, **32** (1932), 171–179.

Reeve, W. D.: "Mathematics for the Secondary School" (New York: Henry Holt and Company, Inc., 1954), pp. 141–142.

Swain, Henry: "How to Study Mathematics" (Washington, D.C.: National Council of Teachers of Mathematics, 1956).

Walters, Margaret E.: How to Study Arithmetic, *School Science and Mathematics*, **34** (1934), 848–852.

7

PLANNING FOR EFFECTIVE TEACHING
AND LEARNING

No responsible person goes into a serious undertaking without having pretty clearly in mind what it is that he wants to accomplish. If the undertaking is to extend over any considerable but limited period of time, the person responsible for it sets up a schedule of stages in which successive parts or aspects of the undertaking are to be accomplished. Such an over-all schedule is necessary in order to keep the progress of the undertaking on a reasonable and realistic time basis, prevent lagging and waste, and ensure that the necessary activities are carried on in appropriate stages or at appropriate times. Within each of the separate stages it will be necessary to give careful definition and organization and timing to the more detailed component activities required for accomplishing the objectives set up for that stage. Whether the undertaking be the construction of a skyscraper, the manufacture of automobiles or pharmaceuticals, or the production of a newspaper, its progress toward its goal can be efficient only to the degree that it is carefully and intelligently planned, in both its long-range aspects and its details.

So it is with the undertaking with which we are specially concerned here: the teaching of mathematics. If it is to realize its objectives, it needs to be well planned, both in its broad considerations and in respect to the direct classroom activities. The teacher should be concerned with all phases of planning, but especially with those which have to do with the direct classroom activities in the courses which he is to teach. No part of the teacher's job is more important than this, because it is what gives direction to all the activities of teaching and learning. Without careful planning the goals of instruction can be attained, if at all, only by some fortuitous combination of circumstances. Of course, even wise planning may not wholly assure the success of an undertaking, but it can measurably increase the likelihood of success.

It is probably true that many teachers of mathematics give too little attention to planning their work. In many cases they are not to blame for this. The heavy instructional loads which most teachers carry, together with the various extracurricular responsibilities which they are expected to assume, leave them with little time for reflective consideration of their work.   It is nevertheless unfortunate that any circumstances should prevent them from having enough time to plan their work with care.   To be able to capitalize on situations as they arise is an inestimable asset to any teacher, and experienced teachers often become exceedingly skillful at it, but it is seldom wise even for an experienced teacher to trust entirely to the inspiration of the moment.   Careful planning is the only insurance which teachers can provide against oversights, lost opportunities, wasted time, and inefficiency in their work.

The Curriculum in Mathematics as a Stage of Planning.   Actually, planning for the mathematical education of the students begins with the planning of the curriculum.   Here decisions are made, at least with respect to the courses which are to be offered, and here policies are established for the counseling and guidance of students with respect to the courses offered. This is generally considered to be an administrative function.   Indeed, administrative considerations sometimes must predominate in determining what courses can be offered.   This is not a desirable situation, but there are circumstances, especially in very small schools, in which it seems to be inevitable.

But even under such circumstances the mathematics teachers should have a voice in the decisions which are reached at this stage of planning. They should be given the privilege and responsibility of making recommendations, and weight should be given to their recommendations. Certainly this would be true in the larger schools, where restrictions on the kinds of courses that can be offered are not so tight as they may be in the very small schools.   By the same token, the mathematics teachers should look upon this not only as an opportunity but as a responsibility which they cannot lightly disregard.   They, better than anyone else, can be aware of the educational implications of various programs of mathematics courses, and their well-considered judgments can be influential in the establishment of sound mathematical programs in the schools.

Provision for Individual Differences as a Stage in Planning.   It is axiomatic that, if instruction is to be really effective, it must reach the individual students and promote their learning as individuals, and individuals differ greatly in their interests and abilities.   The problem of adapting instruction to individual differences has existed whenever and wherever the group receiving instruction has consisted of more than one student, but since early in this century it has occupied a much more prominent place in educational thought than it ever occupied before.   There are several reasons for this, the most important one being that the problem itself has become much more acute and pressing than it was before.   The unprecedented and bewildering growth of the secondary school has been accompanied by a decline in the average intellectual ability of the student population while the spread of the range of abilities has been accentuated. As a result, the always questionable practice of giving identical instruction to all students in an unselected group has become more questionable than ever.   If the instruction for the group is geared to a level which will challenge the abilities of the better students, then students of mediocre ability will miss much of it and will tend to lose interest or will resort to memorizing, while the inferior students will soon fall hopelessly behind and become discouraged.   On the other hand, if the instruction is adapted to the limited abilities of the slow students, then the superior students will soon lose interest because the work will not challenge their best efforts.   It may be noted parenthetically at this point that the importance of really challenging the best efforts of the best students is now receiving belated recognition.   In either case the situation not only will result in inefficient instruction but may easily become a fertile breeding ground for discontent, loss of interest, and possible disciplinary difficulties.

School administrators as well as teachers have now become keenly aware of this problem and its implications.   It is now recognized that the only way of meeting this educational dilemma efficiently is through differentiation of instruction and requirements, to provide, in some measure at least, learning activities appropriate to the capacities of the students.   Recent courses of study, professional books and articles, and the prefaces of nearly all recent textbooks in secondary mathematics bear witness to the urgency of the problem and the effort which is being put forth to provide suitably differentiated materials and methods of instruction, to the end that profitable work may be provided for all students.

Impressive evidence of the widespread concern over this matter can be found in the space and attention given to it in a recent yearbook of the National Council of Teachers of Mathematics.[1]   Here are assembled fifteen articles on the subject of differentiated courses and curriculums in mathematics.   Twelve of these articles describe courses or programs of courses specially designed from one standpoint or another for the special groups or categories of students they are to serve.   The remaining three articles are concerned with the guidance of students with respect to their selection of courses from among those available.   The courses and curriculums described exhibit uniformity of general purpose but not of detail.   The variety of criteria employed in planning these courses is suggested by the Table of Contents of Part One of this yearbook.   The fifteen articles, with indication of the states from which they are reported, are grouped under five main classifications as follows:

[1] Emerging Practices in Mathematics Education, "Twenty-second Yearbook" (Washington, D.C.: National Council of Teachers of Mathematics, 1954), pp. 1–99.

1. Providing a Differentiated Curriculum through a New Organization of Content
   a. An Emerging Mathematics Curriculum (Florida)
   b. A Curriculum Development to Capitalize on the Interrelationships of the Many Areas of Mathematics (California)
   c. The Development of a Differentiated Curriculum (California)
   d. Mathematics for the Consumer (Washington, D.C.)
2. Providing Differentiated Curriculums in Schools Where Homogeneous Grouping is Feasible
   a. A Differentiated Curriculum for Homogeneous Groups (Illinois)
   b. Using Homogeneous Grouping to Lead Pupils to Their Own Highest Levels of Achievement (Wisconsin)
   c. A Mathematics Program for Grade XII (New Hampshire)
3. Providing Differentiated Curriculums in Schools Where Homogeneous Grouping is Not Feasible
   a. Adjusting Work within the Class to the Varying Abilities of its Members (Ohio)
   b. Methods Used to Provide Differentiated Curriculums within the Classroom (New York)
   c. In Small High Schools, Many Purposes—Many Curriculums (Pennsylvania)
4. Differentiated Curriculums Resulting from Pupil, Parent, Teacher, and Community Planning
   a. Geometry Developed through Pupil-Teacher Planning (Illinois)
   b. Working Together in Developing the Mathematics Curriculum (Kansas)
5. Guidance for the Optimum Use of Differentiated Curriculums
   a. The Importance of Early Guidance at the Junior High School Level (Michigan)
   b. Guidance in the Mathematics Program (California)
   c. The Mathematics Teacher's Part in Effective Guidance for Optimum Use of Differentiated Curriculums (Massachusetts)

These classifications and titles clearly indicate a wide diversity of motivations and approaches to the problem, but a common broad purpose is evident throughout.   This attempt to provide for individual differences among students through appropriately differentiated courses represents a phase of planning.   Indeed, it touches all stages of planning.   It finds its broadest manifestation in the long-range considerations that guide curriculum planning.   In particular, the double-track or multiple-track plan which was discussed in Chap. 4 represents simply a long-range plan to provide appropriate kinds of courses for students of different abilities.

Apart from the matter of separate and different courses per se, this attempt to provide for individual differences has taken a number of forms, prominent among which may be mentioned ability grouping or homogeneous grouping, differentiated assignments, honors courses, directed study, and even individual instruction.   The latter plan, although theoretically desirable, if viewed solely from the instructional standpoint, largely precludes the valuable social element which can be had only in group instruction.   It is subject to such obvious practical limitations that it can never become widely used as a normal procedure in our secondary schools.   The other plans, however, are all more or less adaptable to school conditions as they exist.

Ability Grouping.   The plan which most people have come to associate most readily with provision for individual differences is the arrangement generally called "homogeneous grouping" or "ability grouping." As the name implies, it consists essentially of grouping the students in such a way that disparities in the abilities or interests within a given group will be reduced as far as possible.   The great objection to the traditional miscellaneous grouping has been that instruction inevitably becomes geared to some one level of ability, to the consequent disadvantage of all students whose capacities are either above or below that particular level.   The plan of ability grouping, while it would by no means entirely eliminate individual differences within any group, would materially reduce the range of abilities within each group and thus tend to reduce the seriousness of the problem.   To quote Stokes:[1]

Grouping of students with superior mental ability into special schools and special classes has been tried in a number of school systems.   Although there has been little research reported, it is generally felt that this practice has many advantages.   When a child is placed in a group of equally capable children, he is stimulated to use his intellectual powers to a fuller extent because standards of achievement are higher.   He is more likely to develop better and more efficient work habits and is less likely to develop tendencies toward laziness and misuse of time.

It must be acknowledged, however, that ability grouping is not an end in itself, but only a means by which the work of the teacher is simplified to the extent that differentiation of instruction to meet the needs of all pupils is possible since there is less variability in the group.   In a homogeneous group of gifted students much more material can be covered, less time can be spent in drill, and a larger number and variety of enriching learning experiences which are so necessary to the superior child can be made available.

Neither teachers nor school officials are entirely agreed on the effectiveness or desirability of ability grouping.   It has sometimes been charged that the plan is undemocratic and that its psychological effect upon the students is not a wholesome one.   In particular, some individuals feel that it attaches a stigma to some of the classes and accentuates a feeling of inferiority on the part of the weaker students.   Others, however, deny this.   They assert that the plan is more democratic than unselected

[1] William Glenn Stokes, Enrichment for Superior Ninth Grade Algebra Students, unpublished doctoral dissertation (Nashville, Tenn.: George Peabody College for Teachers, 1957), p. 7.

grouping in that it facilitates the adjustment of each student's work so that incentive will be increased and students will be enabled to work at their own optimum rates and thereby be encouraged to put forth their best efforts.

This debate is not new.   Individual cases could be cited in support of either of these points of view, and there is undoubtedly some validity to the arguments on both sides of the question.   We do know that homogeneous grouping has been used for a number of years with apparent success in many of the larger cities, and there is reason to believe that its acceptance as a sound principle is increasing rather than decreasing. This would seem to reinforce the belief that its advantages probably outweigh any disadvantages it may have.   The most serious administrative limitation is that the plan is of no use to the very small schools, since it can be used only in schools where there are enough students to justify having two or more class sections in the same grade or the same subject.

There have been numerous adaptations of the plan, but the basic principles and *modus operandi* are well defined.   The principal variants consist of its use in the following ways:

1. Providing different courses for students who are in the same grade but who differ widely in mathematical interests and potential.

2. Providing different sections of the same course so that, of the students who will take that course, those having differing degrees of mathematical potential may be grouped in separate sections.

Until comparatively recent years the differentiation of students for homogeneous grouping was based mainly on the results of intelligence tests.   More recently it has come to be generally felt that, while such tests are important, they alone are not a wholly satisfactory criterion. Increasing reliance is being placed upon supplementing these indexes of general intelligence by other considerations such as the expressed desires of the students and their parents, prognostic tests, marks in previous courses in mathematics, reading ability, and teachers' estimates of probable success in subsequent mathematics courses.

Certainly the employment of any pattern of homogeneous grouping would represent a phase of planning and would require a great deal of careful thought.   The actual subject matter of each course or of each section of a course would have to be considered and defined with great care.   Specific objectives and units of study would have to be agreed upon and set up.   Time allotments would have to be established.   The criteria that would govern the placement of students in various courses or sections would have to be worked out.   Thus preplanning is importantly involved here all along the line, with respect to policy and administrative procedures as well as to the objectives and details of the various courses or sections.

Differentiated Assignments. The foregoing discussion has centered on long-range or broad-scale plans for providing appropriate learning activities for students of varying interests and abilities. The devices of differentiated curriculums and homogeneous grouping represent means through which, at least in part, the attainment of this objective may be facilitated. But even the most sanguine advocates of these measures will readily concede that they represent only a first stage of progress. Even with a multiple-track program of different courses and with a number of homogeneous sections within a given course, there will still exist substantial differences among the students within any given class or section. Here again, then, we are faced, in a sense, with the same problem as before. Even if the range of abilities has been somewhat diminished, the problem itself is actually accentuated. At this stage it cannot be solved by administrative planning; it is something that has to be both planned and handled by each individual teacher. He cannot delegate sections of the class or parts of the work to his assistants, because normally he will have no assistants. Whatever is to be done he must do himself. Thus if he is to give more than casual or incidental attention to the problem, he will have to do a good deal of careful planning as well as a good deal of hard work.

One method of adapting instruction to individual capacities and interests within a class is the use of differentiated assignments for students whose abilities and rates of work are not alike. This plan has met with favor because it can be used even in schools which are too small to permit homogeneous grouping. While it tends to complicate the work of the teacher, it has much to commend it from the standpoint of instructional effectiveness.

Methods of providing differentiated assignments have taken a number of forms and variations. In classes that are not too large, the differentiation can sometimes be made almost on an individual basis, perhaps with little organization and with the assignments planned through liaison between each individual student and the teacher. The theoretical advantages of such a method are clear. Unfortunately, in most cases it has practical limitations which are also manifest, and which in effect preclude its general use in large classes. Other methods are needed in such cases, and they must be methods that can be more highly organized so that the work assigned can be given in different categories. Two such methods which are in common use may be called the *contract* type of assignment and the *multiple-level* type of assignment. These have certain similarities but they should not be regarded as being identical.

The Contract Type of Assignment. Under the contract type of assignment, each unit of work is organized in such a way that the accomplishment required for a bare passing grade is specified as the minimum contract which all students are required to execute. Other contracts calling for additional work or work of a more difficult nature are set up as requirements for successively higher marks. As commonly set up, each successive contract presumes or specifies that the requirements for all the lower-level contracts be satisfied, and that certain additional requirements also be met. These additional requirements may be qualitative or quantitative or some combination of both. The following illustration represents a set of contracts that was used by one teacher to cover a marking period (in this case, the second month in the second semester in a seventh-grade mathematics class).

D Contract

1. Be able to find the area of any square, rectangle, parallelogram or triangle, when dimensions are given.
2. Hand in at least half as many problems as the average of the class.
3. Take all required tests.
4. Have an average rating of at least 5 on your workbook.
5. Be able to find the volume of any cube or rectangular prism when the dimensions are given.
6. Be able to estimate the area of an irregularly shaped figure by using graph paper.
7. Have a good attitude and be pleasant and industrious.
8. Meet any other requirements that may be added and posted here.

C Contract

All the D Contract plus the following:
9. Be able to find the area of any trapezoid, dimensions being given.
10. Be able to find the perimeter and area of any circle if the radius or diameter is known.
11. Solve problems based on areas and volumes of figures mentioned above.
12. Hand in at least four-fifths as many problems as the average of the class.
13. Have an average rating of at least 6 on your workbook.

B Contract

All the C Contract plus the following:
14. Be able to explain how we got the formulas for the areas of the triangle, parallelogram, and trapezoid.
15. Hand in more problems than the average of the class.
16. Have an average rating of at least 7 on your workbook.
17. Hand in at least one acceptable out-of-class project.

A Contract

All the B Contract plus the following:
18. Hand in 20 per cent more problems than the average of the class.
19. Have an average rating of at least 8 on your workbook.

20. Make an outline of notes covering the important things in the month's work and be prepared to give a 5-minute review discussion of this, using only the notes as your guide.

21. Take a private 10-minute oral examination.

22. Hand in at least three acceptable out-of-class projects.

The contract plan is exceedingly definite in specifying the requirements for each grade or mark, so that students can know at any time about where they stand. It has two disadvantages, however. One of these is that superior students are generally required to execute all the details of the minimum contract before passing on to the higher ones, and often much of the work of the minimum contract is rather simple and uninteresting routine which fails to interest or challenge the more capable students. The other disadvantage is that the preparation of the various contracts in suitable form, and the large amount of record keeping which is necessary, place a severe burden of extra work on the teacher. Unless these details are carefully planned and systematically carried out, this might even become so burdensome as to impair his effectiveness in the actual instructional work. This problem becomes particularly acute when facilities for duplicating assignment sheets and other instructional materials are inadequate.

The Multiple-level Type of Assignment. The contract plan is but one method of providing for individual differences within a class. Another method which is somewhat less stereotyped, but which is probably used more widely, is the multiple-level type of assignment. This approach emphasizes quality and caliber of achievement rather than mere quantity. Its aim is not so much to provide detailed specifications of requirements for the various marks as it is to provide assignments appropriate in nature and difficulty to the abilities of the individual students. This method of differentiation usually provides assignments at two and sometimes three levels of ability. In most cases it is easier to administer than the contract plan, and it avoids some of the objections to that plan. There is much to be said in favor of this method of differentiating assignments, and most of the recent textbooks in secondary school mathematics recognize its potential value. It is frequently mentioned in the prefaces of textbooks, and many of the current textbooks make some provision for facilitating this type of differentiation, in respect both to large units or chapters and to subtopics within units or chapters. Usually this is done through the sets of exercises provided. Such terms as "optional problems," "starred problems," "investigation problems," and "honor problems" are commonly found in connection with lists of exercises, while on a larger scale, chapter or unit summaries and reviews are often arranged under such headings as "easy exercises," "harder exercises," and "honor work."

Assignments differentiated on this basis can be used equally well whether they are made on a day-to-day basis or on a chapter or unit basis. The following description of a case in which this method was used in a plane geometry class presents a good illustration of how it may be employed to advantage.

A class in plane geometry was to spend between two and three weeks on the study of a unit dealing with certain properties of circles. In the class of about twenty-five students there were five who had demonstrated marked superiority and interest in geometry and who liked to investigate their problems and theorems independently, as if they were puzzles to be solved. For this particular unit the teacher proposed to these five students that they work out the essential parts of the unit entirely independently, without any help from the teacher, the textbook, or each other. They were told that, if they wished to do this, they could copy out the statements of all the theorems (more than a dozen) in the unit, but must then make no further reference to their books. Moreover, they were told that, if they decided to take this assignment, they need not even attend the class meetings, but could work during those periods in the study hall. At the end of the time set for the study of the unit they would be asked to turn in complete written proofs for as many of the theorems as they could manage to develop. They were not compelled to take this assignment, but they were given a choice of taking it or doing the work in the usual manner along with the rest of the class.

Without exception the five elected the plan for independent work. During the two and a half weeks that the class spent on the unit, these five students worked individually and independently at devising proofs for the theorems included in their assignment, without any help, even from the textbook. At the end of the time they turned in their written work. Study of these papers revealed that three of them had succeeded in developing satisfactory proofs for all the theorems. A fourth had made a mistake in reasoning on one theorem, and a fifth had mistakes in two theorems. At least two of these five students had formulated correct statements of a generalized theorem which would include some of the given theorems as special cases. The teacher reported that these students took pride in their work, and he felt the assignment had provided motivation of the best kind for them. In his opinion it had not only increased their interest in developing the necessary proofs but had also served to keep their efforts pitched to the limits of their high abilities.

Other Plans of Providing for Individual Differences. An interesting variant is reported by Stokes,[1] who provided 25 units of enrichment material for superior students in ninth-grade algebra to several classes in different schools. These units were used simply to supplement the

[1] *Ibid.*

regular work of the classes throughout the year.   No plan of homogeneous grouping was employed, but the enrichment units were given only to the superior students.   These students attended the classes only four days a week.   On the fifth day they spent the time in the library working on the enrichment units.   The report[1] says, in part:

In this experiment a group of superior students in mathematics, who were provided with enrichment material and an opportunity to work on the material without teacher supervision, was compared with another group of superior students in mathematics who were not provided with the enrichment material. Students in both groups were enrolled in ninth-grade algebra classes which met five fifty-minute periods per week for a school year of nine months.

The summary of the results of this study suggests that use of the enrichment units probably contributed materially toward attainment of the objectives for which they were designed and at the same time did not interfere with mastery of the basic material of the course.   On the basis of certain test scores it is pointed out that the group of superior students using the enrichment units showed better achievement in algebra than the group of superior students who did not have the enrichment units. It is also pointed out that even the nonsuperior students showed higher achievement in algebra in the classes where the superior students were given enrichment units than the nonsuperior students did in classes where the enrichment units were not used.   Observations of the work of the classes and discussions with participating students and teachers tended to support the belief that this kind of special provision for superior students is administratively feasible and that it can operate to the advantage of all the students.[2]

Somewhat allied to the plans mentioned above, but differing from them in certain respects, is the proposal for so-called honors courses.   The underlying idea of the honors course is to relieve particularly brilliant students of unnecessary tedium and waste of time and at the same time challenge their best mathematical efforts.   It recognizes the fact that there are occasional students for whom much of the normal work of the class is easy to the point of being boresome, and it proposes to afford the opportunity for such students to direct their efforts toward special problems which lie definitely beyond the normal scope of the course. In other words, it proposes to offer the brilliant student the opportunity for original and largely independent study of special mathematical topics not contemplated for general class study.   Honors courses have not come into very general use in high school, probably because they are off the beaten track and involve extra work in individual supervision and

[1] *Ibid.*, p. 45.
[2] *Ibid.*, p. 86.

planning on the part of the teacher. As a means for capitalizing the abilities of the very superior students, however, the plan has much to commend it. When it has been given a fair trial, it has more than justified itself in the mathematical growth and the stimulation of interest which have resulted.[1]

Levels of Planning. The considerations which need to be taken into account in endeavoring to make mathematical instruction yield its best dividends are varied in character. The long-range or over-all objectives of the curriculum and of each course call for long-range planning which may often involve cooperative efforts of the administrative, supervisory, and instructional staffs. In military parlance this would probably be called strategic planning. It would be primarily concerned with courses and administrative policies and measures, and it would consider units or major sections of each course mainly from the standpoint of their contributions and their placement. It would hardly go into the detailed objectives and activities.

This latter, however, is very important, and it is wholly a responsibility of the supervisory and instructional staff. It might be called intermediate-range planning. Examples of this kind of planning are often found in syllabuses or courses of study. At this level of planning the teacher or supervisor must consider not only the units or major subdivisions which are to be included in the course but also the specific objectives of each unit and the learning activities and subject matter which appear to provide the best avenues for attaining them.

On the other hand, it would not ordinarily be feasible to lay out, so far in advance, the detailed sequence and schedule of activities to be carried on in each individual class period from the beginning to the end of the unit or block. Unforeseen interruptions and delays, as well as unexpected opportunities for clarification and enrichment, frequently occur even during the course of a class period, and they often require revision not only of the immediate day's plan but also of the plans for subsequent days. Consequently, the detailed daily lesson plans can hardly be made to advantage for more than one or two days ahead. In military terms this might be called short-range or tactical planning, in contrast to the strategic or long-range planning and the intermediate-range planning discussed above.

Planning a Schedule for a Course. It has been suggested that the layout plan for a course may best begin with a days-and-pages schedule. The main use of such a device is that it does provide a schedule which, if fol-

---

[1] For discussion of this topic see Howard F. Fehr, Mathematics for the Gifted, *Bulletin of the National Association of Secondary-School Principals*, **38** (1954), 103–110, and Florence L. Elder, Providing for the Student with High Mathematical Potential, *Mathematics Teacher*, **50** (1957), 502–506.

lowed, will ensure that no principal part of the proposed coverage will be omitted from the course.   In making such a schedule, the course, as represented in the textbook, should first be laid out into the main chapters or units that are to be included.   Opposite this will be set the total number of days that are available for the course.   Then these two layouts must be fitted or matched to each other so that, at least on paper, all the work to be included in the course can also be included in the number of days available.   After the days-and-pages schedule is blocked out for the major units or chapters, it can be refined into a contents schedule by weeks, and even by days if desired.   Usually this will require some adjustment of preliminary estimates and perhaps the curtailment of certain units or the omission of certain topics.   If this is necessary, it is much better to make the adjustment at the outset than to wait and have to correct the inevitable maladjustment after the course is started.

In laying out a time schedule for a course there is always the likelihood that a few days will be lost, as far as instruction is concerned, during the semester or the year.   Actually this likelihood amounts almost to a certainty in many schools.   Unscheduled interruptions and delays are almost certain to occur.   Football games, illness, special meetings, unexpected holidays, and other things may cause dismissal of classes. When this occurs, the reduction of available days entails a corresponding reduction in the amount of work that can be included in the course. Then, too, even experienced teachers operating under well-planned schedules are likely to encounter some necessary slowdowns during the course. These considerations imply and emphasize the importance of leaving a few buffer days or catch-up days in the time schedule for the course. They imply also the importance of weighing the different units and the different parts of each unit on the scales of relative importance.   If some units or parts of units must be omitted from the course, they should be things of lesser importance.   Only by careful study and preplanning can the principle of relative values be systematically applied to the different parts and worked into the plan of the course, and only by leaving some leeway in the form of buffer days can there be much assurance of having enough time even for all of the things of prime importance in the course.

The Daily Lesson Plan.   The day-to-day planning of the details and sequence of each day's work must fall to the lot of each individual teacher.   It is a continuing responsibility and it is of the greatest importance, because the daily lesson plan for a class determines just what learning activities will go on in that class during that period.   Any teacher who goes before a class without having well in mind an orderly plan for the things he expects to do or to have the students do during the period is running a grave risk of wasting time and dissipating effort. Experienced teachers may not need actually to write out a detailed plan for each lesson, though many do so anyway, but young and inexperienced teachers will find it a great help to do so. Indeed, the very act of writing the plan out forces a crystallization of the plan in the teacher's mind. This in itself is an important step toward a successful consummation of what is planned. It is true that daily lesson plans often do need to be modified to take advantage of unforeseen circumstances or to adapt the work to unavoidable delays. But the teacher who can make such needed modifications against the backdrop of a well-ordered plan will be in a much stronger position than the teacher who does not bother to plan each day's work with care.

Lessons have sometimes been classified by the principal types of activity that are contemplated for the lessons. Reeve mentions and illustrates seven of these: the inductive development lesson, the drill lesson, the deductive development lesson, the review lesson, the examination, the appreciation lesson, and the conversational lesson. Subsequently he mentions another—the study lesson—which he feels should not properly be classified as a type of lesson, though he emphasizes the extreme importance of the activity.[1] Such classifications are doubtless useful for purposes of discussion and illustration, and they can be very helpful in focusing the teacher's mind on the principal kind of activity in which he wants the class to be engaged on any particular days. The terms are descriptive and suggest concisely what these kinds of activities are. To select the type of lesson which he wants to conduct on a particular day with a given class, the teacher is forced to consider the main objective toward which he wants to point the activity.

There still remains, however, the need to decide upon the details of the period's work and the ordering of these details. Apart from such routine matters as taking the roll, the number of kinds of activity which may be included in the learning-teaching situation is not great. Most of them would be included in the following list:

1. Testing for any of several purposes
2. Explaining or discussing new concepts or procedures
3. Drilling or reviewing
4. Directing the work of students at chalkboard or at seats (directed study or directed learning; may include laboratory activities)
5. Assigning work to be done by the students

Each of these kinds of activity requires intelligent planning if it is to serve its purpose. A test designed for diagnostic purposes will probably differ not only in the use to which it is to be put but also in the time

---

[1] William David Reeve, "Mathematics for the Secondary School" (New York: Henry Holt and Company, Inc., 1954), pp. 125–147.

which is required from a quiz set up for a drill exercise. Explaining or discussing new concepts in a developmental lesson requires that the teacher clarify in his own mind, and ahead of time, the precise things upon which he wants to focus the discussion. It also requires that he consider well just how the explanation can best be made, what illustrations will best serve his purpose, and how he can secure participation in the discussion by the members of the class. The intelligent assignment of work to be done by the students demands consideration of its aim and of its suitability for the students in respect to length and difficulty.

Not all of the activities listed above will be required in each day's work. Some periods will be devoted entirely to testing or to developmental discussion. On other days, during the assimilation stage, supervised study may well occupy most of the period. A brief discussion for purposes of motivation can often be helpful in such cases. Drill work, review, the making of assignments, and short quizzes should be scheduled in the period's activities at times when it is judged that they will yield the greatest advantage, and this may vary from day to day.

The essence of a good daily lesson plan lies in two things: (1) the careful estimation and selection of those activities which give the most promise of good dividends in terms of the immediate objectives and (2) the arrangement of these activities into a properly ordered schedule, with approximate time allotments, so that the period may be used to best advantage.

The following examples illustrate how a simple check list of fundamental activities such as that given above can serve as a guide in lesson planning. Such lesson plans are simple and easy to make. They can ensure that the important activities for a given period are carried on in the best order and that within the limitations of the period appropriate time allowances are made for each.

Some teachers may object that so much detail in the lesson plans would restrict their freedom too much and would tend to mechanize the class period. Of course, this is not the intention and actually it is not the case. The teacher is free to assign any portion of the class period he wishes to any particular activity. It should also be observed that he is free to depart from the plan if circumstances seem to require it; he should never feel a need to adhere to it slavishly. The ordered plan and time allotment is simply a device which compels him to give thought ahead of time to just what things he believes are in the best interests of the class and which gives as much assurance as possible that they will be included to best advantage in the work of the class period.

Before making out a daily lesson plan, the teacher should carefully think through the main things he wants to do and the things he wants the students to do during the class period for which the plan is to be

Plane Geometry   Topic: Proportion

Order of activities	Minutes
Check quiz on review assignment...........	10
Discussion of proportion and of meaning of theorems 1–6, with illustrations..........	25
Drill work.............................	None
Directed study........................	None
Assignment for tomorrow (see back of card).	10

Algebra   Topic: Fractional Equations

Order of activities	Minutes
Test..................................	None
Review briefly principles of solving linear equations...........................	5
Discussion and explanation of fractional equations and how they may be solved. Work out four illustrative cases with the class (see back of card).................	20
Send class to blackboard to work on exercises 1–6, page 144........................	15
Assignment for tomorrow (see back of card).	5

Seventh-grade Mathematics   Topic: Graphs
(Class has worked on this topic for three days already)

Order of activities	Minutes
Review of terms used; kinds of graphs we have studied; what sort of thing each can show best; establishing proper scales; form of notation for labeling and title; importance of neatness and care in making graphs	10
Discussion (brief): interpretation of some statistical graphs provided by company X	10
Assignment of work to be done tomorrow: exercises 8–12, page 186 in textbook. Complete any three of these.................	5
Directed study: class working at seats on tomorrow's assignment.................	20

made. These should be set down precisely in the order in which he
wants them to occur, with estimated time allowances. The lesson plan
should be neither perfunctory nor stereotyped but should be adapted to
taking full advantage of the educational possibilities of the class situation.
Obviously, different activities will receive special emphasis on different

days. On some days most of the time will need to be spent on developmental work, while on other days the main activity will be directed study, and still other days will be given over largely to testing. The wise variation of the class-period activities is a major factor in stimulating interest and preventing boredom and disciplinary difficulties. It is possible, however, to use a general outline form which will be objective enough to serve as a useful guide in planning and, at the same time, be sufficiently flexible to permit adaptation of the lesson plan to any class situation.

A Practical Hint on Planning.   Many a young teacher in beginning his first job is obsessed with the fear that he will run out of anything to say before the class period is over, and thus leave himself and the class at loose ends. If he is at all competent, a little experience will convince him that the contrary is true: there usually is not enough time for all he wants to do. Well-planned discussions which elicit participation by the class will consume time at an unexpected rate, so that the real danger lies in having to leave untouched some of the work that the teacher has hoped and planned to get done during the period. Yet the tendency to overestimate what can be done during the period is very persistent. Sometimes the shortages can be made up in the next period or two by careful replanning and perhaps curtailing the work of succeeding days. If, on the other hand, these shortages are not compensated in some such way and are allowed to accumulate, they can only result eventually in some major hiatus in the course. Unfortunately, this often does occur. Indeed, it is likely to occur unless the teacher adheres pretty closely to a preestablished days-and-pages time schedule. Some people will object that such a schedule is too mechanical and may compel the class to leave some topics before they are fully mastered. But the alternative is to leave some part of the course, and perhaps some major part, wholly untouched.

It is not always easy to make good daily lesson plans to fit with such a schedule. It requires that the teacher give very careful thought to the relative importance of the material presented in the textbook on the work scheduled for each day and also to the nature of the learning activities through which the objectives of the work can best be attained. Usually the textbook discussion will bear on some concepts or processes or relations that are of primary importance, while other parts of the discussion may be only subsidiary or of secondary importance. In planning the day's lesson it is important to highlight only the key concepts or relations and save most of the time for them. Only in this way can the full benefit of the textbook and the teacher's enriching discussion be realized, and only in this way can there be any real assurance of ordered and orderly progress through the course.

With respect to unit or block planning, much the same considerations hold and much the same things may be said. The major difference is in degree and not in kind. It lies in the larger scope of the unit and the fact that it usually covers several days instead of a single day. The same principle of relative importance should govern selection of the elements of the unit to be emphasized, and the danger of overestimating what can be accomplished is just as real here as in planning the daily lesson. Judgment on these matters can mature quickly, and experience can be a great help in this. But even with experienced teachers, hope sometimes overrides judgment, and beginning teachers must face this problem without even the benefit of experience to guide them. It is hoped that observance of the cautions noted above may contribute toward wise planning of units and lessons and thus toward the avoidance of frustration and disappointment.

In Conclusion. Nearly everything that a teacher does in connection with his work requires some kind and degree of planning. Even the details of his lesson plans must be thought through, appraised, and decided upon. If he is to give a test, he ought to decide what particular things he wants to test for, and then he ought to plan the test so that it will reveal, in terms of the objectives, the particular information he wants. To conserve his own time, he ought to try to arrange the test so that the papers can be checked without excessive labor, and this takes careful planning. If he is to present new material in the form of discussion with the class, he should identify ahead of time the main things he wants to bring out, and he should so plan his discussion that it will highlight and emphasize them. Illustrative examples should be selected with care, and ahead of time, instead of trusting to the inspiration of the moment to provide suitable ones. If the work is to include a field trip or a laboratory type of exercise, there are many things that need to be carefully planned ahead of time, because it is hard to adapt or change such work after it is started. The things to be done must be decided upon in advance and with definiteness, equipment and supplies made ready, and careful instructions given to the students. Forgetting to provide some important instruction or some piece of needed equipment can nullify the exercise and result in loss of time and disruption of morale. Drill and review work needs to be very carefully planned lest it be aimless and ineffective, and the same thing may be said of blackboard work by the students. Providing suitable learning experiences for students of superior ability cannot be done incidentally. Directed study can be effective only to the extent to which a proper background has been established and the learning experiences are planned expressly to consolidate and extend this background. Assignments for homework can bear proper fruit only if they are well designed to produce certain predetermined results and are reasonable in their demands upon the student's ability, understanding, and time.   In short, assuming academic and professional competence on the part of the teacher, intelligent planning at all levels provides the key to efficient instruction and effective learning. The key may fit imperfectly or stick a bit at first, but experience and faithful use will smooth and ease its operation.   It is a *sine qua non* and must not be neglected.

A final word of caution should be given with reference to the use of lesson plans.   In planning the work of a class period the teacher must of necessity work on the assumption that the activities of the period will follow a definite course without interruption or deflection.   All experienced teachers know, however, that this assumption is often wrong.   Circumstances which cannot be foreseen inevitably arise at times, and often such circumstances make it advisable for the teacher to depart from his prepared plan.   If by doing so it is possible to capitalize on some unexpected situation and thereby stimulate the interest of the students in their work or repair some unsuspected weakness, the teacher should not hesitate to divert the activities of the period from their charted course.   Normally, of course, the best results will be obtained by following the prepared plans, but the teacher should not feel obligated to follow them with a slavish fidelity which would forbid him to take advantage of such opportunities.   Frequently, the most effective teaching may be accomplished through spontaneous teacher reaction to unexpected student problems and unpredicted teaching situations.

EXERCISES

1. Discuss the importance of long-range planning for mathematical instruction as it is exhibited in curriculum construction and the broad character of the various courses to be offered.   Why should long-range planning be a concern of the administrative officers as well as the instructional staff?

2. Do you agree with the assertion that for most courses in secondary school mathematics the plan of the course is pretty much determined by the textbook that is used for the course?   If this assertion is true, is it a good thing?   Defend your answer.

3. Some textbooks in mathematics contain more topics than can normally be treated adequately and mastered by a class in the time allotted for the course.   Thus it often is necessary to omit some chapters or parts of chapters.   Deciding on what parts to omit and what parts to retain is a very important part of the long-range planning of the course.   Take some textbook in intermediate algebra and list the topics or chapters it contains.   Next, decide which of these topics you would hope to include in a one-semester course, using that text.   Finally, estimate the time that you would need for each.   If the total of your estimates exceeds the time available, revise your time estimates or reduce your list of topics until it fits the usual time allowance of 18 weeks for the semester's work.   Report the list which you decided to retain, tell what topics or chapters you decided to omit (if any), and justify your

decisions. This is an important exercise because it is precisely the kind of thing you will have to do with each course you teach and with each of the textbooks you use.

4. Select a standard textbook in plane geometry and assume that you are to use it next year; then make a time schedule to serve as an approximate guide for the year's work. Assume that you will have 36 weeks of instructional time, including tests and examinations. For each topic or unit which you will include in the course, estimate the time in weeks which you can safely allot to that topic or unit. Such a schedule can be valuable to you in many ways. Make it with care and report it to the class. Present your arguments in support of it, but ask for criticisms and suggestions.

5. Do all the things that are called for in exercise 4, but with respect to some standard textbook in ninth-grade algebra instead of plane geometry.

6. Do all the things that are called for in exercise 4, but with respect to some standard textbook for a year's work in seventh- or eighth-grade mathematics instead of plane geometry.

7. Do all the things that are called for in exercise 4, but with respect to a textbook in trigonometry. Assume that you have just 18 weeks in which to conduct this one-semester course.

8. It is likely that during any semester or year various circumstances may cause unexpected cancellation of classes on a few days. Many teachers feel that it is well to take this into account in making the over-all time schedule for the course. Do you? If so, about how many buffer days per semester would you allow in your time schedule to absorb these lost class periods? Enumerate several possible circumstances that might cause such loss of class time.

9. Why should provision for individual differences through differentiated curriculums be regarded as a stage of planning for mathematical instruction? Report to the class on at least two of the articles in Part I of the "Twenty-second Yearbook of the National Council of Teachers of Mathematics."

10. Explain the aim, philosophy, and limitations of homogeneous grouping as a measure for making suitable provision for the mathematical education of students of different abilities. Do you believe homogeneous grouping is a good thing, assuming that circumstances permit it to be used? Justify your answer.

11. What planning would be entailed in setting up and administering a system of homogeneous grouping? Be as specific as you can.

12. One plan for providing for individual differences in mathematics without homogeneous grouping of students in different classes involves the use of differentiated assignments *within* a class. One well-defined form of this plan is referred to in this chapter as the "contract plan" or the contract type of assignment. Explain how this plan is set up and how it works.

13. Take some section or unit of algebra, geometry, trigonometry, or junior high school mathematics and plan a series of contracts for the unit. Assume that the class for which it is intended includes students with a wide range of ability.

14. Explain the difference between the contract type of assignment and the multiple-level type of assignment as they are described in this chapter. Which do you think would be the easier to plan? Why?

15. Which of the types of differentiated assignments given in exercise 14 do you think would be most effective for a class in which there are exceptionally capable students? Would your answer be the same with respect to a class in which there are no really outstanding students? Explain.

16. Discuss the method used by Stokes for capitalizing the ability and interest of superior students in ninth-grade algebra, as it is reported in this chapter. What special planning would this method involve?

17. Read the article by Elder (see Bibliography) on "Providing for the Student with High Mathematical Potential" and report it to the class. What special planning by the teacher would this require?

18. Is the selection of a textbook for a mathematics course actually a phase of long-range planning? In selecting a textbook from among several in ninth-grade algebra, what are some of the characteristics with respect to which you would want to compare the books?

19. Select some unit, chapter, or section in a standard textbook in algebra, geometry, or general mathematics and make an over-all plan for teaching the unit. Include a detailed list of specific objectives in terms of "things to know" and "things to be able to do." Indicate the parts of the text that would receive special emphasis and estimate the number of class periods that would be required. Present your outline to the class for discussion and criticism.

20. Based on the unit plan called for in exercise 19, decide what items you would want to test for in order to judge the extent to which your students had mastered the unit. Then, based on these specific objectives, devise a test designed to accomplish such an appraisal. Present it to the class for discussion and criticism.

21. From the unit outline called for in exercise 19 select a section that you estimate would require about three class periods to cover. Decide what principal things you would aim at on each of the three days and what particular things you would do or have done to attain your objectives most effectively. Then make out a daily lesson plan for each of the three days, similar to the examples shown in this chapter under The Daily Lesson Plan. Present these lesson plans to the class for discussion and criticism.

BIBLIOGRAPHY

Albrecht, Mary E.: A Teacher Plans Her Day, *Arithmetic Teacher*, **3** (1956), 151–152.

Allen, Frank B.: Building a Mathematics Program: An Adventure in Cooperative Planning, *Mathematics Teacher*, **49** (1956), 226–234.

Baumgartner, Reuben A.: A Mathematics Curriculum for the Gifted, *School Science and Mathematics*, **53** (1953), 207–213.

Berger, Margaret L.: Provisions for Meeting the Needs of the Poorly Prepared Student in Algebra, *Mathematics Teacher*, **43** (1950), 107–111.

Betz, William: The Teaching and Learning Processes in Mathematics, *Mathematics Teacher*, **42** (1949), 49–55.

Blackhurst, J. Herbert: "Principles and Methods of Junior High School Mathematics" (New York: Appleton-Century-Crofts, Inc., 1928), pp. 106–130.

Breslich, E. R.: "The Technique of Teaching Mathematics in Secondary Schools" (Chicago: University of Chicago Press, 1930), pp. 2–27.

———: "Problems in Teaching Secondary School Mathematics" (Chicago: University of Chicago Press, 1931), pp. 26–30.

———: "The Administration of Mathematics in Secondary Schools" (Chicago: University of Chicago Press, 1933), pp. 334–363.

Brown, Claude H.: "The Teaching of Secondary Mathematics" (New York: Harper & Brothers, 1953), pp. 314–318.

Buzetti, Beatrice: An Experiment in Teaching, *Mathematics Teacher*, **48** (1955), 360–365.

Carnahan, Walter H.: Enrichment in Mathematics Teaching, *Mathematics Teacher*, **42** (1949), 14–18.

Clark, John R. (Editor) and others: Emerging Practices in Mathematics Education, "Twenty-second Yearbook" (Washington, D.C.: National Council of Teachers of Mathematics, 1954), pp. 1–99.

Clark, Norman, and Dick Lander: An Honors Program, *Mathematics Teacher*, **48** (1955), 371.

Commonwealth of Pennsylvania, Department of Public Instruction: "A Course of Study in Mathematics for Secondary Schools," *Bulletin Number* 360 (Harrisburg, Pa.: Department of Public Instruction, 1952), pp. 68–248.

Courses of Study. (Many courses of study and curriculum guides contain detailed analyses of subject matter for the various courses, with suggestions for teaching. These courses of study represent long-range and intermediate-range planning. Few of them contain sample lesson plans, but all of them contain suggestions that would help the teacher in making his own daily lesson plans. Such courses of study, printed or mimeographed, are available from numerous states and cities at a nominal cost.)

Dodes, Irving Allen: Planned Instruction, "Twenty-first Yearbook" (Washington, D.C.: National Council of Teachers of Mathematics, 1953), pp. 303–334.

Douglass, Harl R.: Remedial Work in Junior High School Mathematics, *Mathematics Teacher*, **48** (1955), 344–346.

Elder, Florence L.: Providing for the Student with High Mathematical Potential, *Mathematics Teacher*, **50** (1957), 502–506.

Griff, Ernest R.: The Comparative Effectiveness of One-level and Three-level Assignments in Plane Geometry, *Mathematics Teacher*, **50** (1957), 214–216.

Hartung, Maurice L.: High School Algebra for Bright Students, *Mathematics Teacher*, **46** (1953), 316–321, 325.

Hassler, J. O., and R. R. Smith: "The Teaching of Secondary Mathematics" (New York: The Macmillan Company, 1930), pp. 171–195.

Henderson, Kenneth B.: Anent the Discovery Method, *Mathematics Teacher*, **50** (1957), 287–291.

—— and Kern Dickman: Minimum Mathematical Needs of Prospective Students in a College of Engineering, *Mathematics Teacher*, **45** (1952), 89–93.

Irvin, Lee: The Organization of Instruction in Arithmetic and Basic Mathematics in Selected Secondary Schools, *Mathematics Teacher*, **46** (1953), 235–240.

Johnson, D. A., and C. E. Olander: "How to Use Your Bulletin Board" (Washington, D.C.: National Council of Teachers of Mathematics, 1956).

——, Dirk Ten Brink, and Lauren G. Woodby: "How to Use Field Trips in Mathematics" (Washington, D.C.: National Council of Teachers of Mathematics, 1957).

Kidd, Kenneth P.: Improving the Learning of Mathematics, *Mathematics Teacher*, **47** (1955), 393–400.

Kieffer, Mildred, and Anna Marie Evans: "How to Develop a Teaching Guide in Mathematics" (Washington, D.C.: National Council of Teachers of Mathematics 1958).

Kinney, Lucien Blair: The Operational Plan in the Classroom, *School and Society*, **67** (1948), 145–148.

—— and C. Richard Purdy: "Teaching Mathematics in the Secondary School" (New York: Rinehart & Company, Inc., 1952), pp. 304–325.

Klein, Rose: Self-directed Homework, *Mathematics Teacher*, **44** (1951), 463–465.

Latino, Joseph J.: An Algebra Program for the Bright Ninth Grader, *Mathematics Teacher*, **49** (1956), 179–184.

Lee, William: Provision for Individual Differences in High School Mathematics Courses, *Mathematics Teacher*, **40** (1947), 294–297.

Lentz, Donald W.: The High School Principal Looks at the Mathematics Program,

Bulletin of the National Association of Secondary-School Principals, **38** (1954), 40–47.

Ligda, Paul: "The Teaching of Elementary Algebra" (Boston: Houghton Mifflin Company, 1925). (A section on classroom presentation is found with most of the topics discussed.)

Moore, H. S.: Planning for Competency in Arithmetic, *California Journal of Secondary Education*, **19** (1944), 40–44.

Norton, Monte S.: Enrichment as Provision for the Gifted in Mathematics, *School Science and Mathematics*, **57** (1957), 339–345.

Olander, Clarence: A Comparison of Two Methods of Teaching a Unit on Insurance, *Mathematics Teacher*, **48** (1955), 365–368.

————: The Use of a Readiness Test in Teaching a Unit on Signed Numbers, *School Science and Mathematics*, **57** (1957), 131–138.

Payne, Joseph N.: Self-instructive Enrichment Topics for Bright Pupils in High School Algebra, *Mathematics Teacher*, **51** (1958), 113–117.

Potter, Mary: Mathematics for the Lower Fifty Per Cent, *Bulletin of the National Association of Secondary-School Principals*, **38** (1954), 96–103.

Reeve, William David: "Mathematics for the Secondary School" (New York: Henry Holt and Company, Inc., 1954), pp. 124–166.

————: The Problem of Varying Abilities among Students in Mathematics, *Mathematics Teacher*, **49** (1956), 70–78.

Schult, Veryl: Guideposts in Curriculum Planning in Mathematics, *Bulletin of the National Association of Secondary-School Principals*, **38** (1954), 48–53.

Schultz, Margaret, and M. M. Ohlsen: A Comparison of Traditional Teaching and Personalized Teaching in Ninth Grade Algebra, *Mathematics Teacher*, **42** (1949), 91–96.

Schutter, Charles H.: Improving the Quality of Instruction in Mathematics, *School Science and Mathematics*, **47** (1947), 404–408.

Secondary School Curriculum Committee, Report of: The Secondary Mathematics Curriculum, *Mathematics Teacher*, **52** (1959), 389–417.

Sister Mary Corona: Seminars: An Integrating Force in a Program of Concentration, *Mathematics Teacher*, **48** (1955), 209–213.

Smith, D. E., and W. D. Reeve: "The Teaching of Junior High School Mathematics" (Boston: Ginn & Company, 1927), pp. 270–325.

Snader, Daniel W.: A Program for Individualizing Instruction in Mathematics, *Mathematics Teacher*, **38** (1945), 116–119.

Sobel, Max: Providing for the Slow Learner in the Junior High School, *Mathematics Teacher*, **52** (1959), 347–353.

Sokol, Irwin N.: Divide and Conquer, *Mathematics Teacher*, **48** (1955), 368–370.

Syer, Henry W., and Peter J. Ingeneri: Multi-sensory Aids in Mathematics, *School Science and Mathematics*, **49** (1949), 134–140.

Vance, E. P., Julius H. Hlavaty, Richard S. Pieters, and Leroy Sachs: "Program Provisions for the Mathematically Gifted Student in the Secondary School" (Washington, D.C.: National Council of Teachers of Mathematics, 1958).

Vaughn, William D.: Some Drill Techniques for Arithmetic, *Mathematics Teacher*, **50** (1957), 436–437.

Vollmar, Robert, and Philip Peak: "How to Use Films and Filmstrips in Mathematics Classes" (Washington, D.C.: National Council of Teachers of Mathematics, 1958).

Westmeyer, Paul: Just Stand Out of the Way, *School Science and Mathematics*, **57** (1957), 643–646.

Wirszup, Izaak: Some Remarks on Enrichment, *Mathematics Teacher*, **49** (1956), 519–527.

8

EVALUATION OF INSTRUCTION

The effectiveness of instruction is usually determined by means of checking accomplished results against objectives undertaken. Measures of achievement have thus long been employed as an integral part of the educational program. An efficient program of evaluation, however, does not consist merely in the effort to check the completed process but rather in the continual appraisal of student progress toward the attainment of preestablished aims. Such a program should be outlined in terms of significant instructional objectives and used for more efficient pupil guidance. There is probably no more accurate barometer of the fundamental philosophy of any curriculum than a careful analysis of its evaluation program; the techniques used; the aims, objectives, and functions implied; and the interpretation and use of obtained results.

Nature and Purposes of Evaluation.[1] The emergence of pupil guidance as a significant responsibility of every educational program has placed new emphasis on the function of evaluation. No longer is this function defined in terms of the mere measurement of achievement of ill-defined goals. Standards of achievement have been more clearly defined, more carefully differentiated, and better adapted to different kinds of capability and individual levels of attainment. Furthermore, the program of evaluation has been extended beyond the mere measurement of proficiency of performance with basic skills to incorporate efforts to measure the development of interests and appreciations and discriminate between the varying degrees of aptitude in a given subject field. Also, the techniques of evaluation include not only the giving of tests, whether standard or teacher-made, but also interviews, informal observations, anecdotal records, pupil projects, aptitude and inventory tests, and other methods of obtaining evidence relating to pupil development.

Thus, evaluation can perform a very important function in the educative process. It should no longer be considered merely as a separate pro-

---

[1] For current and contemporary information on evaluation procedures see the department Testing Time, in *Mathematics Teacher*, and "Twenty-second Yearbook of the National Council of Teachers of Mathematics," part five.

cedure to be used at convenient intervals for the purpose of determining marks; rather it should be thought of as a continual process closely related to each aspect of the total program of pupil development. The major responsibilities of a truly effective evaluation program may thus be considered to be the following:

1. To provide a basis for more intelligent guidance of teaching and learning through appraisal of aptitudes and diagnosis of errors
2. To evaluate instructional procedures
3. To measure the attainment of instructional objectives and provide an adequate basis for reporting pupil progress
4. To provide guides for the development of more effective educative experiences
5. To take inventory of pupil readiness
6. To secure information for use as an aid in seeking intelligent and effective parent and community cooperation

The teacher of mathematics has the responsibility of determining the contribution that mathematics can make to the educational development of the individual and then designing a program of evaluation sufficiently comprehensive to measure progress toward maximum benefit from all phases of that contribution. In order to measure progress efficiently, the techniques of measurement must be so flexible that ready adaptation may be made to the characteristic differences that exist among individual abilities, in curriculum demands, and in guidance criteria. Such flexibility should in no sense interfere with the comprehensiveness of the program of evaluation. It is also important that the testing techniques be characterized by balance of emphasis between factual and functional objectives, between tangible and intangible outcomes, between the how and the why, between mere recall and integrated thinking, and between measurement as a check on the completed process and as an aid to more effective instruction.

A satisfactory evaluation program should be further characterized by *continuity*. For efficient guidance there must be a continual check on the student's progress, not only from the standpoint of immediate accomplishment but also from the standpoint of retention. Furthermore, the use of this check for prognostic and diagnostic purposes should be emphasized fully as much as its use as a measure of achievement.

If the evaluation program is to be thoroughly comprehensive and balanced, it must neglect no significant aspect of the subject matter covered and it must take into account all the important objectives which have been set up. Since it can command but a limited part of the school time, it must obviously consist of only a sampling of subject matter and problem situations. Thus the real task of such a program is to use data of varied types collected through several different media to shape a composite appraisal picture of each pupil as an individual and as a member of his group.   Care must thus be exercised to ensure that the sampling is truly representative of all the important aspects of the total program.

In the preparation of the instructional program the experienced, well-trained teacher should enjoy a certain freedom from curriculum restraint. There should not be too much dictation of the material to be covered in a specified period of time.   This also implies freedom in the curricular materials and the testing techniques to be used in the evaluation program.   On the other hand, the inexperienced teacher should seek the counsel of the supervisor or administrator in setting up objectives of instruction and in selecting testing techniques and constructing instruments for measuring student progress toward the attainment of the objectives.

The formulation of a sound philosophy of evaluation is but a necessary prerequisite to the construction of a satisfactory program of evaluation. With the above characteristics as guiding criteria the teacher or administrator may proceed more safely with the technical details incident to the selection or construction of valid and reliable instruments of measurement for use in any particular instructional situation.

Whether the problem is to provide an evaluation program from the point of view of the entire curriculum or of a specific subject matter field, there are at least five steps to be followed in setting up efficient testing techniques, viz.:

1. Determination of those significant aims and objectives which are to be the goals of instruction
2. Provision of pertinent behavior situations to guarantee a valid measure of student reactions
3. Securing a reliable record of the student reactions
4. Accurate and systematic tabulation of the record as an aid in the deduction of implied results
5. Intelligent interpretation of the results in terms of student needs and as an aid to more effective instruction

Evaluation has a very definite function in the learning process which takes place in secondary mathematics; the program of evaluation should be designed in terms of the functional aims as well as the factual aims of mathematical instruction.   Is the instructional program such that functional learning and factual learning supplement each other?   Are the students learning the why as well as the how?   Are they building up integrated funds of information rather than stores of segregated bits of factual knowledge?   Is the program of instruction such that it will provide the student with the techniques of critical thinking?   Will it develop the ability (1) to distinguish between essential and unessential data, (2) to determine the reliability of facts and the reasonableness of results and conclusions, (3) to generalize circumspectly from known facts to unknown situations and new problems, (4) to evaluate arguments, ideas, and conclusions, critically?   Carefully selected techniques of evaluation should be used in determining to what extent these aims have been realized by pupils, both as individuals and as groups.   Futhermore, it should be constantly emphasized that the most significant functions of effective evaluation include not merely use as an aid in determining pupils' marks but use as an aid to the improvement of instruction as well.

The Techniques of Evaluation.   The determination and perfection of techniques to be used in the evaluation of mathematical instruction is a definite responsibility of teachers of mathematics.   These techniques, in the main, consist of teacher judgments and teacher-made or commercially produced tests.   Teachers should be extremely conscientious in their efforts to evaluate student effort, and, in those situations which do not submit themselves very well to measurement scales, appraisals should be based on discriminative and impartial judgments arrived at after careful deliberation.   Such judgments may be made through the medium of oral recitations in class, comparative class observations, the personal interview, the anecdotal record, and the prolonged case study.

If prepared tests are to be used, the teacher will at times have to consider the comparative advantages and disadvantages of standardized[1] and teacher-made tests.   Each has certain advantages over the other.   The standardized test possesses norms which provide for more equitable comparisons between groups than can be made by teacher-made tests.   They are usually constructed by individuals of wide experience and preparation in both subject matter and the techniques of testing.   This increases the likelihood of greater reliability and validity.   Standardized tests are usually subject to a greater degree of objectivity in administering and in scoring.

On the other hand, it is probable that standard tests which are used year after year may exert some "backward influence" which might partially nullify their validity so far as the content of the work of a particular class is concerned.

A distinct administrative advantage of the standardized test is that it diminishes the time which the teacher needs to devote to the details of a testing program.   This, however, in the minds of some is a questionable

---

[1] See the following yearbooks prepared by O. K. Buros: "Educational, Psychological, and Personality Tests of 1933, 1934, 1935" (1936), pp. 14–17, 40–41, 53; "Educational, Psychological, and Personality Tests of 1936" (1937), pp. 10–12, 27–28, 35–36; "The Nineteen Thirty-eight Mental Measurements Yearbook" (1938), pp. 14–42, 83–84, 116–119; "The Nineteen Forty Mental Measurements Yearbook (1940), pp. 268–314; "The Third Mental Measurements Yearbook" (1949), pp. 399–442; "The Fourth Mental Measurements Yearbook" (1953), pp. 483–527; "The Fifth Mental Measurements Yearbook" (1959), pp. 561–615.

advantage, the argument being that thoughtful effort on the part of the teacher in the details of test construction might make a distinct contribution in the direction of improved instruction.   The use of such extramural tests as those prepared by the College Entrance Examination Board and the Board of Regents of the University of the State of New York, as well as some standardized tests designed primarily as final examinations, should be definitely restricted to the purposes for which they were designed and the situations to which they are related.

One of the major advantages of the teacher-made test over the standard or extramural test is its flexibility and its adaptability to local situations and to repeated evaluations.   Tests of subject-matter mastery should include the material which the class has studied and no other material. They should emphasize those things that have been emphasized in the class, and no item should have much place in a test for a particular class unless that class, in its study, has given some attention to that item or topic.   It must be recognized that individual differences exist among classes and teachers just as they exist among individual students.   Extramural tests can take some account of different levels of difficulty, but they cannot take account of differences in details of subject matter or emphasis or differences in the methods of presentation and the points of view of different teachers.   Only the teachers themselves can make tests which will do so.   Other advantages of teacher-made tests over standardized tests lie in their relative inexpensiveness and their inexhaustible availability.

When the tests to be used are to be constructed by the individual teacher or by groups of teachers, there are two major problems to be considered, viz., (1) What is to be tested? and (2) What is the most effective method of testing it?   The answers to these two questions are to be found in the answers to certain supplementary questions.   What are the instructional objectives to be measured?   Is the test to be designed primarily for the purpose of measuring the attainment of standards, or is it to serve as a medium of instruction or as an aid in the educational guidance of the individual pupil?   What are the distinguishing characteristics of prognostic, diagnostic, and achievement tests?   Such questions as these must be settled by the teacher before he will be able to construct an entirely satisfactory test.

Another question of special importance in this connection is whether an essay-type test or a new-type test is better suited to the particular situation.   If the teacher is interested in having the test reflect something of the student's ability to organize and integrate information, then the essay-type test probably provides the better medium.   There are certain types of mathematical subject matter that seem to limit themselves largely to the essay-type or problem-type of test, e.g., solving verbal problems, solving geometrical originals, proving theorems, and constructing geometric figures.   The objective tests, on the other hand, offer the opportunity of covering a wider range of material as well as very greatly restricting any subjectivity which might affect the results of the evaluation program. Such tests are likely to be more reliable than tests of the essay type, although the latter, if carefully constructed, may have a high degree of validity.   Objective tests certainly give opportunity for a wider range of sampling, and for this reason they have certain advantages over essay-type tests in the matter of prognosis and diagnosis.   For the same reason they make possible the inclusion of a more comprehensive range of items in measuring achievement.   However, while their objectivity makes them easy to score and reduces the personal element in scoring, the translation of scores into marks or grades may in some measure offset this advantage. Aside from the fact that they are generally not good tests of organizing ability, their chief disadvantage lies in the fact that the construction of really good objective tests requires much time, considerable experience, and great care.

Such tests are made in various forms, and the determination of which of these forms is most suitable for a particular situation is sometimes a real problem.   One must know and weigh the functions, advantages, and limitations of the different forms such as true-false, direct recall, multiple-response, completion, and matching and decide which one will lend itself most advantageously to the case in hand.

In any case, whether essay-type or objective tests are being constructed, the following criteria should be observed with the utmost care:

1. A test should be as highly objective as possible.   The element of personal interpretation should be minimized in the determination of the correctness or incorrectness of student reactions to behavior situations.

2. A test should be reliable.   The reliability of a test is determined by the consistency with which it measures that which it does measure. There are many sources of unreliability, not all of which are attributes of the test itself.   The behavior of the examiner, the mental and physical condition of the student, and the conditions under which the test is given have a great deal of influence upon the reliability of the results obtained from any test.   Certain other causes of unreliability are inherent within the test itself, e.g., ambiguity in the instructions for taking the test, lack of clearness in statement of problems and questions, inadequate sampling of the items of information to be tested, inefficient methods of scoring, and erroneous interpretations of test results.

3. A test should be valid.   A test can be valid only in so far as it accomplishes for a selected group of pupils the specific purpose for which it was designed.   Two significant attributes of validity are reliability and objectivity.   However, their presence does not guarantee the validity of a test. To be valid the test must be further characterized by that comprehen-

siveness and discriminative power most pertinent to the particular function for which it is designed.   These criteria imply that the teacher must not only be thoroughly familiar with the objectives of instruction for the material to be tested but must also be well versed in the techniques of apt and precise phraseology and efficacious organization.

4. A test should be economical of the teacher's time.   The amount of time required for the construction, administration, and interpretation of a test should not be excessive.   The time element, however, is a function of the expected returns from the test.

5. A test should be "student-conscious."   The elements of the test should be couched in nonambiguous language, and reasonable tasks should be set for reasonable periods of time.   In test items designed to measure understanding of a principle or ability to apply a principle, computation should be minimized.

6. A test should motivate the best efforts of the students.   The questions should be so worded and presented that they will discourage guessing and bluffing.   The use of the "catch question" should be minimized. However, occasional use of such questions might be justified from the point of view of stimulation of accurate thinking.   A test should never be used as a means of punishment but should always tend to create in the mind of the student the attitude that it is worthwhile taking.

7. A test designed to discriminate between students' abilities must provide for measurement of the entire range of abilities.   If anything like accurate discrimination between students abilities is to be approximated, there must be questions easy enough that all students can answer them and questions so difficult that perfect scores would be highly improbable, if not impossible.   Some questions should be so designed that the student will have the responsibility of distinguishing between essential and nonessential data.

Prognosis and Guidance.   As an aid to more effective pupil guidance, tests have been used to analyze present status of mastery and to predict possible future achievement.   Such tests should be provided not only to measure mechanical ability and functional information, but also to make inquiry into students' interests, aptitudes, work habits, and study skills.

The inventory test is used for the purpose of "taking stock" of mathematical information and ability.   It should show what a student knows about a certain topic.   Under the modern philosophy of mathematical education the student has many opportunities to learn something of elementary algebra and a good deal of intuitive geometry by the time he enters the secondary school.   As he proceeds up the instructional ladder, seasonal inventory tests carefully placed and skillfully used will prevent a great deal of unnecessary repetition of experience on the part of the student and waste of effort on the part of the teacher.   They will also serve somewhat in the capacity of insurance against the monotony of learning which might result from student familiarity with teacher-selected material. Such tests may also be used effectively to bring to light the background which the students have for the study of new units and thus aid in the guidance program. The construction of an inventory test on a unit of instruction is not essentially different from the construction of a final achievement test on the same unit. The use of two such comparable tests, one before and the other after the teaching of the unit, will serve as a good indicator of the learning that takes place during the unit. Such a test on exponents and radicals is given here with its tabulation chart. There is also given the tabulation chart for a similar test, identical in form, which was given at the end of the unit. A comparative study of the two tables will give information concerning each pupil and the class as a whole on the learning situations recorded in the test.

Test: Exponents and Radicals

1. How many square roots does a number have?_____.
2. 5 is a square root of____because____times____is____.
3. If $x = \sqrt{y}$, then_____ = y. (Complete this statement.)

4.   The hypotenuse of this triangle is____feet long.

5. Construct geometrically a line $\sqrt{3}$ inches long.
6. (a) $\sqrt{2}$ = _____; (b) $\sqrt{3}$ = _____; (c) $\sqrt{5}$ = _____.
7. (a) $\sqrt{\dfrac{a^2}{b^2}}$ = _____; (b) $\left(\dfrac{4}{7}\right)^2$ = _____.
8. The simplest way to express $\sqrt{x^2y}$ is_____.
9. In the expression $\sqrt[3]{x^2}$ the index is (a)____and the exponent is (b)____. The sign $\sqrt{}$ is called a (c)____sign.
10. $x^{3/2}$ means the (a)____root of the (b)____power of (c)____.
11. (a) $\dfrac{x^5}{x^3}$ = _____; (b) $x^{3/4} \div x^{1/2}$ = _____; (c) $a^{3/2} \cdot a^{1/4}$ = _____.
12. (a) $x^5 \div x^5 = x^{(\ )}$. (Supply the exponent in the answer.)   (b) To what *number* is the above answer equal?_____.
13. (a) $a^5 \div a^7$ = _____.   (b) Does a^{-3} equal $\dfrac{1}{a^3}$?_____.
14. $\sqrt{73}$ is between____and____. (Fill blanks with two consecutive whole numbers.)

An examination of Table 8-1 reveals the fact that, as a whole, this unit constituted new material for the entire class. The meaning of square root, item 2 of the test, was generally understood and no time needed to be spent on its development. Futhermore, the teacher was able to determine those pupils, B, E, F, and H, who would probably need special attention.

Table 8-2 gives the record of responses after the period of instruction on the unit. It reveals that pupils A, E, F, and G needed further indi-

Table 8-1. Pupil Responses before Studying the Unit

Questions:	1	2	3	4	5	6			7		8	9			10			11			12		13		14	Pupil standing
						a	b	c	a	b		a	b	c	a	b	c	a	b	c	a	b	a	b		
Pupil:																										
A	x	x					x					x	x		x	x	x									8
B																										0
C		x				x	x					x	x					x						x	x	8
D		x										x	x		x										x	5
E	x	x																								2
F		x										x			x											3
G		x								x								x			x		x			5
H		x											x													2
Class standing	2	7	0	0	0	1	2	0	0	1	0	4	4	0	3	1	1	2	0	0	1	0	1	1	2	
Familiar material		x																								

Table 8-2. Pupil Responses after Studying the Unit

Questions:	1	2	3	4	5	6			7		8	9			10			11			12		13		14	Pupil standing
						a	b	c	a	b		a	b	c	a	b	c	a	b	c	a	b	a	b		
Pupil:																										
A	x	x	x	x	x	x	x	x	x			x	x	x	x	x	x	x						x		17
B	x	x		x	x	x	x	x	x	x		x	x	x	x		x	x	x		x	x	x		x	20
C	x	x		x		x	x	x	x	x	x	x	x	x	x	x	x	x	x	x	x	x		x		21
D	x	x		x	x	x	x	x	x	x	x	x	x	x	x	x			x	x	x	x	x	x	x	22
E	x	x		x	x	x	x	x	x	x		x	x	x	x	x	x	x						x		17
F	x	x		x		x	x	x	x	x		x	x	x	x		x	x						x		15
G	x	x		x	x	x	x	x	x	x		x	x	x	x		x	x			x	x	x		x	19
H		x		x	x	x	x	x	x	x	x	x	x	x	x	x	x	x			x	x	x	x	x	21
Class standing	7	8	1	8	6	8	8	8	8	7	3	8	8	8	8	5	7	7	3	2	5	5	4	6	4	
Need to reteach			x								x								x	x			x		x	

vidual attention on certain specific items and that, from the point of view of the entire class, items 3, 8, 11b, 11c, 13a, and 14 should be retaught.

In the prediction of mathematical achievement some of the most important factors seem to be comprehension of general mathematical techniques, classroom attentiveness, originality, habits of study, and general intelligence. The most efficient prediction seems to be accomplished through a combined use of prognostic tests, intelligence tests, and teachers' marks. Also, personality ratings have been found to be very effective in the prediction of success in freshman engineering mathematics.[1]

As a corollary to their use as an aid in prediction of achievement, prognostic tests can be used to reduce the number of failures either by eliminating those who are unprepared, or unable for any cause, to proceed further with mathematical study or by providing a basis for the construction of a differentiated mathematical curriculum. Such tests should also serve as an aid in the vocational and educational guidance of pupils and in the better classification of pupils. The discovery of superior ability and unusual aptitude in mathematics is just as important a function of prognosis as is the discovery of the inferior or average.[2]

For the construction of efficient prognostic tests in mathematics the teacher should be familiar with those abilities and interests essential to further progress. Mathematical tests which are to be used as an aid in vocational guidance should be based on a knowledge of those mathematical skills, concepts, and principles incident to success in any chosen vocation. The general characteristics of comprehensiveness, discriminative power, reliability, validity, balance, and flexibility must then be carefully observed in the framing and organization of the test items.

Diagnosis and Remedial Teaching. Probably one of the most significant steps toward improved instruction that has been taken in recent years is that of incorporating into the instructional program plans for discovering learning difficulties and detecting needs for remedial teaching. Such plans call for the intelligent use of inventory and diagnostic tests along with personal interviews to discover and analyze pupil difficulties with a view to setting up specific remedial measures to correct errors and remove difficulties. The characteristics of an efficient program of diagnosis may be summarized as follows:[3]

1. Such diagnosis must be made in connection with worthy objectives of a good educational program.

2. It must be objective, reliable, and valid.

3. It should be as specific as the desired outcomes permit and as the possibility of localization of symptoms allows within the limitations of practicality.

[1] R. D. Perry, Prediction Equations for Success in College Mathematics, *Contribution to Education* 122 (Nashville, Tenn.: George Peabody College for Teachers, 1934).

[2] An important program of this type is the advanced placement program of the College Entrance Examination Board. (See "Fifty-third Annual Report of the Director," 1955).

[3] Ralph W. Tyler, Characteristics of Satisfactory Diagnosis, "Thirty-fourth Yearbook of the National Society for the Study of Education" (Bloomington, Ill.: Public School Publishing Company, 1935), part II, chap. 6, pp. 95–111. Quoted by permission of the society.

4. It should yield results that would be comparable over a period of time and between groups of students.

5. It should be sufficiently precise to note progress during small units of time.

6. It should be comprehensive.

7. It should be appropriate to the educational program.

8. The person making the diagnosis must understand the educational program and be familiar with the fundamental problems of children.

Such a program should be keyed to bring to light distinct weaknesses in learning which call for specifically planned remedial action. An important byproduct of any diagnostic program which is carefully constructed will be the discovery of latent interests and abilities which need to be challenged. A second important byproduct of the diagnostic program can be the evaluation of instructional procedures. Have they been relatively effective or ineffective? Answers to such questions must be sought in a carefully structured composite picture of individual or group reaction to a specific diagnostic testing pattern. This is particularly true if the tests have been designed for diagnosis of basic understandings, insights into problem solving, and intelligent interpretation of results as well as proficiency in fundamental skills.

The intelligent use of such a program of diagnosis is an important aspect of effective teaching. Its real value, however, definitely will be dependent upon a carefully planned follow-up remedial program and a careful check on and interpretation of attained results.

Self-diagnosis by Students. One of the most important functions of tests as an aid to the improvement of instruction is student use of tests to secure evidence concerning individual development. Such tests, called "practice tests," may be either oral or written, and they can play a very important role in the assimilative period of instruction. They can aid the student in self-diagnosis, and they should never be used by the teacher in any other capacity than to help the student discover for himself information concerning his status of achievement in intelligent understanding of subject matter, the speed and accuracy with which he can perform the prescribed operations, and his relative progress as a member of his class group. Such tests must be shaped to reflect individual efficiency in the perspective of group activity.

Oral tests may be used with material that calls for responses which can be readily obtained and simply stated. They may be administered through pointed questions promiscuously, yet evenly, distributed over the entire class or through the medium of team contests. The two principal keynotes of successful oral practice are speed and accuracy of response.

Written tests may be used for both the simple-response and the difficult-response type of practice. As in the case of the oral tests, written tests may be shaped to emphasize speed and accuracy. It should be reemphasized at this point, however, that understanding is a major responsibility of instruction in secondary mathematics, and some of the practice tests should be designed to that end.

Some of the different ways of administering written practice tests are (1) all students at board, (2) some at the board and others in their seats, (3) all students in their seats.   In any of the above cases all students may be working on the same assigned problems, or separate groups may be working on separate problems.   These problems may be dictated by the teacher or printed, mimeographed, or otherwise reproduced.   Timed tests frequently serve to stimulate interest and attention through competition with other students or competition with one's own previous time record on similar material.   Precautions which the teacher must observe are as follows: (1) Do not overemphasize speed at the expense of accuracy; (2) provide for check-up and practice on understanding as well as on speed and accuracy; (3) vary the type of practice material to prevent monotony of effort; and (4) do not continue practice to the point of fatigue.

Achievement.   In the measure of achievement the teacher is not merely interested in testing mechanical proficiency in certain fundamental processes and factual information.   He is also interested in the measure of reasoned understanding of concepts, techniques, and principles.[1]   Such a testing program should be so designed that it will compare and discriminate between relative abilities as well as measure retention and understanding of learning.   The selection of test items must be in terms of an authoritative list of ultimate objectives which in turn have been carefully analyzed into immediate aims of instruction in the light of the significant implications and limitations of the local situation.   Although comprehensiveness is one of the important characteristics of an efficient achievement test, it is quite obvious that no such test can be sufficiently comprehensive to include all items of specific information into which an instructional unit may be analyzed.   The test is thus a function of the different items used. They must therefore represent an adequate sampling of the entire unit, and each item must make a significant contribution to the composite power of the test to discriminate between pupils of high and low levels of general achievement.   The validity of any achievement test is largely a function of the success with which each individual test item performs the function for which it was designed.

Just as in the case of prognosis and diagnosis there are several different

[1] For a basic philosophy of such testing and for representative test items see Maurice L. Hartung and Harold P. Fawcett, The Measurement of Understanding in Secondary Mathematics, "The Forty-fifth Yearbook of the National Society for the Study of Education" (Chicago: University of Chicago Press, 1946), part I, pp. 157–174.   Also see "Twenty-second Yearbook" (Washington, D.C.: National Council of Teachers of Mathematics, 1954), part 5, pp. 339–409.

evaluation procedures that can be used for measuring achievement: the standardized tests, the informal teacher-made tests, observations, interviews, anecdotal records, and pupil reports and projects. While standardized tests are available for many different purposes, there are cautions that should be observed in their use. The content of such a test may not conform closely enough to the local program of instruction, and it can vary widely, from author to author, in tests designed, theoretically, for the same general purpose. A comparison of local scores with published norms can thus be inaccurate and misleading. Futhermore, such tests are valid only in the context of the objectives for which they were designed. Interpretations of results should keep these limitations in mind.

Teacher-made tests have the advantage of being constructed entirely in the context of the local teaching situation. The objectivity of such tests, however, usually is not so well defined as in the case of standardized tests. Also, the question structure of teacher-made tests frequently fails to reflect as high a level of expertness as does that of the standardized tests. In the construction of an achievement test for a specific instructional unit and for a given group of pupils the teacher should use the following criteria as guides in selecting the content and shaping the questions:

1. The different levels of achievement potential within the group should be recognized.

2. For each level the test should provide an approximately equal number of items.

3. The items should hold the pupils responsible for concepts, principles, and understandings as well as for basic skills.

4. The items should be selected and worded in the context of reasonable expectations of individual and group performance for the specific instructional unit.

5. The items should be so constructed that they discriminate between different levels of ability.

6. The items should be such that they lend themselves to reliability in scoring.

Both standardized tests and teacher-made tests have their advantages and limitations. Each type of test can make significant contributions toward effective evaluation of achievement. But whether the two types of test are used separately or combined to secure the benefits of both, there remain gaps to be filled in before the true picture of either individual or group achievement can be composed. The observation of performance, the personal interview, the analysis of anecdotal records, and the studious appraisal of projects and reports, each and all can make significant contributions to the intelligent evaluation of pupil progress.

Interpretation and Use of Results. The significance of any program of evaluation is very definitely dependent upon the interpretation and use of the results obtained. It is highly important that the results of a given test be interpreted and used in the context of the function for which the test was constructed and administered.   For example, the results from a test designed solely for diagnostic purposes should never be used for the purpose of measuring achievement and then assigning grades.   There are sometimes fundamental differences in the construction of such tests, to say nothing of the moral obligation of the teacher to play fair with the student.

In many cases it is necessary that the teacher be familiar with certain simple but fundamental statistical procedures in order to derive maximum benefit from a testing program.   The techniques of classifying and tabulating data; grouping into significant class intervals; determining range of distribution; computing measures of central tendency, variability, and relationship; and ranking scores are the more important statistical measures with which the teacher should be familiar in order to summarize efficiently the results of a testing program.

Not only must the teacher have a certain amount of mechanical proficiency in the techniques for tabulating and analyzing test data but also he must be able to make logical inferences from such findings.   He must know the appropriateness of various measures and the extent and limitations of their implications.   The conclusions drawn must be consistent with the fundamental assumptions underlying the tests and the statistical measures used.

In the measure of achievement the teacher must know the difference between a test score and a grade.   Futhermore, he must know when test scores should be translated into grades and be familiar with the recommended techniques for careful conversion.   He must know how to detect a typical class error from a diagnosis test, and he must be able to determine whether particular detected errors imply the need for group or individual remedial measures.

Teachers should be familiar with the various purposes and limitations of each aspect of a functional testing program.   For maximum value the results should be used within the domain they are designed to serve, in the effort to construct from all sources of relevant information a composite, yet comprehensive, picture of the individual student.

EXERCISES

1. Distinguish between diagnostic, prognostic, and achievement tests as to characteristics and function.

2. Name different ways in which each type of test may be used in the improvement of instruction in mathematics.

3. How specific should one be in the formulation of the objectives for testing?

4. What are some of the recommended measures for improvement of essay-type examinations?

5. Contrast the relative effectiveness of different kinds of new-type tests (true-false, multiple-choice, completion, etc.).

6. Discuss the relative merits of factual and functional testing in secondary mathematics.

7. What are some recommended procedures for measuring mathematical aptitude?

8. What is meant by the validity of a test?

9. What is meant by the reliability of a test?

10. Give examples of material from secondary mathematics which you consider not well adapted to objective tests.

11. In test construction how much importance should be given to "range of difficulty" and "distribution of item difficulty"?

12. Briefly evaluate the advantages and disadvantages of extramural tests.

13. What are some of the common errors in secondary mathematics that call for remedial work?

14. What are some of the more important techniques for discovering pupil errors?

15. What are some of the recommended techniques for determining the degree of difficulty of test items?

16. What are some of the recommended procedures for transforming test scores into grades?

17. Compare the relative merits of the per cent and ranking techniques of determining grades.

18. What are some of the recommended techniques for testing appreciation and understanding in secondary mathematics?

19. What are some of the more significant recommendations for improving the program of evaluation in secondary mathematics?

20. What recommendations does the Joint Commission make concerning evaluation in secondary mathematics?

21. What emphasis did the Commission on Post-War Plans give to evaluation?

22. What is the advanced placement program of the College Entrance Examination Board?

BIBLIOGRAPHY

Blick, D. J., and S. E. Braman: Some Practices Used in Counseling Students Prior to Enrollment in Elementary Algebra and Plane Geometry, *School Science and Mathematics*, **54** (1954), 107–115.

Bromley, A., and G. C. Carter: Predictability of Success in Mathematics, *Journal of Educational Research*, **44** (1950), 148–150.

Brown, Claude H.: "The Teaching of Secondary Mathematics" (New York: Harper & Brothers, 1953), pp. 323–354.

Brueckner, Leo J., Foster E. Grossnickle, and John Reckzeh: "Developing Mathematical Understanding in the Upper Grades" (Philadelphia: John C. Winston Company, 1957), pp. 458–501.

Chrisman, E. B.: Let's Examine Our Tests, *School Science and Mathematics*, **47** (1947), 684–687.

Cliffe, Marion C.: The Place of Evaluation in the Secondary School Program, *Mathematics Teacher*, **49** (1956), 270–273.

Cox, H. M.: What Are the Administrative and Guidance Uses of Mathematics Examinations? *American Mathematical Monthly*, **48** (1941), 317–319.

Glennon, Vincent J.: "Testing Meanings in Arithmetic," *Supplementary Educational Monograph* 70, (Chicago: University of Chicago Press, 1949), pp. 64–74.

Greene, H. A., A. N. Jorgensen, and J. R. Gerberich: "Measurement and Evaluation in the Secondary School" (New York: Longmans, Green & Co., Inc., 1943).

Greenspan, P.: Predicting Success in Algebra, *High Points*, **35** (1953), 19–22.

Grever, L. W.: "Evaluating Critical Thinking," unpublished master's thesis (Normal, Ill.: Illinois State Normal University, 1952).

Hartung, M. L.: Evaluating Appreciation of the Cultural Values of Mathematics, *School Science and Mathematics*, **37** (1937), 168–181.

————: Some Problems of Evaluation, *Mathematics Teacher*, **31** (1938), 175–182.

————: A Forward Look at Evaluation, *Mathematics Teacher*, **42** (1949), 29–33.

————: Evaluating Instruction in Mathematics, *Bulletin of the National Association of Secondary-School Principals*, **38** (1954), 138–143.

Hendricks, S. Clifford: Why Not Abolish Tests? *School Science and Mathematics*, **47** (1947), 114–116.

————: For What Shall We Test? *School Science and Mathematics*, **47** (1947), 203–206.

————: How Shall We Test? *School Science and Mathematics*, **47** (1947), 322–325.

————: How Good Are Our Tests? *School Science and Mathematics*, **47** (1947), 470–474.

————: How to Improve Our Tests, *School Science and Mathematics*, **47** (1947), 554–559.

Henry, L. J.: A Comparison of the Difficulty and Validity of Achievement Test Items, *Journal of Educational Psychology*, **25** (1934), 537–541.

Joint Commission of the Mathematical Association of America, Inc., and the National Council of Teachers of Mathematics: "The Place of Mathematics in Secondary Education," *Fifteenth Yearbook* (Washington, D.C.: National Council of Teachers of Mathematics, 1940), pp. 162–186.

Keller, M. W., and H. F. S. Jonah: Measures for Predicting Success in a First Course in College Mathematics, *Mathematics Teacher*, **41** (1948), 350–355.

————, D. R. Shreve, and H. H. Remmers: A Mathematics Diagnostic Program in Purdue University, *Mathematics Teacher*, **35** (1942), 8–14.

Kinney, Lucien Blair, and C. Richard Purdy: "Teaching Mathematics in the Secondary School" (New York: Rinehart & Company, Inc., 1952), pp. 326–351.

Krout, Maurice H.: Psychological Standards in Measuring Achievement, *School Science and Mathematics*, **46** (1946), 803–806.

Lankford, F. G., Jr.: What Are Your Pupils Learning? Some Suggestions on Evaluation, *Mathematics Teacher*, **47** (1954), 208–210.

Layton, R. B.: A Study of Prognosis in High School Algebra, *Journal of Educational Research*, **34** (1941), 601–605.

Lewis, Harry: Evaluation of Mathematics Education, *New Jersey Mathematics Teacher*, **13** (1957), 13–15.

Lindquist, E. F. (Editor): "Educational Measurement" (Washington, D.C.: American Council on Education, 1951).

Lorge, Irving: Evaluation: The New Stress on Measurement, *Teachers College Record*, **42** (1941), 667–679.

MacRae, M., and W. L. Uhl: Types of Errors and Remedial Work in the Fundamental Processes of Algebra, *Journal of Educational Research*, **26** (1932) 12–21.

Meder, Elsa M., and Edwin Eagle: Measurement and Evaluation in the Teaching of Mathematics and Science, *Review of Educational Research*, **18** (1948), 350–363.

National Society for the Study of Education: The Measurement of Understanding, "Forty-Fifth Yearbook" (Chicago: University of Chicago Press, 1946), part I, pp. 138–157.

National Council of Teachers of Mathematics: "The Evaluation of Mathematical Learning," *Twenty-second Yearbook* (Washington, D.C.: National Council of Teachers of Mathematics, 1954), part 5, pp. 339–409, with additional bibliography on pp. 432–434.

Poppen, Henry A.: A Factor-analysis Study of Prognostic Tests in Algebra, *Contributions to Education* 420 (Nashville, Tenn.: George Peabody College for Teachers, 1950).

Progressive Education Association: "Mathematics in General Education," Report of the Mathematics Committee of the Commission on Secondary School Curriculum (New York: Appleton-Century-Crofts, Inc., 1940), pp. 338–382.

Report of the Committee on Tests: *American Mathematical Monthly*, **47** (1940), 290–301.

Rosskopf, Myron F.: The Present Status of Evaluation of Critical Thinking in Algebra and Geometry, *Mathematics Teacher*, **43** (1950), 143–148.

Shaw, Glenadine Sax: Prediction of Success in Elementary Algebra, *Mathematics Teacher*, **49** (1956), 173–178.

Spitzer, Herbert F.: Testing Instruments and Practices in Relation to Present Concepts of Teaching Arithmetic, "Fiftieth Yearbook of the National Society for the Study of Education," part II, "The Teaching of Arithmetic" (Chicago: University of Chicago Press, 1951), pp. 186–202.

Sueltz, Ben A.: The Measurement of Understanding and Judgments in Elementary Mathematics, *Mathematics Teacher*, **40** (1947), 279.

Tyler, R. W.: Characteristics of a Satisfactory Diagnosis, and Elements of Diagnosis, "Thirty-fourth Yearbook of the National Society for the Study of Education" (Bloomington, Ill.: Public School Publishing Company, 1935), pp. 95–111, 113–129.

———: General Statement on Evaluation, *Journal of Educational Research*, **35** (1942), 492–501.

Ullsvik, Bjarne R.: An Attempt to Measure Critical Judgment, *School Science and Mathematics*, **49** (1949), 445–452.

Weitzmann, Ellis, and W. J. McNamara: "Constructing Classroom Examinations" (Chicago: Science Research Associates, Occupational Information Division, 1949).

Woody, Clifford: Nature of Evaluation, *Journal of Educational Research*, **35** (1942), 481–491.

Wrightstone, J. W.: Techniques for Measuring Newer Values in Education, *Journal of Educational Research*, **35** (1942), 517–524.

———, J. Justman, and I. Robbins: "Evaluation in Modern Education" (New York: American Book Company, 1956).

——— and J. I. Krugman: "A Guide to the Use of Anecdotal Records," *Educational Research Bulletin* 11 (New York: Board of Education of the City of New York, 1949).

9

THE PROFESSIONALLY PREPARED TEACHER
OF MATHEMATICS

Possibly the most critical single element in the composite structure of
an effective mathematics program in the secondary school is the teacher.
A poorly prepared teacher can destroy the effectiveness of any carefully
selected and well-organized curriculum with inadequate and unenthusi-
astic instruction, inaccurate and uninformed interpretation, and indifferent and negative attitudes.   On the other hand, a professionally prepared
teacher can use even an inadequately structured curriculum to build an
instructional program of significant merit.   What then constitutes an
adequate program for the professional preparation of teachers of secondary mathematics?

The Professional Preparation of Teachers of Secondary Mathematics.   There
are two equally important aspects of any true profession, viz., significant
knowledge and effective technique.   One cannot be efficiently professional if there is any distinct weakness in either aspect.   A truly functional program of professional preparation must therefore place emphasis
on the acquiring of knowledge significant to the chosen profession and
also on the acquaintance with and use of the more efficient techniques
of that profession.

The Mathematical Association of America, Inc., and the National
Council of Teachers of Mathematics, as well as certain more localized
groups, have made notable efforts through their committees and publications to improve the situation as far as mathematics is concerned.
The interest of these groups has been directed to the better preparation
of teachers as well as to the improvement of the curriculum.   The fact
remains, however, that the teaching of secondary mathematics in the
United States is hardly an established profession.   There are individuals
teaching secondary mathematics whose academic preparation includes
neither a major nor a minor in mathematics.   They have no great
interest in the subject and, in their teaching, can do no more than treat
it in a superficial and fragmentary way.   They have little appreciation
of the values of mathematics, of the role it has played in the evolution

233

of our civilization, or of its possibilities for integrated development. Likewise, there are those who are deficient in their preparation for teaching because of failure to keep informed in the newer developments in mathematics. Some of this failure to keep abreast of the times is due, unfortunately, to inadequate opportunity but, regrettably, much of it is due to indifferent attitude. There are many teachers, however, whose preparation has been adequate in the field of mathematics itself, but who are unhappy and inefficient in their work because they are required to teach one or more classes in other subjects. Their programs of preparation should have been broad enough to enable them to teach in at least one additional field. There are still other teachers who know their subject well but who, because of their lack of patience with student difficulties and their unwillingness to adjust their teaching to the varying abilities of different students, actually destroy the interest of many students in mathematics when, under more favorable conditions, it might have been made to flourish. Such teachers lack that professional attitude which should impel them to discard any sense of intellectual superiority and view the subject through the eyes of the immature student so that they might patiently guide and encourage him in his efforts and stimulate his interest in further exploration of the field of mathematics.

Masterful scholarship in a body of relevant knowledge is an absolute essential for effective teaching, but it must be supplemented by a proficiency in the use of efficient techniques of instruction. Neither should be emphasized to the exclusion of the other, but a proper balance should be maintained throughout the preparation program.[1] We do not want teachers of mathematics to be "teachers who have nothing to teach," neither do we want them to be "mere purveyors of knowledge and promoters of skill."

Significant Knowledge. There is a trichotomy of knowledge significant to the teacher of mathematics which might be classified under the headings of general knowledge, professional knowledge, and specialized knowledge. We are living in an age in which events take place very rapidly. This rapidity of development and its implications for future change tend not only to stagger the imagination but also to encourage a satisfaction in superficiality of information. Things happen too fast for any individual to be able to attempt a very thorough and systematic acquaintance with the fundamentals of all lines of development. We have to be satisfied with a type of superficial information along some lines. It is for such reasons as this that the teacher of mathematics should have a broad

[1] "Report of Commission on Mathematics" (New York: College Entrance Examination Board, 1959), pp. 50–58.
Secondary School Curriculum Committee, Report of, *Mathematics Teacher*, **52** (1959), 389–417.

educational background against which to project his thinking and in which to orient his appreciation of values. Such an informational background should be related to the major areas of human experience and designed to build up a more intelligent understanding of the part mathematics has played in the evolution of modern civilization and a deeper appreciation of its relation to social progress.

A professional attitude should be a *sine qua non* for every teacher of mathematics. The term "professional attitude" is interpreted here to mean an enthusiastic interest in mathematics as a chosen field of study and service, an inspired concept of the value of mathematics in the structure of civilization, and an eager readiness to interpret carefully and thoughtfully those fundamental laws, mechanical processes, generalizing procedures, and possibilities of practical applications which so definitely characterize mathematics as a field of study and endeavor. In addition to providing a general education for cultural background, the program for the professional preparation of teachers of mathematics should equip such a teacher with an integrated philosophy of education, a devotion to teaching as a profession, and a sense of responsibility for the contributions he will be expected to make in his chosen field of work. This body of professional knowledge should be provided through courses designed to acquaint the individual with the place and function of education in our social order, the interrelationships that exist between the various professions, and the manifold opportunities for service which present themselves to teachers; to build up a psychological foundation for sympathetic understanding of the mental, physical, and social characteristics of those to be taught; and to provide opportunities for acquiring a safe minimum of teaching skill through observation of good teaching techniques and actual classroom practice under sympathetic but critical supervision.

Although the cultural background and the body of professional knowledge are essential elements to the program of professional preparation of teachers of mathematics, such a program must not overlook the fact that sound scholarship is a fundamental qualification of the teacher. This scholarship, however, should be *relevant* to the problem of teaching. From the point of view of the teacher of mathematics, what materials provide opportunity for development of *relevant* scholarship? The scholarship that is of service in the advancement of mathematical thought and research is not, in every case, the same as that which can be of service in the education of adolescents and immature thinkers. It is almost proverbial to state that "he who learns that he may know and he that learns that he may teach are standing in quite different mental attitudes."[1]

---

[1] H. S. Tarbell, Report of the Sub-committee on the Training of Teachers, *Proceedings of the National Education Association* (Washington, D.C.: National Education Association, 1895), p. 240.

The specialist in mathematics has need of a synthetic type of scholarship in which he seeks mastery not only of the fundamentals of mathematical thought but also of a closely interwoven chain of logic and of methods of making deductions and implications. His only need for the analytic type of scholarship is as a tool to be used in the aid of mathematical research. He is not primarily concerned with the questions of the place of mathematics in the educational program or of the practical value of mathematics to the average man. He is concerned with mathematical implications rather than with educational implications or practical applications of mathematics except, possibly, by the actuary, engineer, or other professional users of applied mathematics. He is the producer of mathematics.

On the other hand, the teacher of mathematics is the seller of mathematics. It is he who must convince the consumer of the value of his subject and, through the medium of efficient service, secure and retain consumers. He is constantly confronted with questions of the value of mathematics as an asset to the individual and a significant element in the program of general education. His interest in mathematics must embrace its educational implications and practical applications as well as its intrinsic subject appeal. Thus the preparation of the teacher of mathematics should emphasize that type of scholarship which seeks to integrate the subject with broad fields of learning and relate it to general human activity and interest. The teacher must learn to evaluate mathematics in the light of its role in the history of civilization, its contribution to the present social order, and its relation to future progress.

Furthermore, since it is to be his responsibility to assist immature learners in the mastery of mathematics, the prospective teacher of mathematics should not only strive for proficient mastery of the subject but also make every effort to be conscious of the processes by which he arrives at that mastery. He should pause at significant points for moments of reflection in which he should attempt to analyze the learning processes involved and evaluate the materials studied. Competent scholarship, which emphasizes understanding and mastery of fundamentals, must be constantly emphasized. These fundamentals will vary somewhat, according to whether the prospective teacher expects to teach in the elementary school, junior high school, senior high school, or junior college. To supplement this body of minimum essentials every teacher of mathematics should be encouraged to acquire a certain synthetic proficiency in some chosen line of mathematical endeavor to serve as a reserve of information which he might frequently use as an aid to individual exploration in the unknown realms of mathematical knowledge or in the expanding domain of significant applications of mathematical principles and techniques.

Relevant Scholarship for the Teacher of Secondary Mathematics.   The teacher of secondary mathematics should have some appreciation of the part that mathematics has played throughout the centuries of progress. Furthermore, he should have those contacts with the subject matter and history of mathematics that would enable him to formulate an intelligent notion of the meanings of mathematics.   In 1901 Bertrand Russell defined mathematics in words that are superficially facetious but fundamentally significant when he said: "Mathematics may be defined as the subject in which we never know what we are talking about, nor whether what we are saying is true."[1]   In discussing this definition Bell says that it has four great merits: (1) it shocks the self-conceit out of common sense, (2) it emphasizes the entirely abstract character of mathematics, (3) it reduces all mathematics and the more mature sciences to postulational forms, and (4) it administers a resounding parting salute to the doddering tradition that mathematics is the science of number, quantity, and measurement.[2]   Mario Pieri is responsible for the statement that "mathematics is an hypothetico-deductive system," which merely means that mathematics is a system of logical processes whereby conclusions are deduced from whatever fundamental assumptions and definitions there may be hypothesized.   To Benjamin Peirce goes the credit for expressing these thoughts in the more explicit form: "Mathematics is the science which draws necessary conclusions."[3]   To think mathematically is to free oneself by abstraction from any peculiarity of subject matter and to make inferences and deductions justified by fundamental premises.

According to Shaw,[4] there are four significant methods of mathematics which might be stated as follows:

1. Scientific, leading to generalizations of widening scope
2. Intuitive, leading to an insight into subtler depths
3. Deductive, leading to a permanent statement and rigorous form
4. Inventive, leading to the ideal element, and creation of new realms

The competent teacher of mathematics should realize that in any system of constructive thought the validity of the conclusions rests entirely upon the validity and consistency of the assumptions and definitions upon which the conclusions are based.   It is important that students should have this point of view, and the teacher should make every reason-

---

[1] Bertrand Russell, Recent Work on the Principles of Mathematics, *International Monthly*, 4 (1901), 84.

[2] E. T. Bell, "The Queen of the Sciences" (Baltimore: The Williams & Wilkins Company, 1931), pp. 16–17.

[3] Benjamin Peirce, "Linear Associative Algebra," sec. 1, lithographed, 1870. Reprinted in *American Journal of Mathematics*, 4 (1881), 97.

[4] J. B. Shaw, "Lectures on the Philosophy of Mathematics" (La Salle, Ill.: The Open Court Publishing Company, 1918), p. 11.

able effort to assist them in acquiring it.[1] From a logical point of view
the set of fundamental assumptions should be consistent, independent,
and categorical (complete), but pedagogically the only essential requirements are that they be consistent and categorical. An appreciation of
this dependence upon fundamental assumptions and definitions and
previously established theorems should help to develop an if-then mental
attitude which should function in a more intelligent interpretation of
human events. A student in the secondary school is by no means to be
taught the philosophical and logical aspects of non-Euclidean geometry,
but the teacher should be familiar with the high points in the history of
Euclid's famous fifth postulate. He should know of the efforts of mathematicians to demonstrate the dependence of this parallel postulate upon
the remaining postulates of Euclid's fundamental set. He should appreciate the fact that Lobatschevskian and Riemannian geometries are just as
logically sound as the commonly accepted Euclidean geometry; that,
although the Euclidean postulates are accepted because they seem to conform more nearly to the everyday experiences of the world in which we
live, in Poincaré's world of changing temperatures the parallel postulate
would be absurd.[2] The teacher so informed would have a significant
appreciation of geometry as a form of postulational thinking and thus
be better equipped to enhance his teaching by a more harmonious and
effective coordination of sensible pedagogy and sound logic.

Geometry was used in both Egypt and Babylonia as an art of measuring in connection with agriculture, irrigation, and architecture; thus
it was entirely empirical and intuitive without any idea of logical demonstration. Thales (ca. 640–546 B.C.), of Miletus, was the first to conceive
of the idea of establishing truths through formal demonstration, and in
his Ionian school geometry was studied not for its own sake, but as a
general preparation for the study of philosophy. It was Pythagoras
(ca. 572–501 B.C.), a disciple of Thales, and his followers who achieved
the arithmetization of geometry in the famous Pythagorean theorem.
Plato (429–348 B.C.) introduced to geometricians that powerful tool of
the logicians, the analytical method of proof, and one of his most brilliant
pupils, Eudoxus (ca. 408–355 B.C.), introduced the form of demonstration
known as the indirect method of proof.

In about 300 B.C. Euclid wrote his famous "Elements," in which he
made an effort to present a systematic collection of the then current
mathematical knowledge. Though mathematicians, in recent years,

[1] For the description of a very careful effort to teach geometry from this point of
view, see H. P. Fawcett, The Nature of Proof, "Thirteenth Yearbook" (Washington,
D.C.: National Council of Teachers of Mathematics, 1938).

[2] J. W. Young, "Fundamental Concepts of Algebra and Geometry" (New York:
The Macmillan Company, 1911), pp. 15–25.

have been able to point clearly to inaccuracies and inadequacies of Euclid's effort,[1] it still remains true that possibly his greatest contribution to mathematics was the coordination of all known propositions in a simple but logical sequence. This gave to geometry its characterization as a pattern for postulational thinking. Under the influence of Euclid the center of interest in mathematics shifted from Athens to Alexandria. The first Alexandrian school, of which Euclid, Archimedes, and Apollonius were members, lasted until the beginning of the Christian era, during which time mathematics was studied primarily for the interest in the subject itself. The second Alexandrian school, to which belonged such men as Serenus, Menelaus, Ptolemy, Pappus, and Proclus, flourished during the first six centuries of the Christian era. During this period, when utility was the chief objective for the study of geometry, the ideals of education sank to a very low level and there set in an intellectual stagnation that continued to prevent any significant mathematical progress until the Renaissance period.

In order to appreciate the magnificent structure of geometry, one not only must be familiar with this period of synthetic development but must realize that there are three other important periods of geometrical history, viz., (1) the period of analytic geometry, foreshadowed by the work of Archimedes (ca. 225 B.C.), but in reality exerting a significant influence only after the publication of the researches of Descartes (1596–1650) and Fermat (1601–1665), (2) the period of application of calculus to geometry, and (3) the renaissance of pure geometry which began with the nineteenth century.[2] The teacher of secondary mathematics should have firsthand information concerning these epochs of geometrical history as well as direct contact with the outstanding elements of each. He should know something of the systematized use of algebra that characterizes Cartesian geometry as well as the applications of the techniques of infinitesimal analysis to perfect the study of the relationships existing between the points and lines that generate geometrical configurations. He should know something of the theory of projectivity first enunciated by Poncelet (1788–1867) in 1822 and of Gergonne's (1771–1859) principle of duality, which so definitely enriches the theory of the united position of point and line. Such names as Desargues (1593–1662), Pascal (1623–1662), Ceva (1647–1734), Simson (1687–1786), Euler (1707–1783), Malfatti

---

[1] Felix Klein, "Elementary Mathematics from an Advanced Standpoint," II (New York: The Macmillan Company, 1939), pp. 188–208.

Albert E. Meder, Jr., What's Wrong with Euclid? *Mathematics Teacher*, **51** (1958), 578–584.

Bertrand Russell, "Principles of Mathematics," 2d ed. (New York: W. W. Norton & Company, Inc., 1938), p. 161.

[2] D. E. Smith, "History of Mathematics" (Boston: Ginn & Company, 1925), vol. II, p. 331.

(1731–1807), Legendre (1752–1833), Monge (1746–1818), Brianchon (1785–1864), von Staudt (1798–1867), and Steiner (1796–1863) should carry significant connotations for him because they represent progressive development in the field of modern synthetic geometry.

Historically, arithmetic developed out of a need for a system of counting, just as geometry found its origin in the necessity for systematic methods of measurement. The teacher of mathematics should know something of the history and nature of number, the foundation of all arithmetic. The beginnings of the concept of number are hidden in the obscurity of time, but there seems to be evidence that some form of number preceded written history by thousands of years.[1] The evolution of our number system has been a real "survival of the fittest" struggle between various scales and systems of notation and is more or less an anatomical accident. Had the gods decreed that man should have 6 fingers on each hand and 6 toes on each foot, the human race would probably do all of its counting and calculating on the basis of 12 instead of 10. Some argue that this would have worked to the advantage of the practical man, since 12 has more possibilities of factorization than has 10. If, however, the mathematician should decree the base of the number system, he would probably choose a prime, for then there would be economy in symbols, simplification in operations, and eradication of ambiguities.

The definition of abstract number and its elaborate theory possibly forms no part of the necessary preparation of the teacher of secondary mathematics. The teacher should, however, have his thinking about the system of positive integers (natural numbers) oriented within the context of Peano's postulates[2] or an equivalent system.[3] He needs to have a basic understanding of how the process of counting and the concept of the number of objects in a collection give rise to the system of positive integers, where by positive integer we mean a symbol for the number of elements in a set of distinct elements. This notion of positive integer creates an abstract symbol for the designation of a characteristic property of sets of objects between which the correspondence is one to one. Furthermore, he should have at his ready command the basic laws of operation and should understand how these laws and the principle of permanence rationalize the extension of the number system to include negative numbers, rational numbers, real numbers, and complex numbers. He should recognize the teaching responsibilities accompanying each basic extension. Also, he should be able to transmit to his students

[1] Tobias Dantzig, "Number: The Language of Science" (New York: The Macmillan Company, 1930), p. 11.

[2] Howard Eves and Carroll V. Newsom: "An Introduction to the Foundations and Fundamental Concepts of Mathematics" (New York: Rinehart & Company, Inc., 1958), p. 203.

[3] *Ibid.*, p. 195.

some comprehension of the cultural significance of the evolution of this extension along with the concomitant introduction of place value and the concept of a symbol for nothingness.

Etymologically, algebra means the theory of restitution (or transposition) and adjustment—in other words, a theory of equations.[1] In its modern garb it loses none of this significance but, through its laws of operations upon symbolic forms, expands further into a systematic method for the expression and examination of existing relationships. According to Nesselmann,[2] the history of algebra divides itself into three periods: (1) the rhetorical, (2) the syncopated, and (3) the symbolic. The rhetorical period was characterized by the fact that words were written out in full and no symbols were used. The oldest Egyptian, Babylonian, Arabian, Persian, and Italian algebraists represent this period. In the syncopated period the presentation was similar in literary type to that of the rhetorical period, but abbreviations were used. This period began with Diophantus (ca. 275) and extended up to the middle of the seventeenth century. In the symbolic period abbreviations gave way to signs and symbols.

The following examples show this transition from pure rhetorical algebra to that of modern compact symbolism; they show how the same equation would have been written by:[3]

Regiomontanus, A.D. 1464:

$$3 \text{ Census et } 6 \text{ demptis } 5 \text{ rebus aequatur zero}$$

Pacioli, A.D. 1494:

$$3 \text{ Census p. } 6 \text{ de } 5 \text{ rebus ae } 0$$

Vieta, A.D. 1591:

$$3 \text{ in } A \text{ quad } - 5 \text{ in } A \text{ plano } + 6 \text{ aequatur } 0$$

Stevinus, A.D. 1585:

$$3② - 5① + 6☉ = 0$$

Descartes, A.D. 1637:

$$3x^2 - 5x + 6 = 0$$

There are, of course, no clear-cut lines of demarcation between the three periods. Diophantus, in fact, used certain features of all three.[4]

The teacher of secondary mathematics should be acquainted with the extended domain of algebra under the freedom of symbolic abstraction. Under such freedom it is possible to define many different algebras[5] and their companion arithmetics. The concept of a basic algebraic structure

---

[1] Smith, *op. cit.*, pp. 388–390.

[2] G. H. F. Nesselmann, *"Die Algebra der Griechen"* (Berlin: G. Reimer, 1842), pp. 301–305.

[3] L. Hogben, "Mathematics for the Million" (New York: W. W. Norton & Company, 1937), p. 303.

[4] Smith, *op. cit.*, p. 379.

[5] Bell, *op. cit.*, p. 37.

arises from the recognition of the fact that, with the ordinary definition of addition and multiplication, the properties of associativity, commutativity, and distributivity characterize these operations not only with positive integers, rational numbers, real numbers, irrational numbers, and complex numbers but also with polynomials and even more general types of functions as well as with many other sets of elements. Even with slight modifications in the definitions of the basic operations these properties continue to be the basic laws as the operations are applied to more general sets of elements. Thus the concept of algebra is extended beyond a mere symbolization of arithmetic. It assumes individual stature as a definitive structure with specified elements, defined operations, and basic postulates. Such abstractions identify algebra as a truly hypotheticodeductive system, and there come into existence algebras of many different types such as the algebra of matrices, the algebra of symmetry, the algebra of transformations, and the algebra of sets. The concepts of group, ring, integral domain, and field are basic to the study of algebraic structure.

The algebra of the secondary school is the algebra of real and complex numbers. If we restrict this algebra to one of real numbers, we shall have one that is abstractly identical with the metric geometry of three dimensions. This identity is accomplished through the correlation of points on a line with real numbers, a concept that was suggested to the mathematical world by Descartes. Among an infinitude of significant achievements this equivalence has enabled modern mathematicians to set up the criterion of constructibility and thus through the algebraic analysis of geometrical relations to prove definitely that it is impossible to trisect an arbitrary angle, duplicate a cube, or "square a circle" by using *only* the compasses and the unmarked straightedge.

From the secondary school point of view the graph, equation, and concept of function are extremely important. The preparation of the teacher of secondary mathematics should be such that these will be intelligently correlated and understood. The part that coefficients of a function play in determining the shape of its graph, the techniques of construction and proper interpretation of the graph and its application to the solution of numerical equations, and the significance of the graph in the discussion of simultaneous equations constitute some of the contributions that advanced training should make to the professional equipment of the secondary school teacher. He should know the implications of the fundamental theorems of algebra and arithmetic and some of the more important theorems concerning the relation existing between roots of equations and the coefficients, as well as the application of the elementary theory of determinants and eliminants to the systematic study of equations.

In the words of Prof. E. H. Moore, "functionality is the relation or (mathematical) law of connection between two or more quantities or numbers subject to simultaneous and interdependent continuous variation."[1] This concept of the interdependence of magnitudes was recognized by the early Greeks and Egyptians. Two of the most primitive forms in which we find functional dependence expressed are in area formulas and formulas for the relation between arcs and chords. From these crude beginnings the development was slow, and it was not until the latter part of the seventeenth century that the word "function" was associated with the concept of dependence.

Descartes furnished the crystallizing influence in his discovery and development of coordinate geometry. In 1637 he published his "Geometry,"[2] in which he systematized the method of applying algebra to geometry, introduced the notion of variables and constants into the study of geometrical relations, conceived of curves as generated by a moving point, referred these curves to two intersecting lines, and represented them by equations involving two variables, the relation of these variables being determined by the distances from the two lines of reference. It was this notion of expressing curves by algebraic equations that made possible the step from geometry to analysis and thus paved the way for calculus. A few years later Leibniz introduced the word "function" to designate magnitudes involved in Descartes's idea of curves generated by a moving point. The researches of Newton and Leibniz made extensive use of this new concept of the locus of a moving point and by application of the techniques of infinitesimal analysis gave new significance to the implications of functional dependence.

It is interesting to note that Cartesianism also provided the basis for the modern refinement of the concept of function which subdues or subordinates the idea of dependence to the more fundamental idea of relation. The Cartesian frame of reference composed of two intersecting number lines provides the machinery, and the language of sets provides the terminology, for more precise descriptions of many fundamental mathematical concepts. While relation and function are not necessarily restricted to dealing with numbers, the associations expressed through the Cartesian pairing of numbers in graphs provides a basis for a more precise description of the correspondence existing between different sets of elements. This is accomplished through the mechanism of *ordered pairs* such as (x,y), where x is the first element and y the second element of the ordered pair. A *relation* then is merely a set of ordered pairs, and

---

[1] E. H. Moore, Cross Section Paper as a Mathematical Instrument, *School Review*, **14** (May, 1906), p. 318.

[2] This work, which appeared as an appendix to the *Discours de la méthode*, was divided into three books. The first dealt with the products of lines; the second defined two types of curves, geometric and mechanic, and treated of tangents and normals; and the third discussed roots and transformations of equations.

a *function* is a relation in which there is associated with each first element one and only one second element.   Thus the set $(1, -1)$, $(1,1)$, $(4, -2)$, $(4,2)$, $(9, -3)$, $(9,3)$ would be a relation, while the set $(-1,1)$, $(1,1)$, $(-2,4)$, $(2,4)$, $(-3,9)$, $(3,9)$ would be a function.[1]   The teacher should have a clear comprehension of these more modern ideas and be prepared to give an informal interpretation of them to his students.

Along with the study of analytic geometry the study of trigonometry and differential and integral calculus affords unlimited opportunities for coming into contact with the fundamental principles that are essential to an appreciative and intelligent comprehension of the basic interrelationships which give significant structure to mathematics as a field of thought.   The teacher of secondary mathematics should be not only familiar with the numerical aspects of trigonometry as an effective tool in making indirect measurements but also thoroughly informed concerning the fundamental analytic properties of trigonometric functions and the tremendous import of their applicative value.   Also he should know how the method of exhaustions, used by Antiphon (ca. 430 B.C.), Archimedes (ca. 225 B.C.), and others in their efforts to effect the quadrature of the circle, evolved through the method of indivisibles of Cavalieri (1598–1647) and Roberval (1602–1675) into the infinitesimal analysis of Newton (1642–1727) and Leibniz (1646–1716).   Finally, familiarity with the power of calculus as a generalizing technique and its importance as a research instrument in pure and applied mathematics should be considered as a significant part of the subject-matter preparation of the teacher of secondary mathematics.[2]

Significant Professional Techniques.   The demands made on the teacher of secondary mathematics in the modern program of education make it absolutely essential that he know the orientation of his field of work in the entire secondary program; that he be familiar with significant objectives and problems in secondary mathematics; that he know the techniques of selection of textbooks, workbooks, and other teaching equipment; that he be familiar with the fundamental philosophy of significant evaluation of instruction; that he be skilled in the construction, use, and interpretation of tests—factual and functional, standardized and nonstandardized, objective and essay; that he be acquainted with various instructional techniques and know when and how to use them for maximum efficiency; and that he be prepared to assume his share of the responsibility in the pupil-guidance program.

The teacher of secondary mathematics must be thoroughly familiar

---

[1] For a good presentation of the more modern concept of function see Kenneth D. May and Henry Van Engen, Relations and Functions, "Twenty-fourth Yearbook" (Washington, D.C.: National Council of Teachers of Mathematics, 1959), pp. 65–110.

[2] For the individual who is interested in pursuing the discussion of this section still further the Bibliography provides supplementary readings.

with the complementary problems of transfer of training and individual differences. He must know the major sources of student difficulties and how to diagnose these difficulties and plan programs of remedial teaching; he must know how to plan an instructional program and how to adapt this program to different ability groups; he must be enthusiastically interested in mathematics and know the fundamental principles of the psychology of motivation; and he should know how to detect and remedy inefficient study habits and techniques. Finally, the teacher of secondary mathematics should be well versed in the fundamentals of the psychology of learning and their application to materials and methods for better instruction in mathematics of the secondary school.

We might list the above as the necessary technical equipment of the efficient teacher. As a highly desirable, but not absolutely necessary, part of the program of professional education of the prospective teacher we should list skill in the use and interpretation of the techniques of educational research and experimentation.   The teacher should be equipped to read, interpret, and evaluate the published results of experimental investigation and make use of significant findings in the improvement of his own teaching procedures.   It is also very desirable that he be equipped to pursue scientific investigations in connection with his own program and interpret intelligently his findings for the benefit of others.

The Well-prepared Teacher of Mathematics. The foregoing discussion presents what might be called a minimum ideal for the preparation of mathematics teachers. It represents a program which the prospective teacher should at least approximate as nearly as possible. Most beginning teachers, however, must teach in small schools, and in small schools practical considerations generally make it necessary for teachers to teach one or more courses outside their fields of major interest and specialization.   Consequently the prospective teacher of mathematics is virtually obliged by circumstances to prepare himself in at least one other field, and this may compel him to forego some of the advanced work in mathematics which would constitute a desirable part of his preparation.

Recognizing such varieties of demand and keeping in mind the ideal of effective instruction by an enthusiastic teacher with an adequate background of preparation, the Secondary School Curriculum Committee has presented what it recommends as an appropriate guide for the training of teachers of secondary mathematics.[1]

In view of current curriculum demands teachers of mathematics in grades seven through twelve will need to have competence in (1) analysis—trigonometry, plane and solid analytic geometry, and calculus; (2) foundations of mathematics—theory of sets, mathematical or symbolic logic, postulational systems, real and complex number systems; (3) algebra—matrices and determinants, theory of

[1] Secondary School Curriculum Committee, Report of, *Mathematics Teacher*, **52** (1959), 414–415.

numbers, theory of equations, and structure of algebra; (4) geometry—Euclidean and non-Euclidean, metric and projective, synthetic and analytic; (5) statistics—probability and statistical inference; (6) applications—mechanics, theory of games, linear programming, and operations research.

Ideally every teacher of secondary mathematics should have completed successfully a five-year program, emphasizing the above areas and culminating in the master's degree. As a minimum, teachers of mathematics at the seventh- and eighth-grade levels should have completed successfully a program of at least eighteen semester hours, including six semester hours of calculus, in courses selected from the above areas. Also as a minimum, teachers of mathematics in grades nine through twelve should have completed successfully a program of at least twenty-four semester hours, including a full-year program in calculus, in courses selected from the above areas. Both programs should contain fundamental treatments of relevant topics from the foundations of mathematics and probability and statistics. These programs in mathematics should be supplemented by a basic program in education and psychology. As a minimum, a teacher should have completed successfully eighteen semester hours, including student teaching in mathematics, in such courses as: a methods course in the teaching of mathematics, psychology of learning (with particular reference to adolescents), psychology of adjustment (mental hygiene), and tests and measurements. This total program of specialization should be based on a strong program of general education.

The Sub-committee on Teacher Certification of the Cooperative Committee on the Teaching of Science and Mathematics of the American Association for the Advancement of Science has made the following recommendations in its report:[1]

Part 5. Suggested Courses in Mathematics and Science for High School Teachers
of Mathematics
(Given in semester hours)

Suggested courses	A	B	C	D	E	F	4-year total		5th year		5-year total	
							Math	Supporting Science	Math	Supporting Science	Math	Supporting Science
Teachers of math only (senior high school)	12	6	3	3	3	3	30	18	12	6	42	24
Teachers of math only (junior high school)	9	3	3	3	3	3	24	12	9	3	33	15
Teachers with math minor (junior or senior high school)	9	3	3			3	18					

[1] Alfred B. Garrett, Recommendation for the Preparation of High School Teachers of Science and Mathematics, *School Science and Mathematics*, **59** (1959), 287–288.

Notes on Part 5:

1. *Teaching Area:* There are three teaching areas distinguished in this report:
   1. Mathematics in the senior high school.
   2. Mathematics in the junior high school.
   3. Mathematics combined with some other field such as a science, history, or some other field at the junior or senior high level. Even though teaching assignments are not as desirable as those with only mathematics, such combinations must be recognized.
2. *Mathematics Courses:* On the undergraduate level minimum requirements in each section of mathematics are specified. On the graduate level, only the total additional number of hours in mathematics is specified.
   A. *Analysis:* Trigonometry, plane analytic geometry, calculus (at least six semester hours required), solid analytic geometry, advanced calculus, differential equations, infinite series.
   B. *Applications:* Mechanics (statics and dynamics), mathematical physics, astronomy (mathematical), actuarial mathematics (finite differences, interpolation, numerical analysis), uses in behavioral science (theory of games, linear programming, operations research).
   C. *Probability and Statistics:* Emphasizing probability and statistical inference.
   D. *Algebra:* Abstract algebra (fields, rings, groups, linear algebra, vector spaces), matrices, theory of numbers, theory of equations.
   E. *Geometry:* Metric and other geometries (projective, affine, inversive), non-Euclidean geometries, differential geometry, topology.
   F. *Foundations of Mathematics:* Theory of sets, mathematical or symbolic logic, postulates for geometry, postulates for algebra, postulates for arithmetic, the real and complex number systems.
3. *Supporting Science Courses:* Each undergraduate requirement should include a course in physics. The other hours should be chosen from the following: chemistry, biology, astronomy, geology, and meteorology.

After a detailed discussion of what it feels is "an adequate structure for a teacher-education program" the Commission on Mathematics summarizes its recommendations for a preservice training program for teachers of secondary mathematics in these words:[1]

Secondary teachers should include in their preservice preparation courses in modern algebra, probability and statistical inference, elementary and advanced calculus, and geometry. The latter course should stress the foundations of geometry, and the study of geometries other than traditional Euclidean geometry, and should not deal exclusively or even primarily with so-called "advanced" Euclidean geometry.

The future of mathematics in the secondary schools is primarily the responsibility of the teacher of mathematics in those schools. Its status will depend largely upon his ability to present and interpret his subject as

[1] "Report of Commission on Mathematics" (New York: College Entrance Examination Board, 1959), p. 58.

a worthwhile educational venture. The professional preparation of this teacher should equip him with the scholarship and techniques essential to the satisfactory fulfillment of his professional obligation. He must be able to organize and present mathematics in such a way that adolescent boys and girls will be brought not only to a realization of the intrinsic nature and value of mathematics itself but also to an equally clear realization of its role in enabling man to relate, understand, and control his environmental factors and direct his social and economic advancement.

If these ends are to be attained, the training of the teacher must be an organic and continuous process. It should make the teacher unwilling to permit himself to stagnate under a comfortable self-complacency. It should inspire him to incessant effort both in the expanding of his mathematical horizons and in educational experimentation directed toward the improvement of his instructional techniques. The teacher so prepared will not restrict his attention and his instruction to the confines of mere operational mechanics. He will lead his students with contagious enthusiasm into realms of mathematical thought and endeavor which will be both stimulating to their curiosity and intellectual interest and broadly significant to their insights, appreciations, and general cultural development.

EXERCISES

1. Contrast the implications of the following two statements: (a) Mathematics is a tool subject. (b) Mathematics is a fundamental mode of thinking. Give three illustrations of each of these concepts of mathematics.

2. In the teaching of secondary mathematics what emphasis should be placed on mathematics as a tool subject? What emphasis should be placed on mathematics as a fundamental mode of thinking?

3. What have been some of the major influences that have brought about the employment of so many poorly prepared teachers?

4. Why should the teacher of secondary mathematics be thoroughly familiar with the mathematics programs of all lower grades?

5. What contribution can the history of mathematics make to the better preparation of teachers of secondary mathematics?

6. Do you think there should be a differentiation between programs designed to train the teacher of junior high school mathematics, the teacher of senior high school mathematics, and the teacher of junior college mathematics? Defend your answer.

7. What types of courses could be used to provide for such differentiation?

8. What subjects seem to be most frequently combined with mathematics in teaching combinations?

9. In the light of existent studies how many subjects should a prospective teaching candidate be prepared to teach?

10. What do you think should be considered minimum mathematics preparation for the teacher of secondary mathematics?

11. In the light of existent studies from what subjects do you think a major in mathematics should choose a minor?

12. What are the "major areas of human experience" out of which a program of general education should be developed? What contribution can mathematics make to such a program?

13. What would be some of the principal distinctions in treatment in a course in plane analytic geometry planned for prospective teachers and one planned for the prospective research worker in pure or applied mathematics?

14. Answer the question of exercise 13 for a course in algebra.

BIBLIOGRAPHY

Adler, Irving: "The New Mathematics" (New York: The John Day Company, Inc., 1958).

Archibald, Raymond Clare: Outline of the History of Mathematics, *American Mathematical Monthly*, **56**, part II (January, 1949), 1–114.

Bell, E. T.: "The Queen of the Sciences" (Baltimore: The Williams and Wilkins Company, 1931).

————: "Men of Mathematics" (New York: Simon and Schuster, Inc., 1937).

————: "The Development of Mathematics," 2d ed. (New York: McGraw-Hill Book Company, Inc., 1945).

Boehm, George A. W , and the editors of *Fortune:* "The New World of Math" (New York: The Dial Press, Inc., 1959).

Boyer, Carl B.: "The Concepts of the Calculus" (New York: Columbia University Press, 1939).

————: "History of Analytic Geometry" (New York: *Scripta Mathematica*, 1956).

Branford, Benchara: "A Study of Mathematical Education," 2d ed. (New York: Oxford University Press, 1924).

Breuer, Joseph: "Introduction to the Theory of Sets," translated by Howard F. Fehr (Englewood Cliffs, N.J.: Prentice-Hall, Inc., 1958).

Brown, Claude H.: "The Teaching of Secondary Mathematics" (New York: Harper & Brothers, 1953), pp. 355–373.

Brown, John A. (Compiler): Promising Practices in Mathematics Teacher Education, *School Science and Mathematics*, **58** (1958), 25–40, 435–444.

Brown, Kenneth E., and Ellsworth S. Obourn: "Qualifications and Teaching Loads of Mathematics and Science Teachers," Circular No. 575 (Washington, D.C.: U.S. Department of Health, Education, and Welfare, 1960).

Cairns, S. S.: Elementary and Secondary School Training in Mathematics, *Mathematics Teacher*, **47** (1954), 299–302.

Cajori, F.: "A History of Mathematics," 2d ed. (New York: The Macmillan Company, 1931).

Christofferson, H. C.: Creative Teaching in Mathematics, *Bulletin of the National Association of Secondary-School Principals*, **38** (1954), 117–123.

Commission on Mathematics, Report of: "Program for College Preparatory Mathematics" (New York: College Entrance Examination Board, 1959), pp. 48–58.

————: "Appendices" (New York: College Entrance Examination Board, 1959).

Commission on Post-War Plans: Second Report, *Mathematics Teacher*, **38** (1945), 215–220.

Commission on the Training and Utilization of Advanced Students in Mathematics: Report on the Training of Teachers of Mathematics, *American Mathematical Monthly*, **42** (1935), 263–277, 472–476.

Committee on the Subject Matter Preparation of Secondary School Teachers, Report of, *North Central Association Quarterly*, **12** (1938), 439–539.

Committee on the Undergraduate Program, Dartmouth Writing Group: "Modern Mathematical Methods and Models" [Buffalo, N.Y. (University of Buffalo): Mathematical Association of America, Inc., 1958], vols. I and II.

———, Kansas Summer Writing Group: "Universal Mathematics" [Buffalo, N.Y. (University of Buffalo): Mathematical Association of America, Inc., 1954].

———, Tulane Writing Group: "Elementary Mathematics of Sets, with Applications" [Buffalo, N.Y. (University of Buffalo): Mathematical Association of America, Inc., 1955].

Courant, Richard, and Herbert Robbins: "What Is Mathematics?" (New York: Oxford University Press, 1941).

Dantzig, Tobias: "Number: The Language of Science" (New York: The Macmillan Company, 1933).

Davis, David R.: "The Teaching of Mathematics" (Reading, Mass.: Addison-Wesley Publishing Company, 1951).

Eves, Howard: "An Introduction to the History of Mathematics" (New York: Rinehart & Company, Inc., 1953).

——— and Carroll V. Newsom: "Introduction to the Foundations and Fundamental Concepts of Mathematics" (New York: Rinehart & Company, Inc., 1958).

Fehr, Howard F.: "Secondary Mathematics: A Functional Approach for Teachers" (Boston: D. C. Heath and Company, 1951).

———: Goal Is Mathematics for All, School Science and Mathematics, 56 (1956), 109–120.

———: Mathematics Curriculum for the High School of the Future, Teachers College Record, 59 (1958), 258–267.

———: Breakthroughs in Mathematical Thought, Mathematics Teacher, 52 (1959), 15–19.

———: How Much Mathematics Should Teachers Know? Mathematics Teacher, 52 (1959), 299–300.

Glennon, Vincent J.: A Study in Needed Redirection in the Preparation of Teachers of Arithmetic, Mathematics Teacher, 42 (1949), 389–396.

Grossnickle, F. E.: The Training of Teachers of Arithmetic, "Fiftieth Yearbook of the National Society for the Study of Education," part II, "The Teaching of Arithmetic" (Chicago: University of Chicago Press, 1951), pp. 203–231.

Hartung, Maurice L.: Modern Methods and Current Criticisms of Mathematical Education, School Science and Mathematics, 55 (1955), 85–90.

Hogben, Lancelot: "Mathematics for the Million" (New York: W. W. Norton & Company, Inc., 1937).

Joint Commission of the Mathematical Association of America and the National Council of Teachers of Mathematics: "The Place of Mathematics in Secondary Education," Fifteenth Yearbook (Washington, D.C.: National Council of Teachers of Mathematics, 1940), pp. 187–203.

Jones, B. W.: On the Training of Teachers for Secondary Schools, American Mathematical Monthly, 46 (1939), 428–434.

Judd, C. H.: The Fallacy of Treating School Subjects as Tool Subjects, "Third Yearbook" (Washington, D.C.: National Council of Teachers of Mathematics, 1928), pp. 1–10.

Karnes, H. T.: Preparation of Teachers of Secondary Mathematics, Mathematics Teacher, 38 (1945), 3–10.

Kasner, Edward, and James Newman: "Mathematics and the Imagination" (New York: Simon and Schuster, Inc., 1940).

Kingston, J. Maurice: Some Arithmetical Fundamentals of Value to Junior High School Teachers, Mathematics Teacher, 48 (1955), 232–236.

Kinney, Lucien Blair, and C. Richard Purdy: "Teaching Mathematics in the Second-dary School" (New York: Rinehart & Company, Inc., 1952).

Klein, Felix: "Elementary Mathematics from an Advanced Standpoint" (New York: The Macmillan Company, 1932), vols. I and II.

Kline, Morris: "Mathematics and Western Culture" (New York: Oxford University Press, 1953).

Laframboise, Marc A.: The Training of Mathematics Teachers, *School Science and Mathematics*, **55** (1955), 389–392.

Lane, E. P.: Definition and Classification of Geometries, *School Science and Mathematics*, **30** (1930), 50–56.

Layton, W. I.: The Certification of Teachers of Mathematics, *Mathematics Teacher*, **42** (1949), 377–380.

Luce, R. D.: "Some Basic Mathematical Concepts," Studies in Mathematics, vol. I (Reproduced and distributed by the School Mathematics Study Group, with head-quarters at Yale University), (New Haven, Conn.: School Mathematics Study Group, 1959).

MacDuffee, C. C.: Teacher Education in Algebra, *American Mathematical Monthly*, **60** (1953), 367–375.

Mayor, John R.: Special Training for Teachers of Arithmetic, *School Science and Mathematics*, **49** (1949), 539–548.

Meserve, B. E.: "Fundamental Concepts of Algebra" (Reading, Mass: Addison-Wesley Publishing Company, 1953).

———: "Fundamental Concepts of Geometry" (Reading, Mass.: Addison-Wesley Publishing Company, 1955).

———: The Evolution of Geometry, *Mathematics Teacher*, **49** (1956), 372–382.

———: Modern Geometry for Teachers, *School Science and Mathematics*, **58** (1958), 437–441.

Murnaghan, F. D.: The Evolution of the Concept of Number, *Scientific Monthly*, **68** (1949), 262–269.

National Committee on Mathematical Requirements: "The Reorganization of Mathematics in Secondary Education" (Boston: Houghton Mifflin Company, 1923), pp. 126–132.

National Council of Teachers of Mathematics: "The Learning of Mathematics; Its Theory and Practice," *Twenty-first Yearbook* (Washington, D.C.: National Council of Teachers of Mathematics, 1953).

———: "Emerging Practices in the Teaching of Mathematics," *Twenty-second Year-book* (Washington, D.C.: National Council of Teachers of Mathematics, 1954).

———: "Insights into Modern Mathematics," *Twenty-third Yearbook* (Washington, D.C.: National Council of Teachers of Mathematics, 1957).

———: "The Growth of Mathematical Ideas," *Twenty-fourth Yearbook* (Washington, D.C.: National Council of Teachers of Mathematics, 1959).

———: "Instruction in Arithmetic," Twenty-fifth Yearbook (Washington, D.C.: National Council of Teachers of Mathematics, 1960).

National Society of College Teachers of Education: "The Education of Teachers," *Twenty-third Yearbook* (Chicago: University of Chicago Press, 1935), pp. 1–240.

New Developments in Secondary School Mathematics, *Bulletin of the National Association of Secondary-School Principals*, **43** (1959), 1–203.

Newsom, C. V.: A Philosophy for the Mathematics Teacher, *Mathematics Teacher*, **40** (1947), 195–198.

———: Mathematical Background Needed by Teachers of Arithmetic, "Fiftieth Yearbook of the National Society for the Study of Education," part II, *The Teaching of Arithmetic*, (Chicago: University of Chicago Press, 1951), pp. 232–250.

Northrop, E. P.: Modern Mathematics and the Secondary School Curriculum, *Mathematics Teacher*, **48** (1955), 386–393.

Phillips, Clarence: Background and Mathematical Achievement of Elementary Education Students in Arithmetic for Teachers, *School Science and Mathematics*, **53** (1953), 48–52.

Pólya, G.: "Mathematics and Plausible Reasoning" (Princeton, N.J.: Princeton University Press, 1954), vols. I and II.

Pratt, Gertrude V.: What Should a Good Teacher of Mathematics Know? *Pentagon*, **17** (Fall, 1957), 32–36.

Rappaport, David: Preparation of Teachers of Arithmetic, *School Science and Mathematics*, **58** (1958), 635–643.

Reeve, W. D.: "Mathematics for the Secondary School" (New York: Henry Holt and Company, Inc., 1954).

Rosskopf, Myron F.: Professionalized Subject Matter for Junior High School Mathematics Teacher, *Mathematics Teacher*, **46** (1953), 541–547.

—— and R. M. Exner: "Logic in Elementary Mathematics" (New York: McGraw-Hill Book Company, Inc., 1959).

Rourke, R. E. K.: Some Implications of Twentieth Century Mathematics for High Schools, *Mathematics Teacher*, **51** (1958), 74–86.

Schaaf, William L.: Arithmetic for Arithmetic Teachers, *School Science and Mathematics*, **53** (1953), 537–543.

Secondary School Curriculum Committee, Report of, *Mathematics Teacher*, **52** (1959), 389–417.

Small, Dwain E.: The Fifth Year of Teacher Education for Teachers of Mathematics, *Mathematics Teacher*, **50** (1957), 199–203.

Smith, D. E.: "History of Mathematics" (Boston: Ginn & Company, vol. I, 1923; vol. II, 1925).

—— and Jekuthiel Ginsburg: "A History of Mathematics in America before 1900," *Carus Monograph* 5, The Mathematical Association of America, Inc., (La Salle, Ill.: The Open Court Publishing Company, 1934).

—— and ——: "Numbers and Numerals" (Washington, D.C.: National Council of Teachers of Mathematics, 1937).

Stone, M. H.: Some Crucial Problems of Mathematical Instruction in the United States, *School Review*, **65** (1957), 64–77.

Thacker, G. R., and C. B. Read: Courses Desirable for Training Teachers of High School Mathematics, *School Science and Mathematics*, **49** (1949), 611–619.

Turner, I. S.: The Training of Mathematics Teachers, "Fourteenth Yearbook" (Washington, D.C.: National Council of Teachers of Mathematics, 1939).

Van Engen, Henry: Plans for the Reorganization of College Preparatory Mathematics, *School Science and Mathematics*, **58** (1958), 277–285.

——, J. Landin, P. D. Edwards, and L. E. Bush: Teacher Education in Mathematics, *School Science and Mathematics*, **58** (1958), 27–34.

Wilson, Jack D.: Arithmetic for Majors? *Mathematics Teacher*, **46** (1953), 560–564.

Wren, F. Lynwood: Mathematics in Focus, *Mathematics Teacher*, **48** (1955), 514–524.

——: Curiosity and Culture, *Mathematics Teacher*, **50** (1957), 361–371.

—— and J. A. Garrett: The Development of the Fundamental Concepts of Infinitesimal Analysis, *American Mathematical Monthly*, **40** (1933), 269–281.

Young, J. W.: "Fundamental Concepts of Algebra and Geometry" (New York: The Macmillan Company, 1925).

Zant, James H.: The Mathematics and Science Teacher of Tomorrow, *Mathematics Teacher*, **50** (1957), 426–431.

10

SUPERVISION OF INSTRUCTION

In nearly every enterprise which engages the services of any considerable number of individuals, the supervision of the work of these individuals is regarded as an important function essential to the economical and efficient operation of the enterprise. Engineering and construction crews have their foremen, large stores their departmental managers, restaurants their headwaiters, large offices their chief clerks, governmental bureaus and departments their supervisors, and so on through an endless list. It may be taken for granted that those in charge of the operation of business enterprises would not engage the services of these individuals unless they felt that the returns justified the expense.

Viewed from a strictly financial standpoint the business of public education is the largest single business in this country. While it must be regarded as more than a mere business enterprise, it does entail the expenditure of vast sums of money for the primary purpose of instruction. It seems reasonable, therefore, to insist that this instruction be made to yield as large a return as possible. There is both theoretical and experimental justification for the belief that direct supervision can contribute much to the improvement of instruction in the secondary school and thus increase the efficiency of the entire educational program.

The supervision of secondary school subjects has certain broad functions and employs certain broad principles and types of activity which are pretty much the same whether applied to the teaching of mathematics, art, history, or any other subject. It is difficult, if not impossible, to give any adequate discussion of supervision apart from them. The purpose of the present chapter is to consider these basic functions and principles as they apply to the supervision of mathematics. Generality cannot be avoided in the discussion, but if the reader will maintain the point of view of the individual responsible for the functioning of a mathematics department, the application of the discussion to this particular responsibility will be apparent throughout the chapter.

The Need for Supervision in Secondary Mathematics. There is need for the supervision of the work of mathematics teachers in the secondary school. Large numbers of these teachers come into the schools each year fresh from college, with high enthusiasm for their work but with little or no experience in teaching and without much firsthand knowledge of the problems connected with teaching secondary school students. These problems cannot be mastered adequately in the course of one or two years, even under favorable circumstances. Most young teachers can be greatly helped by the guiding advice and counsel of a sympathetic and experienced supervisor for a period of several years after they enter upon their work, and, since the annual turnover in the teaching staffs of secondary schools is relatively high, this period may in many cases include the entire professional career of the teacher.

The need for supervision is accentuated by the fact that the majority of secondary school teachers find it necessary to teach one or more subjects in fields other than those of their major preparation. Thus many mathematics classes are taught by individuals whose primary interest and preparation have been in other fields and whose training in mathematics has been largely of an incidental nature. Complete familiarity with the subject matter to be taught, while not a sufficient guarantee of teaching proficiency, is certainly a necessary condition, and any limitation of such familiarity evidently imposes a severe additional handicap upon the teacher.

Extensive and reasonably successful experience is a great asset to the teacher of mathematics, but such experience itself is sometimes not without its potential disadvantages. In particular, the teacher who has been successful in his work may find it easy to get into a rut and to become complacent about his work and oblivious or insensitive to possibilities of further improvement. Thus even teachers of long experience and substantial training may benefit from appropriate supervisory contacts through being stimulated to professional alertness and scholarly advancement.

In spite of the foregoing considerations, however, if one may judge from its prevailing status, no great amount of importance has generally been attached to supervision of mathematical instruction in the secondary schools. Even its functions and aims have not always been properly understood. As a result, supervision, where it exists at all, is all too often carried on in a sporadic and more or less planless fashion which accomplishes little of value. There are certain situations, of course, more often encountered in the secondary schools of large cities, in which effective supervision exists. On the other hand, even in some larger schools the supervision is often perfunctory and fails to achieve the major outcomes which are properly implied in the term, while in a great many smaller schools supervision is practically nonexistent.

There are several reasons why this is true. Often such supervision as is carried on must be done by the superintendents, principals, or department heads, who have many duties other than those relating to supervision. Department heads must be concerned largely with their own classes and with administrative affairs of the department, while the professional training of the superintendent or the principal of a school only rarely includes much work in mathematics, and will usually have been concerned more with administrative matters than with principles and techniques of supervision. It may be said also that the postponement or neglect of administrative and instructional duties is much more likely to result in immediately and obviously embarrassing situations than is the neglect of supervision. Consequently, in view of universally crowded time schedules and in view of the usually inadequate training in mathematics and in the principles and techniques of supervision, there frequently exists the tendency to subordinate supervisory activities to other matters which may appear to be more immediately pressing. Moreover, teachers often dislike the idea of supervision. Failing to appreciate its primary function, which is the improvement of instruction, many teachers regard supervision merely as personal criticism and as a means through which ratings and possibly invidious comparisons are to be made. Where this point of view persists, teachers are likely to oppose any attempts at supervision and look upon their supervisors with suspicion and distrust. Such an attitude nullifies the beneficial effects toward the attainment of which all supervisory effort should be directed.

If supervision is to result in improved instruction, it must be a cooperative effort. Teachers and their supervisors must have a mutual and sympathetic understanding of supervision: the reasons for it, its aims and functions, and the advantages which may be expected to result from it. Such a feeling provides the only sound basis for thorough cooperation in the enterprise, and it is only through such cooperation that lasting and helpful results may be expected.

Functions of Departmental Supervision. Any means through which the mathematical instruction in a school may be improved is a legitimate and proper function of departmental supervision. It may be taken as axiomatic that the training and competence of the teacher, together with his attitude toward his work and his students, are more influential than any other considerations in determining the effectiveness of instruction. Therefore the most obvious and direct, and perhaps the most important, service which departmental supervision can perform lies in giving that direct counsel, guidance, stimulation, and assistance which will encourage the various teachers in the department to continue their professional development through the study of pertinent subject matter and professional literature. This aspect or function of supervision may be designated as the in-service training of teachers.

There are, however, other ways in which the proper supervision of the department may contribute appreciably, if less directly, to the improvement of instruction. These consist mainly of the provision and maintenance of adequate instructional facilities, the maintenance of cordial and cooperative professional relations with the administrative offices of the school, and the prosecution of research and the dissemination of professional information bearing upon the instructional problems of the department. As illustrative of these other functions of supervision may be mentioned such matters as the following:

1. Selecting and organizing suitable teaching materials for the several classes
2. Preparing courses of study and coordinating the work of the department
3. Comparing the suitability of different textbooks, workbooks, and other published materials for use in instruction
4. Comparing the efficacy of different methods of instruction
5. Establishing and defining suitable standards of attainment for the various courses in the department
6. Planning, inaugurating, and carrying on a systematic program of evaluation of student attainment
7. Maintaining a suitable, convenient, and facile system of departmental records
8. Holding departmental meetings for the consideration of matters of common concern
9. Keeping the members of the department informed with reference to the objectives and activities of the supervisory program
10. Conducting research designed to secure data which may provide sound bases for the improvement of materials or methods of instruction
11. Locating and abstracting worthwhile pertinent articles, research studies, etc., and making the substance of these available in condensed and understandable form to the members of the departmental staff
12. Promoting and maintaining good morale, close rapport, high interest, and friendly cooperation among the members of the department in all possible ways
13. Making special efforts to be helpful to the young and inexperienced teachers through visitation, conferences, and perhaps demonstration
14. Keeping the administrative officers of the school properly informed about any specially meritorious work of individual teachers
15. Cooperating with those responsible for student guidance
16. Keeping the administrative officers of the school informed with respect to the work of the department and maintaining with them reciprocally cooperative relations
17. Keeping the administrative officers of the school informed with reference to departmental needs and making suitable recommendations concerning provision for those needs
18. Evaluating the effectiveness of instruction and submitting the results of such evaluation, together with appropriate recommendations, to the administrative officers of the school

The functions of departmental supervision have been variously classified by different writers.[1] Some of them are mainly of an administrative nature, while others emphasize the coordination of interdepartmental effort, the conducting and reviewing of research work, the organization of instructional materials, the rating of teaching efficiency, the consideration of special problems, and the in-service training of teachers. They all bear either directly or indirectly upon the general problem of improving the quality of instruction.

Improvement of Instruction in Mathematics through Proper Organization and Articulation of Courses. Much of the criticism which has been directed at mathematical instruction in the secondary schools has emphasized the view that the courses are separated into "watertight compartments" and that the program as a whole has lacked unity and continuity. This charge has been made with reference to the courses in algebra and geometry especially. Efforts have been made to correct this situation by organizing courses in general mathematics. These efforts have met with some success in the junior high school courses, especially those for the seventh and eighth grades. In fact, general mathematics has come to be the typical offering for these grades. In the ninth grade, algebra still enrolls more students than general mathematics does, though there are indications that more than half of all ninth-grade students may choose between algebra and general mathematics. Efforts to organize the courses of the senior high school into a thoroughly integrated sequence have not been notably successful, but their interplay is being emphasized more and more in the separate courses. Considerable progress has been made toward integrating the junior college courses, and efforts in this direction continue to gain momentum.

The importance of continuity in mathematical instruction cannot be too greatly emphasized. It is unfortunate for students to feel that the mathematics of the junior high school is unrelated to that of the senior high school and the junior college, or to feel that algebra, demonstrative geometry, and subsequent courses have no points of contact with each other or with the earlier work in arithmetic, intuitive geometry, and the informal algebra of the seventh and eighth grades. This feeling, however, is all too prevalent, not only among students but among teachers as well. Most teachers of secondary mathematics have received their training in traditional segregated courses and have not been made

[1] E. R. Breslich, "The Administration of Mathematics in Secondary Schools" (Chicago: University of Chicago Press, 1933), p. 5; W. D. Reeve, "Mathematics for the Secondary School" (New York: Henry Holt and Company, Inc., 1954), pp. 109–111, 120–122; David R. Davis, "The Teaching of Mathematics" (Reading, Mass.: Addison-Wesley Publishing Company, 1951), pp. 371–387.

emphatically aware of the interrelations of the different branches of mathematics. As a result they, in turn, often fail to emphasize these interrelations in their teaching.

The supervisor may do much to repair this defect in the teacher's point of view. He should point out many instances illustrating the bearing of one course upon another. In particular he should give convincing illustrations of the fact that the more specialized courses which are usually offered in the ninth grade and beyond have their foundations in the earlier courses of the junior high school and that, conversely, many of the mathematical concepts and principles developed in these earlier courses find some of their most important and interesting applications in the work of subsequent specialized courses. It should be made apparent to the teacher that the full enrichment of the work at *any* level of the secondary school cannot be attained unless the teacher has this perspective and is able to envisage the mathematical program in its entirety, with its manifold interrelations. The supervisor who has been able to bring all his teachers to this point of view will have done a great deal to improve instruction all along the line.

From what has been said it is obvious that the supervisor and the teachers in the mathematics department should be given a good deal of freedom in determining what subject matter should be included in the various courses and in organizing the courses of study for the different grades. Unless they are given such freedom, it may not be possible to realize fully the potential benefits which have just been described. Supervision must have a hand in curriculum construction if it is to justify itself completely. To shackle it in this respect is to impair its usefulness.

Improvement of Instruction through In-service Training of Teachers.[1] Of all the functions and activities of the teacher of mathematics, that of conducting the regular classroom instruction bears most directly upon the degree of student mastery of subject matter and its applications and upon the students' attitudes toward the study of mathematics. Since these represent the ultimate objectives of all mathematical instruction, it follows that the most immediate and important function of supervision is the examination and improvement of those activities and characteristics of the teacher which are involved in actually conducting the work of the class. In broad outline these include the following:

Planning units of instruction and daily class period activities
Selecting and organizing the materials of instruction
Direct expository teaching
Making assignments

[1] See Lawrence W. Lavengood, A Mathematics Supervisor Looks at In-service Programs, *Bulletin of the National Association of Secondary-School Principals*, **38** (May, 1954), 181–190 and also Reeve, *op. cit.*, pp. 119–120.

Directing study and training students in effective methods of study

Preparing and supervising appropriate drill, review, and maintenance work

Appraising the achievement of students

Diagnosing difficulties and applying appropriate remedial procedures

Adapting instruction to individual differences

Providing motivation of effort

Handling routine matters and details of class management in an economical and effective manner

There are also other activities and considerations which, although they are perhaps only indirectly related to the work of the classroom, have definite bearing upon the effectiveness of this work and upon the success of the teacher.   Among these may be mentioned the comparison and evaluation of textbooks, workbooks, and other instructional materials; the careful study of individual aptitudes with a view to making a contribution to the educational guidance of the individual students; earnest cooperation with the administrative officers of the school; continuance of interest in professional and academic self-improvement; and the development and maintenance of those personal characteristics which command the respect and cooperative good will of the students.

The need for the continual training of teachers in service is evident. Even if it might be assumed that all teachers are sufficiently familiar with the subject matter of their courses, many of them lack the experience necessary to give them poise and self-assurance and to produce that familiarity with the various techniques and devices which they must have to enable them to plan and conduct the work of their classes with discriminating judgment.   Others, more mature in point of experience, will have developed more or less fixed patterns of thought and work which with the passage of time tend to become less flexible and adaptable to circumstances.

Some tend to become radically enthusiastic over each new technique, device, or point of view, regardless of whether or not its validity and its practicability have been established and confirmed.   Such teachers need to be trained to develop a more penetrating and critical viewpoint which will be characterized by stability and conservatism as well as by open-mindedness and receptiveness to new ideas.   They need to gain the realization that there is no single new panacea which will solve all the problems of teaching.   Others, by way of contrast, will have become so conservative in their viewpoints as to be unwilling to admit any virtue in anything that is new, or even to try out in an experimental way suggestions for the improvement of their work.   They need to have their attitudes modified and liberalized, to become receptive to new ideas while remaining properly critical of them, and to realize that improvement as well as conservation is desirable.

Some teachers are too easygoing, and do not maintain proper order in their classes. In such circumstances it is impossible for either the teacher or the students to work to best advantage. Interruptions occur, time is wasted, attention is dissipated, and little is accomplished. Students are not slow to size up situations of this kind, and, where they occur, the teacher is likely to forfeit a large measure of the respect of his students. This, of course, is about as disastrous a thing as could occur. On the other hand, some teachers tend to be "hard-boiled" and to lack sympathetic appreciation of the motives and reactions of the students. They need to be helped to a realization that the teacher must be more than a disciplinary officer, that freedom is not incompatible with discipline, and that the highest type of orderliness is not a product of inhibition, but the outgrowth of a cooperative attitude. They need to learn that more can be accomplished by wisely guiding the energies of the students into productive channels than by merely suppressing them.

The foregoing are but examples of situations which might be improved through the in-service training of teachers under the counsel of wise and sympathetic supervision. Many others could be given: the planning of work, the construction of tests, the keeping of records, various details of class management, the clarification of the teacher's relations and obligations to the administrative department of the school and to the community, the general relating and adjusting of the teacher's personality and educational philosophy to the immediate instructional situation, and in particular the class-period activities of the teacher. All these present problems upon which teachers need suggestions from time to time; most teachers welcome these suggestions if they are given in a tactful manner and helpful spirit. There is no way in which supervision can contribute more materially and directly to the improvement of instruction or can justify itself more amply than through this in-service training of teachers.

This phase of supervision must be carried on largely through class visitation and conference and at times through demonstration lessons taught by the supervisor. Before the supervisor visits classes, he should make it clear to the teachers that his purpose in visiting is not primarily to criticize, restrict, or prescribe their work, but to help them in every way possible to improve their teaching and find greater satisfaction in it. Because supervisors are not always careful to do this, teachers often have a dread of the supervisor's visits, and, because of the inhibitions and tensions that are thus set up, they fail to do themselves justice. The supervisor can do much to avoid this unfortunate situation if he will preface his visits by laying a groundwork of mutual understanding and confidence.

The supervisor should make his visits as informal as possible, but they should not be haphazard. He should strive to avoid making himself conspicuous, and the class should learn to accept his presence in the room as a perfectly normal thing calling for no detraction of their attention. It is perhaps well to let the teacher know in advance of some of the visits, and especially is this true with reference to the first few visits to inexperienced or new teachers. However, after a time the supervisor should feel that he can come into the classroom at any time without producing any feeling of tension or restraint in the teacher or the students. Above all, the supervisor should avoid doing anything to embarrass the teacher in the presence of the class. It is nearly always a mistake for the supervisor to volunteer suggestions to the teacher during the class period. Any suggestions which he has to make should be mentally noted, but the time to bring them up for discussion is in the subsequent conference and not during the class period. Nothing can destroy the cooperative attitude of the teacher more quickly or more surely than the practice of placing him at a disadvantage in the presence of his students.

As a rule, visits to classes should be followed by conferences with the teachers. These not only give opportunity for the discussion of points where improvement seems desirable and for suggestions toward such improvement but also offer to the teachers opportunities for raising questions and seeking advice. The conference is the main avenue to a wholesome and friendly mutual understanding between supervisor and teacher, as well as to specific improvements in the instruction. Without conferences no constructive benefit can come from supervisory visits. Indeed, the supervisor who visits classes but does not confer with the teachers afterward may actually thereby engender a feeling of active antagonism, since in these circumstances the teachers, not unreasonably, may conclude that he is merely sitting as a judge upon them and is not a helper to whom they may look for counsel and guidance in their work.

The length of the conference will depend upon the nature and the seriousness of the matters to be discussed. Conferences should be scheduled, as far as possible, to suit the convenience of the teacher rather than that of the supervisor. During the conference it is quite as important for the supervisor to comment upon the favorable impressions which he has received as it is for him to offer criticisms and suggestions on points which need improvement. The supervisor should avoid being arbitrary. He should make every effort to justify his views to the teacher, and he should give equal opportunity for the teacher to justify the teaching procedures used or make other suggestions even if they should run counter to his own ideas. Conferences held in this spirit of freedom and open-mindedness can render the program of visitation extremely helpful and stimulating to both the teacher and the supervisor, thus giving to the program the vitality and the truly functioning force which characterize supervision at its best.

Improving Instruction through a Program of Testing and Associated Activities. Testing has been in use as long as education has existed, but it has been used in the schools primarily as a means for assigning marks. Only in recent years has there come a general recognition that the use of tests may serve other important ends. It is now universally recognized, however, that tests can be used not only to measure the results of instruction but also to *improve* instruction, and there is a widespread and growing feeling that this, after all, should be regarded as the most important service which they can render.

In Chap. 8 there is a discussion of the philosophy underlying the testing program in connection with schoolwork and of the principles of selection, construction, use, and interpretation of tests. Consideration is given to the contribution that can be made by the use of standardized achievement tests with broad-base norms as a means of appraising class or school achievement; the functions, nature, and techniques of prognostic testing as a means to effective guidance; the use of inventory and achievement tests as measures of accomplishment; the use of practice or drill tests as devices for the organization and fixation of details and processes and for the perfection of skills; and the role of diagnostic testing in indicating and facilitating needed remedial work.

The important consideration here is that all these particularized forms and uses of tests are fundamentally pointed toward the improvement of instruction. Since this, in turn, is the primary function of supervision, it must follow that the planning of a comprehensive testing program and the advising and guiding of the teachers in the administration of such a program is an important part or phase of supervisory work.

Many teachers have not had the technical training and the experience which are necessary for mapping out a comprehensive testing program wisely, administering it systematically, and translating the findings and the implications into appropriate instructional procedures. It is an important function of supervision to familiarize the teachers with the ways in which they can make tests contribute to the improvement of their teaching, and to offer them constructive, practical suggestions with regard to the selection or construction of appropriate tests and the interpretation and constructive use of the results. This should be, in fact, an important part of the in-service training of teachers, and as such it must be regarded as a definite responsibility of the departmental supervisor.[1]

---

[1] Paul B. Jacobson, The Place of Testing in the Supervisory Program, *University of Illinois Bulletin*, **35**, No. 89 (1938), pp. 1–34. See also Davis, *op. cit.*, pp. 106–122, and Lucien Blair Kinney and C. Richard Purdy, "Teaching Mathematics in the Secondary School" (New York: Rinehart & Company, Inc., 1952), pp. 326–349.

Improvement of Instruction through the Encouragement of Teachers to Seek Self-improvement. One of the major contributions which supervision can make to the general improvement of instruction is the stimulation of a desire for self-improvement on the part of the teachers along both academic and professional lines. That many teachers in the secondary school are inadequately prepared for their work has been noted by countless observers. In spite of rising standards and increasingly rigorous requirements for certification and assignment, the fact unfortunately remains that many teachers must teach courses which are not in their own fields of specialization and for which, in many cases, they have little or no academic background. Moreover, the heavy teaching loads which prevail almost universally in the secondary schools and the multitude of extracurricular duties and activities which teachers are expected to assume exact so much time and effort that teachers have little opportunity for deliberation and reflection. Continual attention to the urgent demands of the moment tends to become a habit which may easily obscure the longer view of the job, with the result that, even when opportunities for systematic study with a view to academic and professional improvement do occur, they are likely to be overlooked or dissipated through the habitual focusing of attention upon immediate details rather than upon larger issues.

This is unfortunate, because instruction cannot reach its maximum effectiveness unless those who give it continue to expand the breadth of their scholarship in the subject-matter fields in which their teaching lies and to give conscious and sustained attention to the improvement of their techniques of teaching. The best teaching is that which is intellectually stimulating to both the students and the teacher, and really stimulating teaching is seldom done by a teacher whose perspective embraces no more than the immediate details of subject matter which he is to teach and the routine activities of the day's work.

The fact that a great many teachers do work under these limitations is not necessarily their own fault. Many of them lack the maturity and experience which would enable them to organize their work more efficiently so that they might find time for systematic advanced study and professional reading, while others lack the vision which would stimulate them to want these things.

Opportunities for self-improvement are not lacking, but they are often obscured by the conditions which have been mentioned. One avenue to academic and professional advancement is attendance at the summer sessions which are held in universities and teachers colleges all over the country. Great numbers of teachers do take advantage of this opportunity every year. Summer schools, however, do not by any means represent the only avenue to self-improvement. Many universities offer both academic and professional work through the medium of correspondence courses and sometimes through extension classes. These courses are relatively inexpensive, and they serve to systematize study and to give it organization and continuity. In addition to these opportunities another type of activity, the summer institute, must be mentioned. Summer institutes for mathematics teachers have recently attained considerable prominence. Supported both by industry and by the government, such institutes represent a determined effort to upgrade mathematical instruction in the schools through courses and activities aimed at deepening the mathematical insights of the teachers. Thus they represent another means, and a very advantageous and productive means, through which teachers can seek self-improvement.

Teachers who for one reason or another find it impossible to pursue any of these regularly organized courses can still plan for themselves systematic programs of study or professional reading, or they can undertake organized studies of certain aspects of their own work. They can do this either through organized study groups or as individuals. Much benefit may be derived from such activities, which can do much to make the instruction more stimulating and beneficial, both to the teachers and to their students, than it otherwise might be.

The unfortunate thing is that most teachers become so engrossed in their immediate problems that the possibilities of carrying on any systematic program of self-improvement escape them. For this reason it should be one of the major objectives of the supervisor to give to his teachers suggestions and continual encouragement in this direction. He should help the young and inexperienced teachers to plan and organize their work so that it may be carried on with as much economy of time as may be consistent with the requirements of the situation. He should keep the experienced teachers aware of the possibilities of improving their techniques and enriching the content of their courses. He should keep all the teachers conscious of the importance of both professional and academic growth, and he should do everything possible to encourage and facilitate their efforts to bring themselves to an ever higher level of competence.

At the risk of repetition, it should be stressed again that academic advancement ought to be continually pursued with vigor and persistence and that it should not be subordinated to the improvement of methodology. Certainly the latter is important, but alone it is not sufficient. The good teacher will be ever seeking to expand his mathematical horizons and deepen his mathematical insights as well as improve his teaching methods. Mathematics is a growing subject, and at present it is growing with almost explosive rapidity. New concepts, new terminology, new notation, new applications are with us, and some of these are, or soon will be, finding a place in the high school courses.   In order to serve their students adequately, teachers of high school mathematics will need to keep abreast of these developments in the field of their chosen discipline itself, no less than they need to keep alert to improved ways of teaching.

As has been said, opportunities for teachers in service to further their mathematical training are not lacking.   Perhaps the avenues of most special interest and widespread effect at this time are the institutes currently being sponsored by the National Science Foundation.   These institutes reflect a widespread concern for the more adequate preparation *in mathematics and science* of the secondary school mathematics teachers.

The supervisor of mathematics has a clear-cut responsibility to encourage and help his teachers to seek self-improvement along academic lines. He should keep alert to opportunities and should keep his teachers informed about such opportunities.   He should encourage them to seek further training in mathematics as well as in methodology, and he should do all he can to facilitate their efforts and increase their aspirations in that direction.

The Place of Research in Supervision.   Research has a dual role to play in supervision.   Some of the practical instructional problems which face the teacher may find their solutions or partial solutions in the published results of research that has been carried on elsewhere.   On the other hand, such problems may legitimately give rise to research in connection with the work within the department itself.   In the one case supervision goes to outside sources for help in answering its questions; in the other, it endeavors to answer them for itself.

Much experimental work has been done in the field of the teaching of mathematics.   However, the published reports of these investigations are for two reasons often of little direct benefit to teachers in service.   In the first place, many of them are not readily accessible except in the libraries of colleges and universities.   In the second place, many of them are so replete with technicalities and detail that most teachers have neither the time nor the technical background needed to evaluate the validity of the procedures employed and to isolate and interpret the significant findings so that they can be translated into practice.   Teachers in active service need to have the results from such studies made available in concise, understandable, and usable form.   Therefore, it is a function of the departmental supervisor to familiarize himself with the published researches which are really significant, to digest them, and to abstract and summarize the important findings of these investigations and make them available to the teachers with suggestions for translating them into practice and incorporating them in their instructional procedures.[1]

[1] Beginning in 1953, annual summaries and digests of research studies in the field of mathematics education have been published.   These are available through the U.S. Office of Education.

Many instructional problems, however, can be investigated by the teachers themselves, and such investigations often turn out to be not only useful in themselves but extremely stimulating to the teachers who conduct them. As a rule they will necessarily be limited in scope, and the findings may be of local, rather than general, importance. In some quarters they might not even be dignified by the title of research. This, however, is beside the point. The important thing is that they represent efforts on the part of the teachers to apply scientific procedures to the solution of instructional problems, and in this way they serve to make the teachers acutely aware of the problems and to lead them to make careful analyses pointing toward practical solutions. The following list represents a number of random suggestions of such problems. It could be indefinitely expanded, since every teacher who trains himself to be "problem conscious" will find many other instructional problems arising in connection with his own work. Perhaps, however, these suggestions may help teachers to become more sensitive to the presence of such problems and to the possibilities for investigating them systematically.

Compilation of a list of specific uses of mathematics in everyday life situations

Compilation of a list of specific uses of mathematics in industry

Compilation of a list of specific uses of mathematics in other fields of work or study

Study of the effect of various devices for the motivation of junior high school mathematics

Analysis of errors in algebra to determine causes

Comparison of treatment of certain topics in algebra in different textbooks

Comparison of sequences of theorems in different textbooks in geometry

Comparison of results of supervised study and the recitation method in first-year algebra

Experimentation with variations of method in teaching verbal problems

Pretesting and growth studies in solid geometry

Study of the effect of the systematic preparation and use of diagnostic tests in plane geometry

Devising appropriate activities in algebra for superior students

Devising appropriate activities in geometry for superior students

Introducing experimentally certain concepts, terminology, and notation of modern mathematics into the work of the high school courses

Noting and reporting to the staff how well and how rapidly students master these new concepts, terms, and symbols and the extent to which students can translate and reexpress conventionally stated problems in terms of the new symbols

Sometimes the efforts of several teachers or of the entire departmental staff may be enlisted in cooperative studies of this sort. Such an arrangement tends to give added interest to the work and to increase the reliability of the results. It is quite possible for investigations conducted by the teachers themselves to yield objective results that will be practically helpful to them in their own work. However, an even greater benefit is derived from the stimulation of professional interest which almost invariably comes about as a result of participation in such investigations.

It is a function of supervision to envisage significant instructional problems, propose them to the teachers for study, and cooperate with the teachers in the formulation of methods for their investigation. The departmental supervisor should take the lead in this. He should have the most comprehensive view of the problems which should be studied and the most discriminating judgment as to which ones are suitable for investigation by the teachers. The administrative officers of the school are not likely to be sufficiently informed about instructional matters within the department, while the teachers are likely to be too greatly preoccupied with the details of their immediate duties to give much attention to the matter of initiating research. The departmental supervisor alone stands in an altogether favorable position to sense fully the need for these activities, enlist the cooperation of the staff members and, if need be, of the administrative officers, and give the greatest measure of encouragement, guidance, and assistance to the teachers in the prosecution of the investigations.[1]

Evaluation of Instruction and the Rating of Teachers. It has been emphasized throughout this chapter that the fundamental purpose of supervision is the improvement of instruction. Obviously, there can be no basis for constructive suggestions for improvement except through the appraisal of the instructional practices and the qualifications and characteristics of the individual teachers. Therefore, the evaluation of instruction and the rating of teachers are necessary functions of supervision, and the responsibility for carrying on the activities incident to these functions must devolve mainly upon the departmental supervisor.

Evaluation and rating will be meaningful and helpful only to the extent to which it succeeds in indicating points of strength and points where improvement is needed. It must be, in fact, a sort of diagnostic process applied to the traits and teaching activities of the teacher. Rating charts of one form or another are commonly used to facilitate and objectify the procedure. They usually consist of lists of items or characteristics which are believed to be important in relation to success in teaching. The majority of the items in most of these rating lists refer to characteristics or traits which are important elements in connection with the teaching of any subject. In a study of 57 of these rating devices Knudsen[2] noted

---

[1] Paul V. Sangren, The Participation of the Classroom Teacher in Educational Research, *Educational Administration and Supervision,* **15** (1929), 593–601.

[2] C. W. Knudsen, "Evaluation and Improvement of Teaching" (New York: Doubleday & Company, Inc., 1932), pp. 212–215.

79 of these traits, and of these not a single one applied uniquely or with special force to teachers of any particular subject. Occasionally, however, there may be found rating devices which have been constructed specifically for the purpose of analyzing teaching in a particular field. Such lists are more definitely helpful to the departmental supervisor in appraising the work of the teachers in his own department than are the lists of the more general traits.

It is important that teachers should have a correct point of view with regard to teacher rating. Too often they feel that its only purpose is to detect incompetencies and that the detection of these incompetencies will result only in censure, demotion, or dismissal. It is true that ratings may be legitimately used for administrative purposes involving matters of tenure, status, and salary adjustments, but formal objective ratings, when employed for these purposes, should be used only in connection with other considerations. They should never be made the sole bases for these administrative adjustments, and this should be made clear to the teachers. The only way to secure a cooperative and helpful attitude toward teacher ratings is to make sure that no misunderstandings exist as to the main purpose of these ratings, viz., the improvement of instruction. Such misunderstandings can best be avoided by encouraging the teachers themselves to participate in the rating process. If rating lists are to be used, they should be made available to the teachers, and the teachers should be encouraged to use the lists in analyzing their own work. In this way they may locate and identify deficiencies in their own teaching. The supervisor should also make ratings of the teachers and should frequently discuss the ratings with the teachers individually. These discussions, if carried on sympathetically and tactfully by the supervisor, will go far to dispel any feeling of antagonism toward teacher rating and bring about improvement with respect to those traits and activities which are found to need special attention.

Making Supervision Effective. The success of any program of supervision will eventually depend upon the characteristics and the activities of the supervisor. It has been emphasized that, if supervision is to eventuate in any thoroughgoing improvement of instruction, it must be a cooperative enterprise in which the cordial participation of the teacher is an indispensable element. It follows that the first major objective of the supervisor must be to gain the confidence of the teachers and acquaint them with the real purposes of the program. This means in effect that the teachers should be made partners in the enterprise and that they should enjoy the full confidence of the supervisor. This will beget mutual understanding and freedom in the interchange of ideas and suggestions and will tend to prevent or dissipate the distrust and suspicion which sometimes unfortunately mark the attitude of teachers toward supervisory activities.

In order to develop this cooperative attitude successfully, the supervisor must be a person of culture, insight, academic and professional ability, and vision. He should have had extensive experience in teaching mathematics in order that he may know and appreciate the many problems which the teachers actually must face in their work and that he may appraise with sympathetic understanding their methods of handling these problems. He must be tactful in his efforts to assist them. He should have a breadth of knowledge and a degree of mastery of the branches and applications of mathematics which will command the respect of the teachers and out of which he may help them to broaden and enrich their academic perspective. He must be familiar with educational movements and developments, both in general and in the field of mathematics in particular. He must know how to appraise educational movements, and he should make their implications clear to his staff.

He should be a master teacher, because there will be times when it will be desirable for him to teach demonstration lessons. The teachers in the department almost certainly will look with skepticism upon the suggestions of one who is unable to incorporate in his own practice those things which he suggests to others. On the other hand, he should manifest at all times a willingness to learn from the teachers, and he should readily acknowledge his appreciation of any helpful suggestions which they are able to give him.

Finally, he must have organizing and executive ability, initiative, and professional vision, because it is he who must take the lead in initiating and guiding the activities directed toward the improvement of instruction within the department and in coordinating and harmonizing the work of the department with the whole educational program of the school. The supervisor who is equipped with these qualifications should have little difficulty in building up a wholesome atmosphere of interest, respect, cooperation, and good will toward the supervisory program, both among the members of the department and among the administrative officers of the school.

A Program for Self-supervision. While this chapter has outlined the functions and methods of supervision in mathematics primarily from the standpoint of the departmental supervisor in a large school, the fact has not been overlooked that most secondary schools are not large schools and do not have special departmental supervisors. However, the problems of supervision are the problems of the improvement of instruction, and these exist in all schools, large or small. Therefore, the intention has been to discuss these problems comprehensively but simply and clearly, so that the suggestions which have been made will not necessarily require the services of a special departmental supervisor to translate them into practice but can be interpreted and adapted to local situations by any member of the school's staff.

In most cases whatever special supervision is given at all must be given by the superintendent or the principal of the school. It is believed that the suggestions contained in the foregoing pages will be helpful to these officers in carrying out this phase of their work. There are many cases, however, when even the administrative officers are so burdened with teaching and with inescapable administrative duties that they literally can find no time for supervision. In such cases the responsibility for the improvement of instruction must be assumed by the teachers themselves.

In the matter of self-supervision the teacher's attention should be confined mainly to the improvement of his instructional activities, the extension of his command of subject matter, and the cultivation of a professional attitude. There is much that he can do in these directions if he is willing to appraise his own work honestly and try to improve the parts of it which appear to him to be most in need of improvement. First, he can analyze his personal traits, his teaching conditions, and his teaching activities. He can make a rating chart by means of which he can subject himself and his work to detailed scrutiny and give it an honest and careful rating. A list of items of the type included in Breslich's suggestions for supervisors' visitation records[1] would form a simple and practical basis for such an analysis and rating.

Having rated his work in this way, he should concentrate his attention first on a few of the important points which seem to be most in need of improvement. These should be analyzed further, if necessary, in an effort to determine in what particulars and in what ways they can be improved to best advantage. After this is done, the teacher will be in a position to make a sound beginning at actually bringing about the desired improvements. It is better not to work on too many points at once. Each fault which is to be corrected will require special attention for a period of time, and the attempt to focus special attention on too many things at a time might result in a dissipation of effort, which, in turn, might be actually detrimental rather than beneficial to his teaching. On the other hand, the teacher will find that well-planned, systematic, and conscientious effort directed toward the correction of a few teaching practices at a time will have a cumulatively beneficial effect and will in the end far more than justify itself.

Finally, in the scheme of self-supervision the teacher can set for himself a systematic program of professional or academic study. Sugges-

[1] Breslich, op. cit., pp. 15–16.

tions along this line will be found in an earlier section of this chapter. Here again, not too much should be attempted at once, but such a program, if moderately planned and consistently pursued, will give added interest and enrichment to his work and will bring an increased measure of satisfaction.

EXERCISES

1. Contrast the need for supervision of mathematical instruction in American secondary schools with the present status of such supervision.

2. Explain why teachers often look upon supervisory activities with suspicion and dislike, and discuss measures which should be taken to counteract this attitude.

3. Enumerate the characteristics or traits which the supervisor should have in order that he may carry on his supervisory program to best advantage.

4. Enumerate matters which would be especially suitable for discussion at the first departmental meeting of the school year.

5. Make a list of topics which could profitably be considered at departmental meetings after the first one.

6. Explain how the proper organization and articulation of the courses in mathematics can contribute to the effectiveness of instruction.

7. Why should both the teachers and the supervisor have a hand in planning the courses of study and selecting textbooks and equipment?

8. Describe explicitly the ways in which the supervisor may help the teacher in planning his work for the year.

9. Discuss fully the reasons why the in-service training of teachers should be regarded as perhaps the most important function of supervision.

10. Adapt or construct a check list for rating the instructional procedures of teachers of junior high school mathematics.

11. In what respects, if any, would you alter this check list to make it particularly adaptable to rating teaching procedures in senior high school or junior college mathematics. Justify your suggestions for alteration or your decision to make no changes in the list.

12. Describe clearly the ways in which prognostic testing may contribute to the improvement of instruction in mathematics. What are the limitations and potential dangers in the use of prognostic tests?

13. Give a detailed discussion of the ways in which diagnostic testing can contribute to the improvement of instruction in mathematics. Illustrate if you wish.

14. Discuss the ways in which research may contribute toward making supervision effective. What are the supervisor's responsibilities with reference to research in the supervisory program?

15. Summarize one comprehensive research study which has bearings on the teaching of secondary mathematics and point out the instructional implications of the study.

16. Select one instructional problem which might be investigated by a departmental staff, state its implications, and outline the procedure which you would recommend for conducting the study.

17. Discuss the responsibilities of the supervisor and the teachers in relation to the educational guidance of students.

18. Discuss the supervisor's responsibilities in the matter of encouraging teachers to seek academic and professional self-improvement and point out possible avenues

to the achievement of this aim. What are the chief obstacles in the way of such self-improvement?

19. Enumerate and discuss the ways in which a complete and convenient system of departmental records may contribute to the effectiveness of supervision.

20. Draft a set of forms for the records which you would want included in such a system if you were the supervisor.

21. Explain clearly the particular ways in which the supervisor can contribute to the improvement of instruction through his status as a liaison officer between the department and the administrative officers of the school.

22. Explain why it is an important function of supervision to see that adequate facilities and favorable working conditions are provided for the teachers.

23. If you were the supervisor of a mathematics department and were required to submit ratings of your teachers to the administrative officers, upon what items would you feel it proper to rate them? Construct a rating scale including these items.

24. What specific advantages could result from the use of such a rating scale? What dangers might it involve? What measures could be taken to minimize these dangers?

25. Why should formal ratings of teachers not be used as the sole basis for promotion, retention, demotion, salary adjustments, or dismissal?

26. Discuss the possibilities of self-supervision by teachers.

27. In the light of an honest appraisal of your own limitations in training and experience, draw up a statement of the specific ways in which you think a competent and sympathetic supervisor could be helpful to you in your effort to become a better teacher of mathematics.

BIBLIOGRAPHY

Allen, Frank B.: Building a Mathematics Program: An Adventure in Cooperative Planning, *Mathematics Teacher*, **49** (1956), 226–234.

Berger, Emil J.: Devices for the Mathematics Classroom, *Mathematics Teacher*, various recent issues.

Brown, Claude H.: "The Teaching of Secondary Mathematics" (New York: Harper & Brothers, 1953), pp. 304–320; 355–373.

Brown, Kenneth E.: In-service Education for Teachers of Mathematics, "Twenty-third Yearbook" (Washington, D.C.: National Council of Teachers of Mathematics, 1954), pp. 238–243.

————: "Analysis of Research in the Teaching of Mathematics, 1955–1956" (U.S. Office of Education Bulletin 4, 1958).

————, Walter H. Carnahan, Mildred Kieffer, and Veryl Schult: "The Supervisor of Mathematics: His Role in the Improvement of Mathematics Instruction" (Washington, D.C.: National Council of Teachers of Mathematics, 1959).

Clark, John R. (Editor) and others: Emerging Practices in Mathematics Education, "Twenty-second Yearbook," (Washington, D.C.: National Council of Teachers of Mathematics, 1954).

Commission on Mathematics: "Program for College Preparatory Mathematics" (New York: College Entrance Examination Board, 1959), pp. 50–54.

————: "Appendices" (New York: College Entrance Examination Board, 1959).

Commonwealth of Pennsylvania, Department of Public Instruction: "A Course of Study in Mathematics for Secondary Schools," *Bulletin* 360 (Harrisburg, Pa.: Department of Public Instruction, 1952), pp. 268–269.

Davis, David R.: "The Teaching of Mathematics" (Reading, Mass.: Addison-Wesley Publishing Company, 1951), pp. 371–387.

Davis, R. B.: Student-centered Review and Rationalized Examinations, *Journal of Engineering Education*, **45** (1955), 736–738.

Deans, Edwina: The Role of the Elementary Supervisor in the Improvement of Instruction in Arithmetic, *Bulletin of the National Association of Secondary-School Principals*, **38** (1954), 167–181.

Dodes, Irving A.: Four Investigations in the Improvement of Mathematics Instruction, *High Points*, **36** (1954), 32–39.

Fehr, Howard F.: Current Problems in Teaching Secondary Mathematics, *New Jersey Mathematics Teacher*, **13** (1956), 12–15.

————: Psychology of Learning in the Junior High School, *Mathematics Teacher*, **49** (1956), 235–240.

————: High School Mathematics for the Second Half of the Twentieth Century, *Bulletin of the National Association of Secondary-School Principals*, **42** (1958), 318–324.

———— (Editor) and others: The Learning of Mathematics: Its Theory and Practice, "Twenty-first Yearbook" (Washington, D.C.: National Council of Teachers of Mathematics, 1953).

Glennon, Vincent J.: A Study in Needed Redirection in the Preparation of Teachers of Arithmetic, *Mathematics Teacher*, **42** (1949), 389–396.

Hach, Alice: Removing the *Dis.* from Dislike for Mathematics, *Mathematics Teacher*, **50** (1957), 65–69.

Hartung, Maurice L.: Evaluating Instruction in Mathematics, *Bulletin of the National Association of Secondary-School Principals*, **38** (1954), 138–143.

Hoel, Lesta: A Supervisor Plans a Program through Self-evaluation, *Mathematics Teacher*, **49** (1956), 347–352.

Jackson, H. C.: Better Bulletin Boards, *Mathematics Teacher*, **48** (1955), 358–359.

Johnson, Donovan A.: Readability of Mathematics Books, *Mathematics Teacher*, **50** (1957), 105–110.

Jorgensen, Paul: In-service Institutes for Mathematics Teachers, *Mathematics Teacher*, **51** (1958), 613–614.

Keller, M. W.: What Are You Teaching? *School Science and Mathematics*, **56** (1956), 210–220.

Kidd, Kenneth P.: Improving the Learning of Mathematics, *Mathematics Teacher*, **47** (1954), 393–400.

Kieffer, Mildred, and Anna Marie Evans: "How to Develop a Teaching Guide in Mathematics" (Washington, D.C.: National Council of Teachers of Mathematics, 1955).

Kimball, Roland B.: Improvement of Mathematics and Science Instruction in New Hampshire, *School Science and Mathematics*, **57** (1957), 529–535.

Kinney, Lucien Blair, and C. Richard Purdy: "Teaching Mathematics in the Secondary School" (New York: Rinehart & Company, Inc., 1952).

Kinsella, John J.: Is Research in Mathematics Education Really Necessary? *Mathematics Teacher*, **50** (1957), 300–301.

Lankford, Francis G., Jr.: Summer Institutes for Mathematics Teachers, *Bulletin of the National Association of Secondary-School Principals*, **38** (1954), 192–196.

————: What Are Your Pupils Learning? Some Suggestions on Evaluation, *Mathematics Teacher*, **47** (1954), 208–210.

————: Tips for Beginners, *Mathematics Teacher*, issues since 1954.

Lavengood, Lawrence W.: A Mathematics Supervisor Looks at In-service Programs,

Bulletin of the National Association of Secondary-School Principals, **38** (1954), 181–190.

Layton, W. I.: The Certification of Teachers of Mathematics, *Mathematics Teacher*, **42** (1949), 377–380.

MacLane, Saunders L.: The Impact of Modern Mathematics on Secondary Schools, *Mathematics Teacher*, **49** (1956), 66–69.

Mallinson, George G.: The Five Most Needed Investigations in the Teaching of Science and in the Teaching of Mathematics, *School Science and Mathematics*, **54** (1954), 428–430.

Mayor, John R.: Special Training for Teachers of Arithmetic, *School Science and Mathematics*, **49** (1949), 539–548.

———: Some Thoughts on Teacher Education, *Mathematics Teacher*, **49** (1956), 143–144.

Meder, Albert E.: Modern Mathematics and Its Place in the Secondary School, *Mathematics Teacher*, **50** (1957), 418–423.

Moyer, H. O.: Helping the Slow Learner in Mathematics, *School Science and Mathematics*, **55** (1955), 425–429.

Northrop, E. P.: Modern Mathematics and the Secondary School Curriculum, *Mathematics Teacher*, **48** (1955), 386–393.

Reeve, William D.: "Mathematics for the Secondary School" (New York: Henry Holt and Company, Inc., 1954), pp. 96–122.

Schaaf, William L.: Arithmetic for Arithmetic Teachers [with bibliography], *School Science and Mathematics*, **53** (1953), 537–543.

Schreiber, R. E.: Cumulative Guide to Audio-Visual Materials for Mathematics, *Audio-Visual Guide*, **22** (1956), 14–15.

Secondary School Curriculum Committee of the National Council of Teachers of Mathematics, Report of: The Secondary Mathematics Curriculum, *Mathematics Teacher*, **52** (1959), 389–417.

Stone, M. H.: Some Crucial Problems in Mathematical Instruction, *School Review*, **65** (1957), 64–77.

Swain, Henry: "How to Study Mathematics" (Washington, D.C.: National Council of Teachers of Mathematics, 1955).

Syer, H. W., and D. A. Johnson (Editors): Aids to Teaching, *Mathematics Teacher*, issues from 1948–1954.

Vollmar, R., and Philip Peak: "How to Use Films and Film Strips in Mathematics" (Washington, D.C.: National Council of Teachers of Mathematics, 1956).

Weaver, J. Fred: Research in Arithmetic Instruction: 1958 [annotated bibliography], *Arithmetic Teacher* **6** (1959), 121–132.

Wilcox, Marie S.: The Contribution of the Professional Organizations, *Bulletin of the National Association of Secondary-School Principals*, **38** (1954), 190–192.

Wilson, J. D.: Trends in High School Mathematics, *School Science and Mathematics*, **55** (1955), 462–468.

Wolfe, Raphael W.: Organizing the Mathematics Department in the Montebello Junior High School, *Mathematics Teacher*, **51** (1958), 287–291.

Wren, F. Lynwood: Some Common Problems in the Teaching of Secondary Mathematics, *Bulletin of the National Association of Secondary-School Principals*, **38** (1954), 160–167.

PART II

THE TEACHING
OF THE SPECIAL SUBJECT MATTER
OF SECONDARY MATHEMATICS

PART II

THE TEACHING
OF THE SPECIAL SUBJECT MATTER
OF SECONDARY MATHEMATICS

THE JOB OF THE MATHEMATICS TEACHER

The teacher of mathematics, like all other teachers in the secondary school, is a person of whom many things are expected. His obligations are not confined to the classroom but extend along many avenues to the promotion of the effective functioning of the school and the maintenance of harmonious relations and constructive understanding between the school and the community. The sponsoring of extracurricular activities, cooperation in maintaining a smoothly operating physical organization, participation in counseling and guidance, keeping careful records, making necessary reports promptly, and participation in worthy community interests are but illustrative of the range of demands upon the teacher. It must not be forgotten, however, that his first and foremost obligation is to teach effectively.

Teaching mathematics in the secondary schools is a task which, if seriously undertaken, will challenge the best efforts of the best teachers. It requires more than a thorough knowledge of the subject matter to be taught, though that, of course, is a *sine qua non*. It requires more, even, than a broad perspective of the field of mathematics itself and an understanding of the place and importance of mathematics in any valid scheme of general education. It demands skill in the techniques of teaching each particular topic or aspect of the subject, in developing generalized concepts, in coordinating generalizations with applications, in discriminating between essential and unimportant matters within the subject, in knowing where to place emphasis and where to anticipate difficulties, in detecting difficulties when they do occur, in sensing their precise nature, and in knowing how to help the students avoid or overcome them.

The first task of the teacher in connection with the teaching of any division, unit, topic, or aspect of mathematical subject matter is to decide just what the immediate and definite objectives are, viz., which concepts or items of information the students are to gain from their study of that topic, which skills are to be mastered, which techniques and materials will be most effective in producing the desired results.

277

Economy and clarity of learning will come only in so far as the multitude of details related to the unit are subordinated to the main issues and are organized and integrated around the few really major concepts and skills so that these will stand out in bold relief against the background of contributory detail. Having decided what important things are to be emphasized in a particular unit, the teacher is in a position to view the whole problem in its proper perspective and to organize and present the material of the unit in a more effective manner.

The teacher of mathematics must remain alert at all times to the major objectives of mathematical instruction. If these are to be attained in an effective and economical manner, the teacher must plan his work with at least five things in mind. (1) He must decide what exercises and activities will contribute most effectively to produce the desired understandings and skills. This teaching material should be selected with great care. (2) He must analyze these teaching materials carefully to anticipate the specific difficulties which the pupils are likely to encounter in attaining the objectives of the unit. (3) In order to help the pupils avoid or overcome these difficulties, the teacher must become expert in sensing the procedures and devices that promise to be specifically helpful and must learn to be adept in adjusting his procedure to the requirements of each immediate situation. Explanations and developmental discussion should be pointedly and skillfully organized. Devices and illustrations should be selected with great care. (4) A careful selection and arrangement of motivating materials must be made. The teacher must keep in mind that it is his responsibility to create, stimulate, and maintain interest in mathematics as well as strive for proficiency in skills and the amassing of information. (5) He must give careful thought to evaluation techniques and remedial procedures.

No teacher can do a thoroughly good job of teaching mathematics unless he is willing to make a careful analysis of his job and be guided by that analysis in making his preparations and in conducting the work of the class. The analysis of the instructional problems involved in the teaching of any topic in secondary mathematics seems to divide itself rather logically into six considerations as follows:

1. What background of experience and understanding may the student be expected to have when he begins the study of the topic?

2. What are the particular understandings or abilities which the student should acquire or strengthen through the study of the topic?

3. What activities or procedures on the part of the teacher and student will enable the student to gain the desired understandings and abilities most effectively?

4. What specific difficulties may the student be expected to encounter in his effort to acquire the desired understandings and abilities?

5. What specific suggestions, devices, and procedures will most effectively help the student to avoid or overcome the specific difficulties of (4)?

6. What materials and procedures related to the particular topic will best stimulate and maintain the student's interest?

It is the purpose of Part II to consider some of the more important instructional units of secondary mathematics in the perspective of the above questions.

11

THE TEACHING OF ARITHMETIC

Our word "arithmetic" is derived from the word "$\alpha\rho\iota\theta\mu\eta\tau\iota\kappa\dot{\eta}$," which the Greeks used to contrast the *science of number* with the *art of computing*, or "$\lambda o\gamma\iota\sigma\tau\iota\kappa\dot{\eta}$." This distinction in terminology prevailed until the sixteenth century, when "arithmetic" came to mean both the science of number and the art of calculation. In modern American parlance "arithmetic" is taken to encompass both this composite meaning and the application of number and computation to the analysis and the solution of problems. Both of these aspects are highly important. Teachers of arithmetic should keep themselves constantly alert to this duality so that they may avoid the tendency to overemphasize the art of calculation at the expense of the significance of number relations. Their instructional programs, to be functionally effective, must place as much emphasis on understanding of meanings, relationships, and applications as upon proficiency in the mechanics of calculation.

The Arithmetical Responsibility of the Secondary School. In the seventh and eighth grades arithmetic constitutes the main part of the students' program in mathematics. In subsequent systematic courses in algebra and geometry, arithmetic receives relatively less direct attention. This is not unnatural but it is unfortunate, because the arithmetical groundwork laid in the earlier grades is not sufficiently broad or deep or enduring to meet the needs of mature citizens. There is abundant evidence of need for a systematic reemphasis on arithmetic not only in the ninth grade but in the senior high school as well. The average high school graduate of today is not a great deal more proficient, at least as regards sheer computation and work involving percentage, than he was when he entered the senior high school. Indeed the well-established norms for one of the most widely used standard tests on computation indicate that tenth- and eleventh-grade students do not compute even as well as ninth-grade students and that twelfth-grade students do only about as well as ninth-grade students.[1] Other tests do indicate some improve-

[1] See norms for the Schorling-Clark-Potter "Hundred Problem Arithmetic Test," forms V and W, World Book Company, Tarrytown-on-Hudson, N.Y.

ment from grade to grade but tend to confirm the belief that it slows down materially after the ninth grade.[1] Yet practically every high school graduate will need almost immediately to find a place in business, industry, the armed services, homemaking, or college, and in each of these fields arithmetic is becoming increasingly important. It seems clear, therefore, that the senior high school, as well as the junior high school, has a serious responsibility for both maintaining and extending the arithmetical competence of its students.

It is the responsibility of the elementary school to lay the fundamental groundwork of basic concepts, principles, and skills upon which the arithmetical structure must be built. In constructing its curriculum and formulating its instructional program the secondary school is justified in assuming that the elementary school has met this educational obligation.[2] But even if this assumption is valid, the senior high school still has a responsibility for continuing the enrichment of this background and preventing its atrophy through disuse.

It does not necessarily follow, however, that the arithmetic of the secondary school needs to be taught as a separate subject. It is true that the seventh and eighth grades do have specific responsibility for the extension of decimal fractions to percentage and the development of those skills essential to the understanding and intelligent use of percentage as a fundamental arithmetical tool. The broader mathematical obligation of the seventh and eighth grades, however, is to strengthen and increase the working vocabulary of arithmetical terms, to effect a clearer understanding of basic concepts, relationships, and principles, to develop further facility in the fundamental skills, and to emphasize the abstraction of arithmetical processes to applied problems and life situations.

The ninth grade should continue the emphasis on meaningful arithmetic. In addition to the pure computation involved in the evaluation of formulas and in the solving and checking of algebraic equations, the algebra of the ninth grade provides for the extension of the number concepts to include literal numbers and directed numbers. Once these concepts have been developed, there is need for the generalization of the fundamental operations of arithmetic to these new numbers and to the algebraic expressions they introduce. A further extension of the number concept to include irrational numbers is accomplished in the later work of the senior high school and the junior college. In these extensions the

---

[1] See norms for the Madden-Peak "Arithmetic Computation Test," forms Am and Bm, World Book Company, Tarrytown-on-Hudson, N.Y.

[2] Joint Commission of the Mathematical Association of America, Inc., and the National Council of Teachers of Mathematics, "The Place of Mathematics in Secondary Education," *Fifteenth Yearbook* (Washington, D.C.: National Council of Teachers of Mathematics, 1940), pp. 53–54.

teacher has a heavy responsibility for making clear the important role of definition and consistency as desirable controls.

The measurement problems of geometry and trigonometry offer still further opportunities for emphasis on the fundamental skills and basic understandings of arithmetic. Although the instructional material of the junior high school offers a greater abundance of situations which are more nearly numerical in nature, the responsibility for increasing accuracy and facility in numerical computation does not end here as the student passes on to higher levels of instruction. This responsibility, as does that of building up a progressive increase in the student's understanding of basic concepts and appreciation of arithmetical applications, extends even into the junior college.[1]

The responsibility of the high school for maintenance and extension of arithmetical skills and understanding is well summed up in the following statement from Kinney and Purdy.[2]

Skill in arithmetic deteriorates rapidly owing to disuse. To insure retention of the new skills, taught from time to time, and the maintenance of mastery in processes previously taught, the teacher must provide for the systematic cumulative review of old and new processes, together with a remedial program for individual pupils with special needs.

The importance of arithmetic competence in high school graduates was dramatically revealed by the war. . . . This problem has always been with us but has been further accentuated because pupils with a wider range of abilities have been passed through the grades, owing to a change in policy of the grade schools regarding promotion.

The problem will not be solved, however, by a mere program of mechanical drill periodically administered during the high school period. The difficulty is due not merely to lack of skill but also to the fact that, in the typical high school course, arithmetic processes are not utilized to reveal their relation to more mature problem situations. The high school pupil who has had no arithmetic since the eighth grade has dealt with problems that can be understood by a thirteen-year-old or fourteen-year-old pupil. Unless he has opportunity to apply arithmetic processes and concepts to increasingly mature situations, his arithmetic will rarely be adequate for dealing with problems of the adult. Consequently the program of maintenance must be a part of a sequence in which real problem situations are introduced, and the skills must be applied to situations of increasing maturity.

The Four Fundamental Operations with Integers and Decimal Fractions. By the time they reach the junior high school grades most children should have acquired a fair command of the number combinations and

[1] H. Glenn Ayre, An Analysis of the Performance of College Freshmen on Arithmetic, *Western Illinois State Teachers College Quarterly*, **19**, no. 2 (1939).
[2] Lucien Blair Kinney and C. Richard Purdy, "Teaching Mathematics in the Secondary School" (New York: Rinehart & Company, Inc., 1952), p. 259.

the mechanical rudiments of simple ordinary computation with whole numbers. This does not imply that they will have acquired any great facility in computing or that they will have a complete understanding of the number system itself, or even that they fully understand the mathematical justification of all the procedures they use. It seems certain that many do not. Some, of course, will still have difficulty even in performing the operations, especially division, but most of them can be expected to have attained at least a modicum of skill and some understanding of the principle of place value in writing numbers.

Unfortunately, it is too frequently true that students, even upon graduation from high school, either have failed to take advantage of the opportunity or have not had the opportunity to learn the full significance of place value in the structure of our number system. It not only binds together the thought processes which constitute the rationale of the fundamental operations but also simplifies the mechanics of the several algorisms. It is the keystone of our number system, and thus should receive emphasis throughout the elementary and secondary schools. Indeed, since the seventh and eighth grades are grades in which the concepts and skills of arithmetic should be treated with a fair degree of maturity, they are the ones in which special emphasis should be given to place value and its significance to basic understanding in the effective use of number. In these grades pupils are expected to strengthen the skills and understandings of arithmetic and extend them to include operations with numbers involving computation with decimal fractions and common fractions. These extensions involve certain difficulties. It is important that teachers be aware of them so that steps can be taken to anticipate them and prevent them from becoming serious impediments to the students' genuine mastery of the subject.

The student who has really mastered the fundamental operations with whole numbers should have little difficulty in extending them to numbers involving decimal fractions. The procedures themselves are identical in the two cases. There is one new element, however, in cases where decimal fractions are involved, and that is the proper placement of the decimal point in the answer. This usually causes no difficulty in finding sums or differences, because when the numbers are written carefully columnwise, the decimal point in the sum or difference falls naturally into place in line with the others.

Mistakes are more likely to occur in placing the decimal point in products or quotients than in sums or differences. As a rule such mistakes are due to haste and carelessness, because the decimal point is too often placed by rote rule alone and without any checking to see whether the result is reasonable or not. It is also true that a good many students seem not to be impressed by the seriousness of the error which is introduced by a misplaced decimal point. The comment "But it's all right except the decimal point" is neither uncommon nor insincere on the part of the students, yet it implies unawareness of how serious the error is. Students need to be made and kept sensitive to the fact that even if an answer is numerically correct so far as the sequence of digits is concerned, misplacement of the decimal point represents one of the most serious mistakes that could be made, because such a mistake can make the answer unreasonably large or small. As children learn arithmetic they need to be kept aware that the formal procedures are not divorced from common sense and that the results they get by using these procedures will not be right unless they can be confirmed by common sense.

This suggests a quick, easy, powerful, and in most cases a foolproof method of checking on the placement of the decimal point in a product or a quotient, namely, checking by mental estimate. Consider the product 27.43×12.08, which upon multiplication yields the digits 3313544 and requires that the decimal point be properly placed to give the true value of the product. Since 27.43 is a little less than 30 and 12.08 is a little more than 10, the required product *must* be in the neighborhood of 30×10, which is immediately seen to be 300. Hence the product *must* be somewhere near 300, and this requires that the decimal point be placed after the third digit; that is, the product must be 331.3544. This is readily confirmed by the usual rule, but more significantly, it is confirmed by the student's common sense. From such considerations even young students can readily learn to detect and correct careless misplacements of the decimal point and verify the correct position.

Placement of the decimal point in quotients can be determined and checked through similar considerations. For example, when 87.01646 is divided by 1.06, the sequence of digits 82091 appears in the quotient. The question of placing the decimal point can be resolved immediately by considering that, since the dividend is a little less than 90 and the divisor is just a little greater than 1, the quotient *must* be somewhere in the neighborhood of 90 and must also be less than 90, so it will probably be between 80 and 90. Hence, in order to yield such a quotient, the decimal point *must* be placed after the second digit. That is, the quotient must be 82.091.

Another effective method for placing the decimal point in the quotient is the following one. It is easily observed that $10 \times 1.06 = 10.6$, which is smaller than the dividend, and that $100 \times 1.06 = 106$, which is larger than the dividend. It follows, therefore, that the integral part of the quotient must be a two-digit number, since it lies between 10 and 100. The decimal point is thus to be placed immediately following the second quotient figure. Continued trial of successive powers of 10 is not a difficult procedure for establishing limits between which the quotient must lie. Practice will improve the estimate and reduce the number of trials necessary. Here again confirmation is easily made by applying the customary rule, but it is equally important to have the rule confirmed by the estimate. Indeed, the student's feeling of power and assurance is enhanced by encouraging him to make his preliminary estimate of the answer even before performing the computation. To this end such exercises as the following can be used to great advantage. They can be constructed easily and are unlimited in scope and variety.

Exercise. In the following products or quotients the digits are correct and in the right order. Place the decimal point where it should go, placing zeros if necessary before or after the digits given, and read the correct answer.

$38.501 \times 6.93 = 26681193$	$202.9372 \div 28.03 = 724$
$81.072 \times 39.6 = 32104512$	$129.10072 \div 19.88 = 6494$
$512.47 \times 2.53 = 12965491$	$4284.687 \div 0.965 = 48637$
$70.386 \times 0.945 = 6651477$	$4.654728 \div 89.514 = 52$

The importance of inculcating in students the habit of checking their work by such estimates can hardly be overemphasized. Of course, it does not provide any check on the numerical work, but it does provide a powerful and easy and almost certain way of avoiding blunders through misplacement of the decimal point, and it injects a rationale into the work with decimal fractions which can hardly be attained in any other way. Actually, students almost always enjoy it, and the assurance and confidence which can result may often be of extreme importance with respect not only to the correctness of the work itself but also to the student's attitude toward it.

Of course, when dealing with decimal fractions, the point should always be made that these numbers are fractions. All the principles and techniques used with fractions still apply. The only differences at all are due to a possible simplification in notation due to the fact that the fractions to be used are now restricted to those whose denominators are powers of ten, the base of our number system. In particular the rules for finding the product and quotient of two fractions still apply. For example, the product 27.43×12.08 can be found as the product of the two common fractions $2,743/100 \times 1,208/100 = 3,313,544/10,000$, which may, in turn, be written as the decimal fraction 331.3544. Such procedure displays the reason why there are as many digits in the fraction part of the product of two decimal fractions as there are in the sum of the digits in the multiplier and the multiplicand. Similarly, the quotient $87.01646 \div 1.06$ can be found as

$$\frac{8,701,646}{100,000} \div \frac{106}{100} = \frac{8,701,646}{100,000} \times \frac{100}{106} = \frac{82,091}{1,000}$$

which can be written as the decimal fraction 82.091.

Such demonstration provides the rationale of the inverse rule used to find the number of digits in the fraction part of a quotient. Incidentally, once the rule for multiplication is established, the inverse relationship of division to multiplication could be used to obtain the corresponding rule for division.

Probably the most immediately direct and systematic physical application used to explain and illustrate decimals in arithmetic is the money system of the United States. Built as it is directly on the decimal system of notation, it forms a practically perfect physical illustration of that system, and it has the advantage of being familiar to everyone. Excellent as it is, however, it offers but a single means of illustration. Another, intrinsically just as good though less familiar to most people, is found in the metric system of weights and measures, which, of course, is an important element of the mathematics program in its own right. It is specifically recognized in the check list of the Committee on Post-War Plans as one of the 29 fundamental components which should be included in the mathematical education of all children. However, because it is not the system of weights and measures in most common use in this country, few people learn anything about it through informal everyday experience in the way they learn about money. As a rule, if it is learned at all, it is learned in school as a part of the work in mathematics, and its introduction generally occurs after the study of decimal fractions is begun.[1] This, of course, imposes a drastic limitation on its use in *developing* the concept of decimal fractions but does not impair its later usefulness as a means of illustrating and strengthening this concept. Indeed, if the simple elements of the metric system could be taught concurrently with the subject of decimal notation and decimal fractions, it would seem to afford an excellent opportunity for strengthening and enriching both.

Place Value. The concept of place value is possibly the greatest single simplification and efficiency device in our notational system. It would be difficult to overemphasize its nature and importance. Other number systems have been decimal in nature, and some of them have used place value, but in a rather restricted form. For example, in the Roman system of numeration, which is decimal, a symbol for a small number preceding a symbol for a larger number indicates a subtraction of values and a symbol for a small number following a symbol for a larger number indicates an addition of values. Thus, IX means $10 - 1$ or 9 and XI means $10 + 1$ or 11.

Our more efficient use of place value makes it possible to use only ten individual symbols in the construction of number symbols, no matter

[1] See, for example, "Materials for Grade 8 Mathematics Program" (New York: Board of Education of the City of New York, 1955), pp. 56–58.

how large or how small the value of the number to be represented.   Thus each digital symbol (0, 1, 2, 3, 4, 5, 6, 7, 8, 9) in the symbol for a number might be said to have ascribed to it two values, a *place value* and a *face value*.   In the symbol 1302 the digital symbols have certain values because of the position they have in the symbol: the 1 indicates the number of thousands, the 3 indicates the number of hundreds, the 0 indicates the number of tens, and the 2 indicates the number of ones.   The concept of one-to-one correspondence enables us to determine the face value of each of these digital symbols, i.e., to tell *how many* each symbol represents.   For example, compare the number symbol 1302 with the word "seeded."   There are just as many thousands in the number symbol as there are letters *s* in the word; we call it "one" and use the symbol 1 to indicate the number.   There are the same number of hundreds as there are letters *e*; we call it "three" and write it 3.   There are just as many tens as there are letters *b*; we call it "zero" and write it 0.   There are just as many ones as there are letters *d*; we call it "two" and write it 2. Thus, in such numbers, each digital symbol performs two functions; it is both a numeral and a place holder.

Convention has made of 0, the symbol for the number zero, a much more flexible symbol than any of the nonzero symbols.   While, as indicated in the previous paragraph, it does acquire through one-to-one correspondence the basic property of number—and earlier study of arithmetic has demonstrated that, except for division, it obeys the operational laws which govern integers—convention has decreed that it is proper to use this same symbol in the capacity of a mere place holder.   For example, the distance from the earth to the sun is 93 million miles.   This is a satisfactory measure stated in terms of a large unit, 1 million miles. There are occasions when it is desirable to write this as a numeral.   Since convention has decreed that it is not necessary to use a decimal point in writing a numeral unless it is necessary to indicate the ones position, some scheme for distinguishing the ones position becomes necessary when writing symbols for such numbers as 93 million.   By common agreement and use the symbol has become 93,000,000 rather than some such symbol as 93,xxx,xxx.   The same situation holds for small numbers.   For example, to write 4 thousandths as a decimal, three places are required to the right of the decimal.   Since 4 occupies only one place, some symbol must be used to fill the other two.   While .xx4 is quite satisfactory as far as filling the basic need is concerned, convention has established .004 as the proper symbol.

In spite of the great notational and computational convenience intrinsic to the conventional flexibility ascribed to the symbol for zero, there are some situations in which it is absolutely incorrect to use the symbol in the sense of a mere place holder. For example, consider this box score of a baseball game played in Chicago between New York and Chicago.

New York   000 101 002   4
Chicago   001 000 04x   5

The 1, 2, 4, and each 0 are numbers which tell *how many* runs were scored during each team's respective efforts to score.   The x in the position of the last half of the ninth inning is a mere place holder which convention has established as a proper method for filling out the box score when the home team has already won the game and makes no effort to score any more runs.   The symbol 0 would be entirely incorrect in this position because it has numerical significance in such a box score and hence cannot be used in capacity of a mere place holder.

Proper instructional emphasis on place value can remove computation from the status of mere rote performance.   For example, in finding the sum of 54 and 28, the addends are aligned according to the positional

$$
\begin{array}{r}
54 \\
+28 \\
\hline
82
\end{array}
\qquad
\begin{array}{r}
54 \\
-28 \\
\hline
26
\end{array}
$$

value of the digits. $4 + 8 = 12$, with the 2 recorded in the ones column and the 1 ten added with the other tens to secure a total of 8 tens.   Similarly, in finding the differences, the digits are properly aligned according to place value.   In subtraction, one of the 5 tens must be converted to 10 ones and combined with the 4 ones; then 14 ones less 8 ones is 6 ones, and 4 tens less 2 tens is 2 tens.   Notice nothing is said about "carry" or "borrow."   They are merely convenient words which can be used *if the process is understood and not until then.*   In multiplication, place value is the key to the proper placement of the partial products in order that they may be added correctly.   Previous illustration has been given of how place value can be used to estimate and place trial quotients.

A study of number systems using bases other than ten can be a distinct aid to the teacher and to the better students in attaining a richer understanding of the significance of place value in number symbolism.   In the following brief example we shall agree to use the concept of place value and the customary digital symbols in the forming of number symbols.   Note that two such symbols had to be invented for base twelve.   Ten (*t*) and eleven (*e*) are each less than the base and must be represented by one-position holding symbols.

Care must be exercised in reading this table.   Since no number names have been provided for any base other than ten, the symbols must be read digit by digit.   For example, 10 is *not* ten except in base ten; it is only a

Table 11-1. Comparing Number Systems Using Different Bases

	Base two	Base eight	Base ten	Base twelve
Digital symbols	0, 1	0, 1, 2, 3, 4, 5, 6, 7	0, 1, 2, 3, 4, 5, 6, 7, 8, 9	0, 1, 2, 3, 4, 5, 6, 7, 8, 9, t, e
Base symbols and their equivalents	10 1000 1010 1100	2 10 12 14	2 8 10 12	2 8 t 10
Equivalent numbers	10011011	233	155	$10e$

Conversion from one base to another by division: Divide by the new base with computation made under the old base.

Base eight: To go from base eight to base two, divide by 2. The new symbol is found by writing the remainders in the reverse order: 10, 011, 011.

$$2\underline{)233}$$
$$2\underline{)115}\quad 1$$
$$2\underline{)46}\quad 1$$
$$2\underline{)23}\quad 0$$
$$2\underline{)11}\quad 1$$
$$2\underline{)4}\quad 1$$
$$2\underline{)2}\quad 0$$
$$2\underline{)1}\quad 0$$
$$0\quad 1$$

Base ten: To go from base ten to base twelve, divide by 12. The new symbol is $10e$.

$$12\underline{)155}$$
$$12\underline{)12}\quad 11 \text{ which converts to } e$$
$$12\underline{)1}\quad 0 \qquad\qquad 0$$
$$0\quad 1 \qquad\qquad 1$$

Base twelve: The

Conversion from one base to another by multiplication: (1) Write the number in place-value form in the old base; (2) convert to the new base; (3) make the computation under the new base.

The conversion here is from base two to each of the other bases. The number 10011011 converts into $1(2)^7 + 0(2)^6 + 0(2)^5 + 1(2)^4 + 1(2)^3 + 0(2)^2 + 1(2)^1 + 1(2)^0$ whether in base eight, ten, or twelve.

Base eight:

$$1(2)^7 = 200$$
$$1(2)^4 = 20$$
$$1(2)^3 = 10$$
$$1(2)^1 = 2$$
$$1(2)^0 = 1$$
$$\overline{233}$$

Base ten:

$$1(2)^7 = 128$$
$$1(2)^4 = 16$$
$$1(2)^3 = 8$$
$$1(2)^1 = 2$$
$$1(2)^0 = 1$$
$$\overline{155}$$

Base twelve:

$$1(2)^7 = t8$$
$$1(2)^4 = 14$$
$$1(2)^3 = 8$$
$$1(2)^1 = 2$$
$$1(2)^0 = 1$$
$$\overline{10e}$$

symbol for "one of the base." Read it "one-oh." The symbol 233 in base eight is *not* "two hundred thirty-three"; read it "two-three-three."

This Table 11-1 is to be interpreted as follows:

1. All symbols and computations in any vertical column are to be interpreted in the base which is indicated at the top of the column.

2. The significance of each row across the table is indicated by the label at the extreme left. For example, row 2 shows the respective equivalents of each given base. Row 4 carries illustrations of conversions from one base to another by division. The computations used for illustration are in base eight (in conversion to base two) and in base ten (in conversion to base twelve). Row 5 carries illustrations of conversion from one base to another by multiplication. The illustration shows the conversion of 10,011,011 (base two) to each of the other bases being considered. Place value gives to 10011011 the meaning

$$1(10)^{111} + 0(10)^{110} + 0(10)^{101} + 1(10)^{100} + 1(10)^{11} + 0(10)^{10} + 1(10)^{1} + 1(10)^{0}$$

which converts into

$$1(2)^7 + 0(2)^6 + 0(2)^5 + 1(2)^4 + 1(2)^3 + 0(2)^2 + 1(2)^1 + 1(2)^0$$

The computation for each conversion is then carried out in its respective base.

Percentage. Of all the special topics or centers of attention in arithmetic none has more widespread utility and direct application than the subject of percentage. It is involved in the numerical record and analysis of all kinds of activities from the very simple to the very complex, and to those who understand its language it provides a concise and efficient means of interpreting, comparing, and communicating many kinds of quantitative information. Since it is so closely allied to the subject of decimal notation and fractions, one might conclude that its application would involve no difficulties that are not involved in the study or application of decimals as such. Unfortunately, however, experience indicates that this is not the case. Percentage has been and continues to be one of the most troublesome parts of arithmetic. In spite of its importance as an instrument for analysis and a vehicle for communication, many students fail to attain an assured mastery of it.

Various studies have been made from time to time to determine why students have so much difficulty with percentage, and these have usually taken the form of listing mistakes which students have made on percentage problems. One investigator enumerated 28 specific errors classified under seven categories which he had previously listed as representing the chief skills involved in percentage.[1] Such detailed analyses are impor-

[1] Leo J. Brueckner, "Diagnostic and Remedial Teaching in Arithmetic" (Philadelphia: John C. Winston Company, 1930), pp. 255-256.

tant, and if we were concerned only with the perfection of certain *skills*, the identification of these errors might point the way with sufficient clearness. But teachers ought to be concerned not only with what mistakes are made but why they are made. To point out merely that students do not understand the principle of percentage does not provide much indication of just why they don't understand, or of what could be done to help them understand better. The computational skills involved in the mechanics of percentage are merely those involved in computing with decimal fractions, but they do not suffice for the interpretation and analysis of percentage problems stated in words or drawn from original situations. The latter require an exact understanding of the technical vocabulary and symbolism which has come to be associated with percentage, the ability to interchange different but equivalent forms with assurance, and the habit of meticulously careful analytical reading. The student who thoroughly understands a problem in percentage and who understands the language and symbolism usually will have little difficulty in solving it. As Blackhurst pointed out long ago, "For the pupil who has been prepared properly in fractions and decimals the problems in per cent are almost entirely problems in reading."[1]

The difficulties involved in reading and interpreting percentage problems, however, are by no means trivial. According to Butler:[2]

There seem to be several things that contribute to the confusion that is so prevalent with respect to percentage. The terminology that has come to be universally employed is itself confusing and unfortunate. In the identification of "per cent" with "hundredths" the base number often is not mentioned, though neither of these concepts has meaning except as referred to some base. The further representation of, say, "37 per cent" or "37%" by the decimal fraction "0.37" fails to emphasize the clarifying idea that 0.37 itself means 37×0.01 and that the % symbol merely stands for the decimal fraction 0.01. These alternative representations of the same thing thus tend to add to the student's confusion, especially when such expressions as "0.37%" are encountered. Experienced teachers will verify that students often fail to make any distinction in their minds between "37%" and "0.37%." When the subject is taught by "cases" three explicit rules can indeed be developed for the three explicit relations among the three elements involved, but these tend to become confused in the students' minds, and students often have trouble determining "which case this is." Even the single over-all rule or formula *base* $\times$ *rate* = *percentage* (or $b \cdot r = p$) requires that the rate must be represented by the decimal or common fraction only, and not by use of the % symbol, yet even this is seldom emphasized in the textbooks.

---

[1] J. Herbert Blackhurst: "Principles and Methods of Junior High School Mathematics" (New York: Appleton-Century-Crofts, Inc., 1928), p. 159.

[2] Charles H. Butler, A Note on Teaching Percentage, *Mathematics Teacher*, **48** (1955), 208.

What, then, can be done to make the teaching of percentage more productive of worthwhile results?   The terminology and symbolism associated with percentage without doubt present certain ambiguities and difficulties.   It seems reasonable, however, to believe that more can be done than usually has been done to make percentage intelligible to students and enable them to think about it with clarity.

Nearly all textbooks that treat the subject of percentage stress the solution of problems by use of the rule or formula: base $\times$ rate = percentage. This gives the fundamental relationship of the three elements and provides a pattern for explicit determination of percentage when the base and rate are known.   Most textbooks go further and give explicit formulas for each of the three "cases."   This does, of course, give quicker results when the students have the three formulas before them and the cases of all their problems identified.   But, by the same token, it obviates the need for thinking about the problems and in effect avoids, rather than promotes, training in problem analysis.   Moreover, students often get the formulas confused with each other unless they have them all written out before them.   Failure to identify correctly the given data is a further major source of mistakes.   Also, students frequently fail to check their results by first making rough estimates.   Thus they are at times led through mechanical reaction to a rule to accept results which commonsense estimates would show to be ridiculous.

The only apparent reason for teaching percentage by cases with their accompanying three formulas, is the belief that with typed problems this method will produce answers more quickly than other methods.   But actually, even if that is true, the advantage is more apparent than real, because the same results can be attained about as quickly and with less chance of confusion if all three cases are fed into the one basic formula or rule and the resulting equation solved, when necessary, by a single step which even seventh graders can learn to use easily and with understanding.   As an example, consider this problem: At a school district election, 1,400 people voted.   If this was 35 per cent of all the eligible voters, how many eligible voters were there in all?   Steps in the solution would be as follows.

$$\text{Base} \times \text{rate} = \text{percentage}$$
$$\text{Base} \times (0.35) = (1,400)$$
$$\frac{\text{Base} \times (0.35)}{(0.35)} = \frac{1,400}{(0.35)}$$

Since the *base* (total number of eligible voters) is to be determined, it can be done immediately by dividing each member of the equation by the coefficient 0.35, giving the result indicated in the third line of the solution.

If the objection be raised that this requires a little bit of algebra, one must reflect that the special formula for this case is itself derived by precisely this method.

Furthermore, this difficulty, if difficulty it is, can be greatly reduced by the realization that such emphasis on this fundamental relationship in percentage problems points out that there are always three numbers involved, and that one of them (*percentage*) is the product of the other two (*base* and *rate*). If the product number (percentage) is not known, then the operation called for is multiplication; if it is known, then the operation called for is division.

As in the multiplication of any two numbers, so in percentage are there four associated relations: $p = r \times b$, $p = b \times r$, $b = p \div r$, and $r = p \div b$. Furthermore, the rate, if it is a known number, usually is labeled with the per cent sign. This means that in percentage the problem situation is reduced to being able to distinguish between the number upon which all computation is based (the base) and the number which is derived through multiplication (the percentage).

As either an alternative or a supplementary device the "one per cent method" or "method of unitary analysis" can be used, often to great advantage in clarifying students' thinking. In this method primary attention is focused at the outset on the concept of one single per cent of the base as an entity—a whole "little" number or quantity in itself. If this is done, then such an expression as "63 per cent of the distance" comes to be thought of not just as some part of the required distance but actually as 63 parts, all equal and each being 1 hundredth of the required distance. This obviates the need for translating from per cents to decimal equivalents and so avoids the mistakes which so often accompany attempts to make this translation. Now 63 per cent becomes not 0.63 (a decimal fraction of the whole) but 63 "little wholes." It brings the thinking from the realm of fractions into the realm of whole numbers; from a field of possible uncertainty or confusion into a realm of familiarity. Then if one of these per cents can be found, any number of them can be found by a turn of the hand. It requires only the kind of reasoning one uses in determining the cost of $4\frac{1}{2}$ gallons of gasoline at 35 cents a gallon or the cost of 115 postage stamps at 4 cents each. And no matter which case a percentage problem represents, 1 per cent of the base can always be found. As an example, consider again the problem about the voters, discussed above. Here our problem is clearly to determine the base number, which is the total number of eligible voters. It is given that 35 per cent of this total is 1,400 people. Think of this as 35 little groups of people each containing 1 per cent of the total number of eligible voters, with the total number of people in the 35 groups being 1,400. Now that is exactly equivalent, arithmetically, to such a question as this: If 35 note-

books cost $14.00, or 1,400 cents, how much does each cost? Even
seventh graders know how to find the cost of one notebook under these
conditions, so it is not very hard to lead them to see how to determine the
number representing 1 per cent of the required base. Then, having determined that 1 per cent of the total number of eligible voters is 40 (that is,
$\frac{1}{35}$ of 1,400), it follows that the total number must be 100 times as much,
or 4,000.

Now it is easy also to answer at once such questions as the following
ones: If $47\frac{1}{2}$ per cent of the eligible voters are men, how many men are
eligible to vote? If 3.7 per cent of the eligible voters are at least 80 years
old, how many of the voters are not yet 80 years of age? If the number
of eligible voters increases by 18 per cent in the next 5 years, how many
will there be then?

There are, of course, some drawbacks to this method of analysis. It
certainly requires careful and exact reading and interpretation of the
problems, and the students will learn to handle the method only through
honest, painstaking, and protracted effort on their part and on the part
of their teachers. Some old mental associations and fixed habits will
probably have to be broken down in order that the primary concept of a
single per cent of the base number may come to occupy the focus of attention. This method requires superior teaching, and usually it will not
produce answers as quickly as the use of the formula will. For these and
perhaps other reasons it has not come into widespread use either in textbooks or by teachers. But it does aim at the fundamental objectives of
clear thinking about percentage relationships, and if it is systematically
and persistently used with good teaching and adequate supervision, it can
do much to help students clarify their thoughts on this important aspect
of arithmetic.

There are other considerations which teachers should take into account
as means for clarifying and highlighting the main concepts associated with
per cents and for providing conditions favorable to effective mastery of
this subject. Space limitations preclude detailed discussion of them here,
but one or two should at least be mentioned.

The concepts of *base*, *rate*, and *percentage* and the relation between them
can be clarified and made vivid by the extensive use of graphs, and
teachers should capitalize on this means of strengthening and enriching
the concepts. Most textbooks do employ this device to a limited extent,
but they need to be supplemented. Fortunately, it is easy to find many
examples of graphical illustrations of situations that involve percentage.
Newspapers, magazines, financial reports, business articles, brochures,
and advertising material are rich sources of such examples. Bar, circle,
and line graphs lend themselves readily to use in such illustrations. A
great variety of good illustrations is readily available for study, and it can

be supplemented at will by having the students make graphical illustrations of their own problems. The systematic use of graphs to illustrate problems and principles of percentage can do much to clarify and fix the concepts and principles that are involved.

Teachers need to be sensitive to the fact that problems which involve more than 100 per cent of the base number are especially troublesome to many students. The trouble may often be traced to failure to read carefully or to interpret relations or notation correctly. This, in turn, may result from the habit of expecting the percentage to be less than the base, since this is almost always the case in the early problems used to introduce the subject. Similarly, students often have trouble in cases that involve numbers less than 1 per cent of the base. The trouble in this case usually arises from failure either to interpret correctly or to write correctly the notation representing the fraction of a per cent. These two trouble spots are serious enough to merit the teacher's special attention in planning the work in percentage. In both of these cases the use of graphs can be very helpful for illustrating such problems, and the use of the 1 per cent method described above can make a real contribution to the analysis of such problems.

As a final suggestion, teachers should be warned that poorly graded sets of problems can be a major source of difficulty and frustration to students. In general the authors of textbooks make sincere efforts to provide well-ordered lists of exercises leading gradually from very simple ones to more difficult or complicated ones, but sometimes they do not succeed very well. Yet nothing is more frustrating to students than to be expected to solve problems for which they have not had adequate preparation. A hard problem placed inappropriately early in a list where the students are not ready for it is not only nonproductive but actually destructive of confidence and morale. In planning assignments for classwork or homework the teacher will be well advised to go through in detail any lists of problems that are to be assigned, to be sure that this situation does not arise. Problem lists should always be regarded as self-administering exercises designed to lead the student step by step to increased mastery and insight and self-reliance. Exercises which are out of place in a problem list do not contribute to this objective and should be either eliminated or properly relocated in the list.

Inasmuch as percentage constitutes such a crucial part of the arithmetic of the secondary school, a separate list of references bearing on this topic is given in the Bibliography under Percentage.

Common Fractions. Along with percentage and verbal problems, the fundamental operations with common fractions share the dubious distinction of being the most troublesome parts of arithmetic. The difficulties encountered in the solution of verbal problems will be discussed later in a separate section; this section will deal with some learning and teaching problems associated with common fractions.

The very real and very serious difficulties which many students encounter in working with common fractions may stem from any one or more of several things. One of them is failure to have a clear concept of what a fraction represents numerically. Another is an apparent reluctance to concede that in operations with fractions the numerators and denominators must be given attention separately; that frequently it is not sufficient to think of fractions merely as single numbers as one would think of integers, but rather, as ratios each consisting of two separate parts or as the expressed quotients of two numbers. This is tantamount to nonrecognition of the real meaning of the numerator and denominator and of the role each has in expressing the value of the fraction. Such recognition requires reflective thought, and thinking is hard, and often slow, work. A third source of difficulty lies in the characteristic impatience of youth— the desire to be done with a problem quickly, and preferably in a single step. This, coupled with fuzzy concepts, uncertain thinking, disregard of definitions, and a tendency to speed things up by uncritical use of analogy, can and often does combine to produce in students a state of mind altogether unfavorable to clear thinking. Such a state of mind leads to a willingness to use any device that will produce a quick answer.

Teachers, of course, cannot disregard these things. Failing to get acceptable progress through the necessarily slow process of insisting on clear thinking about fractions and faced with limited time, teachers often have recourse to the only apparent alternative: that of providing the students with ready-made rules. Students usually like to have them, because the rules provide them with patterns that are easy to follow and which do enable them to get quick results. Rules per se are not bad. Indeed, they are very necessary for generalizing and crystallizing procedures and for economizing time and effort. But such rules without accompanying insight are merely arithmetical tools. They may promote computational proficiency but they do not represent genuine mathematical understanding, which alone can lead to intelligent use of any acquired mathematical tools.

While this is recognized by practically all teachers, there are two extreme schools of thought about rules in mathematics. One holds that students should *never* be taught a process until it has been rationalized. The other holds that rationalization will always be easier to understand if students are first given the rule and shown how it works and that the use of the rule or procedure should *always* precede the justification. It is almost certain that neither of these extreme positions is tenable. But without rationalization, whether first or last, genuine growth in mathematical insight cannot take place. The danger in the "rule first, rationalization later" theory is that of time pressure. Inevitably, and perhaps before getting around to the rationalization, comes the need to move on to other things, and to teachers under this pressure the temptation to compromise on reasonable mechanical proficiency in the use of the rules can become very strong.

Too frequently the technique of simplifying fractions, or "reducing fractions to lower terms," is taught as a mechanical process of cancellation.   Such a procedure leads to a confused concept of the significance of cancellation and very often reduces it to a mere crossing out of numbers. Such performance as

$$\frac{4+2}{4+9} = \frac{2}{9} \quad \text{or} \quad \frac{7+3}{7 \times 3} = \frac{3}{3} = 1$$

then may, and not infrequently does, result.   In instruction which leads to this sort of performance, no basic understanding of the interrelationship among the fundamental operations or of the structure of fractions is developed.   It needs to be pointed out to students that the horizontal bar of a fraction indicates a division, that, for example, $\frac{8}{18}$ indicates the division of 8 by 18.   Stress should also be laid upon the principle that division and multiplication are inverse processes, just as addition and subtraction are inverse processes.   Thus, in the multiplication and division of any number by the same number (other than zero) one operation nullifies, destroys, or cancels the effect of the other.   This means simply that the net effect is multiplication, or division, of the given number by 1.   Thus

$$\frac{8}{18} = \frac{2 \times 4}{2 \times 9} = \frac{4}{9} \times \frac{2}{2} = \frac{4}{9} \times 1 = \frac{4}{9}$$

We simplify all of this detail by using the convenient device of cancellation:

$$\frac{8}{18} = \frac{{}^1\!2 \times 4}{{}^1\!2 \times 9} = \frac{1 \times 4}{1 \times 9} = \frac{4}{9}$$

The small 1s should be written in to give emphasis to what has actually taken place.   Similarly, the net effect of adding the same number to and subtracting it from a given number is equivalent to the addition, or subtraction, of zero.   Thus $7 + 2 - 2 = 7 + 0$ (or $7 - 0$) $= 7$.   Cancellation can be used to indicate what has taken place here.   There would be no division, however, but merely a neutralizing which can be indicated by simply crossing out the numbers which neutralize each other: $7 + 2 - 2 = 7$.   In the fraction $\frac{4+2}{4+9}$ the student should be taught that he must think of the operations involved as if the division were expressed in the form $(4 + 2) \div (4 + 9)$. In such situations he can recognize that the additions must be performed before the division and that, since addition and division are not inverse processes, no cancellation is possible.

In this connection, something would be gained by pointing out and emphasizing that mathematicians call 1 the *identity element* for multiplication and division. In other words, if any number is either multiplied or divided by 1, the result is the original number. Futhermore, this leads to the definition of the *inverse*[1] of a number as another number which, when multiplied by the given number, yields 1 as the product. Thus the inverse of 4 is $\frac{1}{4}$, because $4 \times \frac{1}{4} = 1$. Later, in beginning algebra, zero should be developed as the identity element for the operations of addition and subtraction, which, in turn, can lead to the definition of an inverse for those operations. Thus the additive inverse of $+2$ is defined as (-2) because $(+2) + (-2) = 0$, which is the identity element for addition.

Multiplication of fractions usually presents little difficulty. It is generally learned at the outset as a mechanical procedure. It can be made to seem reasonable by giving various concrete illustrations and by identifying such notation as $\frac{1}{3} \times \frac{6}{7}$ with the corresponding verbal expression one-third of six-sevenths. Graphic or geometric illustrations are effective and are easy to devise. Although the procedure actually represents a definition of the product, it is well to give illustrations to show that the results which it gives are in accord with actual experience and common sense.

Products of fractions can often be simplified by cancellation. As a precautionary measure against mistakes it is well to have students form the habit of expressing the product as a single fraction before doing the cancellation. For example, instead of writing

$$\frac{1}{\not{3}} \times \frac{\not{6}^2}{7}$$

it is better for them to write

$$\frac{1}{3} \times \frac{6}{7} = \frac{1 \times {}^1\not{3} \times 2}{{}^1\not{3} \times 7} = \frac{1 \times 1 \times 2}{1 \times 7} = \frac{2}{7}$$

because it systematizes the form and may prevent mistakes due to careless writing. Of course after a student thoroughly understands the full significance of what is taking place, he no longer needs to bother with so much minuteness of detail.

The procedure for dividing by a fraction is familiar to most students who know how to multiply fractions, for the reason that, after a single simple adjustment, the division problem actually becomes a problem in

---

[1] This refers, of course, to the multiplicative inverse, since the additive inverse involves negative numbers, and these are first encountered in algebra.

multiplication.   Few, however, of those who know *how* to divide by a fraction understand *why* the inversion of the fractional divisor and the consequent multiplication actually give the required value.   In a recent poll of 75 college students taking business arithmetic it was found that 73 of the 75 knew how to divide by a fraction but only 2 knew how to justify the procedure.   Here again is a case of a rather familiar process which for the most part is used quite empirically.   Where used correctly it gives correct results.   Unfortunately, however, the word "invert" seems to stand out as the only important thing in the minds of the students, with the result that sometimes they invert the dividend instead of the divisor and then wonder why the result they get is incorrect or perhaps even ridiculous.   The only sure safeguard against such a situation is to get the students to understand the rationale of the procedure.   This need not be a long or tedious matter, for a few rather simple illustrations will usually suffice.

While there are several elementary avenues to satisfactory rationalization, it must be kept in mind that the foundation upon which any approach must be based consists of the facts that (*a*) multiplication and division are inverse processes and (*b*) 1 is the identity element for multiplication and division.   Thus it follows, for example, that

$$16 \div 4 = \frac{16}{4} = \frac{16 \times \frac{1}{4}}{4 \times \frac{1}{4}} = \frac{16 \times \frac{1}{4}}{1} = 16 \times \frac{1}{4}$$

and that

$$9 \div \frac{1}{3} = (9 \times 3) \div \left(\frac{1}{3} \times 3\right) = (9 \times 3) \div 1 = 9 \times 3$$

Unless some effective measures are taken to have the students understand what is actually taking place and see why the process must give the required result, there will always be some danger of mistakes occurring, and at best the students would have attained only a mechanical proficiency without corresponding mathematical insight.   The best teachers will never be content with this.

The greatest source of trouble in this area, however, is the addition and subtraction of fractions, particularly when the fractions have different denominators.   The difficulty stems from the sources that have already been mentioned: the desire of the students for short cuts and quick answers, the time pressure on the teachers and the consequent tendency to give inadequate attention to rationalizing the procedure, the excessive dependence on the mechanical use of rules, and the failure to check results for reasonableness.   Furthermore, there is the additional fact that the procedure here is characteristically a bit more involved than is that in the operations discussed previously.   This, of course, intensifies the pressure on the teacher and tends to diminish any disposition to insist on rationalization and checking, although they are made even more important by the circumstances.

One of the most effective ways of giving meaning to the addition of fractions is the method of unitary analysis, which has already been mentioned in connection with percentage. Under this method as applied, say, to the fraction $\frac{3}{7}$, it would be emphasized that the fraction is made up of 3 "unit fractions" each of which is $\frac{1}{7}$, or

$$\frac{3}{7} = \frac{1}{7} + \frac{1}{7} + \frac{1}{7} = 3 \times \frac{1}{7} = \frac{1}{7} \times 3$$

This decomposition both establishes an identity as shown and suggests the usefulness of identifying the form $\frac{3}{7}$ with the form $3 \times \frac{1}{7}$. But it does more. Through this latter identification (which curiously is seldom used and often not even recognized by students, even though teachers always assume that it is so obvious as to require no comment) a reversal of the decomposition suggests the fundamental concept of the combination of fractions with like denominators, out of which the formal rule grows. That is to say,

$$\frac{1}{7} + \frac{1}{7} + \frac{1}{7} = \frac{1}{7} \times 3 = \frac{1}{7} \times (1 + 1 + 1) = \frac{1 + 1 + 1}{7} = \frac{3}{7}$$

This illustrates what goes on in the combination of fractions whose denominators are alike. The effect of such an illustration, however, will usually be negligible unless two things are explicitly and *separately* emphasized about the single fraction which makes up the sum, namely, (1) how its denominator is determined and (2) how its numerator is determined, and preferably in the order mentioned. This may seem a trivial insistence, but it is not. It is justified by both psychological considerations and practical experience. The matter should not be hurried; it should be soundly established in the minds of the students by both discussion and practice before taking them on to the more troublesome case of combining fractions whose denominators are not alike.

Once the handling of fractions with like denominators is thoroughly understood by the students, the way is open for proceeding to the general case of fractions whose denominators are not necessarily alike. Recalling that for any given fraction an equivalent fraction having any (nonzero) denominator we like can be written, let us then say to the students, "If the denominators are not alike, make them alike. Then we shall know how to combine them." This will, of course, require determination of the least common denominator, the building up of all denominators to this form by writing in the needed factors, and corresponding adjustment of numerators. This is best understood if all the denominators are first written in full factored form and the L.C.D. is also written in factored form and if all these factored expressions are written out separately for reference. For example, consider the sum of the fractions $\frac{5}{42}$ + $\frac{7}{12}$ + $\frac{1}{2}$. Now

$$42 = (2)(3)(7) \qquad 12 = (2)(3)(2) \qquad \text{L.C.D.} = (2)(3)(2)(7)$$

$$\frac{5}{42} + \frac{7}{12} + \frac{1}{2} = \frac{5}{(2)(3)(7)} + \frac{7}{(2)(3)(2)} + \frac{1}{2}$$

$$= \frac{5(2)}{(2)(3)(2)(7)} + \frac{7(7)}{(2)(3)(2)(7)} + \frac{1(3)(2)(7)}{(2)(3)(2)(7)}$$

$$= \frac{10}{84} + \frac{49}{84} + \frac{42}{84}$$

$$= \frac{10 + 49 + 42}{84} = \frac{101}{84} = 1\frac{17}{84}$$

In such cases it is simpler and probably better to use parentheses, as shown, to indicate multiplication. The meaning of this notation will have to be explained to students who have not had any experience with algebra, but this should take little time and cause no difficulty.

At the outset, of course, much simpler cases would be used—examples in which the identification of the L.C.D. can be very easily made at sight—and perhaps the work in the seventh grade should be largely limited to such cases. It is believed, however, that even here the routine illustrated above will do much to build fundamental understanding of the rationale underlying the process and thus remove it from the realm of mere mechanical tools. Even in the seventh grade the generality of the procedure can be enhanced by giving some illustrations of cases in which the L.C.D. is not immediately discernible as a single whole number. The advantage of this will become more and more apparent as the students go on to subsequent work in arithmetic and perhaps in algebra in the eighth and ninth grades and beyond.

Furthermore, even in its simplest form this procedure tends to rationalize the rote process used in the elementary grades for finding the L.C.D. in such situations. It is possible that there may be some students at the seventh-grade level who are not yet sufficiently mature to be able to comprehend such rationalization, even in its simplest form. For such students the rote method of successive multiplications of the largest denominator by the integers 2, 3, 4, etc. will have to continue to suffice.

Everything which has been said in this section applies with equal validity and in all details to both proper and improper fractions. Indeed, since mixed numbers and integers can be written as improper fractions, it can be said to apply to them as well, after they are written in fraction form. Sometimes multiplication, and always division, by mixed numbers can be accomplished most easily by reducing these numbers to improper fractions and proceeding accordingly. It is well to give students some experience in this, both for the understanding of the specific applications and for strengthening the sense of the generality of the methods.

Verbal Problems. To be able to apply correct computation to the solution of genuine problems can be regarded for most people as the end product of the study of arithmetic, for it is here that arithmetic finds its practical usefulness. It is also, for most people, the most difficult aspect of arithmetic. The reason for this is not hard to find. Computation per se resolves itself through rationalization into patterns of procedure which eventually become habituated and used in much the same way as correct habits of speaking. Furthermore, when a computation is presented, the student faces not the question of what he is to do, but only the requirement of doing it.

Problem situations, on the other hand, require not only that the student be able to do the things that need to be done but also that he decide what things need to be done and in what order. Beyond the classification, sometimes made, of certain elementary problems into types such as time-rate-distance problems and work problems, verbal problems follow no special pattern. Every one of them must be thought through. The student has to determine for himself exactly what is required, what data he has available for use, and what things he must do with the data in order to arrive at the information that is required. Moreover, since the main source of verbal problems is usually the textbook, the student has to be able to read and interpret correctly what he reads before he can even begin his analysis of the problem. Thus every problem of this sort presents a double problem to the student: he must first read and analyze the problem and set up his procedure and he must then perform the computations required for obtaining the numerical answer. Of the two parts of the problem, the first typically gives more trouble than the second. Also, the student must be able to recognize in a problem situation the basic characteristics of the fundamental processes. For example, when a problem situation calls for the combining of two or more groups of like objects into a single group, the student must be able to recognize that either addition or multiplication is the process which will accomplish the desired result and that a careful analysis will tell him which of the two to use.

A good many studies have been made in the attempt to identify the causes of student difficulty with verbal problems. Examination of published material on problem solving in arithmetic indicates that much of the difficulty can be attributed to one or more of the following causes:[1]

_____

[1] The order of listing here does not imply relative importance.

1. Computation
2. Lack of reasoning ability
3. Poor procedure or complete absence of systematic attack
4. Difficulty in selecting the processes to be used
5. Failure to comprehend the meaning of the problem
6. Inefficient reading habits
7. Vocabulary difficulties
8. Short attention span
9. Inability to select essential data
10. Carelessness in transcribing
11. Poor eyesight and other physical defects
12. Lack of interest
13. Guessing because of desire for a quick answer

Such a list can be of some help to teachers in trying to identify causes of difficulty with verbal problems experienced by individuals and perhaps to some extent by classes, but it does not provide specific remedies. The causes listed above are not in themselves simple or specific but are individually highly complex. Furthermore, they will seldom, if ever, occur singly. For the most part they are not mutually exclusive but are interwoven and interdependent. For example, difficulty in selecting the processes to be used might be due to failure to comprehend the meaning of the problem, lack of reasoning ability, absence of systematic attack, or inefficient reading habits. Inefficient reading habits in turn may result from lack of interest, poor eyesight, vocabulary difficulties, or short attention span.

The truth is that the solution of verbal problems requires intellectual activity of a higher order and more complex nature than that involved in sheer computation. It requires conceptual understanding, insight, originality, independence of thought, and self-reliance. Some students are more richly endowed with these characteristics than others are. The characteristics are not specifics but complexes, and they usually can be developed only slowly, with painstaking, patient, and unremitting effort.

Efforts have been made and experiments have been carried out to try to determine a best method for teaching problem solving and reducing it to a system. Some of them have been more or less well defined and even given names:

1. The *restatement method,* in which the students are asked to restate each problem in their own words as a means of clarifying the problem.

2. The *analysis method,* in which effort is made to have the student systematically analyze the problem by requiring him to go through the following sequence of steps: (*a*) What is required? (*b*) What is given? (*c*) What operations are to be used? With what numbers? In what order? (*d*) Estimate the answer. (*e*) Solve the problem. (*f*) Check the answer by an estimate.

3. The *method of analogies*, in which the student is given a simple oral problem similar to but shorter than the more difficult written problem.

4. The *method of dependencies*, in which the student is taught to recognize and focus on fundamental dependence relations existing among elements in the problem under consideration. This is, in fact, the central core of the analysis method mentioned above.

5. The *graphic method*, in which the student is taught to use some graphic or diagrammatic scheme to help him identify the elements of the problem and formulate an explicit statement of their relations to each other. This method is rather specially helpful because it exhibits the problems visually and thus makes the relations easier to detect and formulate.

Because of space limitation, it is not feasible to give illustrations of all these methods here, but one illustration of the graphic method will be given because of its special helpfulness. Consider the following problem.

Example. A shipment of coats was received, and all but one of the coats were sold before Christmas. On the following January 2 the marked price on this coat was reduced by 20 per cent, and the next day the coat was sold at its reduced price of $60.00. At this price it still yielded a profit which was equivalent to 25 per cent of the cost of the coat. What did it cost and what was the pre-Christmas marked price?

Fig. 11-1

$$\text{S.P.} = \text{cost} + \text{profit}$$
$$= \text{cost} + 25 \text{ per cent of cost}$$
$$= 125 \text{ per cent of cost}$$
$$= \$60.00$$

whence cost can easily be determined as $48.00.

$$\text{S.P.} = \text{marked price} - \text{reduction}$$
$$= \text{marked price} - 20 \text{ per cent of marked price}$$
$$= 80 \text{ per cent of marked price}$$
$$= \$60.00$$

whence marked price is easily determined to be $75.00.

No single method stands out as the one best method of teaching verbal problems. Each of those mentioned above has given fair results. Teachers ought to become familiar with all the methods suggested above and make use of those which seem best suited to the requirements of each immediate situation, adapting them as needed and perhaps devising other ways of helping students learn to clarify the elements and relations involved in verbal problems.

At the risk of some repetition it may be worthwhile to list a few statements which can serve both as prerequisites to effective problem solving and as suggested ways in which the teacher can help students improve their abilities in this direction.

1. Since the problems are written problems, the students must be able to read.
2. The students must be able to use the fundamental processes of arithmetic.
3. The students must understand the fundamental characteristics of each of the fundamental operations. They must be able to recognize these characteristics in a problem situation.
4. The students must be able to distinguish between essential and unessential data; hence, some definite instructional program may be necessary to aid them in acquiring this ability.
5. The students must be able to distinguish the known from the unknown. Some specific instruction in this may be needed.
6. The students must be able to sense such relationships as may exist among given data and the required information.
7. The students must be able to translate verbal expressions into mathematical symbols. This is one of the most important of all techniques necessary for an intelligent approach to the solving of verbal problems. The teacher should place a great deal of emphasis upon the translation of the English statements of problem situations into their symbolic statements. Attention should be called to the simplification of operations which result from the use of significant symbolism and diagrams.
8. Independence and confidence are great aids in problem solving. Students should know how to estimate and how to check answers.

EXERCISES

1. Construct ten exercises similar to those on page 285 in which the correct value of the product is to be read by estimating the approximate value and placing the decimal point correctly.

2. Construct ten exercises similar to those called for in exercise 1 but applicable to quotients instead of products.

3. Perform the division 2,956 ÷ 473, obtaining the quotient and the remainder. Then explain in detail how the same result could be obtained by repeated subtraction, thus justifying the statement, often made, that "for whole numbers, division is essentially a process of repeated subtraction."

4. Explain as you would to a class the details of performing the division 295.6 ÷ 4.73. Justify each step, including placement of the decimal point by the customary rule, and then show that a rough estimate confirms this placement of the decimal point.

5. Without performing any pencil and paper computations, make rough mental estimates of the approximate values of the following products and quotients: 38.47 × 6.24,

253.19 × 19.41, 85.72 × 12.15, 26.06 × 0.486, 0.0945 × 51.54, 281.6 ÷ 71.12, 165.3 ÷ 85.10, 47.364 ÷ 24.336, 19.528 ÷ 0.493, 0.7238 ÷ 0.0352.

6. Give a report to the class in which you explain and illustrate the use in physics and chemistry of the metric system and its counterpart of numbers written in decimal notation.

7. Bring to class five graphical illustrations of situations involving percentage taken from newspapers or other printed sources but not from textbooks. Give the sources and present an explanation to the class for each of the illustrations.

8. Reconstruct each of the graphical illustrations called for in exercise 7 by using a different kind of graph.

9. Solve and explain the following problems by using the 1 per cent method and illustrating each with a diagram:

a. 29% of　　　　is 145.
b. 72 is　　　% of 180.
c. 88 is　　　% of 28.
d. 13% of 485 is　　　.
e. 0.3% of 220 is　　　.

f. 41% of　　　　is 1,476.
g. 52 is　　　% of 260.
h. 126% of 77 is　　　.
i.　　　is 15% more than 80.
j. 44% less than 350 is　　　.

10. Solve and explain each of the foregoing problems by direct substitution of given values in the basic formula base × rate = percentage, with solution of the resulting equations.

11. Give arguments for and against teaching students to solve percentage problems by cases.

12. Exhibit five problems or details of discussion taken from textbooks which you think may be difficult for students to interpret correctly because of the terminology, the symbolism, or the statement as a whole. Clarify each by a restatement or explanation such as you would give to a class.

13. Explain why the quotient $7/8 ÷ 3/5$ is correctly given by taking the product $7/8 × 5/3$.

14. In teaching the addition or subtraction of mixed numbers some teachers instruct the students to add or subtract the integer parts and the fractional parts of the numbers separately and combine the results. Others have the students change all the mixed numbers to improper fractions, find the sum of these, and then convert this back to a mixed number. Give examples in which you think the first of these methods would be preferable and explain why. Do the same for the second method.

15. What observation should students make from working the following five exercises in the order given? (a) $2/7 + 3/7$, (b) $2/27 + 3/27$, (c) $2/95 + 3/95$, (d) $2/513 + 3/513$, (e) $2/n + 3/n$.

16. What observation should students make from working the following five exercises in the order given? (a) $2/47 + 3/47$, (b) $5/47 + 2/47$, (c) $9/47 + 18/47$, (d) $36/47 − 11/47$, (e) $5/47 + n/47$.

17. Consider the following statement:

$$5\tfrac{3}{7} × 3\tfrac{3}{4} = 5 × 3 + 5 × \tfrac{3}{4} + 3 × \tfrac{3}{7} + \tfrac{3}{7} × \tfrac{3}{4}$$

(a) If the statement is wrong, criticize it. (b) If the statement is correct, justify it. (c) Present an alternative method of performing the multiplication. Which method do you prefer? Why?

18. Select 25 verbal problems from a current textbook in seventh-grade arithmetic or general mathematics and list all the words or expressions occurring in them, the

meanings or interpretations of which, in your opinion, seventh-graders might not be expected to understand clearly.

19. Make ten verbal problems involving fractions which you consider suitable for eleventh- or twelfth-grade students taking a refresher course in arithmetic.

20. Consider the numeral $1{,}451 \equiv 1(10)^3 + 4(10)^2 + 5(10)^1 + 1$ and (a) interpret it in base eight and write its equivalent in base ten; (b) interpret it in base twelve and write its equivalent in base ten; and (c) interpret it in base ten and write its equivalent in base two, in base eight, and in base twelve.

21. Give illustrations to show the significance of place value in addition, subtraction, multiplication, and division.

22. Consider a symbol a/b as a common fraction with its numerator and denominator written in base ten and reduced to lowest terms.   Use the fact that $10 = 2 \times 5$ to explain the following three statements:

a. If b is of the form 2^n, 5^n, or $2^m \cdot 5^n$ ($m < n$), then a/b will convert into a terminating decimal fraction of n decimal places.

b. If b is a prime number and $b > 2$, then a/b will convert into a repeating decimal and the repetend will contain no more than $b - 1$ digits.   (For example, $\frac{2}{7} = .\dot{2}8571\dot{4}$.)

c. If b is of the form $2^n \cdot c$, $5^n \cdot c$, or $2^m \cdot 5^n \cdot c$, where $m < n$ and c does not contain either 2 or 5 as a factor, then a/b will convert into a repeating decimal.   There will be n decimal places preceding the first digit of the repetend.   (For example,

$$1/28 = 1/2^2 \cdot 7 = 0.03\dot{5}7142\dot{8}.)$$

23. Use only inspection to answer questions (a) to (d) about the following common fractions: (1) $\frac{5}{32}$, (2) $\frac{7}{28}$, (3) $\frac{8}{72}$, (4) $\frac{3}{28}$, (5) $\frac{9}{200}$, (6) $\frac{7}{375}$.

a. Which fractions will convert into terminating decimals and which into repeating decimals?

b. In each terminating decimal how many decimal places will be required before it terminates?

c. In each repeating decimal how many decimal places will be required before the first digit of the repetend appears?

d. In each repeating decimal what is the maximum number of possible digits in the repetend?

24. Make ten verbal problems involving percentage which you consider suitable for eleventh- or twelfth-grade students.

25. A dealer ordered eight television sets at the wholesale unit price of $142.80. At what price must he sell each in order to realize a profit of 30 per cent of the selling price?   Explain this problem as you would to a class, using a diagram.

26. Solve and explain the following shop problem if you can.   If you have any difficulties, try to identify them.

Find the time required for roughing and finishing a casting $2'8'' \times 5'4''$ on a planer having a forward movement of 36 feet per minute and a return of 2 to 1, if a feed of $\frac{1}{8}''$ is used for roughing and $\frac{1}{4}''$ for finishing and if clearance for the tool is $4''$ at each end.

27. What is the identity element for multiplication and division?   For addition and subtraction?

28. What is the inverse of 7 under the process of multiplication?   What is the inverse of $\frac{3}{4}$ under the process of multiplication?

29. In a system of numbers let a, b, and c be numbers.   Let $\odot$ be an operation such that $a \odot b = c$.   Let i be the identity element under the operation $\odot$ and let m be the inverse of a under this operation.   Is it true that $a \odot m = i$?   Explain.

BIBLIOGRAPHY

General

Aftreth, Orville B.: Shall We Expose Our Pupils to Errors? *Arithmetic Teacher*, 4 (1957), 129–131.

Arthur, Lee E.: Diagnosis of Disabilities in Arithmetic Essentials, *Mathematics Teacher*, 43 (1950), 197–202.

Babcock, Hyrum: "An Analysis of Problem Solving in Arithmetic" doctoral dissertation, (Berkeley, Calif.: University of California, 1954).

Banks, J. Houston: "Learning and Teaching Arithmetic" (Boston: Allyn and Bacon, Inc., 1959).

Beard, Ralph H.: The Twelve Base, *Mathematics Teacher*, 48 (1955), 332–333.

Bernstein, Allen: A Study of Remedial Arithmetic Conducted with Ninth Grade Students, *School Science and Mathematics*, 56 (1956), 25–31, 429–437.

————: Library Research: A Study in Remedial Arithmetic [with bibliography], *School Science and Mathematics*, 59 (1959), 185–195.

Blackhurst, J. Herbert: "Principles and Methods of Junior High School Mathematics" (New York: Appleton-Century-Crofts, Inc., 1928), pp. 157–160; 169–172.

Boyer, Lee Emerson: "An Introduction to Mathematics for Teachers" (New York: Henry Holt and Company, Inc., 1945), pp. 3–138.

Breslich, E. R.: "Problems in Teaching Secondary-school Mathematics" (Chicago: University of Chicago Press, 1931), pp. 36–81.

Brown, Gerald: An Area of Neglect in the Study of Arithmetic: Mental Arithmetic, *Mathematics Teacher*, 50 (1957), 166–169.

Brueckner, L. J., and F. E. Grossnickle: "Making Arithmetic Meaningful" (Philadelphia: John C. Winston Company, 1953).

————, ————, and John Reckzeh: "Developing Mathematical Understanding in the Upper Grades" (Philadelphia: John C. Winston Company, 1957), pp. 128–342.

Buckingham, B. R.: "Elementary Arithmetic—Its Meaning and Practice" (Boston: Ginn & Company, 1947).

Butler, Charles H.: Some Observations on Teaching Percentage, *Mathematics Teacher*, 29 (1936), 330–333.

————: "Arithmetic for High Schools" (Boston: D. C. Heath and Company, 1953), pp. 141–155.

————: A Note on Writing Fractions, *Mathematics Teacher*, 47 (1954), 527.

————: A Note on Teaching Percentage, *Mathematics Teacher*, 48 (1955), 208.

Christian, Cora C.: Arithmetic in the Upper Elementary Grades, *School Science and Mathematics*, 53 (1953), 171–172.

Christofferson, H. C.: Meanings in Multiplication, *Arithmetic Teacher*, 6 (1959), 148–151.

Commonwealth of Pennsylvania, Department of Public Instruction: "A Course of Study in Mathematics for the Secondary Schools," *Bulletin* 360 (Harrisburg, Pa.: Department of Public Instruction, 1952), pp. 76–79, 197.

Davis, David R.: "The Teaching of Mathematics" (Reading, Mass.: Addison-Wesley Publishing Company, 1951), pp. 146–192.

Delury, D. B.: Computations with Approximate Numbers, *Mathematics Teacher*, 51 (1958), 521–530.

DeMar, Richard F.: An Improved Method of Extracting Square Root, *Mathematics Teacher*, 50 (1957), 445–447.

Dower, Lucie L.: Problem-solving in Arithmetic, "Third Yearbook" (Washington, D.C.: National Council of Teachers of Mathematics, 1928), pp. 223–268.

Flagg, Elinor B.: Developing Confident, Self-reliant Learners in Arithmetic, *School Science and Mathematics*, **55** (1955), 381–388.

Georges, J. S.: Learning to Solve Problems Intelligently, *School Science and Mathematics*, **56** (1956), 701–707.

Gibb, Glenadine, Phillip S. Jones, and Charlotte Junge: Number and Operation, "Twenty-fourth Yearbook," (Washington, D.C.: National Council of Teachers of Mathematics, 1959), pp. 7–64.

Grossnickle, Foster E.: Teaching Arithmetic in the Junior High School, *Mathematics Teacher*, **47** (1954), 520–527.

Grove, Ethel, and others: Posters on Fractions, *School Science and Mathematics*, **51** (1951), 11–13.

Habel, E. A.: Deficiencies of College Freshmen in Arithmetic: Diagnosis and Remedy, *School Science and Mathematics*, **50** (1950), 480–484.

Hamilton, Jean F.: Remedial Arithmetic in the Regular Classroom, *School Science and Mathematics*, **56** (1956), 197–209.

Hannon, Herbert: The Role of Meaning in Teaching the Fundamental Processes, *School Science and Mathematics*, **58** (1958), 83–89.

——— and Pearl L. Ford: "The Role of Meaning in Teaching the Fundamental Processes," *Faculty Contributions, Series 3, No. 1, School of Graduate Studies* (Kalamazoo, Mich.: Western Michigan University, 1956).

Henderson, K. B., and R. E. Pingry: Problem Solving in Mathematics, "Twenty-first Yearbook" (Washington, D.C.: National Council of Teachers of Mathematics, 1953), pp. 228–270.

Hickerson, J. Allen: "Guiding Children's Arithmetic Experiences" (Englewood Cliffs, N.J.: Prentice-Hall, Inc., 1952).

Hoel, Lesta: What Constitutes Remedial Work in Arithmetic? *Mathematics Teacher*, **43** (1950), 19–24.

Jackson, Humphrey: Technique for Drill on Arithmetic Fundamentals, *Mathematics Teacher*, **49** (1956), 47–48.

Jerbert, A. R.: Division by Zero, *School Science and Mathematics*, **49** (1949), 484–488.

Johnson, J. T.: What Do We Mean by Meaning in Arithmetic? *Mathematics Teacher*, **41** (1948), 363–367.

———: The Use of a Ruler in Teaching Place Value in Mathematics, *Mathematics Teacher*, **45** (1952), 264–266.

Kingston, J. Maurice: Some Arithmetical Fundamentals of Value to Junior High School Teachers, *Mathematics Teacher*, **48** (1955), 232–236.

Kinney, Lucien B.: Teaching Percentage for Understanding and Use, *Mathematics Teacher*, **51** (1958), 38–41.

——— and C. Richard Purdy: "Teaching Mathematics in the Secondary Schools" (New York: Rinehart & Company, Inc., 1952), pp. 229–235.

Lane, Fay: We Took the Class Census, *Mathematics Teacher*, **45** (1952), 168–172.

Larsen, Harold D.: "Arithmetic for Colleges" (New York: The Macmillan Company, 1958).

Lentz, Donald W.: Mental Arithmetic, *Arithmetic Teacher*, **4** (1957), 132.

McCormick, Chester A.: Helping Children Discover Arithmetic, *School Science and Mathematics*, **52** (1952), 339–343.

McMeen, George H.: Interaction of "How" and "Why" in Arithmetic, *New Jersey Mathematics Teacher*, **13** (1957), pp. 3–6.

———: Differentiating Arithmetic Instruction for Various Levels of Achievement, *Arithmetic Teacher*, **6** (1959), 113–120.

Mallory, Virgil S.: "Arithmetic Refresher for High Schools" (Chicago: Benj. H. Sanborn & Co., 1943).

Marks, John L., C. Richard Purdy, and Lucien B. Kinney: "Teaching Arithmetic for Understanding" (New York: McGraw-Hill Book Company, Inc., 1958), pp. 192–341.

Moser, Harold E.: Can We Teach Pupils to Distinguish the Measurement and Partition Ideas in Division? *Mathematics Teacher*, **45** (1952), 94–97, 105.

Mueller, Francis J.: "Arithmetic—Its Structure and Concepts" (Englewood Cliffs, N.J.: Prentice-Hall, Inc., 1956), pp. 220–229.

Neuriter, Paul: The Unbroken Mystery of the Broken Number, *Mathematics Teacher*, **45** (1952), 13–16, 18.

Newsom, Carroll V.: Mathematical Background Needed by Teachers of Arithmetic, "Fiftieth Yearbook of the National Society for the Study of Education," part II, "The Teaching of Arithmetic" (Chicago: University of Chicago Press, 1951), pp. 232–258.

Orleans, Jacob S.: "The Understanding of Arithmetic Processes and Concepts Possessed by Teachers of Arithmetic," *Office of Research and Evaluation, Division of Teacher Education, Publication* 12 (New York: College of the City of New York, 1952).

Peeler, Harry: Teaching Verbal Problems in Arithmetic, *Arithmetic Teacher*, **3** (1956), 244–246.

Pikal, Frances: Review of Research Related to the Teaching of Arithmetic in the Upper Elementary Grades, *School Science and Mathematics*, **57** (1957), 41–47.

Reeve, W. D. (Editor) and others: "Arithmetic in General Education," *Sixteenth Yearbook* (Washington, D.C.: National Council of Teachers of Mathematics, 1941), pp. 80–139, 196–224.

―――― (Editor) and others: "The Teaching of Arithmetic," *Tenth Yearbook* (Washington, D.C.: National Council of Teachers of Mathematics, 1935).

―――― and Clarence B. Tuites: "Practical Mathematics Refresher" (New York: McGraw-Hill Book Company, Inc., 1955), pp. 78–90.

Schaaf, W. L.: Arithmetic Taught as a Basis for Later Mathematics, *School Science and Mathematics*, **46** (1946), 413–423.

Smith, D. E., and W. D. Reeve: "The Teaching of Junior High School Mathematics" (Boston: Ginn & Company, 1927), pp. 31, 50, 110–114.

Smith, Rolland R.: "Per Cents in the Seventh and Eighth Grades" *Journal of Education*. **136** (November, 1953), 34–35.

Spitzer, Herbert F.: "The Teaching of Arithmetic" (Boston: Houghton Mifflin Company, 1953).

―――――: "Practical Procedures for the Enrichment of Arithmetic" (St. Louis, Mo.: Webster Publishing Company, 1956).

Stahl, Edgar A.: Improving Problem Solving in Arithmetic, *School Science and Mathematics*, **53** (1953), 746–747.

Stein, Edwin I.: "Refresher Arithmetic" (New York: Allyn and Bacon, Inc., 1948).

Stein, Harry L.: How to Make Arithmetic Meaningful in the Junior High School, *School Science and Mathematics*, **53** (1953), 680–684.

Stokes, C. Newton: "Teaching the Meanings of Arithmetic" (New York: Appleton-Century-Crofts, Inc., 1951).

Sueltz, Ben A.: Important Issues in Arithmetic, *Mathematics Teacher*, **42** (1949), 197–199.

―――――: Reviews of Three State Courses of Study in Arithmetic, *Mathematics Teacher*, **43** (1950), 165–168.

―――――: Drill–Practice–Recurring Experience, "Twenty-second Yearbook" (Washington, D.C.: National Council of Teachers of Mathematics, 1953), pp. 192–204.

————: These Things We Believe, *Mathematics Teacher*, **49** (1956), 19–21.

Swain, Robert L.: "Understanding Arithmetic" (New York: Rinehart & Company, Inc., 1957).

Swenson, Esther J.: Rate of Progress in Learning Arithmetic, *Mathematics Teacher*, **48** (1955), 70–76

Taylor, E. H., and C. N. Mills: "Arithmetic for Teacher Training Classes," 4th ed. (New York: Henry Holt and Company, Inc., 1955).

UICSM Project Staff: Arithmetic with Frames, *Arithmetic Teacher*, **4** (1957), 119–124.

Van Engen, H.: A Selected List of References on Elementary School Arithmetic, *Mathematics Teacher*, **43** (1950), 169–171.

————: The Child's Introduction to Arithmetic Reasoning, *School Science and Mathematics*, **55** (1955), 358–363.

Vaughn, William D.: Some Drill Techniques for Arithmetic, *Mathematics Teacher*, **50** (1957), 436–439.

Volpel, Marvin C.: Solving Percentage Problems by the Equation Method, *Mathematics Teacher*, **47** (1954), 425–427.

Weaver, J. Fred: A Crucial Aspect of Meaningful Arithmetic Instruction, *Mathematics Teacher*, **43** (1950), 112–117.

————: Misconceptions about Rationalization in Arithmetic, *Mathematics Teacher*, **44** (1951), 377–381.

————: Six Years of Research in Arithmetic Instruction; 1951–1956, *Arithmetic Teacher*, **4** (1957), 89–99.

Wisely, Edna: An Approach to Problem Solving, *Arithmetic Teacher*, **4** (1957), 125–128.

Wrightstone, J. Wayne: Influence of Research on Instruction in Arithmetic, *Mathematics Teacher*, **45** (1952), 187–192.

Young, William E.: Language Aspects of Arithmetic, *School Science and Mathematics*, **57** (1957), 171–174.

Percentage

Blackhurst, J. Herbert: "Principles and Methods of Junior High School Mathematics" (New York: "Appleton-Century-Crofts, Inc., 1928), pp. 157–160, 169–172.

Boyer, Lee Emerson: "An Introduction to Mathematics for Teachers" (New York: Henry Holt and Company, Inc., 1953), pp. 75–82.

Breslich, E. R.: "Problems in Teaching Secondary-school Mathematics" (Chicago: University of Chicago Press, 1931), pp. 51–57.

Butler, Charles H.: Some Observations on Teaching Percentage, *Mathematics Teacher*, **29** (1936), 330–333.

————: "Arithmetic for High Schools" (Boston: D. C. Heath and Company, 1953), pp. 141–155.

————: A Note on Teaching Percentage, *Mathematics Teacher*, **48** (1955), 208.

Commonwealth of Pennsylvania, Department of Public Instruction: "A Course of Study in Mathematics for the Secondary Schools," *Bulletin* 360 (Harrisburg, Pa.: Department of Public Instruction, 1952), pp. 76–79.

Larsen, Harold D.: "Arithmetic for Colleges" revised ed., (New York: The Macmillan Company, 1958), pp. 167–173.

Mueller, Francis J.: "Arithmetic—Its Structure and Concepts" (Englewood Cliffs, N.J.: Prentice-Hall, Inc., 1956), pp. 220–229.

Reeve, W. D., and Clarence B. Tuites: "Practical Mathematics Refresher" (New York: McGraw-Hill Book Company, Inc., 1955), pp. 78–90.

Schorling, Raleigh: "The Teaching of Mathematics" (Ann Arbor, Mich.: The Ann Arbor Press, 1936), pp. 204–206.

Smith, D. E., and W. D. Reeve: "The Teaching of Junior High School Mathematics" (Boston: Ginn & Company, 1927), pp. 31, 50, 110–114.

Smith, Rolland R.: Per cents in the Seventh and Eighth Grades, *Journal of Education*, **136** (1953), 34–35.

Stein, Edwin I.: "Arithmetic for College Students" (New York: Allyn and Bacon, Inc., 1957), pp. 173–208.

Volpel, Marvin C.: Solving Percentage Problems by the Equation Method, *Mathematics Teacher*, **47** (1954), 425–427.

12

THE TEACHING OF FURTHER TOPICS
IN ARITHMETIC

Averages. Averages have such widespread use in everyday affairs and are so much a part of the common experience of everyone that attention should be given to their computation and interpretation in arithmetic. Standings of baseball teams, seasonal temperatures, airplane speeds, weight and height charts, mortality tables, and tax rates are but a few of the many applications of averages with which people are concerned. While the *arithmetic mean* of a set of measures is usually what is meant by the word "average," there are several different types of averages. The junior high school is not the place to attempt to understand the technicalities of computation of averages in complex situations. However, simple illustrations can be used to clarify basic distinctions.

The *mode* is a measure of concentration. In its simplest form it is merely that measure for which there is the greatest frequency. The *median* is the middle score of a distribution, and the *arithmetic mean* is the sum of all the scores divided by the total frequency. The example in Table 12-1 representing lengths of standing broad jumps made in a

Table 12-1

Length of jump, in feet	Number of boys making each jump
4.0	3
4.2	1
4.5	3
4.8	5
5.0	5
5.2	10
5.5	1
5.8	1

grade school track meet can be used to illustrate these kinds of averages. The *mode* is 5.2 feet, which means that more boys jumped this distance than any other. The *median* jump is 5 feet, which means that, when the lengths of the jumps are listed in order from shortest to longest with the number making each jump, the fifteenth boy, counting from either end, made a jump of 5 feet. Since half of the remaining 28 is 14, there were 14 boys who jumped a distance of 5 feet or less and there were 14 boys who jumped a distance of 5 feet or more. The average jump, or the arithmetic mean of all the jumps, is 4.9 feet. Although no jump of this length was made, the figure does give a good picture of the lengths of all the jumps. The arithmetic mean can be computed from the measures without making a frequency distribution; the mode and the median cannot.

One of the big disadvantages of the arithmetic mean is that it can be affected very greatly by extreme values. Also, although this measure is usually thought of somewhat vaguely as a sort of middle or "typical" value, it may not be at all typical. The set of numbers 17, 48, 106, 91, and 3 has the same mean or "average" value as the set 53, 53, 52, 55, and 52. The average value does typify the second set very well, but the five numbers of the first set are so diverse that they simply do not run to type at all.

The average is merely one characteristic of a set of values, and it takes no account of diversity or homogeneity. Therefore, it should not be regarded as giving anything like a complete description of the set. On the other hand, it is very useful to be able to make comparisons of even a single characteristic of sets of values, and the arithmetic mean, or common average, provides probably the most simple, convenient, and useful instrument for doing so. It is a group measure which is easily understood, easily computed, simple to use, and in some sense representative of the set of values from which it is derived, even though it may not actually typify the values very well.

The *weighted average* is seldom mentioned except in textbooks on statistics. As a practical tool the method employed in its computation is probably not very important except when large masses of data are involved, something which is not often true of the problems one finds in school arithmetic. But large masses of data are frequently involved in the practical experience of a good many adults, and the classification of the data and the use of the weighted mean can materially reduce the labor involved in computing the average. Stripped of the formalism in which it is sometimes clothed, neither the concept nor the method of computation involves any difficulty beyond the ability of an intelligent seventh-grader. The fact that such examples as the cost of living index appear continually in newspapers and periodicals makes it clear that most adults are at least concerned with averages arrived at in this way, even though they may not have occasion actually to compute them. It would seem desirable that the study of averages, at least in the senior high school, should include some attention to situations in which weighted

averages can be used to advantage and to the way in which they actually
are determined and used.

In their treatment of averages, textbooks on arithmetic are prone to
stress the method of computing averages, but do not, on the whole,
give very much attention to discussing the usefulness and the limitations
of this measure.   Yet these aspects are important, and teachers should
not overlook this opportunity to deepen the insights and enrich the
appreciations of the students.   This is important even in the seventh
and eighth grades, but it is even more important when averages are
studied or used in the later years of the senior high school.   Even adults
who are accustomed to the use of the term often attach to it a specific
significance which is not wholly justified.   Weight charts for persons at
various ages are frequently looked upon with a sort of awe, as if the
figures had been divinely ordained instead of being merely averages taken
from large groups of people, and as if any departure from them should
be regarded as cause for serious alarm.   Persons who worry because they
are 5 pounds "overweight" seldom reflect that the standardizing group
itself undoubtedly contained many people whose weights were below
the average, as well as many whose weights were above the average, and
who perhaps were all equally healthy.

It is for reasons such as the above that a rather strong case is being
made these days for the incorporation into the high school program of
some of the fundamental techniques and concepts of elementary statistics.   The argument is strengthened by the increasing need which,
in the normal course of everyday events, the lay public has for informed
ways and means of analyzing and interpreting the vast amount of propa-
gandizing, advertising, or even informing data with which it is constantly
confronted.   Whether or not one agrees that this is a valid argument for
the incorporation of statistics into the high school program, the fact
remains that we cannot avoid the need for a clear understanding of the
concept of averages.   It must certainly follow then, that when averages
are studied in the secondary school, the work should not be confined
solely to their computation.   The concept of dispersion could and should
be brought in simply and informally along with the study of averages.   In
this way emphasis could be given to the limitations as well as the advantages of the average as a working tool.

Another source of misinterpretation and faulty use of averages occurs
in the treatment of percentage.   One should never average the per cents
(rates) unless they are related to the same base or equal bases.   For
example, let us consider two average daily attendance situations.   In
school A, Table 12-2, we shall ask for the average per cent of attendance
in five different grades on a given school day.   In school B we shall ask
for the average per cent of attendance in a given grade for a 5-day school

week. To get the average per cent of attendance, we shall average the per cents. We shall then analyze the appropriateness of the results thus obtained. Note that the individual per cents are the same in the two cases, thus producing the same average per cent, 70 per cent, for each school. If this were a correct representation of the facts in both cases, then 70 per cent could be used to get the attendance for each grade (school A) or for each day (school B). The totals of these numbers should then give the figure obtained in each case above as the total attendance. As should be expected, and as is shown in Table 12-2, this is the

Table 12-2

	School A				School B		
Grade	Enroll-ment	Attend-ance	Per cent	Day	Enroll-ment	Attend-ance	Per cent
7	40	36	90	Monday	80	72	90
8	70	28	40	Tuesday	80	32	40
9	100	70	70	Wednesday	80	56	70
10	90	90	100	Thursday	80	80	100
11	20	10	50	Friday	80	40	50
Total	320	234		Total	400	280	

case for school B, where the base is constant. But it is not the case for school A, where the base varies from grade to grade. There is a difference of ten students. True, the enrollment figures, particularly for school A, have been exaggerated. This was done deliberately in order to give stronger emphasis to the point being made. The only way to get the correct figure for school A is to divide the total attendance, 234, by the total enrollment, 320. To the nearest whole per cent this is 73 per cent. The grade attendance figures given by this rate per cent check, as they should.

Of course, another situation in which per cents can be averaged is the trivial one in which all rates are the same. This is illustrated by Table 12-3. In either case the average rate is 70 per cent.

Checking by Casting Out Nines. The procedure commonly known as casting out nines is often used in business as a quick, practical way of checking arithmetical operations, especially multiplication and division. The procedure is easily learned, but many people who use it do so empirically without understanding why it works the way it does. Actually, its validity is established through the algebra of residue classes, but without going into that it is possible to convince students of its plausibility and reasonableness by analysis of suitable examples.

The principle rests on a theorem which asserts that for any nonnegative integer, the excess of nines (the remainder left after division by nine) is equal to the excess of nines in the sum of the digits.[1] This would say, for example, that the excess of nines in the number 5,728 is the same as the excess of nines in the sum $(5 + 7 + 2 + 8)$ or 22. This can be verified immediately by direct division, but that alone would carry little conviction that the same principle would apply to other numbers. On the other hand, an analysis such as that given below may well convince students of the generality of the principle.

Table 12-3

	School A				School B		
Grade	Enroll-ment	Per cent	Attend-ance	Day	Enroll-ment	Per cent	Attend-ance
7	40	70	28	Monday	80	70	56
8	70	70	49	Tuesday	80	70	56
9	100	70	70	Wednesday	80	70	56
10	90	70	63	Thursday	80	70	56
11	20	70	14	Friday	80	70	56
Total	320		224	Total	400		280

Let it first be observed that for any integral power of 10 the excess of nines is 1 and that for any single digit 1, 2, 3, 4, 5, 6, 7, or 8 the excess of nines is given by the digit itself. Now consider that

$$
\begin{aligned}
5{,}728 &= 5{,}000 &&+ 700 &&+ 20 &&+ 8 \\
&= 5(1{,}000) &&+ 7(100) &&+ 2(10) &&+ 8 \\
&= 5(999 + 1) &&+ 7(99 + 1) &&+ 2(9 + 1) &&+ 8 \\
&= 5(999) + 5(1) &&+ 7(99) + 7(1) &&+ 2(9) + 2(1) &&+ 8 \\
&= 5(111)(9) + 5 &&+ 7(11)(9) + 7 &&+ 2(1)(9) + 2 &&+ 8 \\
&= 555 \text{ nines} + 5 &&+ 77 \text{ nines} + 7 &&+ 2 \text{ nines} + 2 &&+ 8 \\
&= (555 + 77 + 2) \text{ nines} + (5 + 7 + 2 + 8).
\end{aligned}
$$

Therefore the excess of nines in the right member of this equation must be $5 + 7 + 2 + 8$, or 22, since that would be the residue if all the nines were cast out from each of the numbers in the sum $(5{,}000 + 700 + 20 + 8)$. The residue from 5,000 is 5; that from 700 is 7; that from 20 is 2; and that from 8 is 8 itself. But since $5{,}000 + 700 + 20 + 8 = 5{,}728$, it follows that the residue after dividing 5,728 by 9 must also be $5 + 7 + 2 + 8$, or 22. Put another way, the excess of nines in 5,728 must be

[1] For an excellent discussion of this topic see Harold D. Larsen, "Arithmetic for Colleges" (New York: The Macmillan Company, 1958), pp. 31–34, 82–85.

equal to the excess of nines in 22. Furthermore, since the theorem may now be applied again to the number 22, the excess of nines in 22 must be equal to the excess of nines in the sum $(2 + 2)$ of its digits, which is 4. Thus the excess of nines for the number 5,728 can be found without performing any division at all. It is this characteristic of the process which makes it such a quick and easy checking device.

Modular arithmetic affords a more elegant method of presenting the discussion of the previous paragraph. Such a procedure can be used with supplementary exercises as enrichment material for many students in grades 7 and 8.

If a, b, m, and n are integers such that $n = am + b$, then n is said to be *congruent to b modulo m* $[n \equiv b \pmod{m}]$. Of course, if $b = 0$, then n is exactly divisible by m, or $n \equiv 0 \pmod{m}$. The remainder b is called the *residue of n modulo m*, and it may be positive, negative, or zero. For example, $98 = 14 \cdot 7$, $96 = 13 \cdot 7 + 5$, or $96 = 14 \cdot 7 - 2$; that is, $98 \equiv 0 \pmod{7}$, $96 \equiv 5 \pmod{7}$, or $96 \equiv -2 \pmod{7}$. In modular arithmetic the residue of the smaller numerical value is the one generally used. If

$$n_1 = a_1 m + b_1 \quad \text{and} \quad n_2 = a_2 m + b_2$$

then

$$n_1 + n_2 = (a_1 + a_2)m + (b_1 + b_2)$$

and

$$n_1 n_2 = a_1 a_2 m^2 + (a_1 b_2 + a_2 b_1)m + b_1 b_2$$

This theorem therefore follows:

Theorem. If $n_1 \equiv b_1$ and $n_2 \equiv b_2 \pmod{m}$

then

$$n_1 + n_2 \equiv b_1 + b_2 \pmod{m} \tag{1}$$

and

$$n_1 n_2 \equiv b_1 b_2 \pmod{m} \tag{2}$$

The number 5,728, which may be written as $5(10^3) + 7(10^2) + 2(10) + 8$, is thus seen to be congruent to $5 + 7 + 2 + 8 \pmod{9}$. This sum is 22, and $22 \equiv 4 \pmod{9}$.

Equation (1) of the above theorem provides a method for checking sums and equation (2) for checking products by casting out nines. Furthermore, since subtraction and division are inverse processes to addition and multiplication, respectively, the theorem implies checks for these two operations. For example:

Sum	*Excess of Nines*
45,653	5
24,976	1
70,629 (Excess of nines is 6)	6 = Sum of the excesses

Difference

Note in the above sum that just as $70,629 - 24,976$ must give 45,653, so $6 - 1$ must give 5.

Product		Excess of Nines
381		3
29		2
3429		⑥ = Product of the excesses in the
762		two factors
11049	Check	
		⑥ = Excess in the product

In checking division by this method it is necessary to express the result as an integral quotient with a remainder (possibly zero). Next, subtract this remainder from the dividend. Then the product of the excesses for the divisor and the quotient will equal the excess for the modified dividend. Thus:

$$2,578 \div 23 = 112 \text{ with a remainder of } 2$$
$$2,578 - 2 = 2,576, \text{ which is the modified dividend}$$

Excess of nines for the divisor = $2 + 3 = 5$.
Excess of nines for the quotient = $1 + 1 + 2 = 4$.
Product of these excesses = $5 \times 4 = 20$.
Excess of nines in this product = $2 + 0 = ②$.
Excess of nines in the modified dividend =
excess of nines in $(2 + 5 + 7 + 6)$ =   Check
excess of nines in $20 = 2 + 0 = ②$.

Another important application of modular arithmetic is in the development of tests for divisibility. For example, since $10 \equiv 0 \pmod 2$, it follows that $10^n \equiv 0 \pmod 2$. This fact implies the test for divisibility of any number by 2 is that the digit in ones place be divisible by 2. Similarly, the same test applies for 5. What is a test for divisibility by 4 ($=2^2$) and 25 ($=5^2$)? By 8 ($=2^3$) and 125 ($=5^3$)?

Since any composite number can be broken down into relatively prime factors, the tests for divisibility can be extended to take care of composite numbers. For example, since $6 = 2 \times 3$, the test for divisibility by 6 is the combination of the tests for divisibility by 2 and 3. Such factors must be relatively prime. For example, $18 = 2 \times 9 = 3 \times 6$. The test for divisibility by 18 is a combination of the tests for 2 and 9, and *not* a combination of the tests for 3 and 6. This should be evident, for a number which is divisible by 6 is also divisible by 3.

In concluding this discussion, one thing which is not always made clear should be emphasized. The check which this method affords is not an absolutely certain one. It will not detect mistakes in which the error is any multiple of 9, and in particular it will not detect mistakes resulting from transposition of digits. For example, $381 \times 29 = 11,049$, and the check would indicate that this is correct.   But if the product should be erroneously written as 11,409, this method of checking would not detect the error.   Hence it should be used with some caution, since there is a possibility that it might fail to reveal mistakes that had been made.   On the other hand, if the check numbers (excesses) obtained in using this method do not agree, then it is certain that some mistake has been made in the work.[1]

Square Root.   The objectives for the study of square root are two: a clear understanding and appreciation of the meaning of the square root of a number and the knowledge of how to determine its exact or approximate numerical value.   Children are usually introduced to square roots in the seventh or eighth grade in connection with the inverse process of squaring numbers.   Through explanation with relatively small numbers which are perfect squares the concept can be, and usually is, developed without difficulty.   High school students may have trouble giving a precise definition of the square root of a number, but they generally understand what the term means.

On the other hand, few of the students see any clear connection between the meaning of a square root and the traditional method by which they have been taught to compute the value.   Nor could they be expected to do so.   The classic method, still found in most textbooks, is a notable example of an algorithm which to the beginner appears to be completely empirical and arbitrary.   The fact that it gives correct results will seem to him to justify it, but until he has had opportunity to discover through algebra the algorithm for the square of the sum of two numbers, he will have no basis for discovering or reconstructing it for himself.   He can use it only as an apparently arbitrary routine, and the only way he can learn it is simply to memorize it.   But this is precisely the kind of formalism upon which so much criticism of mathematical instruction has been justly focused in the past.   Present-day thinking insists that skill should go hand in hand with understanding.   Therefore an alternative method of computing square roots will be advocated here, a method which derives directly from the definition of a square root, which involves only the familiar procedures of division and averaging, which encourages reasonable estimates, and which is such that the student can understand at every step what he must do next, and why.

Let us first define the square root of a number as one of its two equal factors.   For example, $\sqrt{73} \times \sqrt{73} = 73$.   Let us next recall that in the process of division the divisor and the quotient are two factors whose product is the dividend.[2]   If the divisor and the quotient are equal, each

---

[1] *Ibid.*, pp. 52–55, 83–85, 104–105.

[2] With suitable approximations or remainders, of course, in cases when the division is not exact.

is a square root of the dividend. If they are not equal, the required square root must lie between them. Therefore, if a divisor which is a good approximation to the square root can be estimated, the quotient also will be a good approximation and the average of the two will be a better approximation than either. If a still closer approximation is required, the process can be repeated with this average, or something near it, as the new divisor.

For example, let it be required to find a good approximation to $\sqrt{73}$. Upon reflecting that $\sqrt{64} = 8$ and $\sqrt{81} = 9$ and that 73 is about halfway between 64 and 81, we may reasonably try 8.5 as a divisor and proceed as indicated above.

$$73.00000 \div 8.5 = 8.5882$$

The average of 8.5 and 8.5882 is 8.5441, which by trial is seen to be too small to be satisfactory. We therefore repeat the procedure with, say, 8.54 as a divisor.

$$73.00000 \div 8.54 = 8.548$$

The average of 8.54 and 8.548 is 8.544. By trial, we find

$$(8.544)^2 = 72.999936,$$

or almost exactly 73. Hence $\sqrt{73}$ correct to three decimal places is found to be 8.544. Actually, $\sqrt{73}$ correct to four decimal places is 8.5440.

By successive repetitions the square root can be found to any desired degree of accuracy, but often not more than one repetition is needed, and sometimes none. The approximations converge toward the true value amazingly fast with successive repetitions.

This method is now used in the manuals for computing machines, and it is used in programming square root problems for electronic computers. Moreover, it is beginning to find its way into a few arithmetic textbooks. Its advantages are obvious, since it involves only familiar processes and students can see at every step not only what they are doing but why they are doing it. It forces students to estimate carefully and to review mentally the simple perfect squares without the usual drill procedure, and it gives results as accurate as desired. In comparison with the traditional rule-of-thumb method this alternative method has much to recommend it.[1]

Since economy of time in the actual use of square roots is important, students should become familiar with the use of tables of squares and

[1] For an excellent discussion of the use of this method in connection with a slide rule, see Carl N. Shuster, Approximate Square Roots, *Mathematics Teacher*, **45** (1952), 17–18.

square roots and with interpolation in the tables. When possible, they should be made acquainted with the use of the slide rule for obtaining squares and square roots, and advanced students may well be introduced to the use of logarithms for the purpose. Also, students should be made aware that time and labor may sometimes be saved in finding square roots of fractions or of factorable numbers in which one factor is a perfect square. The principle that

$$\sqrt{ab} = \sqrt{a}\,\sqrt{b}, \text{ or } \sqrt{28} = \sqrt{4}\,\sqrt{7} = 2\,\sqrt{7}$$

is probably more important in algebra than in arithmetic, but there are cases when it can be a time saver even in arithmetic. In attempting to find the square root of a fraction such as $\sqrt{3/7}$ many students even in college work out separate, long approximations to $\sqrt{3}$ and $\sqrt{7}$ and then perform the long division $1.7321 \div 2.6458$ instead of rationalizing the denominator and transforming the expression into the equivalent $\sqrt{21/49} = \sqrt{21}/7 = 4.5826/7$, in which the division is less tedious.

Measurement and Denominate Numbers. People seldom realize the extent to which everybody depends on measurement of one kind or another. We go to work by a clock, which measures time. We buy gasoline by the gallon, which is a measure of capacity, and meat by the pound, which is a measure of weight. Thermometers measure temperature for us; rulers and tapes measure distance; the speedometers on our cars measure speed; pollsters, the popularity of a radio program; and engineers, the tensile strength of materials. In view of these considerations, systematic instruction in measurement should form an important part of the program in arithmetic. The facts of measurement are exhibited and their various combinations and recombinations are made and recorded through the medium of number. About the importance of measurement Morton says:[1]

No arithmetic course is complete without opportunities to learn how mankind has gradually evolved a system of measures and a technique for measuring, to acquire information about measures in common use, to develop some skill in the use of measures and in estimating quantities and magnitudes without measuring, to learn something of the degree of accuracy normally present in measurements, and to gain an appreciation of the role of measurement in modern life.

Among the important concepts which should be but not always are made clear to students, the following should be given special emphasis:

1. What a measurement means
2. The arbitrary nature of units of measure
3. The necessity of having standardized units

[1] R. L. Morton, "Teaching Arithmetic in the Elementary School," vol. III, "Upper Grades" (Morristown, N.J.: Silver Burdett Company, 1939), p. 282.

4. Clear concepts of the most common units of measure
5. Specific relations among some of the common units

These things will require considerable discussion, demonstration, and illustration by the teacher.   There are many excellent articles, books, and brochures which provide most interesting and dramatic accounts of the evolution of our units and systems of measurement.   The teacher who familiarizes himself with the fascinating story of measurement will be able to present it to his classes in such a way as to stimulate their interest, clarify their concepts, and enlist their enthusiasm in attaining the objectives mentioned above.

Of special interest in this connection is the metric system of measure. While it is not the commonly used system in the English-speaking countries, it is used over much of the world, and it is universally used in scientific circles.   Its interesting history, foundation, and structure, and the fact that its units, direct and derived, are based on our common decimal number system, emphasize the importance of having students become familiar with it.   Indeed, it was designated by the Committee on Post-War Plans as one of the 29 items that form the basis of general mathematical literacy.   Study of the metric system should be directed particularly toward giving the students clear physical concepts of the common units such as meter, centimeter, millimeter, kilometer, square centimeter, cubic centimeter, gram, and kilogram; proper knowledge and use of the nomenclature; and the ability to make correct interconversions both among units of the metric system itself and between these and units in the English system of weights and measures.

The numbers which are used to express measurements have attached to them such labels as 8 miles, 74 degrees, 5 pounds, and 18 minutes. The label tells the kind of unit in terms of which the measurement has been made, and the number tells how many of these units the given magnitude was found to contain.   Such numbers are called *denominate* numbers.   Everybody is so familiar with them that nobody stops to think about them.   About the only difficulty which can arise in their use is that which might occur in computing with compound denominate numbers such as 3 weeks 4 days and 2 hours 18 minutes 5 seconds.   For such computations students need to know the common units and subunits of various kinds of magnitudes and they need to be able to make interconversions of minutes and hours; miles, yards, feet, and inches; pounds and ounces; and the like.   Such computations need not be troublesome if the students are taught to look upon them with common sense and not try to clothe them with formalism.   Formal rules are unnecessary and probably are actually detrimental to ease of understanding in such cases.   The student who multiplies 2 yards 2 feet 10 inches by

8 and gives his result as 16 yards 16 feet 80 inches should not be penalized, for he has correctly done what was required.   It should simply be pointed out to him that it is usually preferable to express final results in the largest units possible and that this can now be done easily as follows: The 80 inches make 6 feet 8 inches.   The 6 feet can be combined with the 16 feet to give 22 feet, which can be expressed as 7 yards 1 foot.   Finally, the 7 yards can be combined with the 16 yards to make 23 yards.   Hence, the original answer of 16 yards 16 feet 80 inches can be expressed as 23 yards 1 foot 8 inches.   It should be emphasized that this is no more correct than the original answer but is simply a more convenient form for expressing the same thing.

Common sense should predominate in the treatment of denominate numbers.   There are only a few common scales of measurement which are national in extent, and even in these some units are generally used only by specialists.   But some measures of distance, angular magnitude, weight, area, volume, and time are needed by everybody, and the importance and interrelationships of the common units in these systems should be emphasized.   Everybody should know that there are 12 inches in a foot, 5,280 feet in a mile, 60 minutes in an hour, and 90 degrees in a right angle.   It is doubtful that everyone needs to know that there are $16\frac{1}{2}$ feet in a rod, but everybody should know what a square foot means and why there are 144 square inches in a square foot.   Many details about denominate numbers may well be omitted from the arithmetic of the secondary school, but those parts which are commonly used by many people should not be neglected, and the things that are taught should be taught thoroughly.

The Nature of Approximate Numbers.   The foregoing discussion of measurement and denominate numbers leads naturally to consideration of approximate numbers.   From what sources do they come?   How are they to be used?   What special considerations must be taken into account in computing with approximate numbers?   Until comparatively recent times, such concepts and questions have received no attention in school mathematics except occasional arbitrary instructions for rounding off numbers when so directed.   Since about 1930, some attempts have been made to get more systematic attention given to approximate numbers in textbooks on arithmetic and general mathematics.   This movement, which at first consisted mainly of the efforts of a few dedicated individuals, received support in the second report of the Committee on Post-War Plans and has now begun to bear fruit.

If the teachers of arithmetic had come as far in this direction as the textbooks have, the situation might be regarded with optimism.   Unfortunately, however, most teachers have been brought up in the tradition of treating all numbers as exact numbers.   Moreover, it is simpler and more satisfying to treat them in this way than to deal with them as approximate numbers. Some time and study are required to learn the necessary concepts and the rationale of computing with approximate numbers. Furthermore, the abandonment of well-fixed ideas is never easy and the weight of inertia is heavy. There never seems to be enough time for the things that need to be done, and it is argued that students have enough trouble with arithmetic at best, without bringing in additional complications.

All *exact* numbers result from counting and from applying the fundamental processes to counted quantities. When we say that there are 35 children in the sixth grade, that Jane receives $2 each week as her allowance, or that six eggs make ½ dozen eggs, we mean *exactly* what we say. The counting process sets up a one-to-one correspondence that establishes this exactness. On the other hand, numbers which are estimated results —even though they are based on counting as in the case of the census— or which record the data resulting from measurement are *approximate* numbers. This is true whether we are measuring distance, direction, temperature, or what not. If we say that Jack is 5 feet 6 inches tall, we can only mean that, according to our measuring technique, his height is nearer to this measurement than it is to any other. No measurement can be more precise than the precision of the measuring instrument or more accurate than the relative accuracy of the observation made.

Approximate numbers may arise also from certain mathematical processes which require an infinite number of steps of which only a finite number can be performed. Examples are the extraction of certain roots such as $\sqrt{2}$ and $\sqrt[3]{6}$, the expansion in decimal form of certain nonterminating fractions such as $\frac{2}{3} = 0.666\dot{6}$ and $\frac{1}{7} = 0.\dot{1}4285\dot{7}$, and the evaluation of transcendental numbers such as $\pi = 3.14159 \ldots$ and $e = 2.71828 \ldots$. It should not be inferred from the above remarks that irrational numbers or fractions are necessarily approximate. Whether rational numbers or irrational numbers are exact or approximate depends upon the interpretation of the data involved. If we have a square whose side is exactly 1 unit in length, then $\sqrt{2}$ is the exact length of its diagonal. The actual measurement of this length would, of course, be only approximate.

It should also be stated that exact numbers may be fractional even though the approximation is integral; for example, if lemons are selling at 45 cents a dozen, the 23 cents one pays for ½ dozen is an approximation to the 22½ cents which is the exact price. The context in which any given number is used will frequently play an important part in determining whether it is to be regarded as an exact or an approximate number. An individual who states that he purchased 2 pounds of butter is using the number 2 in an exact sense if he means two 1-pound cartons, whereas the actual weight of the butter only approximates 2 pounds. Furthermore, the use of formulas in practical computations frequently gives rise to approximate numbers either because of the approximate nature of the formula itself (as in the case of the formula $A = 3.14r^2$, or $A = 2\frac{2}{7}r^2$, for the area of a circle and formulas resulting from scientific experimentation) or the use of approximate data in an exact formula (as would result in substituting measurements in the formula $A = lw$ for the area of a rectangle).

Although facility and accuracy in computation with exact numbers is both a desirable and a necessary goal of arithmetical instruction in the elementary school, the secondary school should stress the "exercise of common sense and judgment in computing from approximate data, familiarity with the effect of small errors in measurements, the determination of the number of figures to be used in computing and to be retained in the result, and the like."[1] There is no justification whatsoever, for example, in stating that the circumference of a circle whose radius is given as 3 inches is $2(3.1416)(3) = 18.8496$ inches. The measurement of the circumference can be no more precise or accurate than the measurement of the radius used in finding the circumference. It is, then, very important that the teacher and pupil understand certain fundamental criteria for judging approximativeness[2] and rules for computation with approximate data.

Criteria for Judging Approximativeness. The three principal criteria for judging approximativeness are the position of the decimal point, the number of significant digits, and precision and accuracy.

The Position of the Decimal Point. A number may be said to be correct to within a certain unit (e.g., to units, tenths, hundredths, etc.). The distance from the earth to the sun is usually given as 93,000,000 miles. Here the unit of measurement is 1,000,000 miles, and the measurement is considered correct to the nearest unit. The world record for the 100-yard dash is 9.3 seconds. Here either a second or one-tenth second may be taken as the unit of measurement. The observation is said to be correct to tenths of a second. In such cases as these the number of decimal places in the observation proves to be a criterion for judging approximativeness.

The Number of Significant Digits. Our decimal system of numeration is definitely characterized by the fact that the significance of any particular digit in a number is determined by the position it occupies. In the number 333.3 each three denotes a value one-tenth as large as the one on its left and ten times as large as the one on its right. Thus the number

---

[1] National Committee on Mathematical Requirements, "Reorganization of Mathematics in Secondary Education" (Boston: Houghton Mifflin Company, 1923), p. 7.

[2] By "approximativeness" is meant the closeness with which the approximate number approaches the exact number.

333.3 is given to four significant digits, since each three has a specific relative significance in the make-up of the number. If we consider the numbers 303, 3.03, and 33, it is evident that the presence or absence of the zero affects the relative magnitudes of the threes. In the first two numbers the three on the extreme left is of a magnitude 100 times as great as that of the three on the extreme right, while in the third number the three on the left is only 10 times as great in magnitude as the three on the right. Now consider the numbers, 33, 3.3, 0.033, and 330. It is just as evident that the presence or absence of the zero does not affect the relative magnitude of the threes. In each case the magnitude of the three on the left is 10 times that of the three on the right. In the number 330, as in 0.033, the zero serves merely as an aid in placing the decimal point to distinguish 330 from 33, 3.3, 0.033, 33,000, etc., in which case it is not considered a significant digit. Each of the numbers 303 and 3.03 is given to three significant digits, while each of the numbers 33, 3.3, 0.033, and 330, where zero merely helps to place the decimal point, is given to two significant digits. Similarly, both 93,000,000 and 9.3 are given to two significant digits.

The value of π to seven significant digits is

$$\pi = 3.141593 \tag{1}$$

This value is very frequently stated as

$$\pi = 3.1416 \tag{2}$$

In Eq. (2) the value of π given in Eq. (1) has been *rounded off*. The rules usually given for rounding off numbers may be stated as follows:

1. If a whole number, given to a certain number of significant digits, is to be rounded off to a stated number of significant digits, the digits that are to be dropped should be replaced by zeros. When the digits that are to be dropped are located to the right of the decimal point, the use of the zeros is not correct.

2. If the first digit on the left of those that are to be dropped is 5, 6, 7, 8, or 9, then the first digit on the extreme right of the number, which is to be retained, should be increased by unity. This process is known as "forcing the digit." If the first digit on the left of those that are to be dropped is 0, 1, 2, 3, or 4, then no change is made in the digits retained.

A supplementary rule to number 2 that is frequently used, particularly in more mature circles, is as follows:

2a. If the portion of the number to be dropped consists only of a 5 in the first left-hand position, either alone or followed by zeros, then the first digit on the extreme right of the number to be retained is rounded to the nearest even number.

3. If, after the forcing, the significant digit on the extreme right is 5, a bar should be placed over it in order to indicate that, if there should be a

necessity to drop this 5, the next digit on its left should remain unchanged. For example: 3,464,832 is rounded off to 3,465,000. If it should then become necessary to round off the second number, it would be rounded off to 3,460,000.

If we apply the above rules to round off the numbers 296 and 303 to two significant digits, we obtain in each case 300. The zero on the left thus becomes a significant digit and is underscored to indicate that fact. Whether the zeros to the right of all nonzero digits of an approximate number are significant or not must be determined from an analysis of the situation which produced the number. In the case of a measurement the significance of such zeros can be determined if the precision of the measurement or the unit of measurement is known. In the case of rounded numbers it can be determined only by reference to the numbers from which the rounded numbers were obtained. If only a number, such as 39,000, is given and nothing is known about what it represents or how it was obtained, then there is no way of deciding whether any of the zeros are significant or not. However, all zeros would be significant in 390.00 meters because the two zeros to the right of the decimal point would be used not as an aid in placing the decimal point but to signify that in the application of the specified unit of measurement *no* quantities were found to occupy the two places to the right of the decimal point. Similarly, the zeros in $390 and $390.50 would be significant, except in the case when the amounts were given as mere estimates. Zero is significant whenever it is used other than as a mere place holder to assist in the proper placement of the decimal point.

To illustrate: The following numbers are all correct to five significant digits: 3.2674, 30207, 31260, 312.67, 3126.0, 0.031267, 0.000031267, 0.00030067, 2400.0, 30000.

Precision and Accuracy. Although precision and accuracy are distinctly different as criteria for the measure of approximativeness, they can be most effectively discussed when contrasted with each other. Measures may be precise to within certain specified units such as 1,000,000 miles, 1 mile, 1 second, and $\frac{1}{10}$ of 1 second. Similarly, numbers may be precise to units, tenths, hundredths, etc. On the other hand, a measure or a number may be accurate within a certain per cent of error or a certain number of significant digits.

The most effective measures of both precision and accuracy are in terms of the errors involved. The maximum error (positive or negative) made in any approximation is defined as follows: "If an approximate number is given as correct to k significant digits, then its error is at the most equal to ± 0.5 of a unit in the kth place, counting from the left to the right."[1]

[1] Aaron Bakst, Approximate Computation, "Twelfth Yearbook" (Washington, D.C.: National Council of Teachers of Mathematics, 1937), p. 124.

The *upper* and *lower limits* of the true value of any approximation are obtained by adding this maximum error to, and subtracting it from, the approximate number. The maximum *apparent error* (or *absolute error*) involved in any approximation made to k significant digits is thus seen to be 0.5 of a unit whose magnitude is determined by the kth place of the approximation. For example, the upper and lower limits of the true value of the distance from the earth to the sun are 93,500,000 and 92,500,-000 miles, respectively, so that the limit of the apparent error is 500,000 miles.

In the measure of time for the foot race the upper and lower limits are respectively 9.35 and 9.25 seconds, and the limit of the apparent error is seen to be 0.05 second. *The precision of a measure or a computation is evaluated in terms of the apparent (or absolute) error.*

The two measures 93,000,000 miles and 9.3 seconds are both correct to two significant digits. The per cent of accuracy of a measure or a computation is determined by the *relative error* involved, viz., the ratio of the apparent error to the approximate number. The relative errors, to two significant digits, in each of the above cases are respectively

$$\frac{500,000 \text{ miles}}{93,000,000 \text{ miles}} = \frac{0.5}{93} = 0.0054 \quad \text{and} \quad \frac{0.05 \text{ second}}{9.3 \text{ seconds}} = \frac{0.5}{93} = 0.0054$$

The *per cent of error* in each case is thus seen to be the same, $\frac{1}{2}$ of 1 per cent. One approximation might be far less precise than another and yet be much more accurate. For example, suppose we have the two measurements 0.000341 inch and 1,256 feet. The first measure is much more precise because its maximum apparent error is 0.5 of a millionth of an inch, while that of the second measure is 0.5 of a foot. The first measure is correct to three significant digits and the second to four; the relative errors are respectively

$$\frac{0.0000005}{0.000341} = \frac{0.5}{341} = 0.0015 \quad \text{and} \quad \frac{0.5}{1,256} = 0.0004$$

Thus the per cent of error is 0.15 per cent in the first measurement and 0.04 per cent in the second; in other words, the second measure, although far less precise than the first, is about four times as accurate. *The accuracy of a measure or a computation is evaluated in terms of the relative error or per cent of error made.*

When a common fraction is used in giving approximate data, the denominator of the fraction states the unit of precision used in making the measurement, while the numerator indicates the number of significant digits to which it is read. The unit of precision in each of the following measurements is one-fourth inch: $\frac{3}{4}$ inch, $6\frac{1}{4}$ inches, and $34\frac{3}{4}$ inches. The number of significant digits in each is $\frac{3}{4}$ inch, one; $6\frac{1}{4}$ inches $= \frac{25}{4}$ inches, two; and $34\frac{3}{4}$ inches $= \frac{139}{4}$ inches, three. While $6\frac{1}{4}$ inches has the same numerical value as $6\frac{4}{16}$ inches, there is a great deal of difference in the precision of the two measures. Similarly, there is definite significance to be attached to a measure of $5\frac{0}{8}$ inches as contrasted to one of 5 inches. The maximum apparent error in $5\frac{0}{8}$ inches is $\frac{1}{16}$ inch, while in 5 inches it is $\frac{1}{2}$ inch.

Computation with Approximate Data. In any computation involving approximate data, the result can never be any more precise or accurate than any of the data used. While the rules for such computation may be stated in several different forms, probably the two most satisfactory rules are:

1. In the addition or subtraction of approximate numbers of the same degree of *precision*, perform the operation and retain the result to the same degree of precision. If the numbers are not of the same degree of precision, first round all numbers to the same unit of precision and then proceed with the computation.

2. In the multiplication or division of approximate numbers of the same number of *significant digits*, perform the operation and then round the result to the same number of significant digits. If one approximate number has more significant digits than the other, first round the more accurate number so that it has only one more significant digit than the less accurate number. Perform the operation and then round the result so that it contains the same number of significant digits as the less accurate number.

With some sacrifice in economy of effort but no essential difference in significance of results some writers prefer, for very elementary work with approximate numbers, to simplify these rules to read: In any computation with approximate numbers first perform the required operation with the given numbers just as if they were exact numbers, then round the results: (1) in addition or subtraction, to the same unit of precision as the least precise number used; (2) in multiplication or division, to the smallest number of significant digits that occur in any number used.

The rule for multiplication may, of course, be extended to control the results obtained in raising an approximate number to any given power, and the rule for division to the extraction of indicated roots.

The intelligent use of these rules combined with care in the statement of original data will produce results that can be justified as the best possible results to be obtained from the given data.

If instruction in approximate computation is kept at a level appropriate to the maturity of the students, it need not be confusing to them, and if properly taught and well motivated it can add interest to the course. In Shuster's opinion:[1]

It is not at all difficult to teach the simple rules for computing with approximate data in the seventh, eighth, and ninth grades.   In fact, it is far easier to teach all the student needs to know about the topic in these grades than it is to change the computational habits of graduate students who have always used "exact" computation.

This is not the place to undertake a detailed exposition of the theory of computing with approximate data.   Numerous excellent discussions of the subject that are now available[2] deal adequately with both its mathematical and pedagogical aspects and do so in much greater detail than would be possible here.   On the other hand, it may be desirable to enumerate the central concepts and principles upon which attention would have to be focused in a systematic study of the subject.   The order in which these are listed below represents the order in which they would probably appear in the logical development of the theory of approximations.   They are as follows:

1. What a unit of measurement is
2. Why we can never be certain that any measurement is exact
3. The approximate nature of the number used to record the measurement
4. The apparent (or absolute) error that is always associated with the approximate number and the consequent range of values any of which might be properly represented by the approximate number as written
5. The tolerance (or permissible error) used in industry
6. Estimates as approximate numbers; other ways in which approximate numbers may arise
7. The approximate number as a multiple of the smallest unit in terms of which it is expressed.
8. The concept of precision of a measurement or of an approximate number and the consequent implication with respect to the size of the apparent error
9. The inconsistency involved in the use of "ragged decimals" to represent approximate numbers in sums or differences
10. The accepted principle and the rule for rounding off answers in the addition and subtraction of approximate numbers
11. Significant digits
12. The concept of the relative error of an approximate number and the meaning of accuracy
13. The relation of accuracy to the number of significant digits used in expressing the approximate number
14. Why high precision of an approximate number does not necessarily imply a high degree of accuracy, and conversely

[1] Carl Shuster, Working with Approximate Data, "Twenty-second Yearbook" (Washington, D.C.: National Council of Teachers of Mathematics, 1954), p. 310.
[2] See Bibliography.

15. Why the accuracy of a product or quotient involving approximate numbers depends on the numbers of significant digits in the factors rather than upon their precision

16. The accepted principle and the rule for rounding off answers in the multiplication and division of approximate numbers

This is an imposing array, and it is true that some serious study is required in order to attain clear mastery of these concepts and principles. Such mastery ought to be a part of the equipment of every teacher of arithmetic in the secondary school. On the other hand, it is by no means suggested that all these things be taught in a single sequence or even in a single year. Rather, the instruction should be spread over all the grades from 7 to 12, and the concepts and principles introduced in any grade should be only those which students in that grade can be expected to master satisfactorily.

Using Numbers Expressed in Scientific (Standard) Notation. A very effective method of indicating significant digits, particularly in the case of computation with large numbers, is the scientific (or standard) form of notation. A number is said to be written in the scientific or standard form of notation when it is written as the product of a number between 1 and 10 and an integral power of 10. Any significant zeros would be excluded from the power of 10. For example, the volume of the sun is 1,300,000 times the volume of the earth, while Mars is only 0.150 times as large as the earth. If we use S, M, and E to represent the volumes of the sun, Mars, and the earth, respectively, the above statement may be written in scientific notation as

$$S = 1.3 \times 10^6 E \qquad \text{and} \qquad M = 1.50 \times 10^{-1} E$$

The advantages of expressing numbers in standard, or scientific, notation are not as apparent in the work of the junior high school as they are in grades 11 and 12. It would be perfectly feasible to introduce this notation even in the seventh grade as an alternative way of expressing numbers which are positive integral powers of 10, and to extend it by the end of the ninth grade to include representation of decimal fractions in this form. However, it is not seriously needed as a tool until the eleventh or twelfth grades, when it can be very helpful to students in physics, chemistry, trigonometry, shop mathematics, or any course in which use is made of logarithms or the slide rule or in which extensive evaluation of formulas is required. The main advantage of its earlier introduction is that a good many junior high school students who do not take physics or mathematics in the senior high school might still get some acquaintance with this notation and the way in which it is used.

The particular usefulness of this notation lies in the fact that it provides a means for writing very large or very small numbers in a convenient compact form that is easy to read and work with, and which lends itself well to quick mental estimates and approximations. Consequently, the objectives to be sought are simply clear understanding of the notation and facility in using it to take products, quotients, or square roots of numbers. It is also useful in checking such operations, particularly the position of the decimal point. The only requirements are an understanding of positive and negative exponents and well-supervised practice to such point that the students can work with the notation with confidence and facility and interpret their results with assurance.

Most operations with the slide rule consist of finding products, quotients, or some combination of the two, and a major source of trouble is the proper location of the decimal point in the answer. Of course the ordinary rules for placing the decimal point can apply, but they are inconvenient when several factors are involved or when factors are very large or very small. Mistakes can easily be made in such cases, and it is desirable to have an independent method of checking, because misplacing the decimal point is one of the worst mistakes that can be made. The use of standard notation provides such a check, and it is a check based on common sense. Consider such a case as $(73{,}200{,}000 \times 0.0000211)/0.0045$. Direct computation yields a number with the sequence of digits 34323 but provides no easy way for setting the decimal point. But if these numbers are written in standard notation, they are $(7.32 \times 10^7 \times 2.11 \times 10^{-5})/(4.5 \times 10^{-3})$, which can be rewritten as

$$\frac{7.32 \times 2.11}{4.5} \times \frac{10^2}{10^{-3}} \quad \text{or} \quad \frac{7.32 \times 2.11}{4.5} \times 10^5$$

Now $(7.32 \times 2.11)/4.5$ is shown by even a quick rough estimate to have a value somewhere near 3, and this is to be multiplied by 10^5. Thus when the sequence of digits has been determined as shown above, it is clear that the required answer must be 3.4323×10^5, or $343{,}230$. If the original numbers are approximate numbers, the result should be rounded off accordingly. In this case it would be given as $340{,}000$.

In taking square roots of numbers a slight modification is sometimes needed, because the standard form must now contain a factor of the form 10^n, where n is an *even* integer. Such modifications are easily made. For example, $\sqrt{169{,}000}$ is written as $\sqrt{16.9 \times 10^4}$ instead of $\sqrt{1.69 \times 10^5}$, in order that the result will contain a factor which is an integral power of 10. Thus

$$\sqrt{169{,}000} = \sqrt{16.9 \times 10^4} = \sqrt{16.9} \times \sqrt{10^4} \approx 4.11 \times 10^2$$
$$\approx 4.11 \times 100 \approx 411$$

which is correct to three significant digits as given by the slide rule.

As stated above, the use of scientific notation makes only three demands on the student: an understanding of exponents, knowledge of how to multiply and divide mentally by powers of 10 by moving the decimal point, and the ability to make quick mental estimates of products or quotients of numbers between 1 and 10. The simplicity of the process and the incentive which it could provide probably would justify its introduction on a limited scale in the junior high school. Its usefulness in connection with the slide rule, logarithms, and the evaluation of formulas is undoubted. Students in chemistry, physics, solid geometry, trigonometry, or shop mathematics will find the ability to use this notation an important asset.

Estimating   In view of its importance there is probably no phase of arithmetic which is more neglected than estimating. Everybody gets so involved with the formal processes of computing and with the rationale of analyzing problems that estimation gets overlooked. Yet it is important and it should not be neglected. Indeed, the systematic practice of estimating can be a valuable ally to the student both in the analysis of problems and in checking the reasonableness of solutions. It is indispensable in operating a business or planning any sort of project. Budgets, tax rates, construction bids, merchandising, manufacturing, and a host of other intensely practical things are based on estimates; without intelligent estimates they could not be planned or operated. If students could be kept aware of this, it would help to enrich their arithmetical experience, deepen their insight, and simplify their thinking.

Estimating can be tremendously helpful too in checking the results of computations. It has been mentioned before that students often experience doubt over the proper placement of the decimal point in products, quotients, or square roots of numbers that involve decimal fractions. This is a serious matter, because misplacement of a decimal point is a very bad mistake indeed—much worse than many students seem to realize. But if they become accustomed to making rough estimates of their answers, they are not likely to make this mistake. The estimates do not even have to be very good ones, and they can generally be made mentally with radically rounded-off numbers. For example, 0.327×49.2 yields a product consisting of the sequence of digits 160884 in which the decimal point must be properly placed. If the student reflects that 0.327 is close to $\frac{3}{10}$ and that 49.2 is about 50, it will be clear to him immediately that the product must be somewhere near 15, which is three-tenths of 50. Therefore the only place where the decimal point can make sense in the answer is after the 6. That is, the answer must be 16.0884, since 160.084 is more than ten times as large as the estimated answer, while 1.60884 is only about one-tenth as great as we know the answer must be. If students would consistently use this kind of estimate as a check, or even as a method, for placing the decimal point, there would

hardly be any need for the formal rules.   What is here advocated, however, is not the abandonment of the formal rules for placing the decimal
point, but the use of estimates of this kind as a supplementary check—
a double insurance against a very bad kind of mistake that occurs far
too often.

Other Topics in Arithmetic.   Except for limitations of space it would
be easy to extend the scope of this chapter to include discussion of numerous other topics.   Any extensive survey of courses in arithmetic or
courses in which arithmetic has a prominent role would reveal a wide
variety of objectives, content, and emphasis.   It is doubtful that all
the additional topics that could be mentioned would be found in any
single course.   The orientation of each course will determine at least in
part the topics that will receive emphasis in the course, and the degree
of such emphasis.

While detailed discussion of these further topics cannot be given here,
it may be worthwhile to list some of them.   Among those which represent significant parts or aspects of arithmetic at the secondary school
level are the following:

Simplified or abridged computation	Arithmetic of the shop
Evaluation of formulas	Consumer arithmetic
Ratio and proportion	Informal geometry and mensuration
Inequalities	Graphs
Number systems with bases other than 10	Various social applications of arithmetic
The slide rule	Simple descriptive statistics
Teaching arithmetic with computing machines	

Before undertaking the teaching of one of these topics or aspects of
arithmetic the teacher will do well to subject it to a deliberate analysis
to try to determine the particular objectives toward which the study is
to be pointed, what specific difficulties the students may be expected to
encounter, and what methods can best be employed.   Only in this way
can the work be best organized, presented, and studied to minimize the
difficulties, highlight the important concepts or skills, and in general
bring about the attainment of the objectives so far as this can reasonably
be done.

A False Dichotomy.   More than half a century ago a reaction against
excessive use of formalized drill in arithmetical instruction had begun
to make itself manifest.   As time went on, this reaction took on an
extreme form with the insistence in some quarters that understanding
rather than computational proficiency should be the aim, and some people
went so far as to insist that understanding should be, in effect, the sole
aim in teaching arithmetic.   Such catch phrases as "meaning versus

drill" have formed the captions of many articles and discussions on objectives, subject matter, and methods.

Nobody will deny that there was good reason for this reaction, for it had become evident that exclusive reliance on drill had not automatically produced adequate understanding either of the processes themselves or of their application to problem situations. On the other hand, it should have been clear, as it has now become clear, that proficiency in computation could not automatically develop as an incidental by-product of understanding any more than understanding could emerge as an incidental byproduct of drill. The "meaning versus drill" type of phrase, which has by no means disappeared even yet, implies an "either one or the other but not both" situation which is completely unrealistic and unjustified. Competence in arithmetic does not consist *only* of understanding any more than it consists *only* of skill in computing. The two are complementary parts, and for satisfactory mastery of the subject neither is sufficient without the other. The question of which is the more important is something like asking whether one's right leg or left leg is the more important in walking. The answer is that the question is nonsensical; each leg is as essential as the other, and both are necessary.

Arithmetic must be taught and studied with *both* understanding and computational proficiency as primary objectives, and each of these objectives must be approached through methods appropriate to it. Both are necessary; neither alone is sufficient To think of the one versus the other is to set up a false and vicious dichotomy which is based on superficial thinking and which is completely unrealistic. Instruction based on such a dichotomy and oriented exclusively toward either of these objectives would inevitably lead at best to one-sided learning having little basis for either present application or further extension.

Provision for the Superior Student in Arithmetic. Most of the topics discussed in these chapters are included in the conventional textbooks and syllabuses with the hope that all the students will attain some degree of mastery of them. This being the case, the regular content of the courses is necessarily geared to what most of the students can reasonably be expected to accomplish, and often even this modest coverage is cut down to accommodate slow students. But in all classes there will be some students who could easily handle work beyond the normal assignments, and sometimes even students who are exceptionally talented in mathematics. Although it is not always realized, these have commonly been the most neglected students of all. Teachers are not slow to recognize students of outstanding ability, and because they can do the assigned work without help and often in a small fraction of the time required by other students, they are left pretty much on their own. In the absence of really challenging requirements they often become bored and negligent about doing even the work expected of the class as a whole. Yet these superior students, and especially the really talented ones, are the potential from which the future professional scientists and mathematicians must come. Their talent should not be wasted, but conserved and cultivated with special care.

Various suggestions have been made for ways of making suitable provision for gifted students. In large school systems the superior students are sometimes assigned to special sections where they can progress faster and farther than in other sections. In both large and small schools differentiated assignments within the sections have been used with some success. Other suggestions include assignment of supplementary problems, group or individual projects of various kinds, mathematics clubs, and mathematics contests.

Such administrative and instructional devices have been adequately discussed elsewhere, and the discussion need not be elaborated here. They can provide fairly well for the "better" students, but the highly talented student who is capable of original and independent study can be developed to his fullest capacity only by special individual work.

One suggestion[1] that seems promising is that this can perhaps best be done through a *problems course*, in which the individual student will select, with the approval of the teacher, an area of work in which he is interested and on which he will do independent study and eventually make a formal report to the teacher or the class. This area may, but need not, parallel the regular classwork, and the special work should be done in addition to the regular classwork, not instead of it. It should not be just an interesting but trivial "recreation," but should represent a serious, extended, and sequential study of the chosen area. Successful implementation of such a program would of course imply a highly competent and interested teacher and appropriate library facilities.

At first thought it might appear that such areas for special study would be associated only with the senior high school or with college courses. Upon reflection, however, one can readily identify many topics associated even with arithmetic which could provide avenues for stimulating and worthwhile investigation by highly talented students. The following are examples of such topics:

The history of arithmetic
The metric system
Square root
Tables and interpolation
Magic squares
Cross number puzzles
Computing with approximate numbers

The slide rule
Checking by casting out nines and elevens
Arithmetic on a clock (modulo 12)
Arithmetic in scales of notation other than 10

---

[1] Howard F. Fehr, Mathematics for the Talented, *Bulletin of the National Association of Secondary-School Principals*, **38** (1954), pp. 103–110.

Significant independent investigation of any of these topics would require high intelligence, sound knowledge, insight, intuition, persistence, virtuosity, and insatiable curiosity on the part of the student. These are characteristic of students highly endowed with mathematical talent. Less ambitious projects which might be undertaken by superior but less talented students might include fairly extensive independent work on such things as graphical methods, short cuts in arithmetic, applications of arithmetic in various areas such as banking, insurance, taxation, and sports, and making up lists of original verbal problems. The *Mathematics Student Journal* often publishes interesting problems for investigation.

EXERCISES

1. From newspaper or periodical sources find and bring to class ten examples of cases involving the use of averages. Take two of these and explain (a) how the average reported could be a helpful figure and (b) how, if considered alone, it might be misleading.

2. Take the enrollment figures for 20 different classes in your school and find the average size of the classes by using a guessed mean or estimated mean and combining with it the average of the deviations of the actual figures from it. Consider excesses as positive deviations and deficiencies as negative deviations. Check the result you get by computing the average directly from the original data.

3. Consider the following two sets of integers: $A = \{78, 72, 62, 33, 20\}$ and $B = \{56, 55, 54, 51, 49\}$. (a) Find the average (mean) of each set. (b) For each set find the sum of the absolute deviations of the individual numbers in each set from the average of that set. Then for each set find the average of these deviations. (c) Compare the averages (means) of the two sets. (d) Compare the average deviations in the two cases. (e) Discuss the implications of this exercise. Explain why the use of the averages alone to typify the two sets would be misleading and how one can arrive at a more adequate comparison of the two sets by using their average deviations as well as their means.

4. Five kinds of items in a store are priced as shown in the accompanying table, and the number of items of each kind in stock is given. (a) Compute the average

Item	A	B	C	D	E
Price	$0.60	$4.85	$0.15	$1.40	$0.90
Number of items	20	65	100	35	10

of the five prices. (b) Compute the weighted average price for all the items. (c) Explain why the weighted average gives a better index of the average price of all the items in stock than the mere average of the five prices themselves.

5. Perform the operations indicated in parts (a) to (c) and check the result in each case by casting out nines. Be prepared to explain your work. (a) $5,793 + 8,610 + 2,944 + 877 + 5,555 =$, (b) $2,184 \times 362 =$, (c) $64,833 \div 147 =$.

6. Devise tests for divisibility by 4, 5, 7, 8, 9, and 11. [*Hint:* When the positive residue is greater than one-half the modulus, use the equivalent negative residue. For example, $27 = -1 \pmod 7$ rather than 6 (mod 7).]

7. Which of the following numbers are divisible by 12, 15, 18, or 66? (*a*) 280,764, (*b*) 113,445, (*c*) 3,012,180.

8. Obtain good approximations to $\sqrt{486}$ by each of the following methods and be prepared to explain your work to the class as you would to a class of high school students: (*a*) the traditional method, (*b*) the method of estimating, dividing, and averaging, (*c*) the slide rule, (*d*) logarithms.

9. By interpolation in a table of square roots, give the approximate values of $\sqrt{71.3}$, $\sqrt{34.9}$, and $\sqrt{88.6}$.

10. Explain as you would to a class (*a*) why "stepping off a distance" is properly regarded as an example of measurement, (*b*) why someone else stepping off the same distance might get a different numerical result, and (*c*) why it is important to have standardized units of measure that are known and accepted by everybody as a basis of common understanding.

11. Give a report on the history and evolution of our common system of weights and measures.

12. Give a report on the history of the metric system of measure.

13. Explain as you would to a class how to perform the following operations: (*a*) Add 3 yards 1 foot 9 inches and 7 yards 1 foot 6 inches. (*b*) Subtract 2 hours 44 minutes 15 seconds from 5 hours 2 minutes 8 seconds. (*c*) Multiply 4 pounds 7 ounces by 5. (*d*) Divide 6 feet 5 inches by 15.

14. In the following cases give approximate equivalents as you would want your students to know them:

1 meter ≈	yard	inches	1 kilogram ≈	pound
1 centimeter ≈	inch		1 kilometer ≈	mile
1 inch ≈	centimeters		1 pound ≈	kilogram

15. What error is there in saying that $\frac{5}{15} = 0.33$?

16. Is 48.6 or 48.7 the closer approximation of $^{29}\%$? How much closer?

17. Give the approximation to $\frac{2}{3}$ which has an error $\frac{1}{10}$ as large as the error in 0.667.

18. If cans of a certain kind of food are priced at three for 35 cents, what is the exact price and what is the approximate price of one can?

19. Which of the fractions $\frac{1}{8}$, $\frac{1}{7}$, and $\frac{5}{6}$ give rise to approximate numbers when expanded in decimal form?

20. Give the number of significant digits in each of the following approximate numbers: 2.5, 2.05, 2.50, 0.25, 250, 2,500, 250.0, 0.0025, 0.2500, 205,000, 205,000.0, and 0.00002050.

21. Which is the more precise measurement and which is the more accurate in each of the following cases: 2.56 inches or 3,216 feet; 52.3 seconds or 15 seconds?

22. Of the approximate numbers 47.2, 5.7, 1,238, 0.05, and 265, (*a*) which is the most precise? (*b*) Which of the numbers is the most accurate? (*c*) Write each in the form (the approximate number) ± (its apparent error). (*d*) Give correctly the sum: 47.2 + 1,238. (*e*) Give correctly the product: 0.05 × 265.

23. Determine the maximum apparent error, the relative error, and the per cent of error in each of the following measurements: (*a*) 6.5 feet, (*b*) 0.000020 inches, (*c*) 5 inches, (*d*) $5\frac{3}{4}$ inches, (*e*) 0.005 centimeters, (*f*) 117.200 miles per hour, (*g*) $2^{14}\!\%_{6}$ inches.

24. Determine the relative error and the per cent error in each of the following

measurements: 418.0 feet, 4,180 feet, 46.3 seconds, 4 minutes 46.3 seconds, 25,000 miles. Which of these measurements is the most accurate? Which is the most precise?

25. Find the perimeter of each of these quadrilaterals: (a) 6⅞ inches, 5⅜ inches, 12⅝ inches, and 8⅝ inches. (b) 56.246 inches, 40.300 inches, 35.20 inches, and 27.18 inches.

26. What is the area of the rectangle whose length is measured as 16.72 inches and whose width is measured as 8.46 inches?

27. Give several examples that show how approximate numbers may arise from situations other than measurement.

28. Give several instances in which approximations or rounded numbers are more directly useful than the original numbers and explain why.

29. Express the following in scientific notation: 3,865, 2,604,000, 79.60, 0.154, 0.000553, 512.6, cos 5°23′.

30. Express the following in ordinary notation: 2.65×10^5, 5.34×10^{-2}, 7.953×10^{-11}, 4.49×10^{12}, 6.308×10^0.

31. Express the following numbers in standard notation and, without any actual computation, give rough mental estimates of the answers: (a) $(237 \times 5150)/16$, (b) $(729 \times 0.035)/9.8$, (c) $(6980 \times 0.047)/0.518$, (d) $(44600 \times 0.00923 \times 1.016)/(0.815 \times 254)$.

32. The star Arcturus is about 223,700,000,000,000 miles from the earth. Find this distance in light years if one light year is approximately 5,870,000,000,000 miles. Express the numbers in scientific notation and explain your work.

33. Write out ten numerical problems involving products, quotients, or both, in each of which at least one of the numbers involves a decimal fraction. Then (a) perform the operations indicated, setting the decimal point in each answer by using the formal rules for this purpose, and (b) round off the original numbers to one significant digit each and mentally perform the operations with these rounded numbers to test the reasonableness of your computed answers.

34. Present to your classmates merely the sequences of digits you obtained in part a of exercise 33. Ask them to set the decimal points in the proper places merely by rough estimates and without using the formal rules.

BIBLIOGRAPHY

Arnold, C. J.: An Answer to "Arguments against Universal Adoption of the Metric System," School Science and Mathematics, 51 (1951), 310–315.

"The Amazing Story of Measurement" (Saginaw, Mich.: Lufkin Rule Company, 1957). (Pamphlet.)

Bakst, Aaron: Approximate Computation, "Twelfth Yearbook" (Washington, D.C.: National Council of Teachers of Mathematics, 1937).

———: "Arithmetic for Adults" (New York: Appleton-Century-Crofts, Inc., 1944), pp. 236–259.

Benz, Harry E.: Arithmetic in the Senior High School, "Sixteenth Yearbook" (Washington, D.C.: National Council of Teachers of Mathematics, 1941), pp. 119–139

Bernstein, Allen: A Study of Remedial Arithmetic Conducted with Ninth Grade Students, School Science and Mathematics, 56 (1956), 25–31, 429–437.

Boyer, Lee Emerson: Elementary Approximate Computation, Mathematics Teacher, 32 (1939), 249–258.

———: "An Introduction to Mathematics for Teachers" (New York: Henry Holt and Company, Inc., 1945), pp. 3–138.

Breslich, E. R.: "Problems in Teaching Secondary-school Mathematics" (Chicago: University of Chicago Press, 1931), pp. 36–81.

Brueckner, Leo J., Foster E. Grossnickle, and John Reckzeh: "Developing Mathematical Understanding in the Upper Grades" (Philadelphia: John C. Winston Company, 1957), pp. 343–373, 502–551.

Butler, Charles H.: "Arithmetic for High Schools" (Boston: D. C. Heath and Company, 1953), pp. 203–224.

———— and F. Lynwood Wren: "Trigonometry for Secondary Schools," 2d ed. (Boston: D. C. Heath and Company, 1957), pp. 35–44, 64–67.

Clamurro, Phil: A High-school Teacher Looks at Arithmetic, Mathematics Teacher, 47 (1954), 49–50, 54.

Committee on Materials of Instruction: "The Story of Weights and Measures" (Chicago: American Council on Education, ca. 1940).

Curtis, Herbert J., and Karl Menger: On the Formulation of Certain Arithmetical Questions, Mathematics Teacher, 49 (1956), 528–530.

Davis, David R.: "The Teaching of Mathematics" (Reading, Mass.: Addison-Wesley Publishing Company, 1951), pp. 146–192.

Davis, O. L.: Arithmetic at the School Camp, Arithmetic Teacher, 3 (1956), 157–161.

Fehr, Howard F.: "The Use of Hand-operated Calculating Machines in Learning Arithmetic" (Orange, N.J.: Monroe Calculating Machine Company, Inc., 1956), pp. 2–15.

Finley, George W.: Measurement and Computation, "Third Yearbook" (Washington, D.C.: National Council of Teachers of Mathematics, 1928), pp. 141–148.

Ford Motor Company: "History of the Measurement of Length" (Detroit, Mich.: Public Relations Department, Ford Motor Company, ca. 1940). (Pamphlet.)

————: "How Long Is a Rod?" (Detroit, Mich.: Public Relations Department, Ford Motor Company, ca. 1940). (Pamphlet.)

————: "He Measures in Millionths" (Detroit, Mich.: Public Relations Department, Ford Motor Company, ca. 1945). (Pamphlet.)

Gager, William A.: Approximate Data: Terminology and Computation, "Twenty-second Yearbook" (Washington, D.C.: National Council of Teachers of Mathematics, 1954), pp. 323–338.

Goins, William F., Jr.: Putting More Meaning in the Teaching of Measurement, School Science and Mathematics, 50 (1950), 745–749.

Grossnickle, Foster E.: Teaching Arithmetic in the Junior High School, Mathematics Teacher, 47 (1954), 520–527.

Habel, E. A.: An Experiment in the Diagnosis and Remedy of Errors of College Freshmen in Arithmetic and Radicals, School Science and Mathematics, 51 (1951), 105–113.

Hamilton, E. W.: Field Work Modifies Our Program in Arithmetic, School Science and Mathematics, 51 (1951), 527–531.

Ingham, Carolyn, and Joseph M. Payne: An Eighth-grade Unit on Number Systems, Mathematics Teacher, 51 (1958), 392–395.

Johnson, Donovan A.: A Unit on Our Number System, School Science and Mathematics, 52 (1952), 556–561.

Johnson, J. T.: Decimal versus Common Fractions, Arithmetic Teacher, 3 (1956), 201–203, 206.

Johnson, Vally L.: Proof in Addition by Lateral Addition, School Science and Mathematics, 55 (1955), 544.

Jones, Burton W.: "Elementary Concepts of Mathematics" (New York: The Macmillan Company, 1947), pp. 190–195.

Kinsella, John J.: The Adolescent and Arithmetic, School Science and Mathematics, 50 (1950), 119–124.

Larsen, Harold D.: "Arithmetic for Colleges" (New York: The Macmillan Company, 1958).

Layne, Fay: We Took the Class Census, *Mathematics Teacher*, **45** (1952), 168–172.

Leach, H. W., and George C. Beakley: "The Slide Rule" (New York: The Macmillan Company, 1953), pp. 14–15.

Leonard, John L.: A New Method for Finding Square Root, *School Science and Mathematics*, **50** (1950), 40–48.

Mallory, Virgil S.: "Arithmetic Refresher for High Schools" (Chicago: Benj. H. Sanborn & Co., 1943).

Mason, Hazel L.: "Take Home" Tests for the Eighth-grade Arithmetic Class, *Mathematics Teacher*, **47** (1954), 213–214.

Miller, Ralph C.: Arithmetic for the Twelfth Year, *Mathematics Teacher*, **40** (1947), 221–224.

Moore, Tabbie Mae: More About Casting Out Nines, *Arithmetic Teacher*, **3** (1956), 204–206.

Mueller, Francis J.: "Arithmetic—Its Structure and Concepts" (Englewood Cliffs, N.J.: Prentice-Hall, Inc., 1956), pp. 230–264.

———: A Gratuitous Extrapolation in the Teaching of Per Cent, *Mathematics Teacher*, **51** (1958), 475–476.

Payne, Joseph N., and Robert C. Seber: Measurement and Approximation, "Twenty-fourth Yearbook" (Washington, D.C.: National Council of Teachers of Mathematics, 1959), pp. 182–228.

Pease, Edward M. J., and George P. Wadsworth: "Engineering Trigonometry" (Scranton, Pa.: International Textbook Company, 1946), pp. 214–255.

"Precision: A Measure of Progress" (Detroit, Mich.: Department of Public Relations, General Motors).

Rassweiler, Merrill, and J. Merle Harris: "Mathematics and Measurement" (Evanston, Ill.: Row, Peterson & Company, 1955).

Read, Cecil B.: Arguments against Universal Adoption of the Metric System, *School Science and Mathematics*, **50** (1950), 297–306.

———: Comments on Computation with Approximate Numbers, *Mathematics Teacher*, **46** (1953), 479–483.

Reeve, William David: "Mathematics for the Secondary School" (New York: Henry Holt and Company, Inc., 1954), pp. 208–220.

——— (Editor) and others: The Metric System of Weights and Measures, "Twentieth Yearbook" (Washington, D.C.: National Council of Teachers of Mathematics, 1948).

Reves, George E.: Outline of the History of Arithmetic, *School Science and Mathematics*, **51** (1951), 611–617.

Schaaf, William L.: Arithmetic in the High School [with extensive topical bibliography], *Mathematics Teacher*, **43** (1950), 358–361, 367.

———: The Use of Simple Algebra in Business Arithmetic, *Mathematics Teacher*, **44** (1951), 22–25.

Schiff, Herbert J.: Let Them Measure, *School Science and Mathematics*, **57** (1957), 291–292.

Seeley, Walter J.: The Engineer's Simple Arithmetic, *Mathematics Teacher*, **46** (1953), 565–566.

Shuster, Carl N.: Teaching Computation with Approximate Data, *Mathematics Teacher*, **42** (1949), 123–132.

———: Approximate Square Roots, *Mathematics Teacher*, **45** (1952), 17–18.

———: Working with Approximate Data, "Twenty-second Yearbook" (Washington, D.C.: National Council of Teachers of Mathematics, 1954), pp. 310–323.

—— and Fred L. Bedford: "Field Work in Mathematics" (New York: American Book Company, 1935), pp. 11–17.

Smith, D. E., and W. D. Reeve: "The Teaching of Junior High School Mathematics" New York: Ginn & Company, 1927), pp. 114–118.

Spitzer, Herbert F.: "Practical Procedures for the Enrichment of Arithmetic" (St. Louis, Mo.: Webster Publishing Company, 1956).

Stein, Edwin I.: "Refresher Arithmetic" (New York: Allyn and Bacon, 1948).

——: "Arithmetic for College Students" (New York: Allyn and Bacon, Inc., 1957).

Stern, Catherine: Concrete Representation of Geometric Progression, *Mathematics Teacher*, **44** (1951), 170–176.

Sueltz, Ben A.: Important Issues in Arithmetic, *Mathematics Teacher*, **42** (1949), 197.

Swain, Robert L.: "Understanding Arithmetic" (New York: Rinehart & Company, Inc., 1957).

Tate, M. W.: Notes on Approximate Computation, *School Science and Mathematics*, **44** (1944), 425–431.

Taylor, E. H., and C. N. Mills: "Arithmetic for Teacher Training Classes" (New York: Henry Holt and Company, Inc., 1955).

Trimble, H. C.: The Arithmetic of Growth, *Mathematics Teacher*, **47** (1954), 180–183.

UICSM Project Staff: Arithmetic with Frames, *Arithmetic Teacher*, **4** (1957), 119–124.

Van Engen, H.: A Selected List of References on Elementary School Arithmetic, *Mathematics Teacher*, **43** (1950), 168–171.

Weaver, J. Fred: Misconceptions about Rationalization in Arithmetic, *Mathematics Teacher*, **44** (1951), 369–376.

Wilson, Jack D.: Staking Out New Ground in High School Arithmetic, *School Science and Mathematics*, **54** (1954), 257–266.

Wilt, May L.: A Unit on the History of Arithmetic, *Mathematics Teacher*, **46** (1953), 475–477.

13

THE TEACHING OF ALGEBRA IN THE
JUNIOR HIGH SCHOOL

Algebra has long since acquired the widespread and unenviable reputation of being one of the most troublesome and difficult courses in the entire secondary school program. It has acquired this reputation not so much because of any excessive difficulty in the subject matter itself as because of certain inherent *differences* between algebra and any study which the student will have encountered earlier in his educational career. A large share of the difficulties which students encounter in their study of algebra may be traced to the fact that it presents them a radically new and different approach to the study of quantitative relationships, characterized by a new symbolism, new concepts, a new language, a much higher degree of generalization and abstraction than has been encountered previously; by the fact that, in contrast to arithmetic, algebra is more concerned with the conscious examination and study of processes than with particular answers to particular problems; and by the essential dissociation of many of its parts from intuition and concrete experience.

Too often, however, teachers either fail to recognize the essential significance of these characteristics of algebra, or else, through long-continued familiarity with them, permit them to become sheer habitual reactions. In either case the result is that teachers often fail to take account of the degree and the specific nature of the difficulties which these characteristics involve for beginning students. Unless teachers recognize these difficulties clearly and examine them with sufficient care to formulate specific ways for helping the student avoid or overcome them, the course is likely to degenerate into an aggregate of mechanical manipulations of symbols largely devoid of meaning. It is precisely this situation that has given rise to a large share of the current criticism of algebra as a school subject.

The fact that teachers often have been too preoccupied, negligent, or uninformed to take proper account of them does not mean that these various difficulties are insuperable. On the contrary, experience has shown that through careful analysis and planning and skillful teaching a great deal can be done to obviate or minimize them. No single topic is free of

them.   It is the job of the teacher to analyze each topic, to learn to anticipate the particular difficulties that are likely to occur in connection with
it, and to plan to teach it in such a way that the difficulties may be avoided
or forestalled as far as possible.   Such a practice will go far toward enabling the teacher to explain away those difficulties which cannot be
avoided altogether.

Algebra in the Seventh and Eighth Grades.   In general the algebraic work
to be included in the seventh- and eighth-grade courses should not be
extensive and it should not be formalized to the extent that it will be in
later courses.   Its main objective should be to give the students an introduction to the meaning of certain useful and basic algebraic concepts such
as literal numbers and formulas and the symbolic language of algebra.   It
is not intended that the algebraic work in these grades will lead to any
large degree of technical skill in algebraic operations, nor is it intended
that this work shall be thought of solely in terms of its preparatory values.
Rather it should be conceived as serving the double purpose of extending
the conceptual background of the student as a sound transitional basis
for later work and of providing mathematical experiences interesting in
themselves and more general in nature than those encountered in the
earlier arithmetic.   The Commission on Mathematics in describing the
prerequisites for its recommended program for grades 9 to 12 specifies
the following concepts and techniques from algebra and statistics:[1]

Graphs and Formulas: Use of line segments and areas to represent numbers.
Reading and construction of bar graphs, line graphs, pictograms, circle graphs,
and continuous line graphs.   Meaning of scale.   Formulas for perimeters, areas,
volumes, and per cents—introduced as generalizations as these concepts are
studied.   Use of symbols in formulas as placeholders for numerals arising in
measurement.   Simple expressions and sentences involving "variables."

Of recent years there has been developing in some quarters a feeling
that the first course in algebra would be more properly placed in the school
program if it were in the eighth grade.   The Secondary School Curriculum
Committee has this to say about this suggested practice:[2]

At present it seems unwise to make a blanket recommendation for the placement of algebra in the eighth grade.   It is conceivable, however, that there are
situations in which it is desirable to follow such a program, in which case the
responsibility of the ninth grade will be a follow-up program in algebra.   In such
situations the pupils should be mathematically superior and they should be
taught in homogeneous groups by well-qualified teachers.

[1] Report of Commission on Mathematics, "Program for College Preparatory
Mathematics" (New York: College Entrance Examination Board, 1959), pp. 19–20.
[2] Report of Secondary School Curriculum Committee, The Secondary Mathematics
Curriculum, *Mathematics Teacher*, **52** (1959), 412.

In its 1940 report the Joint Commission stated:[1]

The algebra that has been successfully introduced into grades 7 and 8 up to the present time has been limited largely to the understanding of the basic concepts, evaluation of formulas, and the solution of very simple equations. It seems possible and also desirable to include other algebraic material; but, if it is to prove effective, the work should be carefully planned and should be so organized as to be significant in itself as well as designed to furnish a good foundation for later algebraic study.

However, it was not uncommon then, nor has it been in more recent years, for certain other topics to be suggested as being appropriate for these grades, among them being directed numbers, graphs, and simple verbal problems. In the hands of the skillful teacher these topics can undoubtedly be made meaningful and interesting to young students, provided that the treatment is kept at a level of difficulty commensurate with the experience and maturity of the students.[2]

Although formulas, equations, etc., have been referred to as algebraic "topics," the reader should not get the impression that they are to be treated once, topically, and then relegated to the limbo of "finished work." On the contrary, they should be studied at recurring intervals and in various contexts throughout the course. Formulas and equations, in particular, are so pervasive and so amenable to gradation and adjustment from the standpoint of difficulty that appropriate applications of them can be made in connection with almost any topic which is likely to be considered in junior high school mathematics. Teachers should be alert to opportunities for making such applications and should become adept at using them to best advantage. At the same time, it is necessary to guard against the tendency to become overly zealous with regard to this part of the course. In their enthusiasm teachers sometimes carry the algebraic work to a point of difficulty quite unwarranted in a seventh- or eighth-grade class. It should be kept in mind that the aim of the algebraic work in these grades is by no means an exhaustive coverage of algebra as such, but rather a good and progressively improving mastery of a few of its simpler concepts and processes as they are applied to familiar situations.

It is impossible to make a valid categorical statement of what is the best

[1] Joint Commission of the Mathematical Association of America and the National Council of Teachers of Mathematics, "The Place of Mathematics in Secondary Education," *Fifteenth Yearbook* (Washington, D.C.: National Council of Teachers of Mathematics, 1940), p. 80.

[2] Commonwealth of Pennsylvania, Department of Public Instruction, "A Course of Study in Mathematics for Secondary Schools," *Bulletin* 360 (Harrisburg, Pa.: Department of Public Instruction, 1952), pp. 71, 72, 92–96.

William D. Reeve: "Mathematics for the Secondary School" (New York: Henry Holt and Company, Inc., 1954), pp. 248–250.

arrangement and grade placement of this algebraic work in the seventh and eighth grades. The National Committee on Mathematical Requirements recognized the inadvisability of trying to make such a statement and instead presented five alternative plans. The weight of evidence, however, seems to indicate that, while certain work with simple formulas may be done satisfactorily in the seventh grade, it is better to defer most of this algebraic work until the eighth grade. This was indicated in four of the five plans suggested by the National Committee[1] as well as in the later reports of the Joint Commission[2] and the Commission on Post-War Plans.[3] Today it is reflected in the majority of textbooks prepared in recent years for these grades, as well as in recent courses of study.[4]

Such algebraic work as may be attempted in these grades should be informal, and it should be interesting. So far as possible it should be made to seem useful to the students. There should be little or no technical manipulation of symbols. The problem situations that are presented should be so simple that they can be readily associated with familiar arithmetical or geometrical situations, so that by the process of analogy the appropriate procedures may be made to appear reasonable to the students. The main idea should be to give the students an understanding of the meaning of the language and symbolism of algebra as expressed in the formula and the simple equation and of the simplicity, power, generality, and importance of these mathematical tools.

Probably no better criteria can be found for determining the appropriateness of algebraic material for the seventh and eighth grades than those given by Barber in his excellent monograph on the teaching of junior high school mathematics.[5] Although these were published nearly four decades ago, his clear foresight caught and gave expression to the spirit in which the algebraic work in these grades should be viewed.

Any algebra which may be introduced into these grades should be subjected to three tests. Is it interesting? Is it useful? Is it thought-provoking? And to these there may be added a fourth: Does it prepare for the new algebra of grade nine? . . .

In making his decision as to what algebra is to be used in these grades the

[1] National Committee on Mathematical Requirements, "The Reorganization of Mathematics in Secondary Education" (Boston: Houghton Mifflin Company, 1923), pp. 28-30.

[2] Joint Commission, *op. cit.*, pp. 85-86.

[3] Commission on Post-War Plans, Second Report, *Mathematics Teacher*, **38** (1945), 203-205.

[4] See, for example, "Mathematics in California Public High Schools," *Bulletin of the California State Department of Education*, vol. XXV, no. 4 (Sacramento, Calif.: California State Department of Education, 1956).

[5] Harry C. Barber, "Teaching Junior High School Mathematics" (Boston: Houghton Mifflin Company, 1924), pp. 88-89.

teacher will note that the mensuration formulas are already included in what we call arithmetic. It is, at first, only a question of making the best educational use of such formulas in all the situations in which they are helpful.

It is argued that, by the use of one-letter abbreviations and formulas, and, finally, equations, we can considerably improve the written work in a thoroughly sound manner; and that this provides a single method for handling many kinds of situations, and a method which becomes more and more useful and aids clear thinking as we go ahead with mathematics and its applications.

The common use of the formula and the equation in the technical and the scientific world, even in its elementary and popular discussions, gives color to the claim that a working knowledge of these two tools of algebra has a general informational value which cannot be ignored in this day and generation. On the other hand to teach, in these grades, the old introduction to a mechanical algebra is worse than to teach no algebra at all.

Most of the work in seventh- and eighth-grade algebra will be focused upon the interpretation of graphs and associated concepts, making clear the meaning of literal symbols, the use of these in setting up formulas and simple equations, and the evaluation of such formulas and the solution of such equations.[1] Many commonplace relationships already familiar to the pupil give rise to formulas. Such relationships may be used to advantage by having the pupils translate their verbal expressions into symbolic language. For example, if pencils cost 5 cents each, the pupil readily states that the cost of 2 pencils will be 2 times 5 cents, the cost of 7 pencils will be 7 times 5 cents, and so on. He can be led without difficulty to generalize this situation to give the cost of any number of pencils at this price; i.e., the total cost will be the number of pencils times 5 cents. It is an easy but important step for him now to pass from this verbal statement to the symbolic statement of the same relation, $C = n \cdot 5$, and eventually to the still more general statement $C = n \cdot p$. The evaluation of C for any given values of n and p thus becomes easy and meaningful.

Many familiar arithmetical problems can be made to yield just as satisfactory formulas and equations. Some examples are given in the following table, which could be extended easily.

In any uniform or average-rate motion, distance equals rate
   times time.. $d = r \cdot t$
Simple interest equals principal times rate times time...... $i = p \cdot r \cdot t$
Circumference of a circle equals pi times the diameter...... $C = \pi \cdot D$
Perimeter of a rectangle equals 2 times the sum of the length
   and the width.. $p = 2(l + w)$
The annual rent on a home equals 12 times the monthly
   rent... $R = 12 \cdot r$
Percentage equals base times rate......................... $p = b \cdot r$

[1] See, among others, the following references: Materials for Grade 8 Mathematics, "Mathematics in the Public Schools," (New York: Board of Education of the City of New York, 1955) and the Report of Commission on Mathematics, *op. cit.*, pp. 18–19.

Margin equals selling price minus cost..................... $m = s - c$
Area of a rectangle equals base times height.............. $A = b \cdot h$
The score in a basketball game is the number of free throws
   plus twice the number of field goals made good.......... $S = f + 2g$
The diagonal of a square is equal to the length of one side
   times the square root of 2........................... $d = s \cdot \sqrt{2}$
The volume of a rectangular solid is equal to the product of
   the length, width, and height........................ $V = l \cdot w \cdot h$
The length of the hypotenuse of a right triangle is equal to
   the square root of the sum of the squares of the legs..... $h = \sqrt{a^2 + b^2}$
The number of ounces is equal to 16 times the number of
   pounds.. $n = 16 \cdot p$
The number of gallons in a tank is (about) equal to $7\frac{1}{2}$ times
   the number of cubic feet............................ $g = 7\frac{1}{2} \cdot f$
The number of centimeters is (about) 2.54 times the number
   of inches... $c = 2.54 \cdot i$

The equations which are used should be so simple that the pupil will intuitively know how to solve them. So far as possible they, also, should grow out of familiar problem situations, although there can be no objection to setting up short lists of empirical equations for practice. Consider this problem, for example, If John earned $9.60 for 16 hours work, what was his average wage per hour? This gives rise to the equation $16 \cdot w = \$9.60$, and the pupil's task is to solve for w. Intuition furnishes a sufficient guide for this.

Of equal usefulness is this problem; Fred and Joe picked 40 quarts of cherries one day, but Joe picked 8 quarts more than Fred did. How many quarts did each pick? This suggests the equation $F + (F + 8) = 40$, or $2F + 8 = 40$. By subtracting 8 from each side, the equation becomes $2F = 32$, for which, again, the solution is effected intuitively.

Such equations provide an easy and natural approach to the more formal methods which will be used later. They need not and should not be made difficult. Speed of solution is not a consideration here. The main considerations at this stage should be to ensure understanding of the derivation of the equation, to ensure understanding of the solution, and to develop the habit of using such equations in solving problems.

Ninth-grade Algebra. In the ninth grade more teachers and more students spend more time and effort in a more extensive study of formal algebra than in any other grade in the entire secondary school system. In the combined seventh and eighth grades of the junior high school the total number of students having some contact with algebra is perhaps greater than in the ninth grade, but the algebra treated in these grades is extremely limited in scope and informal in character. On the other hand, the more extensive and formal algebra of the senior high school and the junior college affects only a relatively small group of students who are more highly selected. It is in the ninth grade that the serious study of the subject begins for most students, and it is with this grade that it ends for many of them.   Here the student's interest is either kindled and nourished or allowed to die.   Here he either gains the comprehensions and skills which are necessary for further progress or else fails to gain them and so has his way blocked to the pursuit of further study in this field or to extensive study in many related fields.   All the concepts, principles, and procedures of ninth-grade algebra carry over into the work of later years and in fact form the very foundation of that work.   Thus the ninth grade is the most critical grade so far as algebra is concerned.   Here lies the teacher's greatest challenge and greatest opportunity.

Symbols and Formulas.   The formula, a symbolic statement of relationship between two or more variables, provides an ideal medium for the transition from the earlier work to the more formal and systematic aspects of algebra, and a theme about which a great deal of the work of the ninth grade can be organized.   It involves or is closely associated with a great many of the concepts of elementary algebra; the symbolic language of constants and variables; the concept of dependence and function; graphic representation of relationships; substitution and evaluation; and operations with signed numbers, literal symbols, parentheses, exponents, fractions, radicals, etc.   Thus it forms a core which has points of contact not only with the previous experiences of the students but with many of the topics which will be considered subsequently throughout the ninth-grade course and in later courses.[1]

The ninth-grade student is not entirely unacquainted with formulas even when he begins his study of algebra.   In his previous work in arithmetic and informal geometry he will doubtless have had some contact with such formulas as those for simple interest and for the mensuration of the simplest and most common geometric forms.   If he has had a thoroughly good course in seventh- and eighth-grade mathematics, he should have attained some understanding of the significance and generality of the formula as a shorthand statement of relationships between quantities and as a rule for operation.   He will have had some experience in evaluating simple formulas and perhaps will have constructed or set up a few simple formulas from quantitative situations within his experience.   He thus brings to his ninth-grade work enough background to enable him to use the formula as a point of departure in his work in algebra, and the further study of the formula, in turn, serves to familiarize the student with, and give him experience in the progressive mastery of the new language, concepts, symbolism, and operations of algebra.

The main things which the student should get from his study of formulas through the ninth grade are these:

---

[1] In this connection see Reeve, *op. cit.*, pp. 249–250.

1. An understanding and appreciation of the nature and significance of the symbolism of algebra

2. A clear concept of the meaning of a constant and a variable and the distinction between the two

3. A clear concept and appreciation of dependence and the meaning and relationship of independent and dependent variables

4. The ability to set up simple formulas expressing relationships existing in situations within the student's experience

5. Facility and accuracy in substitution in and evaluation of formulas

6. The ability to represent graphically the relationships indicated by formulas involving two variables

7. The ability to solve formulas, *i.e.*, to transform an implicit relationship into an explicit relationship through application of the laws of algebraic operation

If the teacher will organize the work relating to formulas around these main foci and will consciously plan every exercise and activity so that it will bear upon and contribute to the attainment of one or another of these main objectives, then worthwhile results may be expected. Otherwise, the work is likely to follow a too prevalent piecemeal pattern whose only plan is the order of topics and exercises in the textbook, a pattern in which organization, emphasis, and direction will be lacking and from which any worthwhile outcomes which may occur must be regarded more as welcome accidents than as legitimate expectations.

One of the first of the fundamental tasks which the student faces in the study of formulas and algebra in general is to acquire a good understanding of the real meaning of symbolism. It is customary to introduce students to the notational significance of algebraic symbolism by having them (1) consider common situations in which the relationships between two or more elements are known, (2) state these relationships in words, and (3) abbreviate the verbal statements by substituting letters and symbols of operation and equality for the words. For example, the student may be asked to tell how to find the distance which an automobile traveling at a uniform speed will cover in a given time. His statement will probably be to the effect that the distance is equal to the rate of speed (in miles per hour) multiplied by the time (expressed in hours). He can easily be led to see that, by using letters to represent the verbal expressions, he can write this same relationship more briefly and conveniently as $d = r \cdot t$. That is, in this simple case he has little difficulty in associating the letter d with distance, r with rate of speed, and t with time. He thus gains almost at once the important idea that a letter may stand for a meaning which can be expressed more elaborately in words.

This, however, is not the whole story. Unless the student is made keenly aware not only that the letter is to be associated with a verbal expression (e.g., r for rate) but that it must be identified in any particular instance *with a number*, he is likely to come to the erroneous and meaning-less conclusion that "miles per hour times hours equal miles" or that "feet times feet equals square feet." Such statements are not at all uncom-mon, but they exhibit a lack of clarity with respect to the meaningful use of symbolism. A concept fundamental to the clear and precise use of symbols is that the student be made to understand that they primarily and essentially represent numbers, although they may refer to the enu-meration or numerical measurement of some particular kinds of objects or magnitudes. The intelligent use of symbols probably can be developed most effectively through numerous illustrations of the use of letters to represent such things as lengths of line segments, weights, sizes of angles, or unknown quantities in simple verbal problems or equations. Such illustrations should be closely associated with repeated and carefully supervised practice in the actual evaluation of formulas by the direct sub-stitution of specified numbers and the performance of the indicated opera-tions after the substitutions have been made. The teacher should employ illustrations of these procedures freely, because the immature mind responds much more readily to illustration than it does to definition or verbal direction. During this period of development and early practice in the employment of symbols, the work of the student should be under the close supervision of the teacher in order that any misconceptions and mistakes may be detected and corrected at the outset and so prevented from becoming fixed habits.

Constants, Variables, and Functions. Letter symbols are often used to represent *variables*. The two are not synonymous, because letter symbols are also used at times to represent *constants*. While the concept of vari-able is not to be restricted to the domain of variation, it does provide the language and symbolism for dealing with the principles and problems of variation, and it is indispensable to the complete understanding of for-mulas, equations, and the nature of dependence.

A variable is a symbol that may represent any element from a specified set of elements called its domain. For example, the letter r is frequently used to represent the radius of a circle. Thus the domain of values for r con-sists of all the positive real numbers, since, theoretically at least, there exists a circle for any positive real number which might be specified as the radius. This is not true for negative numbers. If the value of r should be specified as -3, there does not exist a circle with such a number as its radius. Note that in this illustration no thought of variation is expressed. The symbol r is simply used to *stand for* any number that might be used as the radius of a circle. On the other hand, the concept of variation might well be in the picture as, for example, in the use of the symbol t to represent time as it is changing during some specified interval.

A constant is a symbol used to represent a fixed value *during a particular discussion.*   Such symbols as 2, -3, $\sqrt{2}$, $\frac{5}{6}$, and π are constants.   They are fixed in value.   They are known as *absolute constants* in contrast to *arbitrary constants* (or *parameters*) such as the symbol m in the equation of the straight line $y = mx + 3$.   For any particular discussion the value of m may be chosen and it will remain fixed for that discussion, but it may change from one discussion to another.   The value of the absolute constant 3 remains the same for all discussions.   The lines $y = \frac{1}{2}x + 3$, $y = -4x + 3$, $y = 5x + 3$ are straight lines all passing through the point (0,3) but with the respective slopes of $\frac{1}{2}$, -4, and 5.

The ordinary experiences of children furnish innumerable illustrations of both variables and constants.   The fact that many children come through one or more years of work in algebra without any clear understanding of what is meant by either of the terms "variable" and "variation" can mean only that teachers do not take the trouble to present a sufficient number or variety of these illustrations.   Changes in age, height, or weight of individuals, the distance of a moving body from a fixed point, and changes in temperature are but a few examples of many familiar situations which could be used to make the meaning of variation, variable, and constant clear.   If these illustrations are to yield the desired results, however, the teacher must see to it that the attention of the students is focused upon the respective characteristics of each concept, and this emphasis must be made repeatedly and specifically.   One cannot reasonably expect any clear comprehension of any one of the three concepts to emerge as a mere incidental by-product.   They are not difficult to develop, but they must be developed through planned activity if they are to be really understood by any substantial majority of the students.

Just as the concept of variable has suffered through the years because of the inclination of many to restrict it to considerations of variation, so the concept of function has suffered because of similar restrictions to consideration of dependence and dependent variation.   It is true that the concept of function furnishes the language and symbolism for effective consideration of the characteristics of dependence, but it is not to be thought of as being restricted merely to such considerations.   Mathematicians[1] are inclined to emphasize two basic concepts of "function," namely:

1. A function is a set of ordered pairs of elements (a,b) so related that, when the value of a is determined in its set of admissible values, the value of b is determined uniquely in its set.   The two sets are not necessarily distinct.

Thus, the ordered pairs (a,a^2), $(a,\sqrt{a})$, $(a, \sin a)$ are possible functions. If the set of values for both variables is specified as the set of all positive

[1] For interesting and helpful discussions of constant, variable, and function, see chapters III, VIII, and XIII of "Insights into Modern Mathematics," *Twenty-third Yearbook* (Washington, D.C.: National Council of Teachers of Mathematics, 1957).

real numbers, each ordered pair is a function. To any value of the first variable there corresponds a unique value of the second variable. This is illustrated in the table for a few values of a.

a	a^2	$\sqrt{a}$	$\sin a$
1	1	1	$\sin 1$
2	4	$\sqrt{2}$	$\sin 2$
$\frac{1}{4}$	$\frac{1}{16}$	$\frac{1}{2}$	$\sin \frac{1}{4}$

If the set of values for a is specified as the set of all negative real numbers and the set of values for the second variable is specified to be the set of all real numbers, then (a,a^2) and $(a, \sin a)$ are functions, but $(a,\sqrt{a})$ is not. For example, if $a = -4$, then (a,a^2) becomes $(-4,16)$, $(a, \sin a)$ becomes $[-4, \sin (-4)]$ and 16 and $\sin (-4)$ are real numbers. On the other hand, $(a,\sqrt{a})$ becomes $(-4,\sqrt{-4})$ and $\sqrt{-4}$ is not a real number.

2. A function is a rule, expression, or table which defines a specific relationship between two sets (not necessarily distinct) of elements, such that when an element from one set is given, an element from the other set is uniquely determined.

The expression is frequently no more than the formula form of the rule. For example, the rule that "the area of a circle is equal to π times the square of the radius" is more conveniently expressed by the formula $A = \pi r^2$. Caution must be exercised here in the interpretation of just what it is that the formula is and is not. It is a convenient device for selecting the numbers that give us the function defined by the set of ordered pairs of numbers (radius of a circle, area of the circle) symbolized by (r,A). The set of values from which r may be selected is the set of all nonnegative real numbers, and after r is selected, a value of A is easily determined. The formula is *not* the function. The values which define the function do, indeed, meet the conditions of the formula, but there are ordered pairs of values which meet the conditions of the formula but do not meet the conditions of the function. For example, the pair of values $(-3,9\pi)$ satisfy the formula but not the function, since there is no circle with radius -3. Thus, if the function F is the above set of ordered pairs (r,A), it is incorrect to say that $F(-3) = 9\pi$. McShane[1] refers to such incorrect usage as this as using a formula "beyond its domain of validity," and emphasizes that it "can lead to absurdities, not only in mathematics but in any science."

"The *domain* of a function F is the set of all objects x for which $F(x)$ has

---

[1] E. J. McShane: Operating with Sets, "Insights into Modern Mathematics," *Twenty-third Yearbook* (Washington, D.C.: National Council of Teachers of Mathematics, 1957), p. 57.

meaning; in other words, an object x is in the domain of F if and only if there exists some y such that (x,y) is in F [that is, $F(x) = y$]. The *range* of the function F is the set of all objects y which are values of the function; that is, y is in the range of F if and only if there is an x for which the equation $F(x) = y$ is true."[1]

Table 13-1 gives another illustration of how a function may be defined. Here the set of ordered pairs of elements is (t,T), where t represents time and T represents temperature. The domain of the function is the set of even hours of the day from 2 A.M. to 2 A.M., and the range is the set of temperatures (54°, 60°, 61°, 62°, 64°, 66°, 69°, 70°, 71°, 73°). Note that the set of ordered pairs (T,t) would not be a function, since for $T = 61°$ or $T = 62°$ there is not a *unique* determination of a value for t.

Table 13-1

Time	Temperature	Time	Temperature
2 A.M.	61	4 P.M.	70
4 A.M.	61	6 P.M.	66
6 A.M.	61	8 P.M.	62
8 A.M.	64	10 P.M.	62
10 A.M.	69	Midnight	60
Noon	71	2 A.M.	54
2 P.M.	73		

The first symbol in the ordered pair which defines a function is the *independent variable*. It is the variable whose value is arbitrary so long as it is chosen from the domain of the function. The second symbol is the *dependent variable*. It is the variable whose value is determined in the range of the function merely by the assignment of an arbitrarily chosen value to the independent variable.

The more restricted concept of function, namely, the idea of dependence of one element in a situation upon one or more other elements, is not inherently difficult to develop in children. The reason why it is usually so inadequately developed is that specific attention is so seldom given to it. It seems to be one of those outcomes which many teachers wishfully hope for as a by-product of instruction but which they erroneously regard as so sure of occurrence that to give direct and specific attention to it would be a waste of time.

As is the case with most elementary concepts, the best method of development lies in illustration. The concept of dependence is best illustrated by taking cases involving related quantities such as the diameter and circumference of a circle and showing that, when one of these is known, the other is uniquely determined and that a change in either of the two will produce a corresponding change in the other. In this connection it is help-

[1] *Ibid.*, pp. 57–58.

ful to have the students build tables by computing and tabulating the values of the dependent variable (or function) which correspond to arbitrarily assigned values of the independent variable or variables and then make graphs from these tables of variables, as illustrated in Fig. 13-1. It is possible, of course, for students to perform the necessary substitutions and computations in a mechanical way and without *any conscious recognition* of the interdependence of the quantities involved. It is largely because teachers have failed to stress this conscious recognition of dependence and keep it continually in the focus of attention of the students that the notion of functionality has not played the important part it should play in mathematical education. It is not that it is hard to understand, for it is not. If the concepts of dependence and function are to be made

FIG. 13-1. Relation of length of circumference of a circle to length of diameter.

to play an integral and basic part in the mathematical thinking of students, teachers must continually, deliberately, and specifically bring them to the attention of the student and keep his attention centered upon them by repeated illustrations of their occurrence.

The concepts of *dependent* and *independent variables* are implied in the understanding of dependence. But here again the differential characteristics of these concepts are not likely to emerge and stand out with distinctness in the minds of the students unless the teacher directs special attention to them and shows by repeated illustration just *why* they are called variables and why one of them is designated an *independent* variable while the other is called a *dependent* variable.

Attention has already been called to the practice of having students *translate verbal statements of relationships into formulas* by the use of letter symbols to represent the related elements in the situation. There can be little doubt that such practice in translating statements or laws into formulas is of great value in centering the students' attention upon the fundamental concepts which have been discussed and in clarifying these concepts. Probably the simplest and most effective way to give students an understanding start in this use of symbolism is to show them that it may be regarded as a sort of shorthand method of writing down what would otherwise have to be written in a less convenient verbal form. The contrast between the verbal and the symbolic forms and the advantage of the latter can be emphasized by actually writing down the verbal statements of relationships and then "for the sake of convenience" rewriting the statements by using merely the initial letters of the key words rather than the words themselves.   The following examples illustrate this method.

Distance   equals   rate of speed   multiplied by   time
$$d \qquad = \qquad r \qquad \times \qquad t$$
Cost of gasoline   equals   number of gallons   multiplied by   price per gallon
$$C \qquad = \qquad g \qquad \times \qquad p$$

A few such examples will serve to enable most students to get the idea of what is being done and learn to appreciate the significance of the symbolism and the expressed relationships.   However, in order to ensure something distinctly beyond a mere threshold understanding of these concepts, the students should be given a substantial amount of practice in this work, and the practice should be spread over a considerable period of time.

Teaching Students to Solve Linear Equations.   One of the most common and important activities of ninth-grade algebra is the solution of linear equations.   Presumably the student will bring to his study of algebra some understanding of what an equation means, since he will have had experience with simple equations in his previous work in arithmetic and informal geometry and perhaps even with certain very simple equations in which the unknown quantity is represented by a literal symbol.   In all probability, however, his experience in solving equations will have been hardly above the intuitive level.   For example, if confronted with the equation $3n = 24$ and required to find the number represented by n, he will probably reason that, if three n's make 24, then "it stands to reason" that one n will have to be one-third of 24, or 8.

These intuitive reactions are generally sufficient and satisfactory so long as the situation is very simple, i.e., so long as it is possible for the student to keep in mind clearly and simultaneously all the pertinent elements and relationships which are involved in the situation.   On the other hand, the moment a problem situation becomes so involved that he is unable to keep all the elements and their proper relationships clearly in mind at the same time, intuition breaks down, and when this happens, logic must take its place.   In such cases the only recourse is to more formal and powerful tools for the analysis of problem situations.   Such a tool is the algebraic equation.

Since the turn of the century much criticism has been directed against formalism in secondary school algebra.   It is undoubtedly true that the mechanical aspects of algebra have been heavily stressed and that the emphasis placed upon the formal operations has too often given little or no consideration to underlying meanings.   There is a great difference, however, between formalism, conceived in this sense, and the formalization of mathematical procedures. Algebra really consists fundamentally in the generalization and formalization of these procedures, but this formalization need not and should not be divorced from meanings. Rather, it should be conceived as merely an extension of familiar procedures into an environment of number concepts more general and more powerful than those of elementary arithmetic. The student should be taught to look upon the algebraic equation as a device which enables him to investigate easily relationships which would be too complex to be investigated successfully or easily without its aid. It should be explained to him that the solution of formulas or equations operates under certain fixed laws called *axioms*. He should learn the meaning of these axioms. They should be explained to him and illustrated by the teacher in terms of the familiar quantitative concepts of his past experience. After he has thus been given a feeling of the reasonableness of the axioms, he should be given practice in using them not only with arithmetical numbers but with literal numbers as well.

The fundamental operational axioms involved in the solution of linear equations are as follows:

1. If equals are added to equals, the results are equal.
2. If equals are subtracted from equals, the results are equal.
3. If equals are multiplied by equals, the results are equal.
4. If equals are divided by equals other than zero, the results are equal.

The student should learn to react without hesitancy to these axioms. They should become so much a part of him that he will come to apply them as readily to literal numbers as to ordinary arithmetical numbers in an equation.

Linear equations in ninth-grade algebra assume a variety of forms of which the following are illustrative:

$$ax = b \qquad x + a = b \qquad ax + b = c$$
$$\frac{x}{a} = b \qquad a - x = b \qquad x - a = b$$
$$ax + b = cx + d \qquad ax + bx = c$$

While these forms are all variations of a common form, the similarity is usually not immediately apparent to children encountering them for the first time. Moreover, textbooks and teachers are frequently deficient in giving emphasis to this point. As a consequence the different forms are often taught separately, a special technique being developed for each, much as the three cases of percentage are often taught in arithmetic. Such a practice probably makes for quick mastery of the separate techniques but for little else. It is in fact precisely this type of treatment against which the legitimate criticism of algebra has been directed. It does not and cannot make other than an incidental contribution to the development of any real power of generalized understanding and original analysis. It produces little more than the acquisition of certain transitory skills, and so it largely fails in the attainment of its real objective.

A much sounder procedure would be to try to find a single unifying principle which would be applicable to all forms. Such a principle fortunately is available and can be stated in a way which is clearly understandable to ninth-grade students. It can be formulated in three or four key sentences somewhat as follows:

1. In solving *any* linear equation in one unknown for the unknown (we may call it x) the object is to get an equation in which x will stand alone on one side of the equation and will not appear on the other side.

2. In order to do this we must get rid of all the other numerals or symbols which are associated with x on its side of the equation.

3. We get rid of these numerals or symbols by undoing the operations which associate them with x, that is, by applying the processes which are the inverse of those which bind these symbols or numerals to x.

4. If any operation is performed on one side of an equation in order to change its value, the same or an equivalent operation must be performed on the other side of the equation, because if it is not, we shall no longer have an equation in balance.[1]

This principle gives a basis for the solution of linear equations without any recourse whatever to intuition, except the intuitive feeling that the only way to make a number symbol stand alone is to get rid of the other number symbols that are connected with it. It gives emphasis to the character of the equation and lends organization and generality to the solution of linear equations. This, in turn, eliminates any necessity for developing special methods for the different forms. For the student who follows this general plan, the specialized procedures will emerge automatically as he finds need for them, since they are but adaptations of the general plan to particularized forms of the equation.

Example. Let it be required to solve $ax - b = c$ for x. In order to make x stand alone on one side of the equation, it is necessary to get rid of the b and the a from that side of the equation. Since the x appears in only one term, we may first get rid of the other term, b. This is done by adding b to both sides of the equation, since originally b was subtracted from ax and any subtraction can be undone only by the inverse process, addition. This[2] gives $ax = c + b$. It is now necessary to get rid of the a from the left member of the equation. Since the a is a multiplier of x, we can get rid of it only by undoing the multiplication. For

---

[1] See the following listings in the Bibliography: Ligda, pp. 48–52; Hassler and Smith, pp. 277–280; and Davis, pp. 200–202.

[2] This is the equivalent of "transposition," which may be used as a convenient short cut if, and only if, the student understands the full significance of the process.

this purpose we must employ the inverse process, division; that is, we must divide both sides of the equation by a. This will give the required solution:

$$x = \frac{c + b}{a}$$

Sometimes the unknown appears in more than one term. When that occurs, it is first necessary to collect these terms and to factor out the unknown as a common factor. After this has been done, the solution is identical in nature to the one that has just been described.

Example. Let it be required to solve the equation $ax + b + cx = d$ for x.

Solution

1. Collect the terms in x.
2. Factor out x as a common factor.
3. Get rid of the term b from the left member of the equation by subtracting b from both members.

4. Get rid of the multiplier $(a + c)$ from the left member by dividing both members by $(a + c)$.

1. $(ax + cx) + b = d$.
2. $x(a + c) + b = d$.
3. $x(a + c) = d - b$.

4. $\dfrac{x(a + c)}{(a + c)} = \dfrac{(d - b)}{(a + c)}$.

or

$$x = \frac{d - b}{a + c}.$$

Both illustrative examples have attempted to point out the type of reasoning processes involved in the solution of linear equations in one unknown. Nothing has been said about the specific nature of the result. Just what is it that such a process produces? Is it the value of the unknown which, if used to replace the unknown, will produce the desired equality? One does not know until the substitution is made and the equality is tested. In the first example the reasoning is as follows: If $ax - b = c$, then it follows that $ax = c + b$, from which, in turn, it follows that $x = (c + b)/a$. (Note that even this statement does not follow if $a = 0$.) This reasoning simply states that, if $ax - b = c$, then it is *necessary* that x have the value $(c + b)/a$. It *does not say* that $x = (c + b)/a$ is *sufficient* to make $ax - b = c$. This must be tested by substitution (we call it checking the work). The test will reveal that $x = (c + b)/a$ is *both a necessary and a sufficient condition* that $ax - b = c$. Similar reasoning is present in the second illustrative example.

Two further examples are given to illustrate this very important point. For the existence of a unique value of x which will satisfy $ax - b = c$ it is *necessary* that a be different from zero. That this is not sufficient can easily be demonstrated by the fact that, if $a \neq 0$, then $1/a$ has a value, and $x = 1/a$ gives $a(1/a) - b = 1 - b$, which may or may not be equal to c. Furthermore, substitution will reveal that $x = k(c + b)/ka$, $k \neq 0$, is sufficient to give $ax - b = c$. Only $x = (c + b)/a$ is both necessary and sufficient to give $ax - b = c$.

A more homely illustration may be obtained from consideration of the following sentences:

1. To make a 20-cent purchase, it is necessary that one have x cents.
2. To make a 20-cent purchase, it is sufficient that one have y cents.
3. To make a 20-cent purchase, it is both necessary and sufficient that one have z cents.

Any number of cents less than 20 cents could be used to replace x and statement 1 would be true.

Any number of cents greater than 20 cents could be used to replace y and statement 2 would be true.

Only the number 20 could be used to replace z and make statement 3 true.

No process for obtaining the solution of an equation is complete until the obtained solution is checked in the original equation.

It is hardly necessary to give further illustrations. The single unifying principle of getting rid of the unwanted terms, divisors, and multipliers by the application of inverse processes results automatically in the solution of all forms of the linear equation in one unknown. Approached intuitively in the beginning, its complete reasonableness can be made apparent to children without difficulty. Thereafter they should be led to focus their attention on the process per se and to give less and less attention to its concrete numerical setting. Thus eventually it will stand out as a general, abstract, mechanical principle of operation, not devoid of meaning (because it will have been built upon meanings in the beginning) but no longer dependent upon intuition and therefore more certain and more powerful than the earlier and less formal procedures.

The Evaluation and Solution of Formulas. Theoretically the *evaluation of formulas* presents no learning difficulties. Actually, however, students make mistakes in this simple process, and they are not always mistakes in computation. Mistakes in substitution occur with unexpected frequency. These are most often associated with the rewriting or recopying of the formulas with the letters replaced by corresponding numerical values. This type of error can be offset to a considerable degree by having the students make a practice of enclosing in separate parentheses each numerical value which is substituted for a letter. This has a tendency to focus attention upon each quantity as a separate element in the formula and so avoid the confusion of one such element with another. In chalk-board work it is helpful to have the students actually erase one by one the letters in the formula and write in the numerical value of each letter as that letter is erased. This makes the students keenly conscious of the fact that *the* *letters are actually to be replaced by the numbers* and thus strengthens the appreciation of the real meaning of evaluation. While this practice of erasing and rewriting *in situ* cannot be followed so satisfactorily when the work is being done with pencil and paper, something of the same effect can be attained by having each substituted number enclosed in separate parentheses and written in a place which precisely corresponds to the place occupied in the formula by the letter for which the substitution is being made.

The evaluation of formulas involving only two variables can also be tied up with the graphs representing the relationships. Assuming that the graph has been constructed, any value of the independent variable (lying within the domain covered by the graph) may be selected. When this value is referred to the corresponding point on the graph and that point, in turn, to the axis of the dependent variable, the value of the latter is given (at least approximately) at once. To illustrate, use the relation for the number of pounds to the number of kilograms, $P = 2.2K$. If we let K have the value 2.5, Fig. 13-2, we immediately determine P as being (at least approximately) 5.5. Similarly, if K is $5\frac{3}{4}$, the corresponding value of P is found to be about 12.7; for $K = 8$, we get $P = 17.6$; etc.

FIG. 13-2. Relation of pounds to kilograms.

The *solution of formulas* often causes students much difficulty. This is because the students are not made consciously and specifically aware of the general principles underlying the solutions. Indeed, teachers themselves often seem to overlook the general principles. The principles do exist, however, and are quite simple and capable of being applied in an understanding manner by ninth-grade students. They are merely the principles which underlie the solution of all simple equations, whether numerical or literal, integral or fractional, rational or irrational.

The general procedure may be illustrated by considering the formula $A = P + Prt$. Let it be required to solve for t in terms of A, P, and r. Since the letter t occurs in only one term, that term must be retained and all other terms eliminated from that member of the equation. This elimination of elements from one member of the equation (or formula) is always accomplished by *undoing* the operation which binds that element to the rest of the given member of the equation. In this case P is related to Prt by addition.   Hence, to eliminate P from that member of the equation we must undo this addition, or, in other words, we must subtract P from the right member of the equation.   It, therefore, becomes necessary to subtract P also from the left member of the equation.   This (the equivalent of transposing P) gives the equation $A - P = Prt$.

Now since we wish to solve for t, we must eliminate Pr from the right member.   But Pr is bound to t by multiplication.   Hence, in order to eliminate Pr and make t stand alone, we must undo the multiplication by using a process which is the inverse of multiplication, viz., division. Therefore, we divide the member Prt by Pr, and, of course, if we divide one member of an equation by a given quantity, we must also divide the other member by that same quantity.   Thus we get

$$\frac{A - P}{Pr} = \frac{(Pr)t}{(Pr)} \quad \text{or} \quad \frac{A - P}{Pr} = t$$

This principle of "elimination by undoing" (or by applying inverse processes) is perfectly general and is not difficult once the students are brought to see it in its essential simplicity.   It removes the solution of formulas from the status of a bag of tricks and places it upon a reasonable basis.

Apparent complications are introduced when the student is required to solve for a letter that occurs in two or more terms.   In such cases, however, it should be pointed out that it is merely necessary first to group these terms and remove the required letter as a common factor.   The procedure then follows the general pattern indicated above.   To illustrate: let it be required to solve the foregoing formula for P in terms of A, r, and t.   The steps are as follows:

$$A = P + Prt$$
$$A = P(1 + rt)$$
$$\frac{A}{(1 + rt)} = \frac{P(1 + rt)}{(1 + rt)}$$
$$\frac{A}{(1 + rt)} = P$$

Note that, after the right member has been factored, it remains merely to eliminate the factor $1 + rt$ by undoing the multiplication, i.e., by dividing both members of the equation by that factor.

The Teaching of Graphs.   In recent years an increasing amount of importance has been attached to the study of graphs in junior high school mathematics.   Among the several reasons for this may be mentioned the interesting character and the practical importance of graphical devices; the simplicity and power of the graph for presenting data in a condensed, understandable, and striking way; and the increasing prominence of graphical devices in newspapers, magazines, and other current publications.

There are two fundamentally distinct types of graphs, viz., the statistical graph and the mathematical or functional graph. The former is a device used to picture the relationship that exists between several different quantities which are comparable but are not necessarily interdependent, while the latter is used to picture the relationship that exists between two or more variables whose values are so related that they are dependent on each other. Of the statistical graph there are, according to Karsten, four distinct types which may be classified as abstract, geographical, frequency, and historical. The nature of the graph or chart is, of course, a function of the distribution of the data to be represented.[1] Among the more frequently used bases for classifying the functional graph there are (1) type of relation, e.g., linear and quadratic, (2) type of curve, e.g., straight line, circle, parabola, ellipse, hyperbola, sine, and tangent, (3) continuity, and (4) multiplicity of values.

From either point of view the graph is an effective means of presenting data, making comparisons, and depicting relations; it offers untold opportunities for free play of the imagination, the application of simple or ingenious constructive abilities, and the development of an enthusiastic interest in mathematical methods and a more intelligent understanding of fundamental procedures on the part of all those becoming proficient in its construction and interpretation. As the minimum contribution it should make to the program of attaining this proficiency, the secondary school should develop the following abilities:

1. To construct and interpret bar, broken-line, curved-line, and circle graphs in the presentation of statistical data

2. To make comparisons between various comparable statistical graphs

3. To recognize the characteristics of data to be represented by each of these four types of statistical graphs, as well as certain fundamental cautions that are to be observed in their construction and interpretation[2]

4. To construct and interpret a functional graph as referred to a reference frame of coordinates

5. To use the functional graph in solving algebraic equations and to understand the simpler geometric implications

6. To interpret the graph in the light of the functional dependence shown, including simple maximum and minimum values

Frequently the assumption is made that the complete understanding of graphs is implied and guaranteed by the ability to construct them, but

[1] Karl G. Karsten, "Charts and Graphs" (Englewood Cliffs, N.J.: Prentice-Hall, Inc., 1925), p. 675.

[2] For a good discussion of graphs with misleading characteristics see Darrell Huff, "How to Lie with Statistics" (New York: W. W. Norton & Company, Inc., 1954).

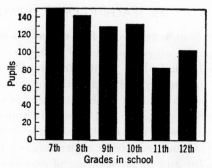

FIG. 13-3. Number of pupils enrolled in a city high school.

Savings	Rent	Food	Clothing	House-keeping	Miscellaneous	Health
10%	14%	28%	14%	10%	17%	7%

FIG. 13-4. Bar graph of a family budget (100 per cent).

A great deal   To some extent   Not much

FIG. 13-5. Do students in a certain school like the school?   (Each figure represents 100 students.)

Rural   Urban   Combined rural and urban

Business 64%   Recreational and social 36%

Business 51%   Recreational and social 49%

Business 55%   Recreational and social 45%

FIG. 13-6. Passenger automobile mileage used for business and social purposes in rural and urban areas.

FIG. 13-7. Men and women licensed to drive.

such an assumption is unwarranted. It is entirely possible for a student to plot a series of points whose coordinates satisfy a particular equation, draw a smooth line through these points, and call this the "graph of the equation" without having any clear realization of the meaning of what he has done. This is not to say that the construction of graphs is unimportant. On the contrary, not only is it extremely important in the development of a full understanding of the meaning of graphs but it also gives valuable review and practice in understanding the meaning of the coordinates of a point and in the solution of equations and the substitution of numbers leading to the evaluation of algebraic expressions. The construction of graphs and the study of their meaning should go hand in hand.

The customary way of teaching students how to construct functional graphs is to give them an equation such as $2x + 5y = 9$ and have them build a table of number pairs which satisfy the equation. They are then shown how to locate points by means of the number pairs. After they have located a few points, they are instructed to draw a smooth line through them. Too often the subject is carried no further. Frequently, teachers fail to give adequate instruction even with reference to such fundamental matters as the dependence of one of the variables upon the other, the arbitrary assignment of values to the independent variables, the naming of the axes, and the selection of suitable scales.

The construction of graphs can contribute little toward the development of adequate concepts of variation, continuity, and dependence if it is taught in this purely perfunctory fashion. These concepts are not likely to enter into the students' thinking unless they are specifically pointed out, not once but many times, by the teacher. Many and varied illustrations should be used. The students will find within their own common experiences many situations involving relationships among variable quantities that may be appropriately subjected to graphical treatment and which, because of their familiarity, will help materially in giving meaning to the graphs.

As an illustration, consider the relationship between the amount of gasoline that goes through a pump at a filling station and the total cost of the gasoline at 34 cents a gallon. This provides an excellent situation for emphasizing the *dependence* of one variable, the cost C, upon another variable, the number of gallons N, the price remaining constant. It can be expressed by the formula $C = 0.34N$. This formula can then be used as a basis for constructing the graph, Fig. 13-9. After the graph has been made, it should be carefully reexamined with attention directed to the way in which it answers such questions as: What happens to the cost as the number of gallons increases? As the cost increases, does the number of gallons increase in the same ratio? Does a decrease in either of the

variables bring about a corresponding decrease in the other?   How does
the price per gallon affect the direction of the graph?   If the price were
increased, how would the direction of the graph be changed?   Approximately how many gallons of gasoline could be bought for $1?   For $1.50?
For $2?   For $3?   Does the graph
show the cost of 8 gallons?   For
any point on the graph should the
ordinate C give a number exactly
0.34 times as great as the number
given by the abscissa N of that
point?   Would the same result be
given by the formula?   If a point
were to move along the graph,
would its ordinate or its abscissa
change the more rapidly?   How
many times as rapidly?   Explain
how the graph shows that the cost
depends on the amount of gasoline
bought.   Explain how the graph
shows that the number of gallons

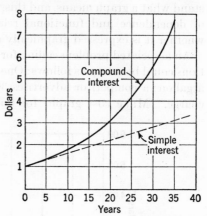

Fig. 13-8. $1 at 6 per cent compounded
annually.

of gasoline one can buy *depends* upon how much money he could spend
for gasoline.

By such questions as the foregoing ones the students can be made conscious of the graph as a device which shows in a striking way the fact and

N	0	2	4	6	8	10	12	14	16
C	0.00	0.68	1.36	2.04	2.72	3.40	4.08	4.76	5.44

Fig. 13-9. Cost of gasoline at 34 cents a gallon.

the precise nature of the dependence of either of the variables upon the
other, the meaning of dependent and independent variables, and the precise way in which a change in either variable inevitably brings about a

corresponding change in the other variable. The students become more clearly aware of the meaning of coordinates. They learn to associate the relationships shown by the graph with those indicated by the formula or equation upon which the graph is based. They learn, in short, to understand what a graph means, and this, in turn, enhances their comprehension of dependence and functional relationship as a permeating principle, whether it is expressed graphically or by means of formulas or equations.

An associated problem calling for the graphs of two simultaneous equations could be set up as follows: One filling station sells gasoline at 34 cents a gallon; a competitor advertises 30 cents a gallon plus 30 cents service charge. Make cost graphs for both stations on the same set of axes.

FIG. 13-10. Comparison of the cost of gasoline at two prices.

This problem involves setting up a second formula, $C = 0.30N + 0.30$, and the construction of another graph along with the one already made and discussed. Questions similar to those heretofore indicated should now be discussed with reference to the new graph, Fig. 13-10.

In addition, such questions as the following should be discussed: With what amount of money could one purchase the same amount of gasoline at the second station as at the first? At which station could one get more gasoline for $1? For 50 cents? For $2? How much more gasoline could be purchased at one station for $4.00 than at the other station? At which station could one buy 10 gallons at the lower cost? At which station could one buy 2 gallons at the lower cost? How much could one save by buying 15 gallons at the station that offered the lower price on this amount? Show how to find this out from the graphs. Does the service charge made by the second station affect the direction of the graph? Does it affect its position? Explain. Does the price per gallon affect the direction of the graph?   Explain.   Would a change in the direction of the graph indicate a change in the price per gallon?   Explain.

Consideration of the direction of a graph leads naturally and easily to the concept of *slope*, which is also to be associated with the rates of change of the two variables and with the coefficient of the independent variable in the formula or equation.   Similarly, the point where the graph crosses the axis of the dependent variable should be associated with the constant term in the equation, and the effect which any change in this constant term has upon the position of the graph should be studied.   The students will be interested in noting that, when the equation is written (rewritten if necessary) in the form $y = mx + b$ (or $C = 0.30N + 0.30$), the b always indicates the point at which the graph crosses the axis of the dependent variable and that the m always indicates the slope.   Thus, by solving any linear equation of the form $ax + by = c$ for y ($b \neq 0$), the student has at his command a method for constructing the graph which is at once less tedious and more meaningful than the method described earlier in this section.

Attention should be called to the fact that the m and b, or the *slope* and the y *intercept*, are two conditions that determine the position of a straight line just as two points determine its position.   The method of determining the x intercept and y intercept from the equation of any line and the use of the two intercepts in plotting the graph of the line should then be emphasized.   All this discussion of the linear equation and its graph should lead to the summarizing generalization: To determine the position of a straight line in a plane, it is necessary to have two independent conditions.

Specific attention to these considerations not only adds interest and value to the study of graphs but, in an easy, natural, and understandable way, provides the beginnings of a sound technical foundation for a real understanding of later work in analytic geometry and calculus. Obviously, more time is required for this sort of treatment of function graphs than would be required for the mere construction of the graphs themselves.   One may feel sure, however, that the thorough discussion of a few instances along the lines which have been indicated will do more to give the students a sense of the functional relationships involved than will the mere rule-of-thumb construction of large numbers of graphs.

The Teaching of Directed Numbers.   The study of directed numbers is an integral part of the study of algebra.   It is also one of the most difficult topics to develop successfully, and teachers and writers are not altogether agreed upon the most satisfactory methods of teaching it.   There is general agreement, however, on the main outcomes which are desired. They may be clearly stated as follows:

1. The student should gain an understanding of the meaning of directed numbers.

2. He should be led to see that the operations with directed numbers are consistent with the operations of arithmetic and that they constitute a more generalized procedure in which the operations of arithmetic appear as special cases.

3. He should gain considerable facility in performing the fundamental operations with directed numbers.

The fact that students fail to attain adequate mastery of these objectives undoubtedly accounts for a great deal of the difficulty which they experience in the study of algebra.

The student's numerical experience prior to the introduction of the concept of negative numbers will have been confined entirely to dealings with the numbers of arithmetic, i.e., with numbers representing quantities actually greater than zero. Up to this time he has used *zero* in two capacities, either as a number or as a place holder in writing numbers such as 305 and 500. Now, however, it becomes necessary to give to zero a new significance. In addition to its use as a number and as a place holder, *zero* will now be regarded as an arbitrary starting point in the number scale from which one may count in either direction; numbers counted in one direction will be called *positive numbers,* and numbers counted in the opposite direction will be called *negative numbers.* Many illustrations of this new use should be given.

The number scale is probably the most satisfactory and helpful of all devices for making clear the nature of positive and negative numbers and for illustrating their characteristics of oppositeness, direction, and position. It should be used, however, in connection with other devices for illustrating the opposite character of positive and negative numbers and the arbitrary selection of the zero, or reference, point. Illustrations of assets and liabilities, north and south latitude, temperatures above and below zero, etc., are helpful in developing the fundamental concepts of oppositeness, direction, and position with reference to an *established* zero, but they present only a partial picture of the nature of positive and negative numbers. They fail to make clear that whether a number is to be regarded as positive, negative, or zero relative to some other number depends not only upon its own position in the scale but also upon the position of the number to which it is referred and that that number may or may not be the previously established zero. Thus we may speak at 3:00 P.M. of an event which happened, say, at 1:00 P.M. The position of the event in time, using 1 hour as a unit, would be indicated by -2 if reckoned from *now* (3:00 P.M.) but would be indicated by $+1$ if reckoned from noon, or by $+13$ if reckoned from the previous midnight, Fig. 13-11.

On referring this situation to the number scale, it is seen that the event's position in time is positive with reference to *any number* that lies to its left on the scale and negative with reference to *any number* that lies to its right on the scale. Thus the statement "all negative numbers are less than zero and all positive numbers are greater than zero" is true only when the preestablished zero is the number to which all other numbers are referred.

The difficulties incident to the mastery of the concept of directed numbers render the topic an unsuitable one with which to begin the study of algebra. In years past, numerous textbooks have introduced directed numbers at the very beginning of the course, but experience has shown that it is better to postpone the topic until the students have become thoroughly familiar with some of the other new and basic concepts, particularly those of letter symbols and formulas.

There is considerable difference of opinion among writers and teachers over the lengths to which teachers should go in the effort to rationalize the operations with directed numbers and explain them in terms of the

Fig. 13-11

familiar operations of arithmetic. It is undoubtedly desirable to have these operations explained in such a way that they will be manifestly consistent with established arithmetical operations. On the other hand, some of the attempts which have been made to rationalize operations with directed numbers more or less defeat their own purpose because, in the attempt to explain the new entirely in terms of the familiar, they so emphasize the illustrative objects that attention is drawn away from the new process rather than being focused upon it. In other words, the thing being illustrated tends to become obscured by the illustration. It must not be forgotten that, after all, we are here *defining* certain operations with a totally new kind of number whose characteristics themselves depend upon arbitrary definition. Therefore, since we are thus extending our number system, obviously the new cannot be explained entirely in terms of the old. Rather, the main concern must be to make clear that the operations with the new (directed) numbers are so defined that they are consistent with the old (arithmetical) operations.

It is in this connection that the students should have their attention drawn to the fact that, with these new numbers, it is no longer impossible to subtract one number from a smaller one. Make sure that they understand why it was impossible previously, while henceforth it will be possible. Also, here is the place for discussion of zero as the identity element for addition and of the significance of addition and subtraction as inverse operations. Make sure that there is clear understanding of what is meant by the statement that numbers $+n$ and $-n$ are inversely related. One is the additive inverse of the other just as surely as n and $1/n$ are inversely related through multiplication.

As soon as the student has acquired an understanding of the nature of negative numbers as contrasted with positive numbers, he should be taught how to perform the fundamental operations with signed numbers. The first of these operations to be undertaken is that of algebraic addition. Here the student is likely to experience some confusion in the beginning, owing to the fact that in arithmetic the sum of two or more

Fig. 13-12

numbers is always greater than either of the addends. Reference to the number scale is useful in clearing up perplexities on this point. It should be carefully reemphasized that addition is a process of "combining" or "taking together." By reference to the number scale it can be made clear why it is that, when a positive number and a negative number are combined, the result will be less than the positive number alone.

The analysis of the addition (combination) of positive and negative numbers is entirely analogous to that of the addition of two or more positive numbers. For example, in finding the sum $2 + 3 + 7$ we start

Fig. 13-13

at the zero point on the number scale (Fig. 13-12) and count two units to the right, since to the right is the direction in which we agree to count positive numbers. Then *from there* we count three more units to the right. Then *from there* we count seven more units to the right. The result of these operations leaves us at a point which is 12 units to the right of zero. Hence we say that the sum is $+12$. In a similar manner the sum $4 + (-7) + 8$ may be found. We start at the zero on the number scale and count 4 units to the right (Fig. 13-13). Then *from there* we count 7 units to the *left* (since this is the direction in which we agree to count negative numbers). Then *from there* we count 8 units again to the right. The result of these movements leaves us at a point 5 units to the right of the zero point on the number scale. Hence we say that $4 + (-7) + 8 = +5$.

Students will have little difficulty in seeing that the addition of negative units offsets or neutralizes a corresponding number of positive units, or vice versa, so that the sum of any series of signed numbers is determined by seeing whether the series contains more negative units than positive ones or more positive units than negative ones, the absolute (or numerical) value of the sum of the series being given by the excess of the one over the other. From these considerations the student may formulate his own rule or method for determining the absolute value and the sign of the algebraic sum.

Simple and easy as this may appear, it requires much carefully supervised practice to fix these ideas and procedures firmly in the minds of the students and to give the students assurance and facility in adding signed numbers. It must not be forgotten that, because this is a new and difficult extension of their mathematical experience, the students will require considerable time and experience to adjust themselves completely to it. It is particularly important that training in the addition of signed numbers not be slighted or unduly hurried, for the reason that the concepts and procedures involved therein form the basis for understanding the subsequent processes of subtraction, multiplication, and division of signed numbers.

In the subtraction of one signed number from another, students may be expected to experience initial difficulty because they may need to revise their idea of the meaning of subtraction. In arithmetic, unless they have been taught to use the additive method, they will have come to regard subtraction as taking one number away from another, and since arithmetic always deals with positive, or absolute, values, the result of subtraction as always less than the minuend. Now, however, it becomes necessary to analyze the process more carefully. The analysis should start with familiar arithmetical examples and then be extended to include both positive and negative numbers. For example, just what does it mean to subtract 5 from 8? One basic interpretation is to find what number is left when 5 units are taken away from an aggregate of 8 units. On the other hand, to speak about taking away "minus 5" units from an aggregate of units would have no meaning. Hence we must make a further and more general analysis of the meaning of subtraction. It is not difficult to point out to students that subtraction can be defined, in a more general way, as the process of finding what number must be added to 5 to give 8 and that, when we find this number, it will be precisely the number which is left when we take 5 away from 8. This definition has meaning when applied to either positive or negative numbers, since the student has already learned that they may be combined by addition. Similarly, the operation indicated by $12 - (-3)$ means that we must find the number which when added to -3 will give 12. Obviously, this definition of subtraction will involve no new difficulties for students who have learned to use the additive method of subtraction in arithmetic.

This may be further illustrated by use of the number scale. Thus, since we are to find what number must be added to -3 to give $+12$, we must start at -3 and count to $+12$. This necessitates moving over 15 units on the scale; since the direction of motion is to the right, the

FIG. 13-14

sign of the result is positive and the result is $+15$. In other words, $(-3) + (+15) = (+12)$, and this is merely another way of saying $12 - (-3) = (+15)$.

Again, take the example $5 - 8$. Here we must count from $+8$ to $+5$. That is, we pass over 3 units on the scale, but this time the direction of motion is to the left; hence the result is -3. In other words, we have the result

$$\text{Subtrahend} + \text{result of subtraction} = \text{minuend}$$
$$(+8) \quad + \quad\quad (-3) \quad\quad = \quad (+5)$$

which is another way of saying that $(+5) - (+8) = (-3)$.

FIG. 13-15

Another effective way of illustrating the subtraction, say, of -3 from $+8$ is as follows:

From	+8	+8	+8	+8	+8	+8	+8	+8	+8	+8	+8	etc.
Subtract	+5	+4	+3	+2	+1	0	−1	−2	−3	−4	−5	etc.
Difference	+3	+4	+5	+6	+7	+8	+9	+10	+11	+12	+13	etc.

Attention should be directed to the fact that, when positive numbers alone are involved and the subtrahends are diminished by unity in successive cases, the differences increase in corresponding fashion. For consistency in operation it is, therefore, essential that the same pattern be followed when negative numbers are used. It is observed that under these conditions, even when negative subtrahends are used, the necessary principle that the algebraic sum of the subtrahend and the difference must equal the minuend is satisfied. Stated in terms of the foregoing discussion of the number scale, it is seen that in every case the difference is obtained by counting from the subtrahend to the minuend, regardless of whether the subtrahend is positive, zero, or negative.

Numerous similar examples exhibiting various combinations of positive and negative numbers should be given, some being explained by the teacher and others being worked out by the students, until the students thoroughly understand the process. As soon as the process is thoroughly understood, the examples should be reviewed, or others given. The students should then have their attention specifically directed to the fact that every subtraction, when analyzed in this way, gives a result which is the same as it would be if the sign of the subtrahend were changed and the problem treated as a problem in addition instead of subtraction. When this point has been made clear, it may be formulated into the rule: To subtract one signed number from another, change the sign of the subtrahend and then treat the problem as an addition problem rather than as a subtraction problem. Henceforth the students should be expected to use this method of subtraction. Its advantages are manifest, because it reduces the process of subtraction to the already familiar process of addition. The rationalization of the method is not intended to be used after the method is understood but is solely for the purpose of showing that the method is consistent with the meaning of subtraction. In spite of the apparent simplicity of the method the students should be given much closely supervised practice in its use.

In the multiplication of directed numbers the law of signs is very simply stated, but its rationalization can be rather complicated. Some writers have gone so far as to recommend the omission of any effort at rationalization. They would have the teacher merely state the rule and leave the understanding to come through use. Such procedure does not satisfy the curiosity that develops in the minds of many students as to why the rules are what they are.

One of the most effective methods of rationalization is to explain multiplication as repeated addition if the multiplier is a positive number. Thus $(+2)(+3)$, to be read $(+2)$ *multiplied by* $(+3)$, means $(+2) + (+2) + (+2) = +6$, and $(-2)(+3)$ means $(-2) + (-2) + (-2) = -6$. Attention should be called to the fact that $(+2)(+3)$ may also be written $(+3)(+2)$, read $(+3)$ *times* $(+2)$, and still mean to add $(+2)$ three times. Similarly, $(-2)(+3)$ may be written $(+3)(-2)$ to indicate the sum of $(-2) + (-2) + (-2)$. Each of these processes can be demonstrated very simply on the number scale.

Since the sign of subtraction is $-$, $(+9) - (+2)$ means that $+2$ is subtracted from $+9$ one time. The result is $+7$, which is the same result as that obtained from adding -2 to $+9$, or $(+9) + (-2)$. In a similar way $0 - (+2)$ is the same as $0 + (-2)$. Since $+ (-2)$ means to add -2 one time and $(+3)(-2)$ means to add -2 three times, so $-(+2)$ means to subtract $+2$ one time and $(-3)(+2)$ means to subtract $+2$ three times. Just as $+(-2) = -2$ and $-(+3) = -3$, so $(-3)(+2) = -6$ and $(+3)(-2) = -6$.

After it has been established that $(+2)(+3) = +6$ and $(-3)(+2) = (+3)(-2) = -6$, attention should be called to the fact that in finding the product of two numbers, *the change of the sign of one of the factors changes the sign of the product.* Opportunity should be provided through practice to become familiar with this fundamental rule of multiplication. The question that should then be raised is what the effect would be if in either of the multiplication examples $(-3)(+2) = -6$ and $(+3)(-2) = -6$ the $-$ sign were changed to a $+$ sign. This provides the opportunity for observing that the familiar product $(+2)(+3) = +6$ is obtained if the rule is applied. After a few practice exercises of this type, the class is ready for this question: What will be the effect if, in either of the multiplication examples $(-3)(+2) = -6$ and $(+3)(-2) = -6$, the $+$ sign is changed to a $-$ sign? The application of the rule gives $(-3)(-2) = +6$. Practice exercises should then be provided for becoming familiar with this last case of multiplication with signed numbers.

As an alternative or supplementary method of rationalizing this process, the following plan has been found to be effective. Exhibit several sets of factors as shown here, using the same multiplicand in every case but with the multipliers diminishing by unity from left to right.

Multiplicand	+5	+5	+5	+5	+5	+5	+5	+5	+5	etc.
Multiplier	+5	+4	+3	+2	+1	0	−1	−2	−3	etc.
Product	+25	+20	+15	+10	+5	0	−5	−10	−15	etc.

By using first only the nonnegative multipliers, attention is given to the fact that, as the multipliers diminish, the products diminish proportionally. If this principle is extended, by analogy and with the control of consistency, to include the cases with negative multipliers, the negative products obtained will be accepted by most students as perfectly reasonable consequences. The fact that this does not constitute a rigorous proof is no indictment of its usefulness as a device for making the principle acceptable to the students. Similar arrangements can subsequently be used in the same way to give a feeling of reasonableness to the proposition that the product of two negative numbers is positive. Thus

Multiplicand	−5	−5	−5	−5	−5	−5	−5	−5	−5	etc.
Multiplier	+5	+4	+3	+2	+1	0	−1	−2	−3	etc.
Product	−25	−20	−15	−10	−5	0	+5	+10	+15	etc.

After suitable rationalization has been made, a few review exercises should then lead to the summarizing of the four cases into the two rules: (1) The product of two numbers which have like signs is positive.   (2) The product of two numbers which have unlike signs is negative.

Opportunity should then be given for practice in the application of the rules to the finding of the product of both arithmetical and literal numbers.   Emphasis should be given to the fact that the numerical value of the product can be obtained by disregarding the signs, and the proper sign can be given to the product through application of the rules.

Whatever pattern of rationalization might be used, the teacher should have it clearly in mind that no proof of the process has been given.   He should also make this fact clear to the students.   The actual situation is that the number system has been extended from the natural numbers, which we now identify with the positive integers, to include zero and the negative integers.   Ultimately, of course, fractions are also included in the extension.

What does it mean to add, subtract, multiply, and divide these new numbers?   The answer to this question is arrived at through definition. We must define each of the operations with the new numbers, and we must be controlled by the practical desirability of consistency of operation with the old, or natural, numbers.   Thus, for example, we define $(+4)(-2) = -8$ because we can interpret this to mean that we subtract 2 four times, which is consistent with the result we should get by subtracting 8.   Since the commutative law of multiplication must hold, it follows that, if $(+4)(-2) = -8$, then $(-2)(+4) = -8$.   The distributive law must also hold.   It states that for any three numbers a, b, and c it is true that $a(b + c) = ab + ac$.   For consistency this law must hold for positive and negative integers.   Furthermore, we know that for any positive number n there exists its unique additive inverse $-n$ such that $(+n) + (-n) = 0$.   Now consider the three numbers -2, $+4$, and -4.   By the distributive law

$$(-2)[(+4) + (-4)] = (-2)(+4) + (-2)(-4)$$

Since $(+4) + (-4) = 0$, it follows that

$$(-2)[(+4) + (-4)] = (-2)(0) = 0$$

By the law of substitution we now have that

$$0 = (-2)(+4) + (-2)(-4)$$

Since $(-2)(+4) = -8$, it follows that the only definition we can give to $(-2)(-4)$ is $+8$, since $+8$ is the additive inverse of -8, and we have

$$0 = (-8) + (+8)$$

Since the quotient obtained by dividing one number by another is a number whose product with the divisor must give the dividend, it must follow that the law of signs for division is the same as that for multiplication. That is, if the signs of the divisor and the dividend are alike, the quotient will be positive; if they are different, the quotient will be negative. This explanation of the law of signs for division is usually quite satisfactory if illustrated by numerical examples, and ordinarily there is no material value in more elaborate attempts to rationalize it.

EXERCISES

1. Make a formula for determining the score earned in a game of contract bridge by setting one's opponents n tricks if the opponents were not vulnerable but were doubled.

2. Make a formula for determining the score of a team in a football game, in terms of t (number of touchdowns), p (number of points on plays after touchdowns), k (number of points on kicks after touchdowns), f (number of field goals), and s (number of safeties).

3. Let a distance be expressed as x yards y feet z inches. (a) Make a formula that will give this distance in inches alone. (b) Make a formula that will give this distance in feet alone. (c) Make a formula that will give this distance in yards alone.

4. Evaluate the formula $s = \frac{1}{2}n(a + l)$ for each of these sets of values of a, n, and l.

a	7	2.6	$\frac{4}{5}$
n	12	5.0	10
l	40	7.8	$6\frac{4}{5}$

5. Given the formula $w = dF/s$, what is the effect on w in each of the following circumstances? (a) d is doubled and F and s remain unchanged. (b) Both d and F are doubled but s remains unchanged. (c) d, F, and s are all doubled. (d) d and F remain unchanged but s is doubled. (e) d is halved, s is doubled, and F is tripled.

6. Explain the results found in exercise 5 as you would explain them to a class, using numerical illustrations.

7. See if you can generalize the results of exercise 5 and your explanations of exercise 6 into general rules, and state those rules.

8. In the two formulas $P = xy$ and $Q = x + y$, compare the effects on P and Q (a) of doubling x but leaving y unchanged, (b) of doubling y but leaving x unchanged, (c) of doubling both x and y.

9. Generalize your results of exercise 8 and state the generalization as a rule of action.

10. For what particular reasons does the formula seem to be the most suitable avenue for introducing students to the study of algebra?

11. How would you make clear to a class the distinction between constants and variables? Between independent and dependent variables?

12. State and justify the things you would emphasize in teaching simple linear equations to ninth-grade students. Prepare a test designed to determine whether these objectives had been attained.

13. Simple linear equations are often presented and taught under various "type forms." What arguments can be advanced in support of this practice? What disadvantages could it have?

14. Select a variety of simple linear equations in one unknown and go through the solutions of these individually and in detail, showing how your plan provides an effective and simple but general method of attacking any of these variations of the simple linear equation.

15. Explain why the solving of an equation is fundamentally incomplete until the obtained values of the unknown have been checked in the original equation.

16. Explain how the checking of solutions of equations gives good training in precisely the same kinds of mathematical activities as those used in the evaluation of formulas. Be specific.

17. The same rules of operation are employed in solving formulas or literal equations as are used in solving ordinary simple equations in one unknown, yet students experience more difficulty in solving formulas than in solving ordinary simple equations. Why is this?

18. Make a list of literal equations that are appropriate for solution by ninth-grade algebra students and involve a variety of operations.

19. Why is it more difficult for students to check the solutions of literal equations than to check the solutions of equations having numerical answers?

20. In this chapter "formalism" in algebra is deplored but the *formalization* of algebraic procedures is held to be important. Review the discussion of these two concepts and make the contrast between the two clear.

21. If the drive shaft of a steel lathe turns through 20 revolutions a minute, a definite relation exists between the number of minutes and the total number of turns. (This simple situation can be utilized as a basis for learning and understanding a good many things about a relationship between two variables and about the formula and graph which exhibit the relationship.)   The following questions and instructions refer to the drive shaft.   Examine them critically, and decide what particular thing or things each could contribute toward helping students understand and interpret the relationship and the modes of representing it.

a. Make a formula giving the relation between the number of turns N and the time in minutes T.

b. By using this formula, make a table of corresponding values of T and N.

c. Draw, label, and scale a pair of perpendicular reference lines or axes.   Then plot a point for each pair of corresponding values in the above table.

d. Explain how you located these points.

e. Will they all lie on a straight line?   Explain why.

f. Draw the straight line through these points.

g. If you used other pairs of corresponding values obtained from this formula to plot points, would the latter points lie on the same straight line as the points of *c*?

h. If you should take some other point on the line and use it to get a pair of corresponding values of N and T, would these values satisfy the formula you set up originally?   Try one and see.

i. Would this be true for all points on the graph?   Test several.

j. Using the graph and taking $T = 3\frac{1}{2}$, find the corresponding value of N.   Explain in words what this means.

k. Using $N = 50$, find by using the graph the corresponding value of T.   Explain in words what this means.

l. Why are N and T called *variables*?

m. Which is the *independent* variable?   Why?   Why is the other called the *dependent* variable?

n. Of what use are the *axes* in making or interpreting a graph?

o. What do we mean when we speak of the *coordinates* of a point?   Explain and illustrate.

p. What is meant by the *abscissa* of a point? The *ordinate?* Explain and illustrate.

q. Must each axis be scaled uniformly?

r. Must both axes be scaled the same?

s. If the unit lengths on both axes were doubled, would the graph have the same direction as before? Explain why or why not.

t. If the unit lengths were changed on one axis but not on the other, would the direction of the graph be changed? Explain why or why not.

u. If the speed of the shaft were doubled after 2 minutes, would the graph change direction? Why or why not? Explain.

v. Why is it advisable to scale and label both axes clearly?

w. If one axis were scaled evenly and the other were scaled unevenly, would the graph of this relationship still be a straight line? Explain why or why not.

x. How far to the right could the graph extend? How far up?

y. A point sliding along the graph would take on changing values of T. Explain what changes in values of N would accompany these changing values of T.

22. The following directions and questions might be given in the study of graphs after negative numbers have been introduced. Consider them in the same ways you did those under exercise 21.

a. Make a graph of the equation $y = 3 - x$.

b. What values can x have? Explain.

c. Is there a value of x for every value of y? Is there more than one?

d. Is there a value of y for every value of x? Is there more than one?

e. Take the difference between the ordinates of two points on the graph and divide it by the difference of the abscissas of these two points. Do the same for two other points. Compare the results. Try this out with still other pairs of points and compare the ratios you obtain.

f. State in words a conclusion you can make from what you did in part (*e*).

g. Make a graph for the equation $y = 3 + \frac{1}{2}x$ on the axes you used for the graph in (*a*).

h. Repeat the things you did under (*e*) and (*f*) for this new graph.

i. Observe that both graphs cross the y axis at the same point. Comment.

j. Does any number in both equations explicitly give you one of the coordinates of this point?

k. From the results of (*h*), does any number in the equation $y = 3 + \frac{1}{2}x$ give the quotient you found? If so, tell clearly in words what you observe about this.

l. Write out several other questions or exercises designed to focus attention on useful or interesting aspects of straight-line graphs.

23. Criticize or support the assertion that the very essence of algebra lies in the generalization of its concepts and the formalization of its procedures.

24. The transposition of terms is a rule-of-thumb method widely used in lieu of either or both of two axioms of elementary algebra. Cite these axioms. Criticize or justify the teaching of transposition as such in ninth-grade algebra.

25. Discuss the proposition that in teaching the operations with directed numbers, there may be danger in overrationalization as well as in overmechanization.

26. Explain as you would to a class in ninth-grade algebra why it is reasonable to accept the principle that $(+a)(-b) = -ab$ and that $(-a)(-b) = ab$.

27. Which is the more important to the average student from the standpoint of later application, the ability to construct graphs or the ability to interpret graphs readily. Does the one imply the other? Discuss the pedagogical implications of your answers.

28. Try to find in current newspapers, periodicals, or books examples of both good

and poor graphs. Exhibit these and comment about their good points and their inadequacies.

29. Do you think drill is needed in learning algebra? Give arguments in support of your viewpoint.

30. Excellent discussions of teaching the solution of simple linear equations are given in the books by Ligda and by Hassler and Smith (see Bibliography). Review the main points in these discussions and report them to the class.

BIBLIOGRAPHY

Adkins, Jackson B.: Goals in Algebra, *Bulletin of the National Association of Secondary-School Principals*, **38** (1954), 10–13.

———: Goals in Algebra, *Mathematics Teacher*, **47** (1954), 368–370.

Barber, Harry C.: "Teaching Junior High School Mathematics" (Boston: Houghton Mifflin Company, 1924), pp. 75–89; 95–109.

Beatley, Ralph: Reason and Rule in Arithmetic and Algebra, *Mathematics Teacher*, **47** (1954), 234–244.

Beberman, Max, and Bruce E. Meserve: The Concept of a Literal Number Symbol, *Mathematics Teacher*, **48** (1955), 198–202.

——— and ———: An Exploratory Approach to Solving Equations, *Mathematics Teacher*, **49** (1956), 15–18.

——— and ———: Graphing in Elementary Algebra, *Mathematics Teacher*, **49** (1956), 260–266.

Bengston, Ray: The "Make 'em Run" Theory, *Mathematics Teacher*, **51** (1958), 10–11.

Blackhurst, J. Herbert: "Principles and Methods of Junior High School Mathematics" (New York: Appleton-Century-Crofts, Inc., 1928), pp. 30–43.

Breslich, E. R.: "Problems in Teaching Secondary-school Mathematics" (Chicago: University of Chicago Press, 1931), pp. 99–102, 107–181, 201–232.

———: "The Administration of Mathematics in Secondary Schools" (Chicago: University of Chicago Press, 1933), pp. 261–287.

Brickley, Raymond S.: Teaching Mathematics [observations by a "student teacher"], *School Science and Mathematics*, **47** (1947), 341–347.

Brown, Claude H.: "The Teaching of Secondary Mathematics" (New York: Harper & Brothers, 1953), pp. 180–204, 209–212.

Brumfiel, Charles: An Introduction to Negative Integers, *Mathematics Teacher*, **49** (1956), 531–534.

Bruns, Walter J.: The Introduction of Negative Numbers, *Mathematics Teacher*, **33** (1940), 262–269.

Carnahan, Walter H.: Note on the Rule of Signs, *School Science and Mathematics*, **49** (1949), 720–722.

Christofferson, H. C.: Teaching Directed Numbers, *School Science and Mathematics*, **47** (1947), 451–459.

Commonwealth of Pennsylvania, Department of Public Instruction: "A Course of Study in Mathematics for Secondary Schools," *Bulletin* 360 (Harrisburg, Pa.: Department of Public Instruction, 1952), pp. 71, 72, 92–96.

Davis, David R.: "The Teaching of Mathematics" (Reading, Mass.: Addison-Wesley Publishing Company, 1951), pp. 162–170, 193–212.

Duke, Mary White: How I Teach Algebra, *Mathematics Teacher*, **47** (1954), 131–134.

Eagle, Edwin: Toward Better Graphs, *Mathematics Teacher*, **35** (1942), 127–131.

Entwhistle, Alice: Subtracting Signed Numbers, *Mathematics Teacher*, **48** (1955), 175–176.

Everett, John P.: "The Fundamental Skills of Algebra," *Contributions to Education* 324 (New York: Bureau of Publications, Teachers College, Columbia University, 1928).

Fulkerson, Elbert: Teaching Equations in First Year Algebra, *School Science and Mathematics*, **48** (1948), 705–711.

Georges, J. S.: Teaching Functional Thinking in Mathematics, *School Science and Mathematics*, **46** (1946), 733–748.

Grove, Ethel L., and others: Substitute Devices for Illustrating Equations, *School Science and Mathematics*, **51** (1951), 388–389.

————: Number Scale for Illustrating All Four Fundamental Processes with Directed Numbers, *School Science and Mathematics*, **51** (1951), 456–460.

Haner, Wendall W.: Teaching the Subtraction of Signed Numbers, *School Science and Mathematics*, **47** (1947), 656–658.

Hartung, Maurice L.: The Order of Operations in Elementary Mathematics, *School Science and Mathematics*, **46** (1946), 752–754.

————: Graphical Methods in Science and Mathematics Teaching, *School Science and Mathematics*, **50** (1950), 200–208.

Hassler, J. O., and R. R. Smith: "The Teaching of Secondary Mathematics" (New York: The Macmillan Company, 1930), pp. 196–296.

Henderson, Lawrence M.: An Alternative Technique for Teaching the Subtraction of Signed Numbers, *Mathematics Teacher*, **38** (1945), 331.

Ingraham, W. W.: Let's Explore It with Straight-edge and Scale, *Mathematics Teacher*, **40** (1947), 27–29.

Jerbert, A. R.: The Algebraic Number Scale, *School Science and Mathematics*, **45** (1945), 40–44.

————: Algebra and Arithmetic, *School Science and Mathematics*, **45** (1945), 528–540.

Joint Commission of the Mathematical Association of America and the National Council of Teachers of Mathematics: "The Place of Mathematics in Secondary Education," *Fifteenth Yearbook* (Washington, D.C.: National Council of Teachers of Mathematics, 1940), pp. 103–106.

Keppers, George L.: Is Algebra a "Tool Subject"? *School Science and Mathematics*, **55** (1955), 296–300.

Kinney, Lucien B., and C. Richard Purdy: "Teaching Mathematics in the Secondary School" (New York: Rinehart & Company, Inc., 1952), pp. 59–99.

Kinsella, John A.: A "Meaning" Theory for Algebra, *School Science and Mathematics*, **47** (1947), 775–780.

———— and Walter H. Carnahan: Putting Meaning into Algebraic Concepts and Relationships, *School Science and Mathematics*, **49** (1949), 19–26.

Klimczak, W. J.: The Solution of Linear Equations and Inequalities, *Mathematics Teacher*, **48** (1955), 460–463.

Koenen, William: Illustrating Simple Transformations, *Mathematics Teacher*, **49** (1956), 467–468.

Lazar, Nathan: A Technique for Giving Meaning to Elementary Mathematics Operations, *Mathematics Teacher*, **42** (1949), 67–68.

Lewis, Eunice: The Pupil Discovers Algebra, *Mathematics Teacher*, **47** (1954), 81–85.

Ligda, Paul: "The Teaching of Elementary Algebra" (Boston: Houghton Mifflin Company, 1925), pp. 1–62.

Lueck, William R.: An Experiment in Writing Algebraic Equations, *Journal of Educational Research*, **42** (1948), 132–137.

Minnick, J. H.: "Teaching Mathematics in the Secondary Schools" (Englewood Cliffs, N.J.: Prentice-Hall, Inc., 1939), pp. 115–151.

National Council of Teachers of Mathematics: "The Teaching of Algebra," *Seventh Yearbook* (Washington, D.C.: National Council of Teachers of Mathematics, 1932).

Olander, Clarence E.: The Use of a Readiness Test in Teaching a Unit on Signed Numbers, *School Science and Mathematics*, **57** (1957), 131–138.

O'Leary, V. C.: Geometric Illustrations in Teaching Algebra, *School Science and Mathematics*, **47** (1947), 802–804.

Peak, Philip: "Efficiency in First-year Algebra," doctoral dissertation, (Bloomington, Ind.: Indiana University, 1954).

Reeve, William D.: "Mathematics for the Secondary School" (New York: Henry Holt and Company, Inc., 1954), pp. 245–275.

Robert, Brother B.: Algebra Teachers—"Take It Easy," *Mathematics Teacher*, **40** (1947), 393–394.

Romig, W. E.: A Technique for Teaching Subtraction of Signed Numbers, *Mathematics Teacher*, **38** (1945), 36.

Rosskopf, Myron F.: What Algebra for Seventh and Eighth Grades? *Mathematics Teacher*, **51** (1958), 377–379.

Running, Theodore R.: Graphical Solution of Equations, *Mathematics Teacher*, **40** (1947), 147–150.

Schaaf, Oscar: Student Discovery of Algebraic Principles as a Means of Developing Ability to Generalize, *Mathematics Teacher*, **48** (1955), 324–327.

Schaaf, William L.: The Use of Simple Algebra in Business Arithmetic, *Mathematics Teacher*, **44** (1951), 22–25.

Schultze, Arthur: "The Teaching of Mathematics in the Secondary Schools" (New York: The Macmillan Company, 1927), pp. 288–312, 332–344.

Shaw, Geraldine Sax: Prediction of Success in Elementary Algebra, *Mathematics Teacher*, **49** (1956), 173–178.

Sites, V.: Logical Approach to $(-a)(-b)$, *Mathematics Teacher*, **40** (1947), 384.

Smith, Brother Albertus: An Attempt to Eliminate Common Errors in Elementary Algebra, *Mathematics Teacher*, **39** (1946), 385–390.

Smith, D. E., and W. D. Reeve: "The Teaching of Junior High School Mathematics" (Boston: Ginn & Company, 1927), pp. 169–216.

Sobel, Max: Concept Learning in Algebra, *Mathematics Teacher*, **49** (1956), 425–430.

Tully, Jean: Teaching Algebra as Generalized Arithmetic, *California Mathematics Council Bulletin*, **7** (1949), 10–12.

UICSM Project Staff: Arithmetic with Frames, *Arithmetic Teacher*, **4** (1957), 119–124.

Uth, Carl: Teaching Aid for Developing $(a + b)(a - b)$, *Mathematics Teacher*, **48** (1955), 247–249.

Van Engen, H.: Logical Approaches to $(-a)(-b) = ab$ and $x^0 = 1$, *Mathematics Teacher*, **40** (1947), 182–185.

Van Waynen, M.: Another Approach to $(-a)(-b)$, *Mathematics Teacher*, **42** (1949), 90.

Van Zyl, Abraham J.: The Formula: The Core of Algebra, *Mathematics Teacher*, **37** (1944), 368–371.

Volpel, Marvin C.: Solving Percentage Problems by the Equation Method, *Mathematics Teacher*, **47** (1954), 425–427.

Washton, Nathan S., and Ethel B. Friedman: A Teaching Unit on Graphs, *Mathematics Teacher*, **48** (1955), 77–81.

Wilt, May L.: A Technique for Solving Simple "Set-up" Equations in One Unknown, *Mathematics Teacher*, **39** (1946), 35–38.

Young, J. W. A.: "The Teaching of Mathematics" (New York: Longmans, Green & Co., Inc., 1927), pp. 292–320.

14

THE TEACHING OF FURTHER TOPICS
IN ELEMENTARY ALGEBRA

Teaching the Solution of Pairs of Simultaneous Linear Equations. The systems of simultaneous linear equations of concern in elementary algebra are limited to only two equations in two unknowns. The three commonly used methods for solving such systems are (1) the graphical method, (2) the method of elimination by substitution, and (3) the method of elimination by addition or subtraction.

The graphical method has many advantages, but it should be based on a clear understanding of what it is that the graph of a relation represents. For example, consider the two relations $y > x$ and $y = -x + 8$ under the following specifications:

Example 1. The domain and range of both relations are to be the same, namely, the set of all positive integers <8. Under these restrictions the complete graph of $y > x$ is the set of points represented by dots in Fig. 14-1. The complete graph of $y = -x + 8$ is the set of points represented by the crosses in the figure. The solution set of the two relations considered simultaneously is, therefore, the set of points represented by the crossed-over dots in the figure: namely, the points $\{(1,7), (2,6), (3,5)\}$.

$$\begin{array}{c} y > x \\ y = -x + 8 \end{array} \Bigg\} \quad \begin{array}{c} 0 < x < 8 \\ 0 < y < 8 \end{array}$$

Fig. 14-1

Example 2. The domain and range of both relations are to be the same, namely, the set of all real numbers. Under these restrictions the incomplete graph of $y > x$ is the set of points represented by the shaded portion of Fig. 14-2. The incomplete graph of $y = -x + 8$ is represented by the straight line. The solution set of the two relations considered simultaneously is the portion of the straight line which crosses the shaded area of the figure.

Furthermore, in consideration of the linear function

$$y = mx + b \qquad m \neq 0$$

it is important that there be a clear understanding of the part the parameters m and b play in determining the graph of the line.   Since $(0,b)$ is a point on the line, it is evident that b is the y intercept of the line.   In Fig. 14-3 the various lines all have the same slope ($m = 2$) but different y intercepts (b varies).   The function represented in this graph is $y = 2x + b$.   On the other hand, in Fig. 14-4 the various lines all have

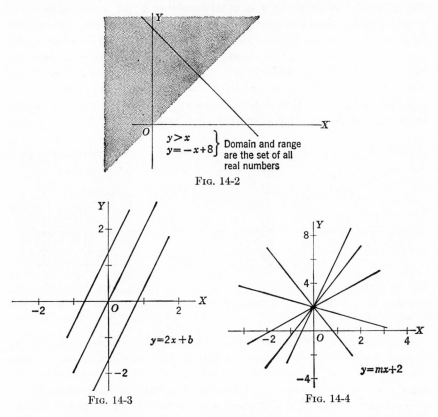

$$\left. \begin{array}{l} y > x \\ y = -x + 8 \end{array} \right\} \text{Domain and range are the set of all real numbers}$$

Fig. 14-2

$y = 2x + b$

Fig. 14-3

$y = mx + 2$

Fig. 14-4

the same y intercept ($b = 2$) but different slopes (m varies).   The function represented in this graph is $y = mx + 2$.[1]

In the above discussion the restriction was placed that m be nonzero. When $m = 0$, the expression $y = mx + b$ reduces to $y = b$, the graph of which consists of the x axis ($y = 0$) and all the lines of the plane parallel to the x axis.   The condition $m \neq 0$ guarantees that the formula

[1] For a more complete discussion of the graphs of such relations see the Report of the Commission on Mathematics, "Appendices" (New York: College Entrance Examination Board, 1959), pp. 8–27, 36–57.   The chapters on the pages referenced are respectively Sets, Relations and Functions and The Linear Function and the Quadratic Function.

which produces the set of ordered pairs of the linear function will contain the symbol representing the first element. Under this restriction the graph of $y = b$ is thus not a portion of the graph of the linear function $y = mx + b$.

The principal advantages of the graphical method lie in the fact that it is interesting and illustrates in a very convincing manner the reason why a solution of such a system must consist of a pair (or set of pairs) of numbers rather than a single number. It affords a very effective method for demonstrating the full significance of the relationships that exist when the equations are consistent, inconsistent, indeterminate, or dependent, Fig. 14-5. This method also proves valuable in developing a clear understanding of just what is meant by *simultaneous linear equations*. Auxiliary advantages are that it gives an excellent review of graphs of linear functions and the associated concepts and procedures.

FIG. 14-5. The graphical method demonstrates the relationships that exist when equations are consistent (a), inconsistent (b), indeterminate (c), independent (a and b), and dependent (c).

Its main disadvantages are two. In the first place it is possible, in general, to get only approximate solutions instead of exact ones. This often introduces apparent discrepancies in checking the solutions and gives the student a consequent feeling of dissatisfaction. Secondly, it is a comparatively slow, tedious, and inefficient method for solving simple linear equations. For this reason, after students have learned the more exact and efficient algebraic methods, they are likely to prefer them to the graphical method.

Aside from any difficulties which the students may experience in the construction of the graphs themselves, the only point of potential difficulty involved in the graphical method is the interpretation of the solution. To assist students in this, the teacher should remind them that any point on any graph has two coordinates (numbers) associated with it, and that these numbers satisfy the equation which was used in making the graph. Therefore, if a point *lies on two graphs at the same time* (say graph A and graph B), its coordinates must satisfy the equation used in making graph A and, at the same time, the equation used in making graph B. Consequently, the coordinates of this point must form a solution of the system. This basic concept is the real crux of this method of solving simultaneous equations, and unless it is strongly emphasized by the teacher, the students may miss the main point of the whole procedure.

If the students have developed a thorough understanding of the meaning of substitution and how to solve and evaluate formulas and literal equations, there is nothing new for them to learn in solving simultaneous equations by the method of substitution. Consider, for example, the system

$$3x - y = -13$$
$$2x + 3y = 17$$

The first step is to solve one of the equations for one of the unknowns in terms of the other. This is merely the solution of a literal equation or formula. The student should select the one which can be solved more easily. In this case he would probably solve the first equation for y and get the result $y = 3x + 13$.

He will now substitute this result for y in the second equation and get a resulting equation in which no term in y appears:[1]

$$2x + 3(\quad y \quad) = 17$$
$$2x + 3(3x + 13) = 17$$

Next he will perform the indicated operations and collect terms:

$$2x + 9x + 39 = 17$$
$$11x \qquad + 39 = 17$$

Then he will solve this equation for x:

$$11x \qquad + 39 = 17$$
$$11x \qquad = 17 - 39 = -22$$
$$x \qquad = \frac{-22}{11} = -2$$

Finally he must substitute this value of x back in the first equation (the one which he originally solved for y) to get the numerical value of y:

$$y = 3(\quad x \quad) + 13$$
$$y = 3(-2) + 13 = -6 + 13 = +7$$

The solution of the system can now be completed by substituting the values obtained in both of the original equations. The first equation is as follows:

[1] Note the use of parentheses.

$$3(\ x\ ) - (y) \overset{?}{=} -13$$
$$3(-2) - (7) \overset{?}{=} -13$$
$$-6\ -\ 7\ =\ -13$$

This checks.   The second equation will be checked in the same manner.

The detailed steps in the foregoing illustration have been given for the purpose of showing how the principles and procedures discussed in Chap. 13 are now applied by the student to this new situation involving a system of simultaneous equations.   In particular it is to be noted that the student does not need to learn or to use in this process anything that is new to him.   He has merely to learn to use familiar mathematical tools in a new setting.   In the process of doing so he receives a most valuable review and a fuller comprehension of the nature of these mathematical tools and, at the same time, gains added proficiency and facility in their use.[1]

It is well to make sure that the students understand the thinking that is back of the process of substitution.   In the above discussion

$$y = 3x + 13$$

gives a formula for finding a value of y which will satisfy the first of the two equations.   This is true for any value which might be used for x, a fact which can be verified by experimenting with a few arbitrarily selected values of x and the corresponding values of y determined by the formula.   When $3x + 13$ is used to replace the y in the second equation, the condition is imposed that whatever value of y satisfies the first equation must also satisfy the second equation.   Imposing this condition on y removes the arbitrariness from x, a fact which should be made clear to the student.   There is now only one value of x which can be chosen, and it is determined by the equation $2x + 3(3x + 13) = 17$ to be $x = -2$.   The formula $y = 3x + 13$ associates one and only one value of y ($y = 7$) with this value of x.   Thus the solution set of the system of equations is $(-2,7)$, which can and should be verified by checking in the two equations.   Actually, the check in the first equation is no more than a check of the computation of the value of y from the determined value of x.   This is due to the fact that $y = 3x + 13$ is but an equivalent form of the original equation $3x - y = -13$.   The real check is the substitution in the second equation.   The process of solving the two equations establishes that $x = -2$ and $y = 7$ is a necessary condition that the two equations be satisfied.   The check establishes it as a sufficient condition.

---

[1] In connection with the detailed steps in the foregoing illustration, the reader may well refer to the sections of the Chap. 13 dealing with symbols and formulas and the solution of equations.

The method of elimination by addition and subtraction is very effective if the method of substitution leads to the substitution of fractions, a complicated combination of symbols, or a maze of parentheses or signs of aggregation.   It is a very simple process and one that is rather easily extended later in the work of the senior high school or junior college to systems of equations in any number of unknowns.   However, the simplicity of the technique should not be allowed to camouflage the basic structure of the process.   Consider the same two equations

$$3x - y = -13$$
$$2x + 3y = 17$$

The process of elimination by addition or subtraction would lead to the multiplication of the first equation by 3 and then to the addition of the transformed equation to the second equation.   This process would produce $11x = -22$, which would then be solved to obtain $x = -2$, and the value would be used in either of the original equations to produce $y = 7$.   Actually, when analyzed in its finality, the values $x = -2$, and $y = 7$ are produced as the solution set of the two equations

$$11x = -22 \qquad\qquad 11x = -22$$
$$3x - y = -13 \quad\text{or}\quad 2x + 3y = 17$$

By what right can it be said that the solution set of either of these two systems of equations is the solution set of the original system?   Of course, the simple answer to this question is that $(-2,7)$ can be verified as the solution set of the original equations merely by substituting these values in the two equations and seeing that the equations are satisfied. Such a check would justify the process used to find a solution set of any system of equations.   A more fundamental question is: How can one be assured that the technique used will produce the solution set of a system of linear equations, if such a set exists?   Consider the original system of equations written in the equivalent form

$$3x - y + 13 = 0$$
$$2x + 3y - 17 = 0$$

The process produced the following identity

$$3(3x - y + 13) + (2x + 3y - 17) \equiv 11x + 22$$

For all values of x the expression on the left is equal to the one on the right.   Hence any value of x which will simultaneously satisfy any two of the equations $3x - y + 13 = 0, 2x + 3y - 17 = 0$, and $11x + 22 = 0$ will also satisfy the third one.   Always the process of solving any equation or system of equations establishes the solution set as a necessary condition that the equations be satisfied. The check alone establishes that it is a sufficient condition. Why is this? For this reason one should never be satisfied with a determined solution set of a given equation or system of equations until it has been carefully checked.

Operations with Fractions. The ordinary operations with fractions which find a legitimate place in elementary algebra include reduction and "stepping up," multiplication and division, and addition and subtraction. The student's experience with arithmetical fractions will serve as a point of departure for beginning the work with algebraic fractions. It would be a mistake, however, to assume that familiarity with arithmetical fractions will eliminate all difficulty in working with algebraic fractions. Algebra lacks the familiar, concrete, intuitive basis which characterizes a good deal of arithmetic, and the student must learn eventually to work almost entirely upon the basis of established rules or patterns of procedure rather than by intuitive methods. These patterns, of course, are merely generalizations of the methods used in arithmetic and so may be developed and explained largely by means of analogy with arithmetical situations. The chief difference to be emphasized is that in algebra the student will find it necessary to confine his attention more and more specifically to the processes by which he works and pay relatively less attention to the particular numerical values of the quantities involved.

Since the use of fractions in elementary algebra is confined largely to the solution of simple formulas and certain types of verbal problems and to the simplification of algebraic expressions, it is neither necessary nor desirable to include highly complicated fractional expressions in the work of the ninth grade.

Many textbooks, both in arithmetic and algebra, introduce the addition and subtraction of fractions before taking up the multiplication and division of fractions. There are those who contend that this plan is psychologically unsound. They argue that multiplication and division are the less difficult of the operations with fractions and hence should be studied first. In accordance with this point of view the plan of organization followed in some of the more recent texts is to consider first the reduction and stepping up of fractions, then the multiplication and division of fractions, and finally the addition and subtraction of fractions.

The student should acquire through his study of fractions the following abilities and understandings:

Understanding of the different aspects of the meaning of a fraction

Understanding of what it means to reduce a fraction to lower terms or to change a fraction to higher terms

Understanding of the nature of the terms of a fraction and how the increase or decrease of the numerator or denominator affects the value of the fraction

Ability and skill in multiplying fractions together or in dividing one fraction by another

Ability and skill in adding or subtracting fractions

In arithmetic various meanings are attached to the word "fraction." Thus

As a *number* a fraction may express:
One or more of the equal parts of a unit
One of the equal parts of a single quantity consisting of one or more units
The quotient of one number divided by another number
As a *relation* a fraction may express:
The ratio which one number bears to another number

The idea which seems to persist most vividly in the minds of most students is that a fraction, when used as a number, is a part or a number of parts of some quantity. This is doubtless because many arithmetical fractions, and even operations with such fractions, can be most easily and concretely illustrated by reference to tangible objects, visible geometric or graphic diagrams, and denominate numbers. Thus the student acquires a sort of intuitive feeling for such a fraction as a part of something. In algebra, however, the precise numerical relationships are not present in the sense that they are in arithmetic; hence it becomes necessary to construct a less intuitive but more definitive meaning. The student must now learn to think consistently of a fraction, if not expressing a ratio, as merely an indicated quotient or an indicated division of one quantity (the numerator) by another quantity (the denominator). Whether the indicated division can actually be carried out exactly or not is immaterial.

If students are to learn to attach this meaning to a fraction, it will be necessary for the teacher to give specific attention to it and focus the attention of the students upon it repeatedly. It may be illustrated and made to appear reasonable by reference to concrete, numerical, geometric, or physical quantities, but it must not stop with such illustrations. There must also be given illustrations in which the precise numerical relations which provide the intuitive basis for the earlier meaning of a fraction are replaced in part or in their entirety by purely symbolic quantities, and students must be specifically trained to regard such expressions as a/b or $(x-3)/2y$ as being fractions just as truly as $\frac{3}{4}$ or $\frac{8}{15}$. The meaning itself must be made to have the status of a definition, so that it may persist even when no intuitive basis exists.

The *reduction of fractions*, as well as the inverse operation of changing fractions to higher terms, involves the general problem of changing the form of a fraction without changing its value. Such changes can always be effected by the operation of a single simple principle, viz., that *the value of a fraction remains unchanged if its numerator and denominator are multiplied or divided by the same quantity.*[1]   Children generally are able to apply this principle quite successfully when working with arithmetical fractions, but they probably do so intuitively and without much conscious recognition of the principle itself.   Evidence of this is found in the fact that, when they come to work with algebraic fractions, they often fail to apply the principle and consequently get such erroneous results as

$$\frac{x+4}{4} = x \qquad \text{or} \qquad \frac{2n+a}{-3n+a} = \frac{2}{-3}$$

Results of this sort are almost certainly due to the failure of the students to realize that this procedure does not constitute division of numerator and denominator by a common factor.   The undefined use of the word "cancellation" probably contributes to this looseness of thinking in many cases.[2]

Students must be kept aware of the fact that the addition or subtraction of like quantities (except zero) to or from the numerator and denominator of a fraction will certainly change not only the form but the value of the fraction, whereas in the reduction of fractions the value of the fraction must be kept intact.   They must also be kept aware that in dividing numerator and denominator by a common factor, the factor must be a divisor of the *whole* numerator and of the *whole* denominator. Continued consciousness of this elementary principle will prevent the occurrence of such errors as this:

$$\frac{3a+5}{a+2} = \frac{3+5}{2} = \frac{8}{2} = 4$$

Most of the mistakes which occur in the reduction of fractions could be avoided by the consistent practice of expressing (rewriting if necessary) the numerator and denominator of the fraction in factored form and enclosing each separate factor, no matter how simple, in its own parentheses.   If this is done, the division, or cancellation, of common factors will be effected with real understanding of what is being done.   Similarly, in changing fractions to higher terms, it is good practice to have the students immediately enclose the numerator and denominator of the original fraction in parentheses at the outset and then write the common multiplier also in parentheses as a multiplier of the numerator and as a multiplier of the denominator.   The consistent use of parentheses in this way serves to keep all factors intact and to prevent students from treating a factor of a part as a factor of the whole.

[1] Division by zero is, of course, excepted, and here multiplication by zero must also be excepted since it would render the value of the fraction indeterminate.

[2] See page 297 for similar discussion with respect to arithmetic.

The *multiplication of fractions* generally causes little difficulty. The principle governing this process is exceedingly simple: the product of two or more fractions is a fraction whose numerator is the product of the numerators of the original fractions and whose denominator is similarly the product of the denominators. It should be illustrated freely by examples drawn from arithmetic, and, by analogy, the application to algebraic expressions can be made without difficulty.

The fractional product can often be reduced to lower terms. Hence it is desirable to have it rewritten as a single fraction, the numerators and denominators of the component fractions being written in factored form with every factor enclosed in its own parentheses. It should be stressed that the numerator of every component fraction must be regarded as a factor of the numerator of the product, and similarly for the denominators. The students will be more likely to keep this consciously in mind if they make a habitual practice of enclosing the individual numerators and denominators of the component fractions in parentheses at the outset, before doing anything else. Thus

$$\frac{4 - x^2}{2 + x} \cdot \frac{x}{2 - x}$$

would be rewritten as

$$\frac{(4 - x^2)}{(2 + x)} \cdot \frac{(x)}{(2 - x)} = \frac{(2 - x)(2 + x)(x)}{(2 + x)(2 - x)} = x$$

In the *division of one fraction by another* it is necessary only to see that the students understand that division is always exactly equivalent to multiplication by the reciprocal of the divisor. They will probably be more or less familiar with this principle from their arithmetic, especially as regards division by a fraction. However, the principle should be clearly explained and numerous illustrations should be given. The student should understand that dividing by a fraction means finding the number which, when multiplied by the divisor, gives the dividend. This is always the test of division. For example, if 7 is divided by $\frac{3}{5}$, the result must be such that the product of itself and $\frac{3}{5}$ will give 7 [or 7(1)]. We must therefore find a number q such that $q(\frac{3}{5}) = 7$. Evidently, q must equal $7(\frac{5}{3})$, since $7(\frac{5}{3})(\frac{3}{5})$ equals 7(1), or 7. Thus 7 divided by $\frac{3}{5}$ equals 7 times $\frac{5}{3}$. Similarly, in the example $a \div (x/y)$, we have $a \div (x/y) = q$. But $q \cdot (x/y) = a$, whence $q = a \cdot (y/x)$. Thus $a \div (x/y) = a \cdot (y/x)$.

As a rule the main difficulties to be anticipated are those incident to the multiplication and simplification of fractions, and these have been discussed in the foregoing paragraphs.

Sometimes students have difficulty in multiplying or dividing fractions by whole numbers. Some writers prefer to treat this as a special case to be covered by the rule: In multiplying or dividing a fraction by a whole number only the numerator of the fraction is to be multiplied or divided by the whole number. Others feel that it is better to have the students regard the whole number as the numerator of a fraction whose denominator is 1, thus bringing the problem under the general procedures for multiplying and dividing fractions. Either of these methods will probably give satisfactory results. The second, however, appears to have certain advantages over the first, in that it gives more unity and generality to the whole matter of multiplying and dividing fractions and obviates the necessity for the special rule. It also has the advantage of applying to the division of a whole number by a fraction, which is not precisely covered by the special rule.

In introducing students to the *addition of fractions* care must be taken to prevent the occurrence of such errors as this:

$$\frac{5x}{a} + \frac{2}{n} = \frac{5x + 2}{a + n}$$

Mistakes of this kind reveal a lack of understanding of the real nature of a fraction and of the real meaning of the numerator (numberer) and the denominator (namer). The students should be kept conscious of the principle that only things of the same kind can be combined by addition or subtraction and that fractions are considered to be of the same kind only if they have like denominators. If students can really get the idea that the denominator of a fraction merely indicates what kind of things are being considered and that the numerator merely indicates how many of these are taken, they will have gone far toward heading off mistakes of the kind described above. Appropriate illustrations of arithmetical fractions are helpful in emphasizing this point because, if sufficiently simple illustrations are taken, the students can immediately check the correctness of their results. For example, they know that $\frac{3}{4} + \frac{1}{4} = 1$, and they can at once see the discrepancy of saying that

$$\frac{3}{4} + \frac{1}{4} = \frac{3 + 1}{4 + 4} = \frac{4}{8} = \frac{1}{2}$$

because $\frac{1}{2}$ is obviously not equal to 1, and they know that the correct answer must be 1. They should be trained to the habit of using some such simple numerical illustration to check up any doubtful operation to see whether or not it is legitimate and correct, and they should learn also to go back to the original meanings of the numerator and denominator to clarify their thinking. To this end it is often helpful to rewrite fractional expressions with the denominators written out in words. Thus $\frac{2}{7} + \frac{3}{7}$ can be written as 2 sevenths + 3 sevenths, in which case the expression becomes similar to the expression for the sum of any like denominate quantities such as 2 dollars and 3 dollars. In other words, this process helps to make clear the idea that fractions are in a sense the same as denominate numbers, the denominator merely telling what kind of thing is being considered and the numerator telling how many are being considered.

The tendency to add numerators and to add denominators is probably a carry-over from the operation of multiplying fractions. It is important that the students get the distinction between these processes clearly in mind so that they will not confuse them.

The first step in teaching students to add fractions is to have them recall the basic principle of addition: Addition can be used only for combining groups of like things. Thus, fractions cannot be added until they have been changed to fractions with a common denominator, for then, and then only, are they groups of like things. The denominator of the sum is the common denominator of the addends, and the numerator is the algebraic sum of their numerators. It is not sufficient, however, merely to tell students this. The teacher should give numerous carefully selected illustrations, working them out at the chalkboard and discussing them with the class while he works. The process is not difficult to understand or perform, but it needs to be explained very carefully and deliberately and to be fixed very carefully in the minds of the students.

Such careful and adequate explanation can give the students an understanding of the addition of fractions, but the fixation of the ideas and the procedure requires that the students shall have a substantial amount of practice in doing the thing themselves. The practice exercises should be selected with great care. They should be very easy at first and become more difficult by gradual stages. The increasing complexity will essentially be in the numerators, since in this first stage only fractions having like denominators will be used. There should be no great difficulty if care is taken, because the only real algebraic work will be the algebraic addition of the numerators. This will essentially be nothing but a review of the algebraic addition of polynomials, with which the students should be expected to have considerable familiarity. The exercises should include fractions whose numerators are of varied types including simple integers and literal monomials, binomials, and trinomials, some of the binomial and trinomial numerators being given in factored form requiring expansion in order to effect the simplification of the resultant sum.

Too much emphasis cannot be laid upon the principle that the transition to the more complicated forms should be made *gradually*. Teachers often assume that little attention need be given to the addition of fractions with like denominators. No greater mistake could be made; the assumption is entirely unwarranted. The fact is that, when the students *really understand* the addition of fractions with like denominators, they are likely to have little difficulty in mastering the addition of fractions with unlike denominators.

When fractions with unlike denominators are to be added algebraically, the students should be firmly impressed with the guiding principle: *if the denominators are not alike, make them alike.* That is, the students should become clearly aware that the first thing to do is to change the given fractions into new fractions whose values are identical with those of the original fractions but whose forms are changed in such a way that they will all have the same denominator. After this has been done, the problem of the algebraic addition of these fractions becomes the already familiar one which has been described above.

While the statement of this principle sounds simple and clear, there are often intermediate details which will tend to obscure the essential simplicity of the matter. Consider, for example, the following case: $3a/(5n + 2) + 5a/(2n - 3)$. Here it is necessary to determine first what the common denominator will be. Since the denominators have no common factor, the common denominator will have to be taken as the product of all (in this case both) of the separate denominators, viz., $(5n + 2)(2n - 3)$. This should always be expressed in factored form. Now, in order to make the first fraction have this common denominator, it is necessary to multiply its denominator (and consequently its numerator too) by the factor $2n - 3$. Similarly the denominator and numerator of the second fraction must be multiplied by the factor $5n + 2$. The two fractions now have the form

$$\frac{3a(2n - 3)}{(5n + 2)(2n - 3)} + \frac{5a(5n + 2)}{(2n - 3)(5n + 2)}$$

in which the denominators are alike. The student may proceed to write the sum by writing the product $(5n + 2)(2n - 3)$ as the denominator of the sum, $\frac{}{(5n + 2)(2n - 3)}$, and then writing in the numerator the indicated sum of the numerators of the transformed fractions: $\frac{3a(2n - 3) + 5a(5n + 2)}{}$. Thus the sum will be written as

$$\frac{3a(2n - 3) + 5a(5n + 2)}{(5n + 2)(2n - 3)}$$

The student should feel that, when he has carried the work this far, he has already completed the essential part of the job of adding the fractions, although it may often be desirable to simplify the expression which he has obtained.   Generally this simplification will consist merely of expanding the indicated products and collecting like terms.   Occasionally it may require a refactoring of the numerator and denominator and the "cancellation" of factors common to both.   However, most problems in the addition of fractions in first-year algebra should be comparatively simple.   Certainly any types which exceed in difficulty the illustrative example discussed above should be reserved for subsequent courses.

Teaching the Solution of Equations Containing Fractions.   Students often have difficulty in solving equations containing fractions even though they may readily solve equations without fractions.   The difficulty generally can be traced to the complicated appearance which the presence of fractions gives to the equation.   Lacking experience with such equations, the student tends to become confused at the outset because he does not know how to start the analysis of his problem.

The student needs to be taught two basic things to help him out of his difficulty.   (1) He must come to understand that equations which contain fractions may be changed into equivalent equations which do not contain fractions and that, when so changed, equations in one unknown may be solved readily because they will then be in the same form as the equations to which he is accustomed.   (2) He must learn how to change an equation containing fractions into an equivalent equation which does not contain fractions.   After he has done this, he has merely to deal with ordinary linear equations concerning which suggestions have been given in the preceding chapter.

A few illustrations should serve both to convince him that it is in general possible to change an equation containing fractions into an equivalent one which does not contain fractions and to make clear to him the method by which this is accomplished.   The method of explanation should be substantially as follows:

Let us consider the equation $\frac{2}{3} + \frac{3}{x} = \frac{5}{6}$, in which we are required to solve for x.   We know how to solve equations without fractions; hence, we could solve this equation if we could change it into one that would contain no fractions.   We could do so if we could get rid of the denominators.   But the only way we can get rid of them is to have a factor in the numerator of each term which is exactly equal to the denominator of that term, so that we may divide both numerator and denominator of each individual term by the whole denominator of that term.

We can get new factors in the numerators of all the terms if we multiply every term in the whole equation by the same quantity, because multiplying a fraction means multiplying its numerator.   We have a right to multiply all the terms in the equation by any common multiplier we wish, because while this changes the value of each individual term, it does not destroy the equation.

We wish, therefore, to find the smallest multiplier which can be exactly divided by the denominator of each fraction in the equation. This multiplier will be, as you know, the least common denominator of all these fractions. In the case of the equation which we are considering in this problem, the L.C.D. will be $6x$, since this is the smallest quantity of which 3, x, and 6 are all exact factors.

Let us therefore multiply each term in the equation by $6x$, whence:

$$\frac{6x(2)}{3} + \frac{6x(3)}{x} = \frac{6x(5)}{6}$$

Now, if we reduce each term to its simplest form by dividing its denominator and numerator by whatever factor is common to both, we have a resulting equation $4x + 18 = 5x$, which has no fractions in it. We can easily solve this equation, since we have solved many others like it.

Students often make mistakes in solving equations containing fractions because they are careless in writing their work down. With special frequency they produce crowded and often illegible work when inserting the L.C.D. as a common multiplier of the numerators of the various terms in fractional equations. The following illustration is not exaggerated:

$$\frac{n}{2n - 8} + \frac{16}{n^2 - 16} = \frac{1}{2} \qquad \frac{n}{2(n - 4)} + \frac{16}{(n - 4)(n + 4)} = \frac{1}{2}$$

$$\frac{n}{2(n - 4)} + \frac{16}{(n - 4)(n + 4)} = \frac{1}{2} \text{ L.C.D.} = 2(n - 4)(n + 4)$$

Such carelessly written work can hardly fail to be productive of mistakes. It can be avoided if the students are taught to do a little planning with regard to the details of form. They should learn to recognize that, where factors are to be inserted, space will be required for writing the factors and that they should provide such space in order that their work will be neat and legible. Thus the foregoing problem might be advantageously written as follows:

$$\frac{n}{2(n - 4)} + \frac{16}{(n - 4)(n + 4)} = \frac{1}{2}$$

$$\frac{n(2)(n - 4)(n + 4)}{2(n - 4)} + \frac{16(2)(n - 4)(n + 4)}{(n - 4)(n + 4)} = \frac{1(2)(n - 4)(n + 4)}{2}$$

$$n(n + 4) + 32 = (n - 4)(n + 4)$$

When the need for space in writing is anticipated and provided for in this way, the written work is invariably improved in neatness and legibility, and the likelihood of mistakes is greatly diminished.   Although this is a matter of form rather than of mathematics, it is by no means a trivial matter.

Sometimes students confuse the procedures involved in solving equations containing fractions with those involved in the addition of fractions. It is important to point out clearly that the two problems are fundamentally different.   In the one case the aim is to find the algebraic sum of certain given fractions.   This obviously makes it necessary to preserve the *original value* of each individual fraction, although its form may be altered.   On the other hand, in solving an equation, both the form and the value of the individual terms may be altered if necessary, provided the *equality* of the two members of the equation is preserved. For this reason, in adding fractions, we may not multiply either the numerator or denominator of any fraction unless we multiply *both* by the same factor, whereas, in clearing an equation of fractions, we have a perfect right to multiply the numerators of *all* the terms by *the same multiplier* without multiplying the denominators at all.   It is important that illustrations of this point be presented and discussed with the students and that they shall come to make a clear distinction between the meanings and the implications of these two fundamentally different problems.

The Solving of Verbal Problems.   The solving of verbal problems is probably the most troublesome part of algebra for most students.   This is not surprising, because here the student must analyze and set up the problem before he can solve it and, except for the dubious practice of classifying certain verbal problems by types, there is no definite pattern for this analysis.   It is true, of course, that for the most part verbal problems involve relationships which may be cast in the form of one or more equations, and those problems which are found in algebra textbooks ordinarily involve relationships that can be represented by relatively simple equations which can be solved without any difficulty once they are set up.   The trouble lies in setting up the equations, i.e., in translating the verbal statements into algebraic language.   Therefore the principal effort of both teacher and students in connection with the study of verbal problems should be directed primarily toward developing the ability to translate the problems into equations.

The difficulty which children encounter in making such translation is quite understandable.   In the first place, most children are not very careful analytical readers.   The recent emphasis in the schools on rapid cursory reading is doubtless appropriate and valuable for many purposes, but it does not lend itself well to the careful analysis of problems.   Analysis is characteristically a slow and tedious process, and the ability to read analytically requires patience as well as concentrated and sustained attention. These characteristics, generally, can be developed to a satisfactory degree only by special training in giving conscious attention to them. The teacher of algebra must assume responsibility for giving this special training in careful analytical reading if he expects to have his students become proficient in solving verbal problems.

One of the material difficulties encountered by children in interpreting the verbal statements of problems lies in the fact that the relationships are not always stated explicitly but are often *implied*. For example, in the familiar distance-rate-time problems relationships between units of measure are implied, such as the number of feet in a mile or the number of seconds in a minute. In the many problems that imply the use of money, the relationships between the various units of monetary value are always assumed as known. Such words as "complementary," "supplementary," and "right triangle" are used to imply pertinent facts or relationships which are not stated explicitly. Hidden implications of this sort may appear so obvious to the teacher that he will perhaps not even be consciously aware of the lack of explicit statement. Often, however, they constitute a real source of confusion to students. The students need to be trained specifically to be on the lookout for these hidden implications, to learn to detect them, and to take them into account in analyzing and setting up the problems.

Closely associated with the difficulties involved in this implicit manner of indicating facts or relationships is the difficulty which sometimes arises from the use of words or expressions whose meanings are not entirely clear to the students. For example, the expression "x less 5" means $x - 5$, while the expression "x less than 5" means either $5 - x$ or $x < 5$, which is a very different thing, although students frequently fail to detect the difference because they do not recognize that the meanings to be attached to the word "less" are not the same in the two expressions.

In the second place, the careful analysis of problems requires much patience, concentrated attention, and the willingness to take the time to write down and organize all relevant data with painstaking care. These are not generally to be regarded as normal characteristics of normal, healthy young children. Children tend to be impatient with problems which they cannot organize intuitively in a moment. They want to get to the answer quickly and are often content to dismiss, with the remark "too hard," any problem involving relationships that cannot be seen and organized at a glance. Development of the ability to give concentrated and sustained attention is not only desirable as a general trait but absolutely necessary in the successful study of mathematics, and it is especially necessary in setting up verbal problems. The students need to be made and kept specifically conscious of this fact and to be trained in the habits implied.

Finally, and perhaps most important of all, students have difficulty with verbal problems because there is no single general pattern according to which all verbal problems can be set up. Certain "general methods" have been proposed and are doubtless helpful in systematizing the analysis, but there is, and can be, no formula which will obviate the necessity for alertness, care, ingenuity, and resourcefulness on the part of the student. The solution of equations, the addition of fractions, and many other operations with symbolic algebraic expressions can be reduced to mechanical laws which operate invariably. It is not so with the setting up of verbal problems. Every problem presents its own peculiar elements, relationships, and requirements which must be studied, interpreted, and organized strictly and solely in the light of the conditions and data stated or implied in the problem itself.

It is true that many of the problems customarily found in the textbooks tend to fall into certain general groupings or types. It is also true that several of these types have characteristic formulas which express the relationships involved. To this extent verbal problems may be classified and their solutions somewhat standardized, and for this reason many authors both advocate and practice the procedure of presenting verbal problems according to type. On the other hand, the component elements and the mathematical relationships involved in one type of problem may be entirely unlike those involved in other types. Thus, while a student may be able to set up and solve type problems when he knows to what types they belong, he may be completely at a loss when he attempts to classify problems by type. For this reason the advisability of teaching verbal problems by type seems questionable, at best. It does tend to produce specific classroom results more quickly than any other method, but they are results which are more in the nature of specific skills than general powers. Some authors suggest compromising the situation by supplementing the type lists of problems by unclassified lists of miscellaneous problems, holding that this secures the advantages of teaching problems by type and at the same time avoids the disadvantages. It would seem that this might be an effective compromise, provided that appropriate emphasis were given to the study of the unclassified problems.

In general, verbal problems lead to equations. Therefore, somewhere in the problem, it should be possible to find at least one quantitative element for which two different mathematical expressions can be obtained. This element may be a particular distance, a particular volume, or any one of a variety of quantitative elements. The equality may be expressed specifically, or it may be merely implied. The search for such an element and for the two different ways of expressing it constitutes the analysis of the problem.

Example. How much alcohol must be added to a pint of 10 per cent solution of iodine to make an 8 per cent solution?

Here the quantitative elements in the problem are the amounts of alcohol, the amounts of iodine, and the total amounts of the solutions. If each of these is considered under both the initial and final conditions, it is seen that the element which remains quantitatively the same in both cases is the amount of iodine. Thus we get the basic equation:

Original amount of iodine = final amount of iodine

By considering now the composition of each solution and designating by n the number of pints of alcohol to be added to the original solution, we may readily get two different expressions for the amount of iodine. A diagram will be helpful in this case.

Fig. 14-6

It is seen from the diagram, Fig. 14-6, that the original amount of iodine is $\frac{10}{100}$ of 1 pint and that the final amount of iodine is $\frac{8}{100}$ of $(1 + n)$ pints. By substituting these expressions in the basic equation given verbally above, we get the equation

$$\frac{10}{100}(1) = \frac{8}{100}(1 + n) \quad \text{or} \quad 10 = 8(1 + n)$$

from which the value of n can be found directly.

Example. Two trains, 350 miles apart, travel toward each other until they meet. Train A travels at an average speed of 55 miles per hour and train B travels at an average speed of 48 miles per hour. How long will it be after they start before they meet?

Here the elements involved in the two situations are distances, rates, and times. One element, which is the same in the case of both trains, is obviously the time. Thus we may set up our basic equation in words:

Time for train A = time for train B

It remains now merely to get two mathematical expressions representing the time in terms of respective distances and rates of speed. To this end the detailed data should now be tabulated in some such manner as the following:

Elements involved	Train A	Train B
Distance traveled, miles..........	x	$350 - x$
Rate, miles per hour.............	55	48
Time (distance/rate).............	$\dfrac{x}{55}$	$\dfrac{350 - x}{48}$

The substitution of these two expressions for the time in the basic equation given verbally above gives the desired equation in algebraic form:

$$\frac{x}{55} = \frac{350 - x}{48}$$

This may be solved for x, the distance traveled by train A, and since the rate is known, the time can easily be computed.

Another, and perhaps easier, approach to this particular problem may be made by reflecting that the total distance is constant and that two expressions for this distance must be equivalent. One such expression is given explicitly in the problem, viz., $d = 350$ miles. Another may be inferred from the fact that the total distance is the sum of the distances traveled by the two trains. Thus we have a basic equation:

Total distance = total distance

(Miles traveled by train A) + (Miles traveled by train B) = (350 miles)

By again tabulating the data, recalling that the trains travel the same number of hours t, and making use of the relation $d = r \cdot t$, we have

Elements involved	Train A	Train B
Rate, miles per hour..............	55	48
Time, hours....................	t	t
Distance traveled, miles..........	$55t$	$48t$

By substitution in the basic equation, we get the simple equation

$$55t + 48t = 350$$

from which the required length of time can be found directly.

The alternative approach to the above example makes it clear that there is considerable latitude in the analysis of many verbal problems and that success depends largely upon the care and ingenuity of the student. The setup of the problem may involve implied relationships which the student must seek in his background of experiences. The student who in his earlier work in arithmetic and informal geometry has

accumulated a rich store of ready information about such relationships
will have a great advantage in the analysis of problems. It is often possible to make graphic or diagrammatic sketches which are helpful in making the relationships among the elements seem concrete and tangible.

The following suggestions, while neither a panacea nor a guarantee of
success, will probably be helpful to students:

1. Read the problem carefully and consider all the elements either expressed or
implied. Assign letters or symbols to represent all elements which are unknown.

2. If possible, make a diagrammatic sketch representing the elements and
the relationships in the problem.

3. Try to find some element which remains quantitatively unchanged throughout the problem, or for which two separate expressions can be obtained to make
the basic equation.

4. Write this basic equation in words.

5. Translate the basic equation into algebraic language, using the data given
or implied in the statement of the problem. It will probably be helpful in this
connection to tabulate the pertinent data.

6. Solve the equation.

7. Check your solution *in the original problem*.

8. Be patient and painstaking. Do not become discouraged.

9. Use particular care to make your written work neat and orderly.

10. In problem situations that are not too involved, it is frequently desirable
to make rough estimates of the answers before attempting to solve the problems.

Selection of Verbal Problems. It is generally felt that one serious limitation to the effectiveness of the work with verbal problems is that so
many of the customary problems are outside the range of the students'
ordinary experiences and therefore do not seem real to the students. It
has often been said, and with entire truth, that many of the problems
are artificial; that they lack reality because the students may feel no
need for solving such problems by algebraic methods. The familiar clock
problems are good examples of this. Why should anybody want to know
the time between three and four o'clock when the hands of a clock will
be together? And, if one *should* want to know this, could he not find
it out more easily by the practical method of actually turning the hands
of his watch to the desired position?

Or again, take such a problem as this: Mary is half as old as Susan.
In 8 years Mary will be three-fourths as old as Susan. How old is each
girl now? Obviously, if this were an actual situation, one would have
to know the ages of the two girls before he could set up the problem, and
the problem could not conceivably have any personal interest or practical
importance to anyone except the acquaintances of the two girls, who
probably would already know the ages.

Many teachers and writers are greatly concerned about this admitted
lack of reality, genuineness, and practical importance in much of our

verbal problem material.   There is evidence, however, that this is not the sole criterion of student interest.   As a matter of fact, many problems that are of the sheer puzzle type and without any practical importance whatever have been found to be highly interesting to students. On the other hand, some problems which contain elements of reality fail to elicit much student interest.[1]

Teachers should be primarily concerned with developing in their students a right attitude toward solving verbal problems.   It is a mistake to try to give the impression that all verbal problems are practical or that the whole benefit to be derived from their study lies in their usefulness.   There seems to be little justification for "dressing up" essentially unreal problems to give them a superficial semblance of reality. In Thorndike's view:[2]

> Such problems, if defensible at all, are defensible as mental gymnastics, and as appeals to the interest in mystery and puzzles.   As such, they are better if freed from the pretence at reality.   "I am thinking of a number.   Half of it plus one-third of it exceeds one-fourth of it by seven.   What is the number?" is better than problems which falsely pretend to represent sane responses to real issues that life might offer.

Breslich rates practicality and reality high in the criteria for suitable problem material but points out[3] that a problem may be practical and still not suitable for elementary algebra:

> The situations of adult life involved in it may be too remote from the pupil's environment to be understood or appreciated.   Problems taken from science and other studies may be ever so real without being real to the pupils who are to solve them.   They may be beyond the mental reach of those students.   The practical situations in a problem may be too complex for the beginner in algebra, and the facts involved may be unknown to him.

Nevertheless, it will be generally conceded that, other things being equal, problems that lie within the experiences of the pupils and exhibit genuine reality and practicality are more desirable than those which lack these characteristics.   The criticism of much of the problem material on this score is a valid one.   Teachers and textbook writers have not been oblivious to the shortcomings of the textbooks in this respect, and in recent years serious efforts have been made to improve the situation. Some progress has been made.   However, problems which are genuinely

[1] See E. R. Breslich, "Problems in Teaching Secondary-school Mathematics" (Chicago: University of Chicago Press, 1931), pp. 183–187; also Jesse J. Powell, A Study of Problem Material in High School Algebra, *Contributions to Education* 405 (New York: Bureau of Publications, Teachers College, Columbia University, 1929).

[2] E. L. Thorndike, "The Psychology of Algebra" (New York: The Macmillan Company, 1923), p. 138.   By permission of The Macmillan Company, publishers.

[3] Breslich, *op. cit.*, p. 186.   Copyright 1931 by the University of Chicago Press.

real and practical, and which at the same time are within the comprehension and experience of young students and which also submit themselves to elementary algebraic analysis, appear to be very scarce.
Teachers should be always on the alert to detect, select, or create such
problems to supplement those found in the textbooks.

Special Products and Factoring. The amount of time and effort generally spent in the study of special products and factoring in the ninth
grade is probably in excess of that which can be justified. The uses of
factoring are mainly confined to work with fractions and to the solution
of certain equations, while the uses of special products are mainly in the
direction of facilitating factoring. Since the equations and fractions
suitable to ninth-grade work are relatively simple, the difficulty of the
factoring and the special products studied in this grade should be in
keeping with the difficulty and the requirements of these applications.
The work in factoring should be confined to expressions involving a
common factor, the difference of two squares, the square of a binomial,
or the quadratic trinomial of the form $x^2 + px + q$. Consequently,
the work in special products need include only the product of a monomial
by a binomial, the product of the sum and difference of two terms, the
square of the sum or of the difference of two terms, and perhaps the
product of two binomials of the form $(x \pm a)(x \pm b)$. Nothing is to be
gained by including special products of the form $(ax \pm b)(cx \pm d)$,
because such products can be found as quickly and with more assurance
by direct multiplication, while the factoring of such products generally
involves trial and should be checked by direct multiplication anyway.

So far as the special products themselves are concerned, the aim is to
enable one to save time by writing the products down without going
through the details of multiplication. So far as their use in factoring
is concerned, the aim is to suggest the factors and enable one to write
them down without the need of going through the details of trying and
checking. The attainment of either of these aims is conditioned primarily upon the following considerations:

1. Knowledge of the type forms of the products to which the various special
sets of factors (in type form) give rise
2. Knowledge of the type forms of the factors to which the various sets of
special products (in type form) give rise
3. Ability to identify a particular pair of factors as belonging to a particular
type and as giving a type product of a particular form
4. Ability to identify a particular product as belonging to a particular type
and as having factors of a particular form
5. Ability to identify each element in a special given factor or product with the
corresponding element in the type form to which it belongs, and to make the
appropriate substitutions

Thus the two fundamental requisites are knowledge of the type forms of the various special kinds of factors and their associated products and ability to recognize, identify, and associate particular cases and particular elements with the general types to which they belong or with the corresponding elements therein.   Consequently, the two foremost pedagogical questions are: how shall the student most effectively be brought to know these type forms, and how may he best become able to identify expressions in particular problems with the special types to which they belong?

Geometrical and arithmetical illustrations will help to rationalize all these type forms and will provide a basis by which the student can easily reconstruct them.   For example, consider the factorization of the difference of two squares:

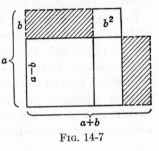

$$a^2 - b^2 = (a + b)(a - b)$$

This geometric illustration, Fig. 14-7, shows clearly why the area represented by the product $(a + b)(a - b)$ is the same area as that represented by $a^2 - b^2$.

FIG. 14-7

Now suppose a is 7 and b is 2.   Then $a^2 - b^2 = 49 - 4 = 45$.   But $a + b = 9$ and $a - b = 5$, and $(9)(5) = 45$.   Thus we may also illustrate arithmetically the fact that $a^2 - b^2 = (a + b)(a - b)$.   The other type forms may easily be illustrated in similar fashion.

To be of much use, the type forms must be learned thoroughly.   They must be understood, and they must also be memorized.   This means that the students must be shown in the beginning that the type forms either result from, or are verified by, actual multiplication.   But it also means that in addition to this the students must have sufficient practice and drill upon these type forms to make the forms themselves become indelibly fixed in their minds.

This drill, however, should not be mere mechanical repetition.   It should be made meaningful through constant illustration and application to specific examples involving both literal and numerical terms.   The students should be kept conscious at all times that their principal job in connection with either writing special products or factoring expressions is to *recognize* each problem as being a special case of one or another of the types which they have learned, to *identify* it with the type to which it belongs, and to make the appropriate substitutions of corresponding terms.   Incidentally, this matter of identification and substitution of corresponding terms is one whose difficulties sometimes are not recognized by the teacher, although it actually constitutes the very crux of the difficulties which many students encounter.   At no point is special attention more needed, and no point seems to be more neglected than this.   There is no better way of ensuring real mastery of special products and factors than to give a well-organized special series of practice exercises on term-by-term identification and substitution.[1]

A topical study of special products and factors is a necessary but not a sufficient condition for permanent mastery. The applications which arise normally in connection with subsequent parts of the course are not in themselves sufficient to ensure continuation of satisfactory mastery even after it has been attained. If the skills are to be maintained, there should be a systematic program of subsequent drills spaced at suitable intervals throughout the remaining part of the course.

Exponents, Powers, and Roots of Numbers. Students will generally have little difficulty in performing operations involving exponents if they understand clearly the meaning of exponents. That so many students make mistakes in these operations is doubtless due to the fact that the laws which govern the operations are too often developed hurriedly and without adequate care to ensure that the meanings are made clear. Results such as the following make it painfully clear that too often work with exponents comes to be a mere meaningless juggling of symbols:

$$a^3 + a^2 = a^5 \qquad (a^2)^3 = a^5 \qquad a^2(b^2) = (ab)^4$$

Such results would be less likely to occur if the concepts of positive integral exponents were adequately developed at the outset, for the laws of operation are simple and inevitable consequences of these concepts.

The meaning of a positive integral exponent is not hard to make clear. The approach is, in fact, suggested in most textbooks through one or two illustrative examples. It is pointed out, for example, that such a product as $(r)(r)(r)$ is written as r^3 for convenience and that the number symbol ³, which is called the exponent in the expression r^3, merely indicates how many times r is to be used as a factor. Then two or three examples are given to illustrate the use of exponents in multiplication and division, the rules are stated, and exercises are given to afford the student opportunity for applying the rules.

The unfortunate thing is that this all seems so familiar and so obvious to the teacher that he is likely to assume that the one or two illustrations offered in the text are sufficient to make the matter equally obvious to the student, which, of course, is not generally the case. Examples of the foregoing type should be given until the students themselves are able to express the results in exponential form, tabulate them, and derive the rules for themselves. When they can do this, they will have the basis for a real understanding of positive integral exponents and of the laws for operating with such exponents. Also, in case they should ever become

[1] The reader may well review at this point the discussion of the solution and evaluation of formulas in Chap. 13.

confused with regard to these rules, they will understand how to take the matter back to original meanings for their analysis of it and to rebuild the laws for themselves.   They should, of course, have plenty of practice and drill in using the laws of exponents as such, after their meaning is understood.   Above all, they should be trained to examine every problem carefully and to be sure that they understand precisely what is called for before proceeding with their work on it.

Since a positive integral exponent indicates *the number of times* the base is to be used as a factor, it is evident that special meanings will have to be attached to zero, negative, and fractional exponents.   We want the meanings to be such that we may operate with the special kinds of exponents under the same laws as those we use for positive integral exponents, so that the results of the operations will be consistent in all respects with the results obtained by using positive integral exponents.

Consider the two laws for operating with positive integral exponents:

Law 1 $\qquad\qquad\qquad a^m \times a^n = a^{m+n}$

Law 2 $\qquad\qquad\qquad a^m \div a^n = a^{m-n}$

If the use of 0 as an exponent is to be so defined that these laws hold, then it is evident from law 1 that

$$a^0 \times a^n = a^{0+n} = a^n$$

It immediately follows that $a^0 = 1$ is a justified meaning to give to the use of 0 as an exponent.

If a similar substitution is made in law 2, we have

$$a^0 \div a^n = a^{0-n} = a^{-n}$$

But since $a^0 = 1$, this may be written

$$1 \div a^n = a^{-n}$$

Thus it immediately follows that a justified interpretation of a negative exponent is that it indicates the reciprocal of the same quantity raised to the corresponding positive exponent.

We cannot give meaning to fractional exponents until we define roots of numbers.   The students should have gained from their arithmetic some understanding of the meaning of square roots and cube roots of numbers and of the symbols $\sqrt{}$ and $\sqrt[3]{}$.   It is best, however, not to assume too much on this point.   The square root of a number should be explicitly redefined as one of its two equal factors, the cube root as one of its three equal factors, etc., and the appropriate symbols should be carefully reassociated with their respective meanings.

As soon as this has been done, resort may be had again to analogy, as follows:

From the definition of square root, $(\sqrt{y})(\sqrt{y}) = y$. Also, if there were a number represented by the symbol $y^{\frac{1}{2}}$ and if it were subject to the laws of multiplication by exponents, then we should have

$$(y^{\frac{1}{2}})(y^{\frac{1}{2}}) = y^{(\frac{1}{2}+\frac{1}{2})} = y^1 = y$$

Now since $\sqrt{y}$ is one of two equal factors whose product is y and since $y^{\frac{1}{2}}$ is also one of two equal factors whose product is y, we may reasonably agree to think of $y^{\frac{1}{2}}$ and $\sqrt{y}$ as representing the same quantity. In other words, we may reasonably agree that $y^{\frac{1}{2}}$ shall have the same meaning as $\sqrt{y}$. Similarly, the corresponding meanings may be attached to such expressions as $y^{\frac{1}{3}}$, $y^{\frac{1}{4}}$, $y^{\frac{1}{5}}$, etc.

Since $(x)(x) = x^2$ and also $(-x)(-x) = x^2$, it follows that

$$\sqrt{y} \cdot \sqrt{y} = y$$

and also $(-\sqrt{y})(-\sqrt{y}) = y$. It thus appears that every number has two distinct square roots, equal numerically but opposite in sign. The number $\sqrt{y}$ is called the principal square root of y. Since $\sqrt{y}$ has been identified with $y^{\frac{1}{2}}$, it follows that $y^{\frac{1}{2}}$ and $-(y^{\frac{1}{2}})$ are also symbols for the two square roots of y, the principal square root being represented by $y^{\frac{1}{2}}$.

Since these meanings have been arrived at by defining these fractional exponents in such a way that they will be subject to the laws of operation formulated for positive integral exponents, we may now apply those laws in such cases as $(y^{\frac{1}{3}})(y^{\frac{1}{3}})$. This obviously gives $y^{(\frac{1}{3}+\frac{1}{3})}$ or $y^{\frac{2}{3}}$. It is equally clear that we have here $(y^{\frac{1}{3}})^2$. It is also clear that $(y^2)^{\frac{1}{3}}$ would give the same result, since $(y^2)^{\frac{1}{3}} = y^{2(\frac{1}{3})} = y^{\frac{2}{3}}$.

By using numerous illustrative examples, carefully selected and arranged to bring out these analogies and identities, the students can be brought to understand what fractional exponents represent. It is well to have them tabulate the different forms of writing such expressions as

$$y^{\frac{2}{3}} \qquad (y^{\frac{1}{3}})^2 \qquad (\sqrt[3]{y})^2 \qquad (y^2)^{\frac{1}{3}} \qquad \sqrt[3]{y^2}$$
$$x^{\frac{3}{4}} \qquad (x^{\frac{1}{4}})^3 \qquad (\sqrt[4]{x})^3 \qquad (x^3)^{\frac{1}{4}} \qquad \sqrt[4]{x^3}$$
$$\cdots \cdots \cdots \cdots \cdots \cdots$$
$$x^{p/r} \qquad (x^{1/r})^p \qquad (\sqrt[r]{x})^p \qquad (x^p)^{1/r} \qquad \sqrt[r]{x^p}$$
$$\cdots \cdots \cdots \cdots \cdots \cdots$$

The careful comparison of the tabulated results of such equivalent forms will lead to a real understanding and generalization of the meaning of fractional exponents. In many cases the students themselves will be able to formulate the general relation that $x^{p/r}$ means the pth power of the rth root of x, or the rth root of the pth power of x. Numerical examples are helpful in making this meaning clear. A considerable amount of practice of the drill type should be given in order to fix the meanings and the identities of the equivalent forms firmly in the minds of the students.

Having now developed meanings and consistent general laws for exponents which may be either positive, negative, or zero and either integral or fractional, it is clear that these laws may now be extended and made applicable to literal exponents as well, since these represent numbers of one or another of the kinds just mentioned.   While the students will have little occasion to use fractional or literal exponents in ninth-grade algebra, the teacher should have a clear concept of the organic and definitive nature of the progressive generalization of the laws to cover all kinds of exponents.

The Use of Parentheses.   In connection with the use of parentheses the principal aims should be to have the students acquire (1) a clear understanding of the meaning of parentheses, (2) the ability to interpret correctly mathematical expressions in which parentheses are used, (3) the ability to employ parentheses correctly in situations where they are necessary or helpful, and (4) the ability to transform expressions involving parentheses into equivalent expressions which do not contain parentheses.

It is questionable whether a topical study of parentheses is either necessary or desirable, although most textbooks in ninth-grade algebra do offer such a treatment.   As Breslich suggests,[1] much of the difficulty which students experience in the use of parentheses in algebra is probably due to the formal way in which the subject is presented to them.   If they can be taught to think of parentheses simply as a symbol which indicates that the terms enclosed therein are to be regarded all together as one quantity, much, if not most, of the difficulty will disappear.   Such a concept will enable the student to make his own analysis of every operation affecting or affected by the parenthetical quantity without the need of having special rules.

The most troublesome cases probably are those involving the "removal of parentheses" containing expressions of two or more terms.   Special rules for the removal are generally given, often without adequate explanation.   Hence students tend to look upon the removal of parentheses in such cases as a mechanical, rather than a rational, process.   There follows a natural tendency to perform the operations with little or no thought of their meaning.

To correct this situation, it is suggested that the students' attention be focused upon the idea of writing an equivalent expression without parentheses rather than upon the removal of the parentheses, and that the latter expression be completely discarded.   Such a case as

[1] Breslich, *op. cit.*, pp. 137–138.

$3x - 4y + 11 - (2x + 3y - 5)$ will then become merely a problem in rewriting. It is apparent that each term must be rewritten with due regard to its sign, and since the entire expression $2x + 3y - 5$ is to be subtracted from the foregoing terms, it is apparent that this means that each of its terms must be subtracted individually. Hence we write $3x - 4y + 11$ and then proceed to subtract, in turn, the terms $2x$, $3y$, and -5. This procedure obviously gives

$$3x - 4y + 11 - (2x) - (3y) - (-5)$$

or $3x - 4y + 11 - 2x - 3y + 5$, which upon collecting terms gives $x - 7y + 16$ as the net result. Thus the expression has been rewritten without parentheses, and it has been accomplished without any special rule for the removal of the parentheses. The whole operation thus becomes one based upon understanding rather than merely upon the authority of an arbitrary rule.

It is probable that a freer and more systematic use of parentheses in such matters as the evaluation of formulas, the solution of literal and fractional equations, the addition of fractions, and various other algebraic operations would do much to prevent mistakes, clarify the meaning, and emphasize the usefulness of parentheses. The foregoing illustration is a case in point. Some mention of this has been made in certain sections of this and the preceding chapter, but for emphasis two additional illustrations will be given here.

1. Given the formula for the sides of a right triangle $h^2 = a^2 + b^2$, let it be required to find the value of h in terms of a and b. Many students will thoughtlessly write, "Since $h^2 = a^2 + b^2$, therefore

$$\sqrt{h^2} = \sqrt{a^2} + \sqrt{b^2}, \qquad \text{or} \qquad h = a + b."$$

The square root is taken of the separate terms of the right member of the equation rather than the right member as a whole. The fact that here $a^2 + b^2$ must be treated as a single quantity could easily be emphasized by writing the equation in the form $h^2 = (a^2 + b^2)$.

2. Given the formula for the volume of a right circular cylinder $V = \pi r^2 h$, let it be required to find the volume of a particular cylinder by using the values $\pi = 3.14$, $r = 1.7$, and $h = 5.5$. The following is not an exaggerated illustration of the careless way in which many students put down their written work for the evaluation of such a formula:

$$V = \overset{3.14}{\cancel{\pi}} \quad \overset{1.7}{\cancel{r}^2} \quad \overset{5.5}{\cancel{h}} = \cdots \cdots$$

Such carelessness in writing is responsible for many arithmetical mistakes. If the students were trained to write out such a form as the following for the evaluation before substituting the numerical values, there would be much less likelihood of mistakes occurring either in the substitution or the subsequent evaluation.

$$V = \quad \pi \;\cdot\; r^2 \;\cdot\; h$$
$$= (\quad)\;(\quad)^2(\quad)$$
$$= (3.14)\;(1.7)^2(5.5)$$
$$= \;\cdot\;\cdot\;\cdot\;\cdot\;\cdot\;\cdot\;\cdot\;\cdot\;\cdot\;\cdot$$

Illustrative Tabular Analysis of a Teaching Problem

Radicals and radical equations

I. What background may the students be expected to have with reference to this topic?
  A. Use of radical sign and index to indicate square roots and cube roots of numbers
  B. Meaning of literal symbols
  C. Meaning and laws of positive integral exponents
  D. Finding square roots and some cube roots, squares and cubes of numbers
II. What are the particular understandings and abilities which the student should acquire or strengthen through his study of this topic?
  A. Things to know:
   1. The precise meaning to be associated with a radical
   2. The precise meaning of rational and irrational numbers
   3. The precise meaning of similar radicals
   4. The fact that in general only similar radicals may be combined by addition or subtraction
   5. The precise conditions under which a radical is said to be in its simplest form
   6. The fact that $\sqrt[n]{a \cdot b} \equiv \sqrt[n]{a} \cdot \sqrt[n]{b}$, and conversely*
   7. The fact that $\sqrt[n]{a/b} \equiv \sqrt[n]{a}/\sqrt[n]{b}$, and conversely*
   8. The fact that in general $\sqrt[n]{a} \pm \sqrt[n]{b} \neq \sqrt[n]{a \pm b}$*
   9. The principles which underlie the solution of radical equations
   10. The meaning of extraneous roots and the necessity as well as the method of guarding against them in the solution of radical equations
  B. Things to be able to do:
   1. To combine similar radicals by addition or subtraction
   2. To change radical expressions of the forms $\sqrt[n]{a \cdot b}$ and $\sqrt[n]{x/y}$ into the equivalent forms $\sqrt[n]{a} \cdot \sqrt[n]{b}$ and $\sqrt[n]{x}/\sqrt[n]{y}$ (and conversely) with assurance and facility
   3. To "simplify" radicals readily
   4. To change radicals with different indices to similar radicals when possible so that they may be combined by addition or subtraction
   5. To solve radical equations
   6. To check the solution of radical equations and detect and discard extraneous roots

* The exceptions to these properties need not be considered here.

III. What activities or procedures will most effectively enable the student to gain these desired understandings and abilities?

Each of the foregoing items should be subjected to a careful individual analysis before teaching. In general, careful explanations by the teacher should be freely illustrated by numerical examples and accompanied by questions and discussion in which both the teacher and the students participate. Understanding should be followed by supervised practice or drill on the skills listed under II*B*. The drill should be specific but with examples sufficiently varied to foster generalization and give the students a feeling of assurance in identifying meanings and recognizing appropriate procedures. Subsequent diagnostic testing and remedial instruction will probably be needed.

IV. What special difficulties may the students be expected to encounter in acquiring the desired understandings and skills?
   A. Learning to simplify radicals such as $\sqrt{54}$ or $\sqrt{3x^3y}$
   B. Learning to simplify fractional radicals such as $\sqrt{a/b}$
   C. Combining radicals which are not given as similar radicals (e.g., $\sqrt{27} + \sqrt{48}$). Instead of reducing these to similar radicals and then combining, some students are likely to say $\sqrt{27} + \sqrt{48} = \sqrt{75}$
   D. Failing to check solutions of radical equations in the original equations
V. What specific suggestions, devices, and procedures will be most likely to help the student overcome these difficulties and avoid these mistakes?

The particular shortcomings listed under IV give rise to mistakes which may be traced to inadequate understanding of the principles involved and to lack of experience in using these principles. Doubtlessly the principles will have to be reexplained and discussed and the procedures will have to be reillustrated, perhaps several times. Each new discussion should aim to produce more complete and specific understanding and should be followed by specific and carefully supervised practice.

Considerable difficulty may be avoided if the students are taught to *write out in detail all the steps in the operations,* as follows:

$$\sqrt{54} = \sqrt{9 \cdot 6} = \sqrt{9} \cdot \sqrt{6} = 3\sqrt{6}$$
$$\sqrt{3x^3y} = \sqrt{x^2(3xy)} = \sqrt{x^2} \cdot \sqrt{3xy} = x\sqrt{3xy}$$
$$\sqrt{a/b} = \sqrt{ab/b^2} = \sqrt{ab}/\sqrt{b^2} = \sqrt{ab}/b$$
$$\sqrt{27} + \sqrt{48} = \sqrt{9 \cdot 3} + \sqrt{16 \cdot 3} = \sqrt{9} \cdot \sqrt{3} + \sqrt{16} \cdot \sqrt{3}$$
$$= 3\sqrt{3} + 4\sqrt{3} = 7\sqrt{3}$$

Students often object to this detailed writing out of all the steps because they feel that it slows up their work. As a matter of fact, however, it really has the opposite effect by materially decreasing the number of mistakes. More important still, it is the best possible guarantee that the students will fully understand what they are doing and why they are doing it.

The foregoing section is illustrative of a pattern of analysis which can be made by any teacher with reference to any topic of algebra. The making of such an analysis serves several useful purposes. It forces the teacher to a consideration of relative values in planning the various parts of his work. This enables him more effectively to disregard non-essentials and build his teaching with appropriate emphases toward the attainment of the really significant outcomes. Again, it gives the teacher a more complete and organic view of the whole topic and enables him to see the various important elements in their relation to each other and to the whole. This makes for freedom, clarity, interest, and effectiveness in the developmental work. Finally, it calls his attention to the specific danger points which are, after all, the critical points in teaching. It forces the careful analysis of every individual concept and process to be taught from the standpoints of anticipating inherent difficulties, tracing them to their specific causes, and then determining specific means for preventing or overcoming them. It will become increasingly valuable if it is revised from year to year in the light of students' mistakes in oral and written work.

No such analysis will ever be complete or perfect, because there will always be unpredictable factors. But every such analysis will be helpful in motivating the work and making it more efficient and effective through the judicious selection and organization of subject matter, the considered allocation of emphasis, and the selection of procedures and devices specifically designed to produce optimum understanding and mastery and to avoid, minimize, or correct specific misunderstandings or mistakes.

Provision for Superior Students. As in arithmetic, algebra classes must be conducted as classes, and the main body of the subject matter must be studied by all the students. Therefore, that which is to be considered as the required subject matter must be kept within the intellectual reach of practically all of the students. Apart from the general developmental discussions, teachers tend to spend more time and effort in helping the poorer students come up to an acceptable level of attainment than in planning ways to help the superior students and the occasional very exceptional student develop their talents to greatest advantage. This is entirely understandable, because the need of the poor students appears the more obvious and more immediately urgent of the two, and it is also the easier to try to satisfy. Appropriate provision for the superior students, and especially for the unusually talented students, cannot ordinarily be made on the spur of the moment, and heavy teaching loads usually leave the teacher little time for the special study and planning that would be required.

Yet the issue is too important to be neglected or ignored, and ways need to be found to facilitate the efforts of teachers in this direction. In Norton's view:[1]

Many of the people involved with the current problem of providing for the gifted pupil in mathematics appear to be in need of specific suggestions for providing for the gifted pupils in their charge: techniques, devices, activities, and other experiences that have been successfully administered and have produced successful results.

In the article from which this quotation was taken the reader will find a considerable number and variety of such specific suggestions under the following headings:

1. Reading and writing activities
2. Individual and group projects in mathematics
3. Additional exercises and supplementary problems
4. Building vocabulary in mathematics
5. Applications of mathematics
6. Mathematical assemblies
7. Mathematical clubs and organizations.

The article also contains a list of 15 specific avenues for enrichment of the student's work. These suggestions, however, are not slanted explicitly toward any particular course or grade.

With particular reference to ninth-grade algebra some provision can be made in several ways:

1. Superior students who have completed the regular assignments may be permitted to work ahead of the class on advance assignments. Often this appears to be the easiest way to meet the situation, but eventually it can give rise to serious problems of instruction and management.

2. Superior students who have completed the regular assignments may be given additional and more difficult problems related to the same topic or unit that the class is currently studying. Unless such supplementary work is provided in the basic textbook, the teacher will need to plan the assignments. Review or "refresher" books or more advanced textbooks in algebra can often be used to economize time in this. The plan may make considerable initial demands on the teacher's time, but it has the advantage of keeping the class together in the sense that at any time all are working on the same topic or unit.

3. Superior students who have completed an assigned chapter or unit ahead of schedule may be permitted to study (perhaps in small discussion

groups where it is feasible) extensions or variations of the work of that unit.   This requires that other texts or reference books be easily accessible.   An interesting variant of this is to have these students critically examine the presentation of this unit in several ninth-grade algebra textbooks and report critical comparisons of the several texts with respect to this unit.   Most better than average students will respond well to such an assignment.   It seems to capture their interest, and the comparisons necessarily elicit the best kind of good, well-motivated study with consequent broadening and reinforcement of their mastery of the unit.

Since about the same major topics or units are presented in nearly all ninth-grade algebra texts, this type of activity could be carried on with respect to practically any unit or chapter.   Individual or group written reports could be required and made to the teacher on each unit studied in this way, and these reports should form a basis for student-teacher or group-teacher discussion.   These reports may provide the teacher with helpful cues to what the students consider the more effective ways of presenting the details of the unit.   Thus they could help the teacher improve his instruction and they might eventually be helpful in the reappraisal or selection of a basic textbook for the class in ensuing years.

4. The extremely talented and interested student will probably be helped most by permitting him to select some topic or area which he would like to investigate extensively and independently, providing him with suitable materials in the way of reference books, and getting him started at his undertaking.   He should be permitted to work on his special study only after he has done the work currently assigned to the class, because sometimes brilliant students are so impatient to get to the superstructure that they would slight the routine necessary to lay a proper groundwork.   His study might extend over a semester or even a year.   He would need to have some guidance and supervision, and to this end he should be required to make progress reports at designated intervals.   Eventually he should be held responsible for both a written and an oral report on his work.   The written report would be supervised by the teacher, and the oral report would be made to a group of perhaps one or more teachers and some of the outstanding students in his own or more advanced classes in algebra.[1]

Concepts of Modern Mathematics in Elementary Algebra.   In view of the recent attention being given to modern mathematics, it may be expected that some of the newer concepts, terminology, notation, and operations will find their way into high school algebra.   This does not mean that the present courses are to be scrapped and replaced by courses in Boolean

[1] For a discussion of this topic see Howard F. Fehr, Mathematics for the Gifted, *Bulletin of the National Association of Secondary-School Principals*, **38** (1954), 103–110.

algebra or symbolic logic. That should not and will not happen. Most of the algebra which we teach today will continue to form the main body of the courses of the future. However, some of this traditional algebra can be both enriched and clarified by introducing some ideas which have not heretofore been included in the high school work.

Probably the most pervasive of these is the notion of *sets* and the operations of union, intersection, complementation, inclusion, etc. as applied to sets. The notion of sets and subsets is a very simple concept. A set is defined simply by some consideration whereby one can determine whether a particular object does or does not belong to the set. Innumerable examples can be given: the set of persons in a given algebra class, the set of chairs in a room, the set of all automobile licenses issued in Michigan in a given year; the set of numbers in a telephone directory, the set of points on a line, the set of positive integers less than 13. Indeed, the idea of sets of objects is one of the earliest concepts which children form. They use sets of objects in learning the names of numbers and in learning to count. Even in such simple matters as distinguishing between different kinds of objects, they are implicitly using notions of sets of things having different characteristics.

In view of these considerations one may reasonably raise the question why children should have any difficulties in studying about sets in connection with algebra. The truth is that there need be very little difficulty at all, because the consideration of sets that is appropriate in connection with ninth-grade algebra should be largely intuitive and informal, and it should be concerned more with establishing foundations of ideas, terminology, and symbolism than with formal proofs of theorems about sets. At the same time, unless this work is carefully presented and unless enough practice is given both in translating the set symbolism into words and in translating verbal statements into appropriate set symbolism, some difficulties may arise. These would seem to stem mainly from three sources.

First, in their early experiences with sets, the attention of the students will usually have been focused either on the individual objects of the set or upon some characteristic that is common to these objects, rather than upon the set itself. Second, the usual operations with sets (union, intersection, complementation, inclusion) are different from the operations of arithmetic and school algebra to which the students have been accustomed. Third, and unquestionably most important, the terminology and symbolism generally associated with sets and operations with sets, and which the students must learn, will be new to them and will seem strange and esoteric at first. Most children will respond readily and correctly to the question, What positive integers are greater than 30 and less than 40? But write on the chalkboard the symbols

Let $\qquad\qquad P = \{x: x = 1, 2, \ldots, 39\}$

and $\qquad\qquad Q = \{y: y = 31, 32, 33, \ldots\}$

Then $\qquad\quad P \cap Q = \{ \qquad\qquad\qquad\qquad \}$

and ask them to fill in the last pair of braces, and they are likely to be baffled unless they have previously been taught how to translate these symbols into words.

Venn diagrams are very useful in helping students clarify the notions of union, intersection, complementation, and inclusion. It is also helpful to give illustrations employing finite sets having small numbers of objects. Not a great deal is known yet about how rapidly or how well high school freshmen can master the rules of operation with sets, but this question is probably not a very important one. It should be repeated that a formal study of the algebra of sets is not advocated for the ninth grade.

At the same time, an introduction to the concept of sets, explanation of the meanings attached to the terminology and symbolism employed, some simple illustrations and perhaps some simple exercises involving union and intersection of sets can bring several advantages. Through these avenues students can be made aware that mathematics is not a subject on which the last word has been written, but a live and growing field and that there are branches of mathematics other than the traditional algebra and geometry which are new and interesting and of growing importance. They can be given a little glimpse into one of these branches and can become acquainted with some of its technical words and symbols. Few high school students realize that there are algebras other than the conventional school algebra that they study. Some acquaintance with the other algebras can do much to broaden the students' mathematical horizons and give added interest to the work of the regular course in which they are enrolled.[1]

EXERCISES

1. Make a careful large-scale graphical solution of the system of equations $2a + 5b = 2\frac{9}{4}$ and $7a - b = \frac{9}{4}$. Consider the domain of each of the variables a and b to be the set of real numbers. Explain your work, estimate the solution as nearly as you

[1] For illustrations of various types of suggested adaptations to elementary algebra see:

Robert R. Christian, "Introduction to Logic and Sets" (Boston: Ginn & Company, 1958).

Report of the Commission on Mathematics, "Appendices" (New York: College Entrance Examination Board, 1959).

W. R. Krickenberger and Helen R. Pearson, "An Introduction to Sets and the Structure of Algebra" (Boston: Ginn & Company, 1958).

Report of the Secondary School Curriculum Committee, The Secondary Mathematics Curriculum, *Mathematics Teacher*, **52** (1959), 398–402.

can from the graph, and tell what the numerical values represent.   Check your solution by substituting the values of a and b in both equations.

2. Consider the two relations: $x + y \geqq 2$ and $2x + y = 4$ with the domains of both x and y the set of integers such that $-3 \leqq x \leqq +4$ and $-2 \leqq y \leqq +5$.

  a. Draw the graph of each relation.

  b. What is the solution set when the two relations are considered simultaneously?

  c. What is the solution set for the two relations when the "is greater than" ($>$) is removed from $x + y \geqq 2$?

3. Rework all parts of exercise 2, but this time let the domains of both x and y be the set of all real numbers.

4. Analyze in detail the reasoning process involved in the solution of the system $5x - 2y = 26$ and $2x + 3y = -1$.

5. Consider the following problem: The length of a rectangle is 2 inches less than twice its width, and its perimeter is 20 inches.   What are its dimensions?   Solve this problem by using just one equation in one unknown.   Then solve it by using two equations in two unknowns.   Show that in the first case you really used two equations in two unknowns but solved one of them mentally.

6. It frequently happens that ninth-grade students who can combine numerical fractions readily have trouble in performing the same operations with fractions involving literal symbols.   What, in your opinion, is the explanation of this?

7. Why is it important that students learn how to factor algebraic expressions before undertaking work with algebraic fractions?

8. In your opinion what are the things that a student must understand in order to take reducible algebraic fractions and reduce them to simpler terms?   Give examples to illustrate why these understandings are needed in order to perform this operation intelligently.

9. Show that in the process of simplifying a fraction or changing a fraction to higher terms the value of the fraction remains unchanged even though the form is changed.   Upon what mathematical principle does this rest?

10. In the process of reducing a fraction or changing it to higher terms the original value of the fraction must be preserved.   Explain why the value of a fraction is changed if the same nonzero number is added to or subtracted from both the numerator and the denominator of the fraction.

11. Point out the potential dangers of using the terms "cancel" and "cancellation" in ninth-grade algebra.   Give examples to illustrate.

12. In dividing one fraction by another, the rule "Invert the divisor, then multiply" is generally used.   Most students know this rule and know how to use it but very few can justify it.   If a student should ask you why the rule is valid, what explanation would you give him?

13. In explaining to ninth graders how to perform the operation $(6n/5) \div 3$, would you teach them to divide the numerator by 3, or would you teach them to regard the divisor as a fraction $3\!/\!1$ and then use the customary rule for dividing by a fraction? What advantage can you see in the method you prefer?

14. When fractions are to be combined by addition or subtraction, is it necessary that the original values of the fractions be preserved?

15. Explain as you would to a class in ninth-grade algebra why fractions can be combined by addition or subtraction only if they have the same denominator.

16. Explain as simply as you can the procedure for converting fractions with unlike denominators into equivalent fractions having the same denominator.   Give the reasoning that underlies and justifies the procedure.

17. Make a list of the specific difficulties and kinds of mistakes which students in

ninth-grade algebra can be expected to make in combining algebraic fractions by addition or subtraction.   Prepare explanations designed to help students overcome these difficulties and avoid these mistakes.

18. If one of your students should write $a/x + 5/(x + 3) = (a + 5)/(2x + 3)$, just what would you do to get him to see his error and understand why it is an error? What would you do to help him understand how to correct his mistake and check his result?

19. From ninth-grade textbooks select ten examples in the addition of fractions which, because of their complexity or difficulty, you consider inappropriate for average ninth-grade students.

20. Build up a set of 50 practice exercises in the addition and subtraction of fractions suitable for ninth-grade algebra.   Start with extremely simple ones and shade gradually into more and more complicated ones.   Never introduce more than one new complication at a time.

21. In adding fractions it is necessary to preserve the original value of each of the fractions involved.   Explain why this is not necessary in solving equations containing fractions.   Explain what it is that *must* be preserved in such equations.

22. In this chapter there is a discussion of some important considerations related to teaching the solution of equations containing fractions.   Give a clear and connected resumé of this discussion, emphasizing its salient points.

23. How do you account for the fact that students generally have more trouble with verbal problems than with other parts of algebra?   Be as specific as you can.

24. Students characteristically have difficulty both in reading verbal problems with understanding and interpreting them correctly and in translating them into the symbolic language of the equation.   How serious is the handicap imposed by these shortcomings?   What, if anything, can be done about it?

25. Verbal problems usually are solved by solving one or more equations arising from the problems.   Explain why, in checking the solutions, it is necessary to check them in the actual statements of the problems and why it is not enough merely to check them against the equations.

26. Read carefully 50 verbal problems chosen at random from ninth-grade algebra textbooks and list any words or expressions found in these problems which you think the students might not understand clearly.   Do you think vocabulary difficulties are a serious source of trouble with verbal problems?

27. Rules and formulas of algebra can often be illustrated effectively by numerical examples.   For instance, the general relation $a^2 - b^2 = (a - b)(a + b)$ can be illustrated by expressing 21 as $25 - 4$, or as $5^2 - 2^2$ and in turn as $(5 - 2)(5 + 2)$, or $(3)(7)$.   Select other algebraic rules and illustrate them in a similar manner.   Do you think this practice would serve to clarify the meanings of the rules to the students?

28. Explain in detail how you would make it clear and convincing to a class that the following definitions are consistent with the laws of operation with positive integral exponents:

$$x^{1/3} = \sqrt[3]{x}, \qquad x^{-3} = 1/x^3, \qquad x^0 = 1$$

29. Does your explanation of the relations set forth in exercise 28 constitute a proof of these relations, or does it merely define fractional, negative, and zero exponents? Explain.

30. What are the reasons for teaching special products and factoring?   Why should they be taught together?

31. Read carefully the chapter or section dealing with special products and factoring in a ninth-grade algebra textbook and make a list of all the words or expressions which you think a good many ninth-grade students might not understand clearly.

32. What special products and what types of factoring are suitable for ninth-grade algebra? Examine some ninth-grade textbooks and see whether you find included any types of factoring which in your opinion are not suitable for the ninth grade.

33. Make up a set of expressions or problems designed to promote understanding and appreciation of the use of parentheses. How important is this? Why? Give illustrations to show how failure to use or interpret the use of parentheses properly may lead to numerical mistakes.

34. Read carefully the reviews of some ninth-grade algebra books. Such reviews can be found in recent issues of *School Science and Mathematics* and the *Mathematics Teacher*.

35. Write a critical review of one recent textbook in ninth-grade algebra.

36. Let $S = \{x: 0 < x < 30\}$ and $T = \{x: 5 \leq x \leq 42\}$, where x is an integer. Then what does $S \cap T$ equal?

37. If a, b, and c are real numbers and if $a < b$ and $b < c$, is it true that $a < c$? If X, Y, and Z are sets, $X \subset Y$, and $Y \subset Z$, is it necessarily true that $X \subset Z$? (Note that in this case the rule for inclusion among sets is an exact counterpart of the rule for inequalities among real numbers.)

38. If a and b are real numbers and $a \neq b$, then either $a < b$ or $b < a$. If A and B are sets and $A \neq B$, is it necessarily true that either $A \subset B$ or $B \subset A$? (Note that sets are said to be equal if and only if they contain exactly the same elements.)

39. Consider the sets $A = \{7, 8, 9\}$ and $B = \{12, 13\}$. In this case note that the set $A \cap B$ contains no elements at all. Such a set is called the *empty* set, or the *null* set, and is usually designated by the symbol $\emptyset$. Give several examples of such sets, e.g., the set of all numbers each of which is less than 5 but greater than 8, or the set of living men who are more than 500 years old.

40. Let $\{a \ldots b\}$ be the set of points on a scaled line and in the interval extending from a on the left to b on the right. Let $A = \{3 \ldots 7\}$, $B = \{5 \ldots 12\}$, and $C = \{8 \ldots 15\}$. Then express correctly in set notation each of the following: $A \cup B$, $B \cup C$, $A \cup C$, $A \cap B$, $B \cap C$, and $A \cap C$.

BIBLIOGRAPHY

Adams, L. J., and Clifford Bell: Installment Buying, *Mathematics Teacher*, **43** (1950), 388–391.

Beatley, Ralph: Reason and Rule in Arithmetic and Algebra, *Mathematics Teacher*, **47** (1954), 234–244.

Beberman, Max, and Bruce E. Meserve: An Exploratory Approach to Solving Equations, *Mathematics Teacher*, **49** (1956), 15–18.

Breslich, E. R.: "Problems in Teaching Secondary-school Mathematics" (Chicago: University of Chicago Press, 1931), pp. 107–232.

Brown, Claude H.: "The Teaching of Secondary Mathematics" (New York: Harper & Brothers, 1953), pp. 180–222.

Butler, Charles H.: Home-made Problems for Algebra, *Mathematics Teacher*, **45** (1952), 384–386.

———: A Note on Writing Fractions, *Mathematics Teacher*, **47** (1954), 527.

Clements, C. Robert: Work Problems Made Easy, *Mathematics Teacher*, **48** (1955), 582–585.

Commission on Mathematics: "Concepts of Equation and Inequality" (New York: College Entrance Examination Board, 1958). (Sample classroom unit for high school algebra students.)

———: "Appendices" (New York: College Entrance Examination Board, 1959), pp. 2–7.

Davis, David R.: "The Teaching of Mathematics" (Reading, Mass.: Addison-Wesley Publishing Company, 1951), pp. 200–209.

Denbow, Carl H.: On the Use of Variators in the Teaching of Algebra, *School Science and Mathematics*, **54** (1954), 65–68.

Duke, Mary White: How I Teach Algebra, *Mathematics Teacher*, **47** (1954), 131–134.

Durell, Fletcher: "Mathematical Adventures" (Boston: Bruce Humphries, Inc., 1938), pp. 47–59.

Ellis, Fred E.: The Function of Verbal Problems in Elementary Algebra, *Mathematics Teacher*, **36** (1943), 230–232.

Fehr, Howard F.: Operations in the Systems of Positive and Negative Numbers and Zero, *Mathematics Teacher*, **42** (1949), 171–176.

Fouch, Robert S.: On the Definability of Zero to the Power Zero, *School Science and Mathematics*, **53** (1953), 693–696.

Fulkerson, Elbert: Teaching Signs in Fractions, *Mathematics Teacher*, **40** (1947), 71–74.

Georges, J. S.: Learning to Solve Problems Intelligently, *School Science and Mathematics*, **56** (1956), 701–707.

Grove, Ethel L., and others: Models for Introducing Special Products, *School Science and Mathematics*, **50** (1950), 662–664.

Hartung, Maurice L., and Robert L. Erickson: Graphical Methods in Science and Mathematics Teaching, *School Science and Mathematics*, **50** (1950), 200–208.

Hassler, J. O., and R. R. Smith: "The Teaching of Secondary Mathematics" (New York: The Macmillan Company, 1930), pp. 239–296.

Hazard, William J.: "Algebra Notes" (New York: Vantage Press, Inc., 1952).

Henderson, K. B., and R. E. Pingry: Problem Solving in Mathematics, "Twenty-first Yearbook" (Washington, D.C.: National Council of Teachers of Mathematics, 1953), pp. 228–270.

Henderson, Ronald: How I Teach Analysis of Verbal Problems, *Mathematics Teacher*, **47** (1954), 275–276.

Ingraham, W. W.: The Graphic Solution of a Problem Involving Simple Linear Equations, *Mathematics Teacher*, **38** (1945), 175–176.

Jerbert, A. R.: Division by Zero, *School Science and Mathematics*, **49** (1949), 484–488.

Keppers, George L.: Is Algebra a "Tool Subject"? *School Science and Mathematics*, **55** (1955), 296–300.

Kinney, Lucien Blair, and C. Richard Purdy: "Teaching Mathematics in the Secondary School" (New York: Rinehart & Company, Inc., 1952), pp. 64–99.

Kinsella, John J., and Walter H. Carnahan: Putting Meaning into Algebraic Concepts and Relationships, *School Science and Mathematics*, **49** (1949), 19–26.

Klimczak, W. J.: The Solution of Linear Equations and Inequalities, *Mathematics Teacher*, **48** (1955), 460–463.

Lewis, Eunice: The Pupil Discovers Algebra, *Mathematics Teacher*, **47** (1954), 81–85.

Ligda, Paul: "The Teaching of Elementary Algebra" (Boston: Houghton Mifflin Company, 1925), pp. 63–209.

Meighan, John N.: Methods of Solving Elementary Systems of Equations in Two Unknowns, *School Science and Mathematics*, **47** (1947), 709–714.

Miller, G. H.: Difficulties in Algebra: A Study, *School Science and Mathematics*, **58** (1958), 714–720.

Minnick, J. H.: "Teaching Mathematics in the Secondary Schools" (Englewood Cliffs, N.J.: Prentice-Hall, Inc., 1939), pp. 115–151.

Mossman, Edith: So-called Shortcuts Often Cause Confusion, *Mathematics Teacher*, **40** (1947), 62–64.

Myers, Sheldon S. (Editor): Applications, *Mathematics Teacher*, **45** (1952), 210–214; 522–524.

Niessen, Abraham M.: The Extension of the Exponent Concept, *School Science and Mathematics*, **48** (1948), 605–610.

O'Brien, Katherine: Problem Solving, *Mathematics Teacher*, **49** (1956), 79–86.

Peak, Philip: Algebra Problems and Problems in Life, *Mathematics Teacher*, **41** (1948), 266–269.

Perisho, Clarence R.: A Non-commutative Algebra, *School Science and Mathematics*, **58** (1958), 727–730.

Reeve, William David: "Mathematics for the Secondary School" (New York: Henry Holt and Company, Inc., 1954), p. 245–294.

Rev. Brother Leo: Making New Exercises from Old Ones, *Mathematics Teacher*, **52** (1959), 307–309.

Rich, Barnett: The Place of the Variable in the Teaching of Mathematics, *Mathematics Teacher*, **48** (1955), 538–541.

Schaaf, Oscar: Student Discovery of Algebraic Principles as a Means of Developing Ability to Generalize, *Mathematics Teacher*, **48** (1955), 324–327.

Schaaf, William L.: "Mathematics for Junior High School Teachers" (Richmond, Va.: Johnson Publishing Company, 1931), pp. 391–431.

——: The Use of Simple Algebra in Business Arithmetic, *Mathematics Teacher*, **44** (1951), 22–25.

Schorling, Raleigh: "The Teaching of Mathematics" (Ann Arbor, Mich.: The Ann Arbor Press, 1936), pp. 108–116.

Schultze, Arthur: "The Teaching of Mathematics in Secondary Schools" (New York: The Macmillan Company, 1927), pp. 312–332.

Singleton, Marilyn C.: An Approach to Solving Word Problems, *Mathematics Teacher*, **51** (1958), 212–213.

Smith, D. E., and W. D. Reeve: "The Teaching of Junior High School Mathematics" (Boston: Ginn & Company, 1927), pp. 183–216.

Sobel, Max A.: Concept Learning in Algebra, *Mathematics Teacher*, **49** (1956), 425–430.

Strickland, Warren: Algebra of Complex Numbers, *School Science and Mathematics*, **58** (1958), 690–692.

Torreyson, Homer C.: Equation Balances, *School Science and Mathematics*, **55** (1955), 104–108.

Tucker, A. N.: On the Meaning, Use, and Importance of Zero, *School Science and Mathematics*, **52** (1952), 443–444.

Van Engen, H.: Logical Approaches to $(-a)(-b) = ab$ and $x^0 = 1$, *Mathematics Teacher*, **40** (1947), 182–185.

15

THE TEACHING OF ALGEBRA IN THE
SENIOR HIGH SCHOOL AND
THE JUNIOR COLLEGE

The subject matter of algebra is very cumulative; hence at the higher levels it makes continual use of the concepts, principles, and operations developed in the ninth-grade work at the same time that new concepts and new principles are introduced and studied. From one standpoint the broader objectives of the instruction at the more advanced level offer certain points of contrast with the objectives of the junior high school. In particular, the elective status of the higher courses implies a somewhat different personnel in such classes. The students are likely to be inherently more interested and capable than typical junior high school students. It is also quite probable that they are studying algebra because of its usefulness in academic or professional fields. In view of these facts, the technical aspects of algebra may legitimately come to occupy a relatively more important place among the instructional aims. This, of course, does not imply any lessening of the emphasis upon understanding, but it does imply a progressively increasing insistence upon the mastery of the algebraic tools.

Qualitatively, the general aims are the same as before, viz., to develop and clarify understandings, to produce familiarity with the terminology, notation, and symbolism of algebra, and to perfect operational facility. The expanding field introduces new difficulties which are offset only in part by added maturity of the students and by the operation of the principle of progressive selectivity. Intelligence and reasonable mastery of prerequisite work are necessary conditions for the successful study of algebra at these higher levels, but they are not in themselves sufficient. The teacher's role is still one of extreme importance, and his effectiveness will depend in great measure upon his ability to anticipate and overcome specific difficulties which the students are likely to have with particular topics.

Review Work in Beginning Intermediate Algebra. In beginning the course in intermediate algebra, teachers generally find it necessary to make some review of the work of the ninth grade. Indeed, most textbooks in the more advanced algebra courses begin with several chapters which are essentially reviews of various phases of the earlier work. Much time may be wasted in this review work, however, unless it is carefully and purposefully planned. It is well at the outset to take a rather careful inventory of the algebraic equipment of the class. This may be done by administering a comprehensive inventory test. If it is done at the beginning and if the results are immediately tabulated and analyzed, it is possible for the teacher to have very soon a fairly accurate picture of the needs of the class for review work. If these tabulated results are used as a basis for planning and conducting the review, it will be possible to concentrate attention on those places where the need is evident and to dispense with unnecessary work on other topics.

There is an advantage in spreading the review over some 2 or 3 weeks and giving it in small doses interspersed with new work instead of concentrating it all in the first few days and leaving it as finished business. If the students get nothing but review work for several days, it becomes tiresome. Some new work offered along with the review provides both variety and incentive. The distribution of time in this way also makes for more effective learning. Among the things which are likely to need special attention in this review work may be mentioned the language of algebra (substitution and evaluation), positive and negative numbers, easy formal work in the fundamental operations, the solution of literal equations, and easy work with fractions.

Need for Teaching Even Simple Details Specifically. Teachers often overlook the very important fact that much of the difficulty which students have with algebra is due to their failure to understand and generalize certain critical *details* of the work or to appreciate the bearing of these details upon the work as a whole. It is not at all uncommon for students to find themselves confused and their progress blocked merely because of lack of understanding of some apparently minor point. In many cases when the proper cue is given or the troublesome detail is cleared up, the student is able to proceed with independence and satisfaction. Many such details appear so familiar, simple, and obvious that teachers do not recognize them as troublemakers, but it is not wise to assume too much in this respect, even in the matter of recognizing equivalent expressions and making proper substitution. The following examples will make this clear.

Frequently students experience difficulty because they fail to *recognize* the equivalence or identity of certain algebraic expressions. This is particularly true with reference to indicated products and quotients, roots, and exponents.   For example, the expressions $x^3/2$ and $\frac{1}{2}x^3$ are precisely equivalent, but even in such simple cases it is not uncommon to find students who are unable to recognize the fundamental equivalence. Other examples of equivalent expressions in which the identity is not always readily discerned are found in such illustrations as the following:

$$\frac{2}{3}\,xy,\ \frac{2x}{3}\,y,\ 2y\,\frac{x}{3},\ \text{and } 2\,\frac{xy}{3}$$

$$\frac{1}{2}\,h(b+B),\ \frac{h}{2}\,(b+B),\ \frac{b+B}{2}\,h,\ \text{and } \frac{(b+B)h}{2}$$

$$\sqrt{7x} \text{ and } \sqrt{7}\cdot\sqrt{x}$$

$$\frac{\sqrt{x}}{\sqrt{y}} \text{ and } \sqrt{\frac{x}{y}}$$

$$\left(\frac{x}{y}\right)^3 \text{ and } \frac{x^3}{y^3}$$

$$x^3y^3 \text{ and } (xy)^3$$

Students also frequently fail to recognize the fact that, whereas in the multiplication of a polynomial the multiplier must be applied to each term in the polynomial, in the multiplication of an indicated product of two or more factors the multiplier is applied to only one factor (any factor) of the indicated product.   Likewise, they do not always recognize that to multiply a fraction means to multiply only its numerator.   Hence such erroneous statements as

$$r(x+y)(a+b) = (rx+ry)(ra+rb) \qquad \text{or} \qquad 3\,\frac{a}{b} = \frac{3a}{3b}$$

are of common occurrence.

Another case in point is found in connection with the substitution of one expression for another in a function or a formula.   For example, the teacher immediately sees in the expression $8x^6 - 125y^9$ the difference of two cubes and associates the expression at once with the form $a^3 - b^3$.   It seems so natural to identify $2x^2$ with a and $5y^3$ with b that it may not even occur to him that the student will have any difficulty. However, it takes specific teaching, deliberately designed to emphasize this particular association, to give the students a feeling of security and assurance in handling such situations.   The acts of recognition, identification, association, and substitution which are involved are things which will be successfully mastered in most cases only if they are taught specifically and if considerable special practice is given in performing them.

Many other illustrations could be given.   There is nothing in these situations themselves which is inherently difficult.   The correct interpretations can invariably be explained easily and to the entire satisfaction of the students by dealing with them deliberately and specifically. Numerical examples are often sufficient, but the students must be continually impressed with the need for associating the specific illustration with the generalized procedure. The trouble is that teachers do not keep themselves sensitive to the fact that the students need to be taught to generalize these details. They take too much for granted. The reason why most students do not react properly to such situations is that they are not taught to do so. The teacher, if he gives any thought to it at all, generally assumes that the principles or the generalizations are so obvious that they need no discussion. It is a fact, however, that this assumption cannot safely be made. The only reasonable assurance of the effective functioning of these recognitions, identifications, and generalizations is to give special instruction and carefully planned practice designed specifically to this end.

This instruction, however, needs to be more than superficial. It needs to stress the basic principles that apply to the different operations, particularly the commutative, associative, and distributive laws. Students need to be kept sensitive to the fact that these laws are taken as axioms and that as such, they provide the formal justification for asserting that two or more algebraic expressions are equivalent, or are names for the same thing. The students in these classes will already have had one course in algebra, and they should now be given a more mathematically mature approach to material with which they had previously worked in an earlier grade.

More about Simultaneous Linear Equations. When more than two equations are involved in a system of linear equations, the most effective techniques for solving are based on the concept of a rectangular array of the coefficients of the system. Such a rectangular array is called a *matrix*. Consider the system of equations

$$x - y + 2z = 5 \tag{1}$$
$$4x - 2y + 3z = 9 \tag{2}$$
$$3x + 4y - 5z = -4 \tag{3}$$

There are basically two matrices associated with such a system of equations, the *coefficient matrix* and the *augmented matrix*. The coefficient matrix is merely the rectangular array consisting of the coefficients of the system. Here it is

$$\begin{pmatrix} 1 & -1 & 2 \\ 4 & -2 & 3 \\ 3 & 4 & -5 \end{pmatrix}$$

The augmented matrix is obtained by annexing to the coefficient matrix the column of constant terms. The augmented matrix of the above system is

$$\begin{pmatrix} 1 & -1 & 2 & 5 \\ 4 & -2 & 3 & 9 \\ 3 & 4 & -5 & -4 \end{pmatrix}$$

The two methods to be discussed here are essentially methods of synthetic elimination in that the process is concerned with the detached coefficients of a system of equations as displayed in the augmented matrix of the system.   No proof will be given of the validity of either technique, but a bit of careful examination will reveal the fact that each technique is closely related to the process of elimination by subtraction.

The Pivotal-element Method.   Consider the elements of the augmented matrix of the system of equations with an annexed column in which each element is the sum of the numbers in the row in which it occurs.   In row

	x	y	z	c	S
(1)	1	-1	2	5	7
(2)	4	-2	3	9	14
(3)	3	4	-5	-4	-2
(2')		2	-5	-11	-14
(3')		7	-11	-19	-23
(3'')			13	39	52

(1) for example, $7 = 1 + (-1) + 2 + 5$.   The technique of the pivotal-element method involves the selection of any nonzero element of the coefficient matrix as the pivotal element.   If there is a 1 among these coefficients, it should be used in order to simplify the computation as much as possible.   Here the coefficient of x in the first equation is 1, and it is chosen as the pivotal element.   The row and column to which this chosen element belongs are then blocked out (here row 1 and column 1).   The augmented matrix is then transformed in the following manner:

1. Each element of the augmented matrix, not included in either the row or column which is blocked out, is replaced by a determinant of order two.   The corresponding elements of the sum column are replaced in the same manner.   For example, the elements of the second row in the matrix of the given system of equations, which are to be replaced, are -2, 3, 9, and 14.

If we use P to represent the pivotal element and R to represent the replaced element, then, for this illustration, P is 1 and R is, in turn, -2, 3,

9 and 14. For equation (3) R will be 4, -5, -4, and -2, respectively, while P, of course, remains 1. The symbol e_{pr} will be used to represent the element in the same row as the pivotal element and the same column as the replaced element, and e_{rp} will represent the element in the same row as the replaced element and the same column as the pivotal element.

2. Construct the determinant

$$\begin{vmatrix} P & e_{pr} \\ e_{rp} & R \end{vmatrix} = PR - e_{pr}e_{rp}$$

for each element which is to be replaced. For example,

-2 is replaced by $\begin{vmatrix} 1 & -1 \\ 4 & -2 \end{vmatrix} = (1)(-2) - (-1)(4) = 2$

3 by $\begin{vmatrix} 1 & 2 \\ 4 & 3 \end{vmatrix} = (1)(3) - (2)(4) = -5$

9 by $\begin{vmatrix} 1 & 5 \\ 4 & 9 \end{vmatrix} = (1)(9) - (5)(4) = -11$

14 by $\begin{vmatrix} 1 & 7 \\ 4 & 14 \end{vmatrix} = (1)(14) - (7)(4) = -14$

The elements in row 3 are replaced in a similar manner.

3. The new element in the sum column must be equal to the sum of the remaining elements in the same row. For example,

$$-14 = 2 + (-5) + (-11)$$

This is a good rapid check, but it is not an infallible check. If the equality does not hold, there is an error. It should be evident, however, that owing to the possibility of compensating errors, the equality might hold even though errors would be present.

4. Continue the process, each time choosing as the pivotal element a nonzero element from the transformed coefficient matrix. Each transformation has the effect of eliminating the unknown for which the pivotal element was the coefficient. For example, if x were eliminated by subtraction from the above system of equations, the resulting system would be the two equations whose coefficients are displayed in rows 2' and 3'. Since 2, a coefficient of y, is chosen as the pivotal element in the second transformation, the row 3'' represents the equation $13z = 39$.

5. From the final equation determine the value of one of the unknowns. Use this value in an equation of the immediately previous system to determine a second unknown. Use these two values to determine a third unknown, and continue until values for all unknowns have been determined. For example, $13z = 39$ gives $z = 3$; use either 2' or 3' to

find $y = 2$; use either 1, 2, or 3 to find $x = 1$. Check in the remaining equations of the original system.

In the above discussion of the pivotal-element technique three equations with simple integral coefficients were chosen. All the computations can be made mentally in all such cases. The process is effective for any number of equations and with complicated coefficients. In such cases computing machines can make the computations effectively and rapidly, the most difficult problem being the control on the proper number of significant digits to retain in the rounding process that becomes necessary.

There are systems of equations which do not produce unique solutions. In such cases some of the unknowns may be expressed in terms of the remaining unknowns. If a system of equations in n unknowns is such that r of the unknowns can be expressed in terms of the remaining $n - r$ unknowns, then the pivotal-element technique will produce proportional rows after $r - 1$ transformations. For example, consider the system of equations

$$2x - 3y + z - u = -1 \qquad (1)$$
$$3x + y - z + 2u = 5 \qquad (2)$$
$$5x - 2y + u = 4 \qquad (3)$$
$$5x + 9y - 5z + 8u = 17 \qquad (4)$$

The augmented matrix with the sum column is

	x	y	z	u	c	S
(1)	2	-3	1	-1	-1	-2
(2)	3	1	-1	2	5	10
(3)	5	-2	0	1	4	8
(4)	5	9	-5	8	17	34
(2′)	5	-2		1	4	8
(3′)	5	-2		1	4	8
(4′)	15	-6		3	12	24

One transformation has produced rows which are proportional, so two of the unknowns may be expressed in terms of the remaining $4 - 2$, or 2, unknowns. For example, from row 2′ $u = 4 - 5x + 2y$. This value used in equation (1) gives $z = 3 - 7x + 5y$. These values will check in equations (3) and (4).

It is important to note that the determinant $\begin{vmatrix} P & e_{pr} \\ e_{rp} & R \end{vmatrix}$ is used to replace the element R, although the pivotal element, P, is not in the first column.

The rows and columns in which P and R occur have no effect on the second order determinant used to replace R.

In the illustrative example the number of equations is the same as the number of the unknowns. This is not necessary.

The Sweep-out Process. This process is quite similar to the pivotal-element process. Again, consider the augmented matrix of the first system of equations. In each row divide all elements by the element which is the coefficient of x in the corresponding equation. (If this coefficient is zero, use the first nonzero element in the row.) This process produces equations (1'), (2'), and (3'). Subtract the elements of row 1' from the corresponding elements of rows 2' and 3' to produce rows 4 and 5, respectively. This has, in effect, eliminated x from the three equations

	x	y	z	c	S
(1)	1	-1	2	5	7
(2)	4	-2	3	9	14
(3)	3	4	-5	-4	-2
(1')	1	-1	2	5	7
(2')	1	$-\frac{1}{2}$	$\frac{3}{4}$	$\frac{9}{4}$	$\frac{7}{2}$
(3')	1	$\frac{4}{3}$	$-\frac{5}{3}$	$-\frac{4}{3}$	$-\frac{2}{3}$
(4)	$[(2') - (1')]$	$\frac{1}{2}$	$-\frac{5}{4}$	$-11\frac{1}{4}$	$-\frac{7}{2}$
(5)	$[(3') - (1')]$	$\frac{7}{3}$	$-11\frac{1}{3}$	$-19\frac{1}{3}$	$-23\frac{2}{3}$
(4')		1	$-\frac{5}{2}$	$-11\frac{1}{2}$	-7
(5')		1	$-11\frac{4}{7}$	$-19\frac{4}{7}$	$-23\frac{4}{7}$
(6)	$[(5') - (4')]$		$13\frac{1}{14}$	$39\frac{1}{14}$	$26\frac{4}{7}$

and produced two equations in two unknowns, y and z. Divide the elements in rows 4 and 5 by the leading nonzero coefficient to produce rows 4' and 5' and then subtract 4' from 5'. This operation has, in effect, eliminated y from the two equations, leaving the one equation $\frac{13}{14}z = 39\frac{1}{14}$, or $z = 3$. This value of z can be substituted in row 4', 5', 4, or 5 to determine a value for y. The values of y and z can then be substituted in any one of the three original equations to determine a value for x. The three values thus determined can then be checked in the remaining two equations.

As in the pivotal-element method, each operation can be checked by the fact that the element in the sum column must be the same as the sum of the remaining elements in that particular row.

Solving Quadratic Equations in One Unknown.   Five methods for solving quadratic equations are commonly taught.   They are (1) solving by the graphical method, (2) solving by inspection (in the case of incomplete quadratics), (3) solving by factoring, (4) solving by completing the square, and (5) solving by use of the quadratic formula.

The graphical method is not strictly an algebraic method and can give only approximate solutions, but it is very valuable in clarifying the meaning and nature of the two roots, just as the graph itself is useful in bringing out certain important characteristics of the function.   There are four essential things for the students to understand: (1) The graph is the geometric picture of a *function* of the independent variable and, as the independent variable takes on different values, the function also takes on different values; (2) since the general form of the quadratic equation is $ax^2 + bx + c = 0$, we seek to find those values of x which will make the function $y = ax^2 + bx + c$ have the value zero; (3) the only points on the graph for which the function can have value zero are those points which are on the x axis; and (4) consequently, the abscissas of those points give the values of the independent variable which satisfy the equation.   These values are sometimes called the *zeros of the function*.   The graph also can be used effectively to show why two real and distinct roots may exist, why the roots are sometimes real and equal, and why, in certain cases, there are no real roots.

Just as in the case of the linear relations, it is important that the student have a clear understanding of just what is represented by a quadratic relation.   Consider the two relations

$$x^2 + y^2 \leqq 25 \tag{1}$$
$$y = x^2 - 5 \tag{2}$$

Example 1.   Let the domain and range of $x^2 + y^2 \leqq 25$ be the set of integers, and for $y = x^2 - 5$ let the domain be the set of integers such that $-4 \leqq x \leqq 4$ while the range is the set of integers such that $-5 \leqq y \leqq 11$.   The *complete* graph for relation (1) consists of all those points marked by dots in Fig. 15-1, and the *complete* graph for relation 2 consists of all those points marked by crosses. When the two relations are considered simultaneously, the solution set consists of all those points common to the two graphs, namely, those marked by a crossed-over dot.   It is the set $\{(0,-5), (-1,-4), (1,-4), (-2,-1), (2,-1), (-3,4), (3,4)\}$.

Example 2.   Let the domain and range of the two relations be the set of all real numbers.   The *complete* graph of the relation $x^2 + y^2 \leqq 25$ will be the circle and the area which it encloses, as is indicated by the shaded portion of Fig. 15-2. The *incomplete* graph of the relation $y = x^2 - 5$ will be the portion of the parabola that is shown in the figure.   When the two relations are considered simultaneously, the solution set will consist of all the points on the portion of the parabola that lies within the shaded part of the figure.   If the condition of "less than"

($<$) is removed from relation (1), then the graph of this relation becomes the circle. In this case the solution set of relations (1) and (2), considered simultaneously, becomes the set $\{(0,-5), (-3,4), \text{ and } (3,4)\}$.

Similar considerations are present when a quadratic relation and a linear relation are considered simultaneously.

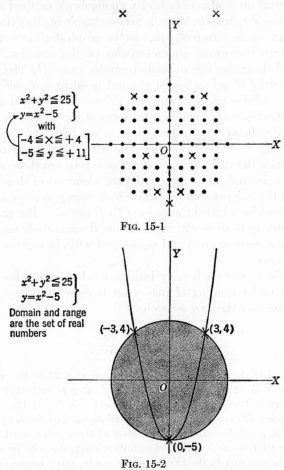

$$\left. \begin{array}{l} x^2+y^2 \leqq 25 \\ y=x^2-5 \end{array} \right\}$$
with
$$\left. \begin{array}{l} -4 \leqq x \leqq +4 \\ -5 \leqq y \leqq +11 \end{array} \right]$$

Fig. 15-1

$$\left. \begin{array}{l} x^2+y^2 \leqq 25 \\ y=x^2-5 \end{array} \right\}$$
Domain and range are the set of real numbers

$(-3,4)$ $(3,4)$

$(0,-5)$

Fig. 15-2

The graph of $y = x^2 - 5$ is a special case of the graph of the quadratic function

$$y = ax^2 + bx + c \qquad a \neq 0$$

The condition $a \neq 0$ guarantees that the function has the characteristics of a quadratic function; it also guarantees the possibility of certain operational procedures which are desirable in dealing with the function. For a proper understanding of the essential characteristics of this function it is necessary to examine the effect which each coefficient in the formula has on the graph.   For the illustrative examples it will be sufficient to specify the set of real numbers as both the domain and range of the function.

Example 3.   The effect of c on the graph of $y = ax^2 + bx + c$, Fig. 15-3.   It should be evident that $(0,c)$ is always a point on the graph; that is, c is the y intercept of the graph.   A comparison of the graphs of the functions $y = x^2 + 2$, $y = x^2$, and $y = x^2 - 5$ is sufficient to show that a change in the value of c merely shifts the position of the intercept on the y axis.   Note that in each of these three cases the curve is open upward and the y intercept is the lowest point on the curve.   It is a *minimum point;* that is, the function has a *minimum value* at this point.

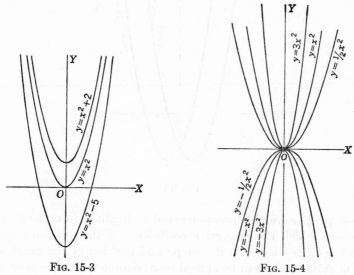

FIG. 15-3   FIG. 15-4

Example 4.   The effect of a on the graph of the function $y = ax^2 + bx + c$. This effect is of two types.   In Fig. 15-4 a comparison of the graphs of the functions $y = ax^2$, where the coefficients a are numerically equal but opposite in sign, will reveal the following facts: when $a > 0$, the curves are open upward and have a minimum point; when $a < 0$, the curves are open downward and have a maximum (highest) point.

Furthermore, a comparison of curves for the equations in which the coefficients a have the same sign but differ in numerical value will reveal that, as a gets larger in numerical value, the curve tends to close up toward the y axis and, as a gets smaller in numerical value, the curve tends to stretch out away from the y axis.

In both of the above examples all of the curves are symmetric with respect to the y axis.   This means that $x = \pm k$ substituted into a quadratic function of the form $y = ax^2 + c$, where $a \neq 0$, will produce the same value for y, namely, $y = ak^2 + c$.

Example 5.　The effect of b on the graph of the function $y = ax^2 + bx + c$. A simple illustration of the effect which a change in b will have on the graph of the quadratic function can be obtained from a comparison of the graphs of the two functions $y = x^2 - 2x - 3$ and $y = x^2 + 2x - 3$.　Here simple values of a and c are used, but they remain the same for the two functions.　The only difference is in the value of the coefficient b.　The effect on the graph, Fig. 15-5, has been to shift along the x axis both the minimum point [from $(+1, -4)$ to $(-1, -4)$] and the axis of symmetry (from $x = 1$ to $x = -1$).

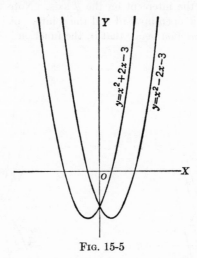

FIG. 15-5

These special examples have portrayed in simplified form the characteristic effects which the respective coefficients of the quadratic function $y = ax^2 + bx + c$ have on the shape and position of the graph of the function.　Each case can be argued more rigorously for the general case by directing attention to the equivalent form of the function

$$y = a\left(x + \frac{b}{2a}\right)^2 + \frac{4ac - b^2}{4a}$$

which exhibits $x = -b/2a$ as the axis of symmetry and the point $(-b/2a, 4ac - b^2/4a)$ as the minimum point (if $a > 0$) or the maximum point (if $a < 0$).[1]

Because it is slow and tedious, the graphical solution should not be required for many problems.　Its purpose will have been served when it has been used in a few cases to clarify and amplify the students' understanding of quadratic equations and their solutions.　The major

---

[1] For a more detailed discussion of the quadratic function see the Report of the Commission on Mathematics, "Appendices" (New York: College Entrance Examination Board, 1959), pp. 36-57.

part of the work with quadratic equations should be concerned with algebraic rather than graphical solutions.

The second method mentioned above—that of solving by inspection— is so simple and obvious that often it is not even listed as a method of solution. The third offers little difficulty to students except possibly in the factoring, and this will merely require careful attention. There is nothing inherently new about the process, but there is one point that may need reexplanation. When an equation such as $x^2 + 5x - 14 = 0$ is given in factored form as $(x + 7)(x - 2) = 0$, it is not always clear to the students why one has the right to set the factors separately equal to zero and thus get two linear equations. The justification for this should be made clear. That is, it should be explained that, if either of the factors is zero, the function itself will be equal to zero and the equation is thus satisfied, and conversely, the *only* way in which the equation can be satisfied is for at least one of the factors to be equal to zero.

In taking up the method of solving quadratics by completing the square, it will be well to review briefly the characteristics of the perfect trinomial square of the form $x^2 + 2bx + b^2$ in order that the students may get well in mind the relation between the coefficient of x and the term free of x. This is the crux of the whole matter, and it should be carefully explained and freely illustrated. It is desirable that the students themselves should make the generalization and be able to state it in words. The generality of this method of solution should be emphasized and contrasted with the lack of generality (in terms of real numbers) of the factoring method. It will not be necessary, however, to spend much time in actually solving equations by this method, since its principal function here is to provide a means for developing the general quadratic formula.

The general quadratic formula is of such special importance and usefulness that it should be thoroughly mastered by every student. Its development requires the use of the method of completing the square and provides an excellent review of operations with literal symbols. The development should be carefully explained, and the students should be tested for their understanding of every step. The formula itself is indispensable, and every student should memorize it and use it until he is perfectly familiar with its form and meaning.

In connection with the study of this formula, the teacher should see to it that the students understand the meaning of the discriminant and that they understand why it is possible, in a quadratic equation under proper hypotheses of reality or rationality of the coefficients, to determine the nature of the roots from a study of the discriminant alone, without solving the equation. To this end it is desirable for the teacher and students to examine and discuss together a variety of quadratic equations with numerical coefficients, after which the students may well be given exercises such as the following.

Exercise. In each of the following quadratic equations the coefficients are rational numbers. Indicate in each case the nature of the roots so far as this can be determined from the discriminant alone. Do not solve the equations.

Equation	Discriminant $b^2 - 4ac$	Nature of roots		
		Real or imaginary	Equal or unequal	Rational or irrational
$x^2 + 7x + 6 = 0$				
$3y^2 + 7y + 2 = 0$				
$2x^2 - 2x + 11 = 0$				
$x^2 - 10x + 25 = 0$				
$5x^2 + x - 7 = 0$				

Exercises of this sort demand and develop insight into the role of the discriminant in determining the nature of the roots and contribute materially to the understanding and appreciation of the generality of the formula. In any discussion of the use of the discriminant, exercises of the form (1) $x^2 - \sqrt{5}x - 5 = 0$ and (2) $2x^2 + 6ix - 9 = 0$ should be used by way of contrast to those listed in the table. The purpose is to place specific emphasis on the importance of the hypothesis of reality and rationality on the coefficients of the quadratic. In example 1 the discriminant is rational but the roots are irrational. (The coefficients are *not* rational.) In example 2 the discriminant is positive but the roots are not real. (The coefficients are *not* real.)

Not infrequently students have difficulty in dealing with equations such as $x^6 + 13x^3 + 36 = 0$. The difficulty almost invariably lies in the failure to recognize that, while this, for example, is a sixth-degree equation in x, it may be regarded as a quadratic equation in x^3 and so may be solved easily for x^3, the values of x itself then being readily found by taking the cube roots of x^3. To help the students become sensitive to the possibility of reducing such equations to quadratic form, a variety of examples should be given, the quadratic form being written out in each case. Thus $x^8 + 5x^4 - 2 = 0$ may be written $(x^4)^2 + 5(x^4) - 2 = 0$, or, if preferred, a different letter, say z, may be substituted for x^4 so that the equation becomes $z^2 + 5z - 2 = 0$. The illustrations should include examples involving radicals and fractional exponents, such as $x + 3\sqrt{x} - 18 = 0$ and $2x^{2/3} + 8x^{1/3} + 12 = 0$. After a number of illustrative examples have been given, the principle may be generalized to help in subsequent recognition of such cases.

In the work of the twelfth grade or of the first year of college algebra there should be extensive applications of the foregoing methods to the solution of quadratic equations in one unknown. This work would necessarily involve the use of radicals and imaginary and complex numbers. The quadratic formula as a general solution should be stressed. Such work may appropriately be extended to include the investigation of certain other general properties of quadratic equations, particularly the relations existing among the roots and the coefficients. It should lead to the subsequent study of quadratic equations and systems of equations in two unknowns.

Many students who are able to apply the quadratic formula explicitly in determining the roots of a given equation find themselves at a loss when confronted with situations in which the formula is implicitly involved. The following illustrative examples are cases in point.

Examples. In each of the following equations determine the real values of k for which the roots will be equal:

$$4x^2 - 12x + k = 0$$
$$2kx^2 + 5x + 1 = 0$$
$$x^2 - 8kx + 4 = 0$$

There usually will be a few students who will be able to sense for themselves the role of the discriminant in such cases, but for many of them it will need to be pointed out and illustrated specifically. In particular it will be necessary to review the fact that the equality or inequality of the roots of such equations is determined solely according to whether the discriminant $b^2 - 4ac$ is or is not equal to zero, and consequently the condition for their equality is that k must be of such value as will make this discriminant zero. That is, the student must come to sense the fact that, in order to produce the required condition and to discover the required value of k, the discriminant of the particular equation must be set equal to zero and the resulting equation solved for k.

The relations between the roots and the coefficients should be carefully developed. Most textbooks give the bare symbolic development of these formulas but are usually lacking in explanatory comment. To supply adequate explanation of the development and pointed comment with reference to applying these relations must be the task of the teacher. He must use a variety of problems which will provide the student with the opportunity of seeing the formulas applied both explicitly and implicitly. For example:

Example. Find the sum and product of the roots without solving.

$$5x^2 - 3x + 8 = 0$$
$$2x + 5 = x^2$$

Example. Given the equation and one root, as indicated; find the other root without solving.

$$x^2 - 11x + 24 = 0 \qquad \text{(one root is 8)}$$
$$2x^2 - 17x + 33 = 0 \qquad \text{(one root is 3)}$$

Example. Given the roots as indicated; write the equations.

Roots are $\frac{5}{2}$ and -6

Roots are k and k/a

Other and varied examples will be found in any text in college algebra. Those which are to be used for illustrative purposes or for practice work should be carefully selected by the teacher. The main criterion should be the extent to which the exercise lends itself to clarifying and emphasizing the particular point in question.

Systems Involving Quadratic Equations in Two Unknowns. The students' previous experience in solving simultaneous equations may be assumed to have been confined to systems of linear equations. In teaching the solution of such systems of equations, many teachers give preponderant emphasis to the method of elimination by addition or subtraction. The disadvantage of failing to give due emphasis to the method of substitution now becomes apparent, because this method is generally applicable to the solution of systems involving quadratics, while the method of addition and subtraction is not applicable in all cases. Therefore it may be advisable, in taking up the study of this topic, to give a *brief* review of the solution of systems of linear equations by substitution. The students should be made sensitive to the importance of the method as a general algebraic method for solving quadratic systems in two unknowns.

Systems of equations involving quadratics fall into two general classes: (1) systems containing one linear and one quadratic equation and (2) systems in which both equations are quadratics. The latter class may be further divided to advantage into homogeneous and nonhomogeneous systems. The special methods and devices used in the solution of these systems vary according to the forms of the equations involved in the particular systems under consideration. Teachers should make every effort to see that students do not use these various devices blindly but are trained to look for the reasons why the devices work. In doing this they will be acquiring the ability to analyze systems of equations and to determine for themselves what procedures will be most likely to yield the desired solutions. It is highly important that the teachers use discretion and care in the selection of problems to be assigned.

Textbooks generally present these devices with appropriate illustrations but often without emphasizing either the peculiar characteristics of the forms to which the various methods are especially adapted or the *reasons why* a particular method is especially suitable for handling a particular form.   It must be the teacher's primary task to see that the students are given insight into the reasons underlying the use of

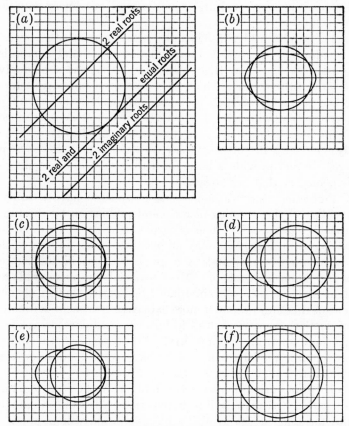

FIG. 15-6. Quadratic systems: (*a*) two real roots, two real and equal roots, two imaginary roots; (*b*) four real roots; (*c*) four real roots (equal in pairs); (*d*) two real and two imaginary roots; (*e*) four real roots (two equal); (*f*) four imaginary roots.

the various devices in particular situations as well as a knowledge of the devices themselves.   Otherwise, rote work is inevitable.

Useful and economical as these special procedures are, the student should not be allowed to forget that as a rule they are merely means for reducing the tedious labor often involved in the more general method of solving one equation for one variable in terms of the other and then substituting the result in the other equation.

The graphical method of solving quadratic systems is a laborious method and, of course, gives only approximate solutions, but it probably gives the average student more real intuitive insight into the nature of the solutions than any of the strictly algebraic methods of attack. In particular, it is useful in explaining why a system containing two quadratic equations has four solutions (real or imaginary) and why a system containing one quadratic equation and one linear equation has only two solutions.

The set of graphs in Fig. 15-6 includes representation of all types possible in quadratic systems. A thorough discussion and comparison of such graphs as these and their associated equations should give the students an intuitive basis, which they too often fail to get, for interpreting the solutions of such systems. Moreover, the use of graphs in this connection will give the student an initial acquaintance with some of the basic concepts of analytic geometry. In this way it serves not only to clarify his present work in algebra but also to stimulate his interest in and provide a basis for a thorough understanding of the analytic geometry that lies ahead.

Ratio, Proportion, and Variation. Most students have a fairly clear understanding of the meaning of ratio and proportion by the time they reach the eleventh grade. The concepts of ratio and proportion are used, at least intuitively and by implication, even in the arithmetic of the elementary school and to a greater extent in the subsequent work of the junior high school. Most textbooks in ninth-grade algebra or general mathematics contain some systematic, though elementary, treatment of this subject, and a more extensive treatment is found in the study of similar geometric figures in intuitive and demonstrative geometry and in numerical trigonometry. Consequently, students in the advanced courses may be expected to have some familiarity with the concepts and techniques of ratio and proportion.

The concept of variation also will be familiar to the students, but with intuitive rather than analytical implications. In all probability the form and meaning of the symbolic representation will be new. However, since it is often more convenient and effective to use the variation form of notation than the proportion form, the systematic analytic study of variation should undoubtedly find a place in the advanced work in algebra. It is not a particularly difficult topic to teach, but it needs to be taught thoroughly. Such explanation as may be given in the textbook will necessarily be condensed and will need to be materially supplemented by the teacher.

The teacher should have in mind two specific objectives: (1) to see that the students get a clear understanding of what is meant by direct variation, inverse variation, and joint variation and (2) to see that the students learn how to set up these relations in the form of equations involving a constant of variation and understand why the equations necessarily represent the different types of variation. A variety of illustrative formulas, graphs, and problems can be used effectively to bring out the meaning of the equations $y = kx$, $y = k/x$, $x = kyz$, $y = kx^2$, $y = kx^2/z^3$, etc. Innumerable examples involving variation may be drawn from arithmetic, geometry, physics, and other sources. The following illustrative examples are designed to give the students training in translating verbal statements of relationships into equations of these types. In each case the student should be asked to translate the statement into an equation involving a constant k and to indicate the numerical value of k where he can.

1. The perimeter of a square varies directly as the side.
2. The area of a square varies directly as the square of a side.
3. The circumference of a circle varies directly as the radius.
4. The volume of a sphere varies directly as the cube of the radius.
5. The base of a rectangle of constant area varies inversely as the altitude.
6. The strength of an electric current (amperage) varies directly as the voltage and inversely as the resistance.
7. The amount of simple interest varies jointly as the principal, rate, and time.
8. The volume of a confined gas varies directly as the absolute temperature and inversely as the pressure.
9. The intensity of illumination from a given source varies inversely as the square of the distance from that source.

Many applications should be given in the form of problems in order that the students may become thoroughly familiar with these forms and acquire the ability to apply them correctly in appropriate situations and use them with proficiency and assurance. The students will realize, of course, that there are many situations involving variation in which the relationships are so complex that the mathematical laws governing them are not known. They should be impressed, however, with the fact that, whenever we can set up an analytical representation of the mathematical law governing such variation, we are thereby providing ourselves with a powerful instrument for studying and predicting the behavior of the variables.

The study of variation affords an excellent opportunity to clarify and emphasize the nature of functional relationship and functional thinking. In fact, the concept of variation is inseparable from the concept of function, and the two should be stressed together, both concepts being abstracted and clarified through the interweaving of graphic illustrations and numerical evaluation of formulas of polynomial functions. The concept of continuity should be emphasized in connection with the graphs of such functions. This concept should be associated with the concept of the *changing values* of the variables. These, in turn, are to be associated with the shifting coordinates of a point moving at will on the graph, and the graph itself should be associated, through these notions, with the formula or function which it represents. Proper attention to these concepts and associations of ideas will go far toward developing a real idea of the nature of variation at the same time that it gives clear emphasis to the general notion of dependence as an aspect of functionality.

Arithmetic and Geometric Progressions. The first fundamental necessity in teaching progressions is to see that the students become really sensitive to the way in which the progressions are built up, i.e., the precise way in which each term after the first one is obtained from the preceding term. There are two approaches to this problem. Textbooks generally start by giving in each case a definition of the type of progression being discussed, calling attention to its distinguishing characteristic (the common difference between two consecutive terms or the common ratio of the one to the other), giving a few numerical illustrations, presenting in symbolic form the first few terms, and proceeding then to the development of the formula for the nth term. In this procedure the definition and the concept forms the starting point, and the numerical examples merely illustrate, supplement, and enrich the concept.

Some teachers feel, however, that better results are to be secured by more or less reversing this order of things. Under this plan various simple numerical illustrations of progressions are presented at the beginning without any definite laws or conditions governing the relations among the terms being given. The students are merely asked to try to find the way in which each series is built up or to discover for themselves the characteristic relation governing each of the series. This approach obviously stresses discovery rather than definition as a starting point. After the student has discovered the relations governing several progressions, he is asked to formulate a statement expressing this relation for each type of progression and finally to express these laws or relationships symbolically as formulas for the nth term of the series. It is held that many students can do this if the illustrative series are simple and appropriately chosen.

Advocates of this approach contend that students who discover the relationships for themselves are likely to understand the characteristic laws better, remember them more vividly, and apply them more readily than those who start with ready-made definitions and formulas. There are probably some grounds for this contention. There is no conclusive evidence, however, that either of these approaches is markedly superior to the other. In either case numerical illustrations are indispensable, and in either case it will probably be necessary for the teacher to help many of the students in setting up the symbolic formula for the typical nth term in the particular type of progression being considered.

Derivation of the formulas for the sums of the first n terms demands careful attention. Some texts offer "simplified proofs" which avoid explicit application but require tacit assumption of the principle of finite induction. This does not seem to be justifiable practice. Rather, the proofs of these propositions afford simple, yet very effective, means for introducing the students to the important technique of proof by mathematical induction. The procedural pattern in the application of the principle of finite induction to these particular propositions is simple in content but of sufficient general import to offer real opportunity for the development of basic understanding of this important mathematical technique.

The most serious difficulty which most students encounter in the study of progressions is in knowing how to go about the insertion of a given number of arithmetic or geometric means between two given numbers. This difficulty can easily be dispelled, however, if the students can be made sensitive to the fact that all they need to do is to find the common difference or the common ratio and that they can do this in either case by taking the formula for the nth term and solving it for the common difference or the common ratio in terms of the other elements of the formula. For several reasons it is better for them to carry out these solutions as they are needed rather than to memorize the formula for d and r. Besides reducing the amount of memorizing, it enhances the students' understanding of the formulas and provides excellent practice in the solution of literal equations.

Arithmetic and geometric progressions have extremely interesting and important applications which should be pointed out to the students. In any linear function, for consecutive integral values (in terms of any real unit) of the independent variable, the corresponding values of the function form an arithmetic progression, and conversely. This may be illustrated both graphically and numerically. Doubtless the most important general application of the geometric progression is the compound interest law. Here the teacher has the opportunity to emphasize the usefulness of geometric progressions by showing that this law is applied not only to the computation of compound interest but also to important problems in various fields. The following examples are illustrative:

Chemistry: problems associated with the disintegration of radioactive substances

Physics: the adiabatic law for gases; rates of cooling

Biology: problems associated with the growth of colonies of bacteria and abnormal tissue growth

Economics: problems of investment, insurance, debt funding, and installment buying

Sociology: problems associated with population growth

The study of harmonic progressions is a topic which has important but highly specialized application, and it is usually taught (or retaught) in connection with these applications. It is of less general interest than arithmetic and geometric progressions and is often omitted even from courses in college algebra. The same may be said with reference to the convergence of certain infinite geometric series. Because of the specialized application of these topics, no discussion of them will be given in the present chapter.

Complex Numbers. In introducing students to the study of imaginary and complex numbers it is well to review the previous steps in the extension of their number concepts from positive integers to common and decimal fractions and later to irrational numbers and negative numbers. They will be interested in realizing that each of these extensions was made in response to a need; that, when situations were encountered which could not be interpreted or explained adequately by use of positive integers alone, fractions were invented to do the job; and similarly for negative numbers. The point should be stressed that these new kinds of numbers have been sheer *inventions* made to serve a purpose and that they take their meanings from definition. This having been established, the students will tend to be in a receptive frame of mind for further extension of their number ideas.

The meaning of an imaginary number should be made clear at the outset. There should be no mystery about it, and there need be none. An explanation along the following lines will make clear the meaning which is to be attached to such numbers and will dispel much of the intellectual reservation and even antagonism which often exists with reference to this radically new concept.

Let us consider some negative number, say, -9. Can we find its square root? The $\sqrt{-9}$ cannot be $+3$, because $(+3)(+3) = +9$; nor can the square root be -3, because $(-3)(-3) = +9$. In fact the square root of -9 cannot be any positive number and it cannot be any negative number, because the square of either a positive or a negative number is positive. Obviously it cannot be zero. What then can it be? The only kinds of numbers we know about up to now are positive and negative numbers and zero. Since the square root of -9 cannot be either of these, we must *invent* another kind of number which we shall *define* as being the square root of a negative number and which we shall *call* an *imaginary number*. This is, in fact, what mathematicians have done. They have recalled that the square of the square root of any number gives that number (i.e., $\sqrt{7} \cdot \sqrt{7} = 7$; $\sqrt{23} \cdot \sqrt{23} = 23$; etc.), and they have said that, since this is the meaning of a square root, it must be true that $\sqrt{-9} \cdot \sqrt{-9}$ must be equal to -9. Since they call both nonnegative and negative numbers *real* numbers and since $\sqrt{-9}$ cannot be a real number, they call it an *imaginary* number. Other imaginary numbers are $\sqrt{-48}$, $\sqrt{-2}$, $\sqrt{-1}$, $\sqrt{-364}$, etc. The special symbol i is used to denote the imaginary number $\sqrt{-1}$.

This explanation will, of course, need to be amplified by the teacher, but it indicates the main avenue along which the students' thinking should be directed. It should be made clear that, in thus defining imaginary numbers, we make them subject to all the normal laws of operation which we use with real numbers. It is very important that students understand this clearly, and this understanding is facilitated, and confusion avoided, by the consistent use of the symbol i in place of the radical $\sqrt{-1}$. Thus there is no difference between applying the laws of exponents, the law of signs in multiplication, etc., to numbers expressed in terms of i and applying these laws to numbers expressed in terms of x or y or a or any other literal symbol. The peculiar cyclic nature of the successive integral powers of i often makes it possible to simplify the results of such operations, but this characteristic itself is a direct consequence of the laws of exponents applied in the usual manner to the number i, and of the definition of that number.

The principal points at which difficulty may be anticipated are the establishment of the definition and meaning of imaginary numbers, the definition of the symbol i, the firm fixation of the principle that *operations* with numbers in terms of i are carried on in exactly the same fashion as operations with numbers expressed in terms of any other letter, and the establishment of the successive positive integral powers of i which give a recurring series of numbers $+i$, -1, $-i$, $+1$.

When these properties of imaginary numbers have been well established in the minds of the students, the subsequent definition of and work with complex numbers should present little difficulty. Care must be taken in defining equal complex numbers. Conjugate complex numbers must also be defined. The principle of combining real parts and imaginary parts in the addition or subtraction of complex numbers can be readily explained by the fundamental law that only like terms can be combined. The real parts themselves are obviously like terms, as are the imaginary parts, while the real and imaginary parts are, just as obviously, unlike terms.

The generality of complex numbers, i.e., the fact that a complex number may be either a real number, a pure imaginary, or a combination of the two, is intriguing to most students when they come to understand and appreciate it. This generality may be made clear by considering that in the general form of the complex number $a + bi$ the a and b are any real numbers. Therefore if $a = 0$, the complex number becomes $0 + bi$ or simply bi, a pure imaginary. On the other hand, if $b = 0$, the complex number becomes $a + 0i$ or simply a, a real number.

The geometrical representation and treatment of complex numbers is extremely interesting to students and helps to make their concepts of these numbers much more tangible. This work is not extremely difficult and may well be introduced even in the eleventh grade, at least to the extent of making the students familiar with the method of representing complex numbers graphically and with the basic principles of simple vector addition. For twelfth-grade or college students who have had trigonometry, this work may well be extended to include the representation of complex numbers in trigonometric form, multiplication of two numbers in polar form, De Moivre's theorem, finding the nth roots of a complex number, and the division of complex numbers expressed in polar form.

The Teaching of Logarithms. Most students make their first acquaintance with logarithms when they study trigonometry. This acquaintance too often is limited to the use of logarithms as a means of reducing the laborious computation incident to the solution of triangles. It is certainly true that logarithms have played an important role in this connection, but students should not be left with the impression that logarithms are a part of trigonometry per se, or that their usefulness is limited to numerical work in this branch of mathematics. Actually, the theory of logarithms is algebraic, and the application of logarithms in trigonometry is incidental rather than organic. The systematic study of logarithms should therefore form a part of the second year of algebra, and the analytic properties of logarithms should be developed in connection with their inverse counterpart, exponentials.

It is best to start out by explaining that for present work logarithms are to be regarded merely as exponents, that a table of exponents can be useful in making certain computations, and that we merely apply the laws of exponents when we use logarithms for finding powers and roots of numbers and for multiplying or dividing numbers expressed as powers of a common base. A review of these fundamental properties, laws, and uses of exponents can be made by taking some convenient small positive integer as a base and building a partial table of exponents of numbers with respect to that base. For example:

Base 2		*Base 8*	
$2^0 = 1$	$2^4 = 16$	$8^{0/3} = 1$	$8^{5/3} = 32$
$2^1 = 2$	$2^5 = 32$	$8^{1/3} = 2$	$8^{6/3} = 64$
$2^2 = 4$	$2^6 = 64$	$8^{2/3} = 4$	$8^{7/3} = 128$
$2^3 = 8$	etc.	$8^{3/3} = 8$	$8^{8/3} = 256$
		$8^{4/3} = 16$	etc.

By using the first of these tables (extended if desired), simple operations in finding powers and roots, products, and quotients can be performed. Thus,

$$\sqrt[3]{64} = \sqrt[3]{2^6} = 2^{6/3} = 2^2 = 4$$
$$4 \cdot 4 = 2^2 \cdot 2^2 = 2^{2+2} = 2^4 = 16$$
$$64 \div 4 = 2^6 \div 2^2 = 2^{6-2} = 2^4 = 16$$

It will be obvious to the student, however, that these tables or any other tables similarly constructed would be very limited in their application. For example, the first table above contains no logarithms for 3, 5, 6, 7, 9, 10, or any other number which is not an integral power of 2. The logarithms of such numbers, with reference to the base 2, would necessarily be fractional since the numbers lie between numbers which are integral powers of 2. A similar observation should be made, of course, with reference to a table similarly constructed with any positive number as a base. However, the students should also be told that, although they do not know how to determine these fractional exponents, there are methods by which they can be computed and really serviceable tables compiled. They should also be reminded that, since our number system is a decimal system, the number 10 would seem to be a more convenient base than 2 or 8 or any other number, because the integral powers of 10 give our familiar units of enumeration, viz., 1, 10, 100, 1,000, etc.

By this time the stage is set for introducing the students to the system of common logarithms in which the base is 10. The following step-by-step procedure has been found effective in producing understanding of this system and skill and facility in its use. The order of the steps is important because each new idea or principle developed rests upon those preceding it and, in turn, provides an additional idea or principle as a basis for those yet to come. The key sentence or idea in each step is italicized. The teacher may enlarge upon these italicized statements and give such explanations, illustrations, and practice as may be desired. Some suggestions are given.

1. *Any number in the decimal system can be expressed as an integral power of 10 or as the product of two factors, one of which is between 1 and 10, the other being an integral power of 10.*

$$32.78 = 3.278 \times 10^1 \qquad 35,200 = 3.52 \times 10^4$$
$$0.346 = 3.46 \times 10^{-1} \qquad 0.00682 = 6.82 \times 10^{-3}$$

Give considerable practice in writing numbers in this way. Such consideration would afford further opportunities for calling attention to the nature and importance of scientific notation (see page 332). If the students have difficulty in determining the integral power of 10 to be used, the following rule will be helpful: place the pencil point after the nonzero digit on the extreme left of the given number and count to the position of the decimal point. The number of digits (or places) thus counted gives the integral power of 10 to be used. Counting to the right in this way indicates a positive power of 10, while counting to the left indicates a negative power of 10. It may be noted in passing that this integral power of 10 is the characteristic of the logarithm of the number, but it is better not to use the terms "logarithm" or "characteristic" until a little later.

2. *If we could express all numbers between 1 and 10 as powers of 10, then it is evident that we could express all numbers in the decimal system as powers of 10.* Point out that this follows from the fact that every number in the decimal system can be expressed as an integral power of 10 or as the product of such a power of 10 by a number between 1 and 10. Refer to the illustrations under step 1 above.

3. *Any number between 1 and 10 can be expressed either exactly or approximately as a power of 10.* Do not try to prove this, but make it appear plausible. Remind the students that since $1 = 10^0$ and $10 = 10^1$, then surely any number between 1 and 10 must be expressible (at least approximately) in the form 10^x, where $0 < x < 1$. For example, if $x = \frac{1}{3}$, we have $10^{\frac{1}{3}} = 2.154$ (approximately), or 2.154 is approximately 10 to the one-third power. Similarly, $10^{\frac{1}{2}} = 3.162$ (approximately); $10^{\frac{2}{3}} = 4.641$ (approximately); etc.

4. *Mathematicians have given us a table of numbers between 1 and 10 expressed as powers of 10.* Make it clear that the numbers in the left margin of the table of logarithms should be read as if there were a decimal point after the first digit at the left in the number. This is, in fact, the number for which the logarithm is given in the table, since only mantissas are given, and these, themselves, are logarithms only of numbers between 1 and 10. This number will be the first of the two factors referred to in step 1. It may also be explained to the students that the omission of the decimal point in the numbers printed in the tables makes for convenience and for the conservation of space. When the students have learned to read and interpret the numbers in the left margin of the table of logarithms in this way, have them refer to their tables of mantissas and read from these the powers of 10 representing various numbers between 1 and 10. For example, $5 = 10^{.69897}$; $3.27 = 10^{.51455}$; $7.84 = 10^{.89432}$; etc. For the present have the students think of these as exponents rather than as logarithms. Point out that the decimal point precedes the first figure in the number taken from the table, whether it is printed there or not. Give practice in reading and writing down these exponents and in interpreting them.

5. *We can make certain computations by use of this table alone so long, and only so long, as the numbers we use are between 1 and 10 and the answers are also between 1 and 10.* Give practice, using examples in multiplication and division and in finding powers and roots, but be sure that at this stage no number used or answer sought is less than 1 or greater than 10.

6. *We may now use our tables for any positive numbers.* Give practice in multiplication, powers, roots, and appropriate division, but for the present avoid division that would lead to negative exponents. This is a problem in itself. In connection with the use of the tables for the inverse cases, teach the students to express the numbers as the product of two factors. For example, have them express $10^{3.82367}$ as $10^{.82367} \times 10^3$.

7. *We are now ready to begin thinking, speaking, writing, and working in terms of logarithms instead of exponents.* Some practice, but not a great deal, will be needed now in reviewing and associating the logarithmic form with the exponential form.

Examples

Exponential form	Logarithmic form
$8 = 2^3$	$\log_2 8 = 3$
$100 = 10^2$	$\log_{10} 100 = 2$
$a = b^c$	$\log_b a = c$

In each case the logarithm is the exponent, but explain to the students that in the common system of logarithms the base 10 is understood and is generally not written.

Now give considerable practice in the use of the logarithmic form and notation in finding products, roots, powers, and quotients. Negative characteristics should still be avoided.

Example. Find the product of 782 and 3.96.

$$\log 782 =$$
$$\log 3.96 =$$
$$\overline{\log product =}$$
$$Product =$$

At this stage of development it is probably advisable to emphasize that previously the practice work was for understanding, but now it is mainly for efficiency.

8. *Special difficulties with logarithms with negative characteristics.* Go back to the exponential form for a little while.

Example. Find log .0342.

$$.0342 = 3.42 \times 10^{-2} = 10^{.53403} \times 10^{-2} = 10^{-2+.53403}$$

This, however, cannot be written as $10^{-2.53403}$ because the .53403 is positive. It is sometimes written as $10^{\bar{2}.53403}$. A more convenient way of writing the same thing is $10^{8.53403-10}$. In logarithmic form this would be given as log .0342 = 8.53403 − 10.

Considerable special practice will be needed on this, and it should be very carefully supervised until the students have acquired a substantial understanding of the nature of negative logarithms and reasonable proficiency in handling the special notation which it is necessary to use.

Having learned how to use the table of natural functions and the table of common logarithms, the student should have no difficulty in understanding the meaning or mastering the use of the tables of logarithms of the trigonometric functions. These tables are not, in fact, indispensable but are provided merely to speed up the work. The question of whether or not to use cologarithms is debatable. Some teachers and writers feel that cologarithms are nonessential and superfluous, while others prefer to have them used. This matter is probably of little moment and may safely be left to the judgment of the individual teacher.

An explanation of the slide rule, showing how its construction and use is based upon the principles of logarithms, will add interest and value to the study of logarithms.

Logarithmic and Exponential Functions. If two variables are so related that the first can be expressed as some function of the second and the second can be expressed as some function of the first, then the two functions are said to be *inverse* to each other. For example, if $y = f(x)$ and $x = g(y)$, then $g(y)$ is the inverse of $f(x)$ and $f(x)$ is the inverse of $g(y)$. Thus, if $y = 7x + 2$, then the inverse function is $x = (y - 2)/7$. This is an example of two inverse algebraic functions.

Logarithmic and exponential functions have this inverse relationship, since either can be expressed in terms of the other. Thus if $y = a^x$, then by taking logarithms of both members we get log $y = x$ log a, or $x = (\log y)/(\log a)$. Similarly, if $y = \log_a x$, then $x = a^y$; hence it is possible to take a function given in either form and convert it into an equivalent inverse expression in the other form.

As a part of mathematical literacy beyond the most elementary level, it is important for students to become aware of this inverse relationship between logarithmic and exponential functions. As an instrument in the study of analytic geometry, calculus, statistics, and subsequent courses it is necessary for students to understand this relationship and be able to make interconversions with assurance and facility. This objective has often been sadly neglected, to the detriment of the students, who too often have been taught only how to use logarithms numerically.

Other Topics in Algebra. In a volume such as this it is impossible to consider in detail the teaching procedures connected with all the topics of intermediate and college algebra. It is hoped that the preceding pages will in some measure have set a pattern for the study of such problems. It is hoped further that the discussion will encourage teachers to apply themselves assiduously to the task of specifying the major relationships and concepts to be developed in connection with each topic and discovering the main characteristic difficulties which the study of each topic presents to the students.

Among the topics which are of first-rate importance at their appropriate levels but which it has not been possible to discuss in this chapter may be mentioned the binomial theorem, special properties of functions and equations of degree higher than second, permutations and combinations, probability, determinants, mathematical induction, general theorems on algebraic functions and equations, and the mathematics of investment and insurance.   In concluding this chapter, a few general suggestions may be made with a view to helping teachers plan their instruction in these and other topics effectively.

Perhaps the most important objective of mathematical instruction at the higher levels is the development of the ability to understand *generalized* principles and concepts and to apply these generalizations properly to particular situations or problems.   At the same time, this seems to present to students greater difficulty than almost anything else.   It is therefore a matter to which special attention needs to be given very consistently.   The following examples may be cited by way of illustration.

1. The recognition of type forms in factorable expressions which in themselves may be rather complicated, such as

$$12y^3 - 4y^6 + x^{2a} - 9 \qquad \text{(difference of two squares)}$$
$$a^3 + 8b^3 + c^3 + 6a^2b + 12ab^2 \qquad \text{(sum of two cubes)}$$

2. The recognition of possibilities for reducing equations or expressions to standard forms which can be more readily handled, such as

$$x^{16} + 5x^8 + 6 = 0 \qquad \text{(quadratic equation in } x^8)$$
$$x^4 + x^2 + 1 = 0 \qquad \text{(factorable by difference of two squares)}$$

3. Determination of the nature of the roots of a quadratic equation from investigation of the character of the discriminant

4. Understanding the generality of the relations given by the remainder theorem, the factor theorem, the fundamental theorem of algebra, the theorems giving relations between roots and coefficients, etc.

5. Understanding the significance of the procedures used in solving and checking literal equations and formulas

6. Applying the formula for the rth term in a binomial expansion for a given value of r, and similarly applying other generalized formulas to the determination of values in particularized cases

It is important that instruction be carried on at suitable levels of difficulty and expectation.   Nearly all textbooks in eleventh- and twelfth-grade algebra include topics and treatments which are appropriate for college algebra but are beyond the ability of the even better than average eleventh-grade student.   It is unreasonable to expect from the average eleventh-grade student the degree of mastery of these topics which may legitimately be expected of superior twelfth-grade students or those taking college algebra.   There is an unwarranted, though not unnatural, tendency among teachers to assume that all the material in a textbook is suitable for the students in the grade in which the textbook is used. In connection with any given topic the teacher should try to decide how far he can profitably carry his particular class in relation to that topic and what should be the nature and difficulty of the exercises which he should use and the assignments he should make. It is to be expected that a cyclic treatment of topics in algebra will generally produce better results than too intensive treatment, carried beyond appropriate levels, in any one year. Thus, instead of trying to teach all of factoring in the ninth grade, a few simple and easily understandable cases are given in that grade. In the eleventh grade these are reviewed and more difficult ones considered, and this process is repeated in subsequent years. The work should always challenge the best efforts of the students, but if it is carried beyond their capacities, it will lose its meaning and value.

Finally, the elements of time, practice, review, application, and maintenance are of extreme importance. They are all involved in a program of instruction that looks to a fundamental mastery of algebra. The great generalities do not emerge in an instant or a year. They are the result of a long process of assimilation and familiarization. They require not hours but years of concentrated attention and sheer hard intellectual work, beginning with simple concepts and proceeding to ever more difficult and abstract relationships. Rome was not built in a day, nor is there any quick, easy short cut to a real mastery of algebra. Persistent review and practice, both in the skills of algebra and in their application, is required. Otherwise, the skills and understandings will deteriorate through disuse.

Under a program of subject matter selected to present a reasonable challenge to ability, to provide a gradual expansion of the horizon of mathematical understanding, and to demand an incessant program of maintenance, the student may expect to arrive at a *real mastery* of algebra. Such a mastery of appropriate subject matter of algebra not only will provide that student with a sound basis for exploring mathematics at its higher levels but also will give him a richness of insight into the related fields of science.

Provision for Superior Students. Students who take algebra beyond the ninth grade usually do so voluntarily, through some special interest in the subject. The problem of motivation is thus less acute, and some degree of selection with respect to mathematical aptitude will have been operative. At the same time the subject is sufficiently demanding that the regular work of the course will call forth serious effort on the part of most of the students. There will be a few, however, for whom the regular work is easy, and there may be an occasional student for whom the regular course is not much of a challenge. These are the students who possess that rare combination of mathematical insight and originality which marks them as potential leaders in mathematics, and the shortage of such leaders is regarded in high places as a matter of grave and increasing concern.

We cannot afford to let mathematical talent go to waste. Yet this will happen unless students of exceptional talent are given work which will call forth their interest and their best efforts. For those students who are simply above average, varied assignments with perhaps less routine work and more emphasis on relatively difficult problems may suffice. It is usually easy to find some such problems in the regular textbook or in collateral textbooks. They may be oriented to the unit or to topics currently being studied by the class, but this need not be the case. Students with marked ability and a taste for originality will often take keen delight in working on challenging problems which may be quite unrelated to the current work of the class. Such journals as the *Mathematics Student Journal*, the *Pentagon, School Science and Mathematics*, and the *Mathematics Teacher* are good sources of problems suitable for this purpose, as are some of the numerous books on mathematical recreations.

Once in a while one may find a student not merely superior but of truly exceptional insight and endowed with insatiable curiosity and the capacity for sustained effort. Such a student may work with more keen interest in carrying on independently an intensive investigation of some collateral topic than in working on short-term special assignments. Serious work of this kind should be encouraged, though with suitable safeguards. For high school students such topics as the following could serve as foci for such investigations: theorems about polynomials of higher degree; properties of determinants; exponential and logarithmic functions; mathematical induction and the binomial formula; permutations, combinations, and probability; notation for and operations with sets; elements of symbolic logic.

Only the student who is capable of a high order of independent and sustained work should be given this sort of collateral assignment. The teacher's role will be to recommend appropriate reference works, to receive and comment on the progress reports that the student will make from time to time, and to appraise the final oral and written reports that should be presented. This will make extra work for the teacher, but if the assignment is well carried out, it can yield high dividends.

One caution is in order. Special projects of this kind should be regarded as complementing but not replacing the regular course in algebra, and such assignments should be made only with the most careful discrimination. Sometimes the enthusiasm of highly capable students makes them impatient with the need to master routine but necessary skills and details. But such neglect of fundamental groundwork imposes severe limitations on eventual progress, and it should not be permitted. Talented students may not require as much time as their less capable classmates to acquire the necessary details and skills, but they should be held responsible for their mastery, just as the other students are.

EXERCISES

1. The usual way of beginning the second year's work in algebra is to give a concentrated and extensive review of the fundamental operations. What are the reasons for this? What disadvantages does it entail? Can you suggest a better plan? What is it?

2. Use both the pivotal-element and sweep-out processes to solve these systems of equations:

$$
\begin{array}{ll}
(a) &
\begin{aligned}
x + y + z + u &= 5 \\
2x - y + z - 2u &= -1 \\
x - 2y + z - 2u &= -1 \\
3x + 2y - 2z + u &= 0
\end{aligned}
&
(b) &
\begin{aligned}
x + y + z + u &= 3 \\
2x + 2y + 3z - u &= 8 \\
z - 3u &= 2 \\
3x + 3y + 5z - 3u &= 13
\end{aligned}
\end{array}
$$

3. Consider the two relations $y \geq x^2$ and $y^2 = 8x$ (1) with the domain for both x and y the set of integers such that $-3 \leq x \leq +8$ and $-5 < y < +10$ and (2) with the domain for both x and y the set of real numbers. (a) Draw the graph of each relation. (b) What is the solution set when the two relations are considered simultaneously? (c) What is the solution set for the two relations when the "is greater than" ($>$) is removed from $y \geq x^2$?

4. List the specific things you would want your students to know or be able to do as a result of their study of quadratic equations in their second year of algebra?

5. What difficulties would you expect your students to encounter in their work with quadratic equations? How could you help them avoid or overcome these difficulties? Consider each separately and be as specific as you can.

6. Construct a diagnostic test designed to locate and identify such of the specific difficulties called for in exercise 5 as may persist even after the unit has been studied.

7. Give reasons for the appropriateness of teaching logarithms in the algebra course rather than in connection with the trigonometry course.

8. Make a list of the main outcomes you would strive for in teaching logarithms and exponentials in a second course in algebra. Why is it desirable to teach these two topics together?

9. Prepare a set of 50 exercises, well graduated with respect to increasing difficulty or complexity, designed to lead students to clear understanding and increased facility in the use of common logarithms for numerical work. This should include multiplication, division, roots, and powers.

10. Prepare a list of 25 exercises designed to enrich understanding of the relation between logarithmic and exponential functions and to produce facility in converting from one form to the other.

11. The invention of logarithms forms an extremely interesting chapter in the history of mathematics. Prepare and give a fairly full account of this mathematical development.

12. What specific outcomes should be sought in work with radicals? What specific difficulties can students be expected to have in connection with this work?

13. Show that the equation $\sqrt{3x - 5} + \sqrt{2x + 3} + 1 = 0$ has no solution, although the derived quadratic equation obtained by transposing and squaring does

have two real solutions.   (Such problems illustrate and emphasize the importance of thoughtful checking of algebraic work.)

14. Given: $f(x) = x^2 - 5x + 28$ and $g(x) = 12 - 5x + x^2$.   Many students, if instructed to write the correct expressions for $f(12)$ or $g(h + 17)$, would report that they could not do it.   Do you think this is because of mathematical disability or do you think it is due mainly to not knowing how to interpret the notation used?   How important is this question?   Discuss.

15. With reference to exercise 14 what are some steps you would take to remedy the situation?

16. Make a list of 20 practice exercises designed to make students feel assurance in the use and interpretation of the function notation referred to in exercise 14.

17. Compare the treatments of ratio, proportion, and variation in several textbooks. Enumerate the specific objectives.   List and illustrate specific difficulties which students are likely to encounter in the study of this topic.

18. The resistance of a wire to the passage of an electric current is directly proportional to the length of the wire and inversely proportional to the square of the diameter.   Write this as a variation equation, using R, L, and D to represent resistance, in ohms; length, in feet; and diameter, in mils, respectively; and K to represent the constant of variation.

19. A 24-gauge copper wire of diameter 20.1 mils and length 150 feet has a resistance of 3.85 ohms.   Compute the constant of variation K and determine the length of 30-gauge copper wire (diameter 10.0 mils) required to make a coil whose resistance is 75 ohms.   Explain the part which the constant K plays in the solution.

20. Compare the treatment of progressions in five different textbooks in college algebra.   Which do you like best, and why?   What do you think should be included in the study of this topic?

21. Show how the compound interest law, and consequently the study of annuities and the mathematics of life insurance, are based upon a geometric progression.   Give illustrations to show applications of the compound interest law to fields other than finance.

22. Enumerate and illustrate the main properties of inequalities.   Take five high school textbooks in algebra and see how many of them give any treatment of inequalities.   Should this topic receive any attention in high school algebra?   Comment.

23. The study of inequalities often receives no attention in high school algebra and little attention in college algebra.   What do you think is the reason for this?   Criticize or justify this practice, giving arguments to support your position.

24. Graph each of the following and discuss each graph: $y = 3$, $y \geq 3$, $y < 3$, $y < -1$, $y \leq x$, $y \geq x - 1$, $3y < 2x$, $y = x^2$, $y \geq x^2$, and $y < x^2$.   Take the domains of x and y to be the set of real numbers.

25. Prove the remainder theorem and show that the factor theorem is actually just a special case of the remainder theorem.   Do you think students generally get the full significance of the remainder theorem?   If not, why don't they?

26. Explain to the class the principle of mathematical induction.   As an illustration of this principle, prove that, if n represents any positive integer, then

$$\sum_{n=1}^{n} n(n + 1)(n + 2) = \tfrac{1}{4}n(n + 1)(n + 2)(n + 3)$$

27. Make a list of specific difficulties which students may be expected to encounter in the study of one of the following topics and suggest ways of helping them avoid or overcome the difficulties: progressions, logarithms, irrational roots, determinants,

complex numbers, inequalities, quadratic equations, equations of third or higher degree, mathematical induction, binomial theorem, permutations and combinations, and probability.

28. What advantages, if any, accrue to students from the practice of checking their own solutions of, say, quadratic equations or equations involving radicals?

29. What advantages, if any, accrue to students from having printed answer lists available for some of the problems they are to solve? What disadvantages may attend this practice?

30. See if you can find, in textbooks on algebra, ten illustrative cases in which you think students might have trouble in getting clear interpretations because of ambiguities, lack of clearness, or other reading difficulties.

31. Write up a critical review of one recent textbook written for the second course in high school algebra.

The next four problems were taken from the Problem Section of *School Science and Mathematics*. Present your solutions.

32. Solve for x: $\sqrt[3]{e^{2+x}} \sqrt[4]{e^{4-x}} \sqrt[5]{e^{5x-1}} = 1$.

33. If $\log (x + z) + \log (x - 2y + z) = 2 \log (x - z)$, show that x, y, and z are in harmonic progression.

34. Find two numbers such that their sum multiplied by the sum of their squares is 5,500 and their difference multiplied by the difference of their squares is 352.

35. Eliminate x and y from the following system of equations: $x^2y = a$, $x(x + y) = b$, $2x + y = c$.

36. *School Science and Mathematics* has for many years regularly carried a Problem Section in each issue. Consult current or past volumes of this journal and compile a list of several algebraic problems that might appropriately be suggested for independent study for superior students in high school or college algebra.

37. Assume that you have discovered in your class a student of extraordinary ability who does the regular work of the class with little effort and who wishes also to carry on an independent study of transfinite numbers. Compile a list of suitable references which you would recommend for him.

BIBLIOGRAPHY

Andree, Richard V.: A Simple but Fruitful Arithmetic, *Mathematics Teacher*, **50** (1957), 58.

Bacon, Ralph Hoyt: Integral Solutions of $x^2 + y^2 + z^2 = r^2$, *School Science and Mathematics*, **47** (1947), 155–164.

Bakst, Aaron: Evaluation of Determinants, *Mathematics Teacher*, **45** (1952), 183–186.

————: The Teaching of Collegiate Mathematics, *School Science and Mathematics*, **52** (1952), 462–463.

Barnes, George: An Easily Constructed Chart for Finding the Roots of Quadratic Equations, *Mathematics Teacher*, **50** (1957), 40–42.

Barnett, I. A.: Reasoning Problems in Mathematics, *School Science and Mathematics*, **40** (1940), 548–556.

Beberman, Max, and Bruce E. Meserve: Graphing in Elementary Algebra, *Mathematics Teacher*, **49** (1956), 260–266.

Bellman, Richard: Inequalities, *Mathematics Magazine*, **28** (1954), 21–26.

Bennett, Albert A.: A Note on "Variable," *Mathematics Teacher*, **48** (1955), 464–468.

Bennett, Howard C.: A Graphical Method Useful in Solving Certain Algebraic and Trigonometric Inequalities, *Mathematics Teacher*, **46** (1953), 82–85.

Boyer, Lee Emerson: "An Introduction to Mathematics for Teachers" (New York: Henry Holt and Company, Inc., 1945), pp. 435–456.

Breslich, E. R.: "Problems in Teaching Secondary-school Mathematics" (Chicago: University of Chicago Press, 1931), pp. 201–232.

——: "The Administration of Mathematics in Secondary Schools" (Chicago: University of Chicago Press, 1933), pp. 273–287.

Brown, Claude H.: "The Teaching of Secondary Mathematics" (New York: Harper & Brothers, 1953), pp. 256–267.

Brown, Elizabeth F.: Roots and Logarithms, *Mathematics Teacher*, **49** (1956), 544–547.

Brown, James P.: Further Deciphering of the General Trinomial, *Mathematics Teacher*, **48** (1955), 586–587.

Clair, H. S.: The Laws of Algebra and Modern Algebra, *School Science and Mathematics*, **53** (1953), 29–33.

Clements, C. Robert: Work Problems Made Easy, *Mathematics Teacher*, **48** (1955), 582–585.

Coffman, Raphael T.: An Elementary Approach to the Use of the Rate of Change Concept for Solving Problems, *Mathematics Magazine*, **30** (1956), 81–90.

Colinese, S. J.: Logarithms Made Easy, *Industrial Arts and Vocational Education Magazine*, **37** (1948), 239–243.

Commission on Mathematics, Report of: "Appendices" (New York: College Entrance Examination Board, 1959), pp. 29–63, 74–93.

Conkwright, Nelson B., and J. D. Heide: The Solution of Simultaneous Linear Equations, *Mathematics Teacher*, **38** (1945), 177–180.

Cordrey, William A.: Applications of Quadratic Equations, *Mathematics Teacher*, **38** (1945), 120–125.

Danieley, James Earl: Individual Differences and the Teaching of Algebra, *High School Journal*, **31** (1948), 69–72.

Davis, David R.: "The Teaching of Mathematics" (Reading, Mass.: Addison-Wesley Publishing Company, 1951), pp. 245–282.

Diamond, Louis E.: Introduction to Complex Numbers, *Mathematics Magazine*, **30** (1957), 233–249.

Dubisch, Roy: A Problem in Elementary Algebra, *Mathematics Teacher*, **40** (1947), 39.

Eves, Howard: The Irrationality of $\sqrt{2}$, *Mathematics Teacher*, **38** (1945), 317–318.

Fehr, Howard F.: Operations in the Systems of Positive and Negative Numbers and Zero, *Mathematics Teacher*, **42** (1949), 171–176.

——: "Secondary Mathematics: A Functional Approach for Teachers" (Boston: D. C. Heath and Company, 1951), pp. 36–73, 123–167.

Fouch, Robert S.: On the Definability of Zero to the Power Zero, *School Science and Mathematics*, **53** (1953), 693–696.

Friedman, B.: Teaching Mathematical Induction, *School Science and Mathematics*, **41** (1941), 279–280.

Goodrich, Merton Taylor: Teaching Mathematical Induction, *School Science and Mathematics*, **40** (1940), 472–476.

Gruenberger, Fred: Imaginaries, *Mathematics Teacher*, **47** (1954), 11–12.

Hazard, William J.: "Algebra Notes" (New York: Vantage Press, Inc., 1952).

Jerbert, A. R.: Division by Zero, *School Science and Mathematics*, **49** (1949), 484–488.

——: Simultaneous Linear Equations, *Mathematics Teacher*, **45** (1952), 48–50.

Jones, Phillip S.: Complex Numbers: An Example of Recurring Themes in the Development of Mathematics, *Mathematics Teacher*, **47** (1954), pp. 106–114, 257–263, 340–345.

Keller, M. Wiles: What Are You Teaching? *School Science and Mathematics*, **56** (1956), 210–220.

Kinney, Lucien Blair, and C. Richard Purdy: "Teaching Mathematics in the Secondary School" (New York: Rinehart & Company, Inc., 1952), pp. 64–102, 195–202.

Klimczak, W. J.: The Solution of Linear Equations and Inequalities, *Mathematics Teacher*, **48** (1955), 460–463.

Lange, Lester H.: Another Encounter with Geometric Series, *School Science and Mathematics*, **55** (1955), 472–476.

Lariviere, R.: Two and Two Are Not Always Four, *Mathematics Magazine*, **30** (1957), 273–275.

Larsen, H. D.: The Teaching of Collegiate Mathematics, *School Science and Mathematics*, **52** (1952), 267–268.

Law, Carol: Arithmetical Congruences with Practical Applications, *Mathematics Magazine*, **32** (1958), 221–227.

Lyda, Wesley J.: Concerning the Irrationality of $\sqrt{2}$, *Mathematics Teacher*, **39** (1946), 176–177.

MacLane, Saunders: The Impact of Modern Mathematics on Secondary Schools, *Mathematics Teacher*, **49** (1956), 66–69.

Manheimer, Wallace: Some Classroom Problems from the Field of Atomic Energy, *Mathematics Teacher*, **47** (1954), 86–90.

McGaughey, A. W.: The Imaginary Number Problem, *American Mathematical Monthly*, **64** (1957), 193–194.

Meserve, Bruce E.: Using Geometry in Teaching Algebra, *Mathematics Teacher*, **45** (1952), 567–571.

———: Foundations of Algebra, *Mathematics Teacher*, **50** (1957), 356–360.

Miller, J. H.: Difficulties in Algebra: A Study, *School Science and Mathematics*, **58** (1958), 714–720.

Mirsky, Robert: Streamlining the Proof of the Binomial Theorem, *Mathematics Teacher*, **48** (1955), 96.

Mode, Elmer B.: The Commutative Law, *Mathematics Teacher*, **38** (1945), 108–111.

Morris, Richard: Mathematical Induction for Freshmen, *National Mathematics Magazine*, **12** (1938), 183–187.

Newsom, C. V.: The Teaching of Collegiate Mathematics, *School Science and Mathematics*, **52** (1952), 130–132.

Niessen, A. M.: Illustrations of the Versatility of the Binomial Theorem, *School Science and Mathematics*, **46** (1946), 855–860.

Nowlan, F. S.: The Solution of a Radical Equation, *Mathematics Teacher*, **46** (1953), 490.

O'Brien, Katherine: Problem Solving, *Mathematics Teacher*, **49** (1956), 79–86.

Payne, Joseph H.: Self-instructive Enrichment Topics for Bright Pupils in High School Algebra, *Mathematics Teacher*, **51** (1958), 113–117.

Peters, Max: An Introductory Lesson in Logarithms, *New Jersey Mathematics Teacher*, **13** (1957), 3–6.

Pillans, Harry T.: Common Pupil Difficulties with Basic Concepts of Logarithms, *School Science and Mathematics*, **39** (1939), 763–765.

Prag, Lewis D.: A Device for Teaching Logarithms, *Mathematics Teacher*, **45** (1952), 378–380.

Ransom, W. R.: Elementary Calculation of Logarithms, *Mathematics Teacher*, **47** (1954), 115–116.

———: Second Order Interpolation, *School Science and Mathematics*, **55** (1955), 460–461.

Read, Cecil B.: Does Unity Divided by Zero Equal Infinity? *School Science and Mathematics*, **52** (1952), 736.

Reeve, William D.: What Price Factoring? *Mathematics Teacher*, **45** (1952), 497–502.

———: "Mathematics for the Secondary School" (New York: Henry Holt and Company, Inc., 1954), pp. 245–300.

Rich, Barnett: Variation Applied to Problem Solving, *Mathematics Teacher*, **40** (1947), 158–165.

————: The Place of the Variable in the Teaching of Mathematics, *Mathematics Teacher*, **48** (1955), 538–541.

Ringenberg, L. A.: Numbers and Number Systems, *Mathematics Magazine*, **32** (1958), 265–276.

Schaaf, William L.: Meaning, Rigor and Discipline in Secondary Mathematics, *Mathematics Teacher*, **44** (1951), 259–261.

————: Logarithms and Exponentials, *Mathematics Teacher*, **45** (1952), 361–363.

————: Notes on Advanced Algebra, *Mathematics Teacher*, **46** (1953), 199–201.

Schack, Arthur: Two Forms of Mathematical Induction, *Mathematics Magazine*, **32** (1958), 83–85.

Schultze, Arthur: "The Teaching of Mathematics in Secondary Schools" (New York: The Macmillan Company, 1927), pp. 288–352.

Scott, C. H.: Dimensional Analysis, *School Science and Mathematics*, **57** (1957), 32–36.

Selby, S.: A Note on Logarithms, *Mathematics Teacher*, **48** (1955), 59–60.

Shepherd, W. L.: Motivating the Study of Determinants, *Mathematics Magazine*, **28** (1955), 280–281.

Shuster, Carl N.: The Calculation of Logarithms in the High School, *Mathematics Teacher*, **48** (1955), 322–323.

Sleight, N.: Logarithms and Algebra, *School Science and Mathematics*, **49** (1949), 737–748.

Sobel, Max A.: Concept Learning in Algebra, *Mathematics Teacher*, **49** (1956), 425–430.

Spiegel, M. R.: Reciprocal Quadratic Equations, *American Mathematical Monthly*, **59** (1952), 175–177.

Stabler, E. R.: Demonstrative Algebra, *Mathematics Teacher*, **39** (1946), 255–260.

UICSM Project Staff: Words, Words, Words, *Mathematics Teacher*, **50** (1957), 194–198.

Utz, W. R.: Maxima and Minima without the Calculus, *School Science and Mathematics*, **57** (1957), 263–266.

Weiner, L. M.: A Direct Proof of the Binomial Theorem, *Mathematics Teacher*, **48** (1955), 412.

Whitford, D. E., and M. S. Klamkin: On an Elementary Derivation of Cramer's Rule, *American Mathematical Monthly*, **60** (1953), 186–187.

Wilt, May L.: Logarithmic Functions, *Mathematics Teacher*, **40** (1947), 133–135.

Yates, Robert C.: Solving Symmetric Equations, *School Science and Mathematics*, **54** (1954), 234–235.

16

THE TEACHING OF GEOMETRY IN THE JUNIOR HIGH SCHOOL

According to the Commission on Mathematics there are three main objectives for the study of geometry in high school.[1] They are:

1. The acquisition of information about geometric figures in the plane and in space
2. The development of an understanding of the deductive method as a way of thinking, and a reasonable skill in applying this method to mathematical situations
3. The provision of opportunities for original and creative thinking

The third objective is, of course, a major objective of instruction in geometry whether in the junior high school, senior high school, or junior college.   The second objective is a principal responsibility of the senior high school.   The first objective is primarily the concern of the junior high school.

The geometrical experience of the student entering the junior high school has been somewhat limited and quite casual.   It has extended from the more or less incidental perceptions of size, shape, and position that take place during preschool days to the more systematic treatment of measurement, drawing to scale, and calculation of perimeters, areas, and volumes in the arithmetic of the sixth grade.   The geometrical information of the preschool and elementary-school period has been acquired largely through manipulation and computation.   It is the function of the junior high school (1) to systematize this information and extend it to some of the broader and more general aspects of the geometry of everyday life, (2) to aid the student in becoming familiar with the basic geometrical concepts and in understanding the fundamental techniques, such as the use of the straightedge, protractor, compass, and the techniques of measurement and construction, (3) to acquaint the student with the characteristics of good geometrical notation, and (4) to bridge the gap from the largely manipulative type of geometric experiences to the more formal logical processes of demonstrative geometry.   Such a geometry

[1] "Report of the Commission on Mathematics" (New York: College Entrance Examination Board, 1959), pp. 22–23.

has been called "intuitive," but it is rather a geometry *sui generis* which is characterized by intuition, experiment, and an informal approach to the more formal processes of demonstrative geometry.   To omit any one of these three aspects would be to give an imperfect description of the province and function of the geometry of the junior high school.

Committee Recommendations.   While the major concern over the high school program in geometry has been directed at the senior high school, it has been recognized that the foundation for effective work at that level must be laid in the junior high school.   Experimental materials are being prepared and tried out in selected schools throughout the country. While such experimentation should, and will, continue for several years, the Secondary School Curriculum Committee and the Commission on Mathematics felt it urgent that they include in their reports recommendations pertinent to basic aspects of the geometry program at both the senior and junior high school levels of instruction.

The Secondary School Curriculum Committee has this to say:[1]

1. The learning experiences in geometry that precede the one-year [senior high school] course should be *valuable in themselves* and not solely as prerequisites for the deductive geometry that is to follow.   We must remember that we are concerned with the education of all youth, not merely those who are college-capable. This consideration is particularly important in grades seven and eight.   In these grades there must be provided a program of instruction which is appropriate for pupils whose future study of geometry must be confined largely to its applications, as well as one which is appropriate for those who will later study geometry as a deductive system.

2. Those learning experiences that are designed as preparation for deductive geometry should not require any great amount of verbalization of theorems that are to be proved later in the formal course.   The time can be employed to better advantage in developing certain concepts that provide a foundation for the subsequent study of deductive proof.   In cases where it is necessary to deal with statements pertaining to congruence, similarity, relations between the sides of a right triangle, etc., there should be constant emphasis on the difference between proof and experimental verification.

The report then proceeds to outline the program for grades 7 to 9 in this fashion:

Grades seven and eight (the introduction or observation stage):
Drawing, both freehand and with straightedge and compass
Drawings that represent three-dimensional objects
Perspective drawing
Conjectures based on inductive and intuitive reasoning
Use of measuring instruments, ruler and protractor

[1] Report of the Secondary School Curriculum Committee, *Mathematics Teacher*, **52** (1959), 406.

Recognition of the fact that all measures are approximate

Relative error; distinction between precision and accuracy

Experiments designed to test conjectures about the areas and volumes of certain solids

Construction of templates for some solids

Concepts: Application of set language to geometry; the set of points on a line, the set of lines on a point, the set of lines on a plane, the set of planes on a line, intersection of two sets; one-to-one correspondence; simple locus problems in two and three dimensions; congruence, ratio, similarity, concurrence of lines, collinearity of points; "inside" and "outside" of a closed curve; the if-then form of a statement; exercises which are "open-ended" in the sense that the pupil is given a certain set of data or a certain drawing and asked to draw as many conclusions as he can.

The above material might well constitute 20 to 30 per cent of that presented in grades seven and eight.

Grade 9:

Liberal use should be made of geometric drawing in illustrating problems wherever possible. The one-to-one correspondence idea should be applied to the number scale and to the development and use of the Cartesian coordinate system.

The Commission on Mathematics does not list any specific geometric content for the ninth grade, but it does describe a program for grades 7 and 8 in these words:[1]

Geometry

Measurement: The ability to operate with and transform the several systems of measure, including the metric system of length, area, volume, and weight. Geometric measurements, including length of a line segment, perimeter of a polygon, and circumference of a circle, areas of regions enclosed by polygons and circles, surface areas of solids, volumes of solids, measure of angles (by degrees). The student should know the difference between the process of measuring and the measure of the quantity. Ability to apply measurement to practical situations. Use of measurement in drawing to scale and finding lengths indirectly.

Relationships among geometric elements: These include the concepts of parallel, perpendicular, intersecting, and oblique lines (in a plane and in a space); acute, right, obtuse, complementary, supplementary, and vertical angles; scalene, isosceles, and equilateral triangles; right triangles and the Pythagorean relation; sum of the interior angles of a triangle. The use of instruments in constructing figures; ideas of symmetry about a point and a line.

An Analysis of the Content of Junior High School Geometry. In its Guidance Report the Commission on Post-War Plans of the National Council of Teachers of Mathematics presented a check list of twenty-nine items in terms of which functional competence in mathematics was

[1] Report of the Commission on Mathematics, *op. cit.*, p. 19.

Table 16-1. Content of Junior High School Geometry

Vocabulary	Instructional purposes	Instructional methods

Geometric Objective: Line Segment

Vocabulary	Instructional purposes	Instructional methods
broken line curved line distance equal segments graph horizontal intersecting length line line segment mid-point oblique parallel perimeter perpendicular perpendicular bisector ratio scale straight line transversal "units of length" vertical	1. To acquaint the pupil with meaning and use of lines and line segments 2. To teach the techniques of drawing and measuring line segments *a.* To develop reasonable competence in estimating lengths 3. To teach drawing to scale 4. To instill an appreciation of the need for careful and significant notation	1. Observing lines in classroom, on models, in pictures, in geometric design, on athletic field. Introduce ideas such as "as the crow flies," the shortest distance between two points 2. Illustrate and emphasize the use of straightedge in drawing a straight line; the use of the ruler, compass, and squared paper in measuring and comparing lengths; the use of both English and metric units of length; the approximation of lengths and distances; the approximate nature of measurement; the use of drawing instruments in making simple geometric diagrams 3. Draw to scale simple diagrams, such as the classroom, gymnasium, football field, baseball field, basketball and tennis courts. Draw many graphs in which the student must select an appropriate scale 4. Show the advantage of both types of notation, viz., lettering both end points and using a single small letter to represent the line segment. Emphasize the significance of simple notation in algebraic discussions relating to line segments

Geometric Objective: Angle

Vocabulary	Instructional purposes	Instructional methods
acute angle adjacent angles alternate interior angles angle base angles of a triangle complementary angles corresponding angles degree	1. To teach the concept of what an angle is; both the static and dynamic aspects of angle 2. To teach pupils to recognize and classify different types of angles 3. To teach pupils the technique of angular	1. Use of board compass, shears, hands of clock, or some similar instrument to develop the concept of an angle as the amount of opening between two lines 2. Observation and discussion of angles found in the environment. Development of the concepts of acute angle, right angle, obtuse angle, and straight angle 3. Frequent use of the protractor in measuring and drawing angles of

Table 16-1. Content of Junior High School Geometry (Continued)

Vocabulary	Instructional purposes	Instructional methods

equal angles
exterior angle
inscribed angle
obtuse angle
opposite angles
parallel
perpendicular
protractor
right angle
side of angle
straight angle
supplementary
  angles
vertex
vertical angle
	measurement
	a. To develop reason-
	   able competence in
	   estimating sizes of
	   angles
	b. To teach use of pro-
	   tractor
	4. To instill an apprecia-
	   tion of careful and sig-
	   nificant notation
		various sizes. Comprehension of
		what is meant by "size of an angle."
		Construction of simple designs in-
		volving angles of various sizes.
		All right angles are equal
		
		4. Develop three types
		  of notation for the
		  angle, viz., $\angle ABC$,
		  $\angle B$, $\angle \beta$. Show ad-
		  vantages of each

Geometric Objective: Fundamental Constructions

altitude
angle
bisect
bisector
circle
compass
construct
equal
equilateral
line segment
median
mid-point
parallel
perpendicular
perpendicular
  bisector
protractor
right angle
straightedge
triangle
	1. To bisect a line segment
	
	2. Construct a perpendicu-
	  lar to a line (*a*) at a
	  point on the line, and
	  (*b*) from a point outside
	  the line
	
	3. To bisect an angle
	
	4. Construct an angle
	  equal to a given angle
	
	5. To make applications
	  of the fundamental con-
		1. Make several constructions and use
		compass to compare line seg-
		ments. Draw designs which make
		use of construction. Show that
		points on ⊥ bisector are at equal
		distances from extremities of line
		segment
		2. Make several constructions. Meas-
		ure the resulting angles to show
		that they are right angles. Bring
		out that construction is really draw-
		ing perpendicular bisector of a por-
		tion of the line segment. Draw
		designs using these constructions
		3. Make several constructions, and
		use protractor to compare resulting
		angles. Obtain angle of 45° from
		one of 90°, etc. Drop perpendicu-
		lars from points on bisector to sides
		of angle, and use compass to com-
		pare these lengths. Draw designs
		using this construction
		4. Make several constructions.
		Check each by the protractor and
		some by cutting the angles out and
		placing one on the other to see if
		they fit
		5. Construct angles of 60°, 45°, 30°, etc.
		Construct equilateral triangle, regu-

Table 16-1. Content of Junior High School Geometry (Continued)

Vocabulary	Instructional purposes	Instructional methods
structions		lar hexagon, parallel lines, circular graphs. Construct altitudes, medians, bisectors of angles, or perpendicular bisectors of sides of triangles. Divide circle into three, four, six, or eight equal parts

Geometrical Objective: Circle

arc area center central angle chord circle graph circle circumference compass concentric diameter equal inscribed angle locus pi (π) radius secant segment of circle tangent	1. To teach the concept of circle and develop an appreciation of the extent to which circles are used 2. To teach the definition of circle and the formulas for circumference and area	1. Observation of circles in art, architectural designs, nature, machinery, clothing designs, etc. 2. A circle is a curved line all points of which are the same distance from the center. The radii of a circle are equal. Develop an understanding of radius, diameter, circumference as the distance around the circle (circumference and perimeter should be related). To develop an understanding of the relationship between diameter and circumference, have pupils measure the diameters and circumferences of circular objects such as cans, plates, saucers, watches, etc., and calculate the ratio to three or four significant digits in each case. The formula should then be set up. The formula for area should be merely stated without development. There should be many applications. The circle as the path of a moving point
	3. To teach the application of concepts and formulas related to circles in problems of mensuration	3. Use many varied instances of circles in design and construction
	4. To teach the technique of drawing circles	4. Teach use of compass and string (at board). Point out that, when using a string to draw a circle on the blackboard, a right-handed person should always start with right

Table 16-1. Content of Junior High School Geometry (Continued)

Vocabulary	Instructional purposes	Instructional methods
		hand as far around to the left as possible and draw the circle clockwise while keeping the chalk perpendicular to the string at all times (a left-handed person would want to draw the circle counterclockwise starting with left hand as far around to right as possible). Draw many designs using circles
	5. To study positional relationships of line and circle and of two circles	5. A line may contact a circle in no points, one point, or two points. Discuss the significance of each position. Emphasize the fact that there are at most two points of contact Two circles may be in one of six possible positions with respect to each other; concentric, tangent (two positions), intersect, not intersect, coincident. Emphasize that there are at most two points of contact for two distinct circles

Geometrical Objective: Polygons

Vocabulary	Instructional purposes	Instructional methods
acute-angle triangle altitude area base congruence congruent diagonal equiangular equilateral formula hexagon isosceles trapezoid isosceles triangle obtuse triangle octagon parallelogram perimeter polygon	1. To acquaint pupils with the fundamental properties of triangles 2. To acquaint pupils with	1. Analysis of the various types of triangles and the part angles play in their make-up. Sum of the angles equals 180°. Study of congruence and similarity through experiment. Constructing and fitting triangles of the three types (a.s.a., s.a.s., s.s.s.) to test for congruence and (a.a.a.) for similarity. Relations between corresponding parts of congruent and similar figures. Ratio and proportion. Shadow ratio in right triangle. Nature and properties of isosceles, equilateral, and right triangles. The angles of an equilateral triangle are all equal; the base angles of an isosceles triangle are equal. Pythagorean relation 2. Sum of angles of quadrilateral

Table 16-1. Content of Junior High School Geometry (Continued)

Vocabulary	Instructional purposes	Instructional methods
quadrilateral rectangle regular rhombus right triangle scalene triangle similar similarity square symmetry trapezoid triangle vertex (vertices)	the fundamental properties of quadrilaterals 3. To study characteristics of certain regular polygons 4. To apply the fundamental principles of measurement 5. To develop an appreciation for, and an ability to use, significant notation	equals 360°. Nature and properties of parallelogram, rectangle, square, rhombus, and trapezoid. Similarity and congruence. Ratio and proportion. Parallelism of sides. Base and altitudes 3. Equilateral triangle, square, hexagon, octagon. Construct many regular polygons and use designs which emphasize them. Emphasize equality of angles and of sides 4. Study of perimeters and areas with establishment of basic formulas. Develop fundamental understanding of each concept and its calculated value 5. Call particular attention to the triangle, in which capital letters represent vertices and the corresponding small letters the opposite sides. It is desirable to use small Greek letters for the angles. The use of capital letters for vertices of all polygons should be emphasized. The use of b for base, h for height, A for area, and p for perimeter is recommended. In the case of trapezoids it is recommended that b_1 and b_2, or b and b', be used to represent the two bases

Geometrical Objective: Indirect Measurement

angle angle mirror angle of depression angle of elevation congruent distance	1. To find distances and angles by congruent triangles: *a*. To become familiar with the congruency of triangles because of the equality of two	1. Construct and test for congruence several triangles with equality of s.a.s. and a.s.a. Determine lengths of inaccessible distances (through buildings, across swamps, etc.). Use surveying instruments, and make constructions with ruler and

Table 16-1. Content of Junior High School Geometry (Continued)

Vocabulary	Instructional purposes	Instructional methods
length ratio ruler sextant similar tape measure "the more commonly used units of measurement" transit	angles and an included side *b.* To become acquainted with the congruency of triangles because of the equality of two sides and an included angle	compass. Further practice in measuring lengths and angles
	2. To find distances and angles by means of similar triangles: *a.* To become familiar with the similarity of triangles because of the equality of angles *b.* To become familiar with the similarity of triangles because of ratios of corresponding sides *c.* To become familiar with the concept of the "shadow ratio" as a basis for the better comprehension and use of the tangent ratio	2. Construct and test for similarity several triangles whose angles are equal, also whose sides are proportional. Find the heights of flagpoles, trees, buildings. Develop the concepts of angle of elevation and angle of depression. Develop the use of the shadow ratio (the ratio of an object to its shadow) as a technique for using a known height to find an unknown height. Point out the constancy of the angle for equal shadow ratios
	3. To find distances and angles by scale drawings	3. Develop the use of ratios in scale drawings and emphasize the convenience of the use of graph paper in drawing to scale. Make scale drawings of many familiar designs

Geometric Objective: Solids

altitude cone cube cylinder diagonal edge face formula	1. To develop the ability to draw solids and see solids in proper perspective	1. Point out some of the elementary aspects of looking at objects in perspective (looking down a railroad track, looking at pictures of rooms and their contents, the movie screen, etc.). Practice drawing the simpler solids so that they really look like what they are supposed

Table 16-1. Content of Junior High School Geometry (Continued)

Vocabulary	Instructional purposes	Instructional methods
length, width, height plane prism pyramid rectangular solid space sphere surface surface area units of volume vertex volume	2. The recognition of solids and their importance 3. The study of properties of solids	to be. Emphasize that lines that are behind planes should be lighter than others and dotted, etc. If colors are used, all lines lying in the same plane should be of same color 2. Seek pictures of such solids; look for them at home, at school, at work, at play. (For example, the chalk box, classroom, church steeples, silos, baseballs, basketballs, tennis balls) 3. Build up through experiment the relation between corresponding parts and formulas for surface areas and volumes. Bring out the various plane sections

Geometric Objective: Geometric Dependence

change dependence formula ratio variation varies	1. To acquaint the pupil with some of the more elementary and yet fundamental aspects of dependence in the study of geometry	1. Use the various formulas for perimeter, area, and volume as background for raising pertinent questions concerning the behavior of one aspect of a geometric situation for given changes in other, associated aspects of the same situation

Geometric Objective: Informal Reasoning

axiom conclusion definition hypothesis postulate reason	1. To bridge the gap between the intuitive and experimental geometry of the early junior high school and the more formal geometry of the senior high school	1. Give many opportunities for the pupils to replace direct measurement and observation by simple inferences. Try to develop an appreciation for the need of logical reasoning. Show the importance of analysis of situations to bring out the implications involved

Geometrical Objective: Numerical Trigonometry*

angle degree right angle acute angle	1. To develop the ability to sketch good working drawings for problems involving trigonometric	1. Explain and discuss the meanings of the trigonometric functions, and show, by various illustrations, how they are used to determine dis-

* This will be discussed more fully in Chap. 18.

Table 16-1. Content of Junior High School Geometry (Continued)

Vocabulary	Instructional purposes	Instructional methods

right triangle
hypotenuse
leg
opposite side
adjacent side
similar
ratio
proportion
scale drawing
sine
cosine
tangent
height
distance
horizontal
vertical
	solution from conditions stated verbally
	2. To develop an understanding of the meaning of the sine, cosine, and tangent of an angle
	
	3. To develop an interpretation of each of these functions in each of the following two ways:
	  a. As a ratio
	  b. As a numerical multiplier
	4. To develop the ability to use tables of sines, cosines, and tangents
	
	5. To develop the ability to use trigonometric functions to determine distances and angles without actual measurement
	6. To develop an appreciation of the method and usefulness of trigonometry
		tances and angles without actual direct measurement
		2. Strengthen the students' understanding of these meanings and applications by giving varied types of problems to be solved by using trigonometric functions
		3. Discuss and illustrate how trigonometric methods are used in practice by surveyors and engineers
		
		4. So far as possible, have the students carry on appropriate field problems, using instruments to collect their own primary data and using trigonometric methods to obtain final results

defined.[1] Of these twenty-nine items twelve related specifically to the geometry of the junior high school. The recommendations of the Secondary School Curriculum Committee and the Commission on Mathematics seem to reemphasize the specifications of the Commission on Post-War Plans.   Table 16-1 summarizes the best current judgment on what should be the geometric content of the junior high school curriculum and presents suggestions for the implementation of this program.

Basic Competence in Geometry.   At the end of a program of instruction such as that outlined in Table 16-1 the student should be familiar with the elementary ideas of shape, size, and position of basic geometric

[1] Commission on Post-War Plans, Guidance Report, *Mathematics Teacher*, **40** (1947), 317–318.

forms in both plane and space.   He should have an appreciation of the following:

1. The significance of symmetry as fundamental to design and construction
2. The implications of congruence and similarity in the relationships existing between geometric configurations
3. The nature and importance of direct and indirect measurement
4. The pertinence of dependence to the better understanding of the intrinsic characteristics of various fundamental geometric figures
5. The need for a more substantial verification of facts and establishment of truths than mere measurement, observation, or experimentation

Such a program in geometry in the junior high school should equip the student with a basic competence which will be of significant value to him whether he chooses to terminate his study of mathematics or pursue it to higher levels of abstraction and applications.

EXERCISES

1. What are some of the more important current trends which relate to the geometry program of the junior high school?
2. Give a specific statement of your interpretation of the function of geometry in the junior high school.   What authority can you cite to substantiate your point of view?
3. In what sense should the geometry of the junior high school be experimental?
4. In what sense should the geometry of the junior high school be intuitive?
5. What attention should be paid to direct and indirect measurement in the geometry program of the junior high school?
6. How much emphasis should be paid to the techniques of computing with approximate data in the geometry program of the junior high school?
7. To what extent should recreational projects be used as instructional aids in the geometry program of the junior high school?
8. How much attention should be given to the concepts, configurations, formulas, and techniques of solid geometry in the junior high school?
9. To what extent should attention be given to the formal proof of propositions in junior high school?
10. To what extent do you think the geometry of the junior high school should be used as background for the senior high school?

BIBLIOGRAPHY

Archer, Allene: Aids for Junior High Mathematics, "Twenty-second Yearbook" (Washington, D.C.: National Council of Teachers of Mathematics, 1954), pp. 134–142.
Beeman, W. E.: Originality in Geometry, *Mathematics Teacher*, **50** (1957), 589–593.
Betz, William: The Transfer of Training, with Particular Reference to Geometry, "Fifth Yearbook" (Washington, D.C.: National Council of Teachers of Mathematics, 1930), pp. 149–198.

————: The Teaching of Intuitive Geometry, "Eighth Yearbook" (Washington, D.C.: National Council of Teachers of Mathematics, 1933), pp. 55–164.

Buchman, Aaron: Symmetry and Congruence, *School Science and Mathematics*, **43** (1943), 356–357.

Burns, Francis H.: The Use of Models in the Teaching of Plane Geometry, *Mathematics Teacher*, **37** (1944), 272–277.

Davis, Kenneth S.: Geometry for Everyone, *Mathematics Teacher*, **35** (1942), 64–67.

Dobbs, Olive P.: Intuitive Geometry Comes to Life, *School Science and Mathematics*, **40** (1940), 221–225.

Fawcett, Harold P.: Geometry for All Laymen, *Mathematics Teacher*, **35** (1942), 269–274.

Hertzig, M.: Notes on the Teaching of Geometry in Junior High Schools, *High Points*, **40** (1958), 68–70.

Johler, W. W.: Seeing Solid: Attacking the Major Difficulty Met by Students of Solid Geometry, *Journal of Education*, **125** (1942), 253–254.

Johnson, D. A.: "Paper Folding for the Mathematics Class" (Washington, D.C.: National Council of Teachers of Mathematics, 1957). (Pamphlet.)

Joint Commission of the Mathematical Association of America and the National Council of Teachers of Mathematics: "The Place of Mathematics in Secondary Education," *Fifteenth Yearbook* (Washington, D.C.: National Council of Teachers of Mathematics, 1940), pp. 63–65, 78–91, 210, 246–247.

Miller, A. Brown: How Intuitive Geometry Serves the Community, *Mathematics Teacher*, **34** (1941), 339–342.

National Committee on Mathematical Requirements: "The Reorganization of Mathematics in Secondary Education" (Boston: Houghton Mifflin Company, 1923), pp. 26–60, 78–91, 99–113, 161–171.

Payne, Joseph N., and Robert C. Seber: Measurement and Approximation, "Twenty-fourth Yearbook" (Washington, D.C.: National Council of Teachers of Mathematics, 1959), pp. 182–228.

Price, H. Vernon: An Experiment in Fusing Plane and Solid Geometry, *School Science and Mathematics*, **49** (1949), 199–203.

Reeve, W. D.: Informal Geometry in the Junior High School, *School Science and Mathematics*, **56** (1956), 371–380.

Scannell, A., and M. Fridrich: Finding Art in the Geometry Classroom, *School Arts*, **55** (1956), 33–34.

Sister Mary Fides: Geometry Decorates Our Lunch Room, *Catholic School Journal*, **54** (1954), 20–21.

Smith, D. E., and W. D. Reeve: "The Teaching of Junior High School Mathematics" (Boston: Ginn & Company, 1927), pp. 59–66, 133–168, 229–269, 308–320.

17

THE TEACHING OF GEOMETRY IN THE SENIOR HIGH SCHOOL

The informal geometry of the junior high school will constitute the complete geometry program of many students. For those who continue their study of geometry in the senior high school, intuition and experiment will still be an effective aid, but the major purposes of instruction will be to instill in the students an appreciation of the significance of logical demonstration; to acquaint them with effective methods of clear impartial thinking, critical evaluation, and intelligent generalization; to train them in the techniques of discovery of truth; and to introduce them to the meaning of mathematical rigor and precision.

The demonstrative geometry of the senior high school should aim to develop the habits of independent and careful thinking rather than strive to present the subject matter of geometry as a *finished* model of deductive thinking. It is extremely important that each pupil do his own thinking, observing, and comparing and that new ideas, statements, truths, and theorems be discovered by the pupil himself. Teachers should therefore give thoughtful and conscientious consideration to the most effective means of attaining these goals of instruction. Each teacher should have a clear comprehension of the nature of proof and the significance of demonstration. He should know something of the relative effectiveness and the distinguishing characteristics of the various techniques of careful thinking. He should be skilled in the methods of application and generalization of geometrical subject matter.

The Nature of the Program. From the Third Report of the Committee on Geometry[1] we have the statement that

It is generally agreed that the important facts of geometry can be mastered below the tenth grade through inductions based on observation, measurement, constructions with drawing instruments, cutting and pasting, and also through simple deductions from the foregoing inductions as well as from geometric notions intuitively held.

[1] Ralph Beatley, The Third Report of the Committee on Geometry, *Mathematics Teacher*, **28** (1935), 334.

Thus it would seem that the responsibility of senior high school geometry is entirely defined within the province of postulational thinking. This does not imply the mastery of a significant body of theorems any more than it implies intelligent comprehension of the methods involved in arriving at and establishing the truths embodied within such theorems. There is a definite propaedeutic value in the mastery of a number of geometric theorems which is to be neither overlooked nor minimized. In the main, however, such academic value is overshadowed by the importance to the individual of the technique of discovery, evaluation, and establishment of truth. The clear statement of definitions, the critical analysis of assumptions, the careful weighing of evidence, and the impartial deduction of implied conclusions are invaluable contributions which the intelligent study of demonstrative geometry may make to the general education of senior high school pupils.[1]

Furthermore, students should be led to an appreciation of the postulational structure of geometry. They should recognize that different geometries with distinct basic postulates can be structured, some infinite and some finite.[2] They should have the opportunity to know of the existence of non-Euclidean geometries as well as Euclidean, projective as well as metric, and of the basic distinctions between such classifications of geometrical subject matter. Also they should have their consideration of geometric configurations oriented in three dimensions as well as in one and two dimensions, and the techniques they use should be extended to include those basic to analytic coordinate geometry as well as those basic to synthetic pure geometry.

One of the major problems that confront the teacher of demonstrative geometry is to teach the pupil to reason without reference to unestablished circumstantial evidence. For example, in proving a theorem related to triangles, a pupil is inclined to think in terms of a right triangle if one of the angles looks like a right angle, or in terms of an equilateral triangle if the diagram looks as if the three sides are equal. The pupil's attention should be called to the dangerous pitfalls of inaccurate reasoning that lie behind such diagrammatic camouflages. An inexperienced pupil is likely to use such special diagrams and is just as likely to draw general conclusions from specific situations. Emphasis should be given to the necessity for drawing accurate diagrams with ruler and compass in situations that demand them, such as construction problems, prescribed written work, or any situation which places a great deal of emphasis on accuracy of figure. Freehand drawings that are approximately accurate

---

[1] A very interesting study to read in this connection is H. P. Fawcett, The Nature of Proof, "Thirteenth Yearbook" (Washington, D.C.: National Council of Teachers of Mathematics, 1938).

[2] Burton W. Jones, Miniature Geometries, *Mathematics Teacher*, **52** (1959), 66–71.

may be used occasionally, particularly for the drawing of figures that are purely demonstration figures, such as in proofs of theorems or solutions of original exercises where the emphasis is on the method of attack. In every case the argument for the establishment of a truth should place the figure in the background, i.e., only known and established facts related to the figure should be used.

The above remarks do not intend to imply that there will be no place for intuition in senior high school geometry. A great many of the intuitive truths from junior high school geometry should be accepted as a background for senior high school geometry. Furthermore, there should be opportunities for experimentation and intuitive thinking in senior high school geometry. The teacher must make sure that a clearly defined distinction is drawn between the techniques and functions of experimentation, intuition, and demonstration. The subject matter of geometry offers a body of materials concerning which individuals can think impartially and critically and about which they can form conclusions entirely uninfluenced by their emotions. It is for this reason that the study of geometry can be used so effectively as a means for demonstrating and analyzing the techniques of careful argumentation and clear thinking.

Committee Recommendations. No area of the secondary school mathematics curriculum has received more critical study than has the geometry program. This has been due to the recognized inadequacies of the traditional pattern of Euclidean geometry that has dominated the high school program.[1] The Secondary School Curriculum Committee devoted four pages of its report to the discussion of this problem.[2] Likewise, the Commission on Mathematics devoted better than five and one-half pages of its report to the same problem,[3] and an additional two pages to presenting a proposed outline for a geometry program for grade 10.[4] Though there is some divergence in these two reports, particularly concerning the relative emphasis to be devoted to synthetic geometry and analytic (algebraic) geometry, there is a great deal of agreement on fundamental questions relating to an improved program in geometry. In particular, the two reports agree on the desirability of (1) the use of techniques and concepts from coordinate geometry, (2) an integrated treatment of plane and solid geometry, (3) more careful attention to the postulational struc-

[1] Albert E. Meder, Jr., What's Wrong with Euclid? *Mathematics Teacher*, **51** (1958), 578–584.

[2] Secondary School Curriculum Committee, Report of, *ibid.*, **52** (1959), 404–408.

[3] "Report of the Commission on Mathematics" (New York: College Entrance Examination Board, 1959), pp. 22–28.

[4] *Ibid.*, pp. 38–39. Also see the second volume of the report, entitled "Appendices," pp. 109–174, for discussions and illustrative examples of possible revisions in the treatment of the geometry program of the secondary school.

ture of geometry, (4) providing opportunity for students to learn of the existence of geometries other than the Euclidean type, and (5) capitalizing on a basic geometric foundation which should be recognized as the responsibility of the junior high school.

The Secondary School Curriculum Committee, in placing a stronger emphasis on the synthetic study of geometry, underscores the need for "a sharper delineation of the meaning of deductive proof." They state that this implies a need for a better understanding of the nature of an indirect proof and for becoming familiar with the distinctions and relations between a theorem and its converses, inverses, and contrapositives. Also, they make the very important point that "the kind of thinking that pupils are called upon to do in solving geometric originals is somewhat like that required of the mature classical mathematician.[1]

Indirect Proof.[2]   In Chap. 3 the nature of the indirect form of argumentation is discussed.   Since there are many situations in geometry which can be investigated most effectively by applying the techniques of indirect proof, it is desirable to examine the procedure more in detail in such a context.   One feature of the indirect proof which frequently proves to be troublesome is the clumsy wordiness inseparable from the verbal statement of the denial of the hypothesis.   This use of negative statements can become very confusing.

A plan that has been used very satisfactorily in overcoming this difficulty is that of writing out separately the complete and careful statements of the two contradictory propositions in step 1 *and then substituting for each of these statements a single identifying symbol.*   The Greek letters θ and ϕ were chosen merely because it was felt that they were not likely to be confused with the customary symbols used in identifying points, lines, etc.   The choice turned out to be a happy one for another reason, viz., the newness of these symbols aroused the curiosity and interest of the students and, as a by-product of this focusing of attention, the mechanical outline of indirect proof tended to crystallize in the students' minds more quickly and more definitely than had been expected.

The use of these symbols made it possible to eliminate a great deal of the verbal confusion mentioned above, and to shorten both written and oral exposition, with a corresponding increase in understanding of the mechanics and the nature of indirect proof.

To illustrate, let us consider the proposition concerning two straight lines perpendicular to the same line.   The demonstration following the outline described, but not employing the symbolic representation of the contradictory statements, would be set up in some such manner as the following:

[1] Secondary School Curriculum Committee, *op. cit.*, p. 407.
[2] See the Report of the Commission on Mathematics, "Appendices," *op. cit.*, pp. 116–119.

Theorem. Two straight lines, lying in the same plane and both perpendicular to the same straight line, are parallel to each other.

Given. $a \perp l$ and $b \perp l$.

To prove. $a \parallel b$.

FIG. 17-1

Proof

1. Either $a \parallel b$ or a is not $\parallel b$.	1. Contradictory statements.
2. Suppose a is not $\parallel b$.	2. Tentative assumption.
3. If a is not $\parallel b$, then a intersects b.	3. Definition of $\parallel$ lines.
4. In this case we should have two lines both $\perp$ a line from the same point, which is impossible.	4. One and only one line can be drawn from a point perpendicular to a line.
5. $\therefore$ It is not true that a is not $\parallel b$.	5. Because this assumption leads to a contradiction of a previously proved theorem.
6. $\therefore a \parallel b$.	6. If one of two contradictory propositions is false, the other one must be true.

This is a perfectly correct and valid proof, but its statement is rather confusing in step 5, where it is necessary to use the double negative or else avoid the use of the word "parallel."

If this proposition were set up in the symbolic form which has been described, the argument could be developed as follows (the same diagram and statement of hypothesis and conclusion may be used):

1. $\theta \ldots a \parallel b$, $\phi \ldots a$ is not $\parallel b$.	1. Two contradictory statements.
2. Suppose ϕ is true.	2. Tentative assumption.
3. If a is not $\parallel b$, then a intersects b.	3. Definition of $\parallel$ lines.
4. In this case we should have two lines $\perp$ a line from the same point, which is impossible.	4. One and only one line can be drawn from a point perpendicular to a line.
5. $\therefore \phi$ is not true.	5. Because the assumption led to a contradiction of a previously proved theorem.
6. $\therefore \theta$ is true.	6. If one of two contradictory statements is false, the other one must be true.

Observe that the statement "ϕ is not true" is much more concise and less confusing than the verbal statement "it is not true that a is not parallel to b." Moreover, experience has shown beyond doubt that the use of this symbolic representation of the two possibilities in setting up the theorem distinctly increases the students' perception of the essentially contradictory nature of the two statements and clarifies for them the mechanics of the proof.

There are, of course, cases in which the setup of the problem contains more than two possibilities. Take, for example, the following:

FIG. 17-2

Theorem. If two angles of a triangle are equal, the sides opposite these two angles are also equal.

Given. $\angle B = \angle C$.

To prove. $AB = AC$.

Proof

1. $\theta \ldots AB = AC$,
   $\phi \ldots AB \neq AC$,
   or $\begin{cases} \phi_1 \ldots AB > AC, \\ \phi_2 \ldots AB < AC. \end{cases}$

1. Contradictory statements which involve all possible cases.

2. Suppose ϕ_1 true, then $\angle C > \angle B$, contradictory to hypothesis.

2. If one side of a triangle is greater than a second side, the angle opposite the first side is greater than the angle opposite the second side.

3. Suppose ϕ_2 true, then $\angle B > \angle C$, contradictory to hypothesis.

3. Same reason as step 2.

4. $\therefore \theta$ is true, and $AB = AC$.

4. All other possible relationships between AB and AC have led to contradictions of the hypothesis.

In the above two illustrations the argument proceeded directly from the negation of the conclusion to the implication of the negation of the hypothesis. This is, as was pointed out on page 72, the proof of the contrapositive of the given theorem, and it is equivalent to proving the original theorem. Not all indirect arguments are of this type. Another technique is to establish that the contradiction of the conclusion leads to the implication of a known inconsistency. This procedure is illustrated in the following proof of the converse of the first of the above two theorems.

FIG. 17-3

Theorem. If a line is perpendicular to one of two parallel lines and lies in the plane of these lines, then it is perpendicular to the other.

Given. Two parallel lines l_1 and l_2 with line $l_3 \perp l_1$ at A and meeting l_2 at B.

To prove. $l_3 \perp l_2$.

Proof

1. Either $l_3 \perp l_2$ or l_3 is not $\perp l_2$.

1. Contradictory statements which involve all possible cases.

2. Assume l_3 is not $\perp l_2$.

2. Tentative assumption.

3. Through B, and in the plane of l_1
and l_3, draw $l_4 \perp l_3$.

4. $l_4 \parallel l_1$.

4. Two straight lines lying in the same plane and perpendicular to the same straight line are parallel.

5. $l_2 \parallel l_1$.

5. By hypothesis.

6. There are two lines through B, both $\parallel l_1$, which is impossible.

6. A contradiction of the parallel postulate.

Although the indirect proof is a very powerful instrument in the investigation of truth, it is at times dangerous. One using the indirect type of argument can very easily become guilty of reasoning in a circle, i.e., using the theorem in question either explicitly or implicitly as a reason in its proof. This, however, is but one type of faulty argument which can be the source of error in any form of deductive proof whether direct or indirect, synthetic or analytic. The teacher should be aware of these sources of error and shape his instructional program to ensure against them. Probably the most prominent and persistent are the following:[1]

1. Omission of statements
2. Inclusion of irrelevant statements
3. A disregard for a correct order of statements
4. The use of reasons not yet established
5. Reasoning in a circle, i.e., the use of the proposition in question as a reason in its proof
6. The confusion of definitions with theorems
7. The confusion of the hypothesis with conclusion
8. The confusion of a statement with its converse and inverse

Converse, Inverse (Opposite), and Contrapositive. The analysis of geometric truths and proofs frequently demands a familiarity with, and the intelligent use of, the converse, inverse, or contrapositive of some theorem or theorems. An introduction to a clear understanding of these descriptive terms may be secured by examining a simple theorem containing only one hypothesis and one conclusion.

Theorem. If a triangle is equilateral, then it is isosceles. (Obviously true.)

Converse Theorem. If a triangle is isosceles, then it is equilateral. (Not necessarily true.)

Inverse Theorem. If a triangle is not equilateral, then it is not isosceles. (Not necessarily true.)

Contrapositive Theorem. If a triangle is not isosceles, then it is not equilateral. (Obviously true.)

In this simple case the method of derivation of the different types of theorems is rather evident. For a theorem with one hypothesis and one conclusion:

[1] Harry Sitomer, "If-Then" in Plane Geometry, *Mathematics Teacher*, **31** (1938), 326–329.

1. The converse theorem is obtained by interchanging the hypothesis and conclusion.

2. The inverse (or opposite) theorem is obtained by taking the contradiction of the hypothesis as the new hypothesis and the contradiction of the conclusion as the new conclusion.

3. The contrapositive theorem is obtained by taking the contradiction of the conclusion as the new hypothesis and the contradiction of the hypothesis as the new conclusion.

If H represents the hypothesis of a given theorem and C the conclusion, the above definitions may be stated diagrammatically as follows:

Theorem. If H is true, then C is true.
Converse Theorem. If C is true, then H is true.
Inverse Theorem. If H is not true, then C is not true.
Contrapositive Theorem. If C is not true, then H is not true.

It must be remembered that, as was demonstrated in the truth tables of page 73, the fact that a theorem is true makes no implication about the truth or falsity of the statement in its converse or its inverse. The truth of each must be investigated upon its own merits. The law of contraposition, however, states that a theorem and its contrapositive are equivalent, i.e., if one is true, the other is true, and if one is false, the other is false.[1]

The above definitions must be modified for theorems that involve more than one hypothesis or more than one conclusion. The following definitions have been suggested as satisfactory generalizations:

1. The converse of a theorem may be obtained by interchanging *any* number of conclusions with an *equal number* of hypotheses.[2]

2. An inverse of a proposition having one conclusion may be formed by contradicting one of the hypotheses and the conclusion.[3]

3. A contrapositive of a theorem containing more than one hypothesis and only one conclusion may be obtained by the interchange of the contradictory of one of the hypotheses with the contradictory of the conclusion.[4]

[1] N. Lazar, The Importance of Certain Concepts and Laws of Logic for the Study and Teaching of Geometry, *Mathematics Teacher*, **31** (1938), 170.

[2] *Ibid.*, p. 107. It would be better to say, "A converse of a theorem . . . " since the definition provides for more than one converse of a theorem which contains more than one hypothesis and one conclusion.

[3] *Ibid.*, p. 159. Although the concept of "inverse of a proposition" may be extended to theorems with more than one conclusion, the logical difficulties involved seem to make it advisable to restrict the definition to the one given above for geometry in the secondary school.

[4] *Ibid.*, p. 218. The definition given above represents a rewording of the definition given by Lazar in the reference. Contradictory statements are to be interpreted as satisfying the conditions specified on p. 77 (this book). Lazar points out that a less restricted definition may be given for a contrapositive of a theorem (*ibid.*, p. 170), but

As an illustration of the nature of converse propositions, consider the following:

Theorem. If two right triangles have the hypotenuse and a leg of one equal respectively to the hypotenuse and a leg of the other, the triangles are congruent.

Fig. 17-4

Hypotheses	*Conclusions*
△ ABC and $A'B'C'$ (Fig. 17-4)	△ are ≅.
H_1 . $\angle C$ and $\angle C'$ are rt. $\angle$s.	C_1 . $a = a'$.
H_2 . $c = c'$.	C_2 . $\angle B = \angle B'$.
H_3 . $b = b'$.	C_3 . $\angle A = \angle A'$.

There is a temptation on the part of the immature pupil to consider the statement that the triangles are congruent as the one conclusion of the theorem.   Upon analysis, however, it is seen that there are in fact many conclusions, since equality of any pair of corresponding parts of the two triangles follows as a consequence of the three stated hypotheses. Only the three basic conclusions are listed above for purposes of the desired illustration.   Symbolically the above theorem may be written

$$(H_1)(H_2)(H_3) \rightarrow (C_1)(C_2)(C_3)*$$

It is then evident that the following converses can be obtained by the interchange of one hypothesis and one conclusion.

1. $(H_1)(H_2)(C_1) \rightarrow (H_3)(C_2)(C_3)$ 4. $(H_1)(H_2)(C_2) \rightarrow (C_1)(H_3)(C_3)$
2. $(H_1)(C_1)(H_3) \rightarrow (H_2)(C_2)(C_3)$ 5. $(H_1)(C_2)(H_3) \rightarrow (C_1)(H_2)(C_3)$
3. $(C_1)(H_2)(H_3) \rightarrow (H_1)(C_2)(C_3)$ 6. $(C_2)(H_2)(H_3) \rightarrow (C_1)(H_1)(C_3)$
                   7. $(H_1)(H_2)(C_3) \rightarrow (C_1)(C_2)(H_3)$
                   8. $(H_1)(C_3)(H_3) \rightarrow (C_1)(C_2)(H_2)$
                   9. $(C_3)(H_2)(H_3) \rightarrow (C_1)(C_2)(H_1)$

Careful examination of these nine theorems reveals the fact that in each case but one there is a combination of hypotheses sufficient to give congruent triangles.   The exception is theorem 6, in which case the hypothesis would imply the ambiguous case for a triangle.   In each theorem, however, which involves H_1 as one of the conclusions there is

---

that logical difficulties make the one cited above more desirable for elementary geometry (*ibid.*, pp. 170, 218).

* The symbol → is to be read "implies."

not necessarily a true statement. Thus, of the nine converse theorems, only six (1, 2, 4, 5, 7, 8) are necessarily true theorems.

Since converse theorems may be obtained by the interchange of two hypotheses with two conclusions and of the three hypotheses with the three conclusions, we have the following additional converses of the original theorem:

10. $(H_1)(C_1)(C_2) \rightarrow (H_2)(H_3)(C_3)$
11. $(H_1)(C_1)(C_3) \rightarrow (H_2)(C_2)(H_3)$
12. $(H_1)(C_2)(C_3) \rightarrow (C_1)(H_2)(H_3)$
13. $(C_1)(H_2)(C_2) \rightarrow (H_1)(H_3)(C_3)$
14. $(C_1)(H_2)(C_3) \rightarrow (H_1)(C_2)(H_3)$
15. $(C_2)(H_2)(C_3) \rightarrow (C_1)(H_1)(H_3)$
16. $(C_1)(C_2)(H_3) \rightarrow (H_1)(H_2)(C_3)$
17. $(C_1)(C_3)(H_3) \rightarrow (H_1)(C_2)(H_2)$
18. $(C_2)(C_3)(H_3) \rightarrow (C_1)(H_1)(H_2)$
19. $(C_1)(C_2)(C_3) \rightarrow (H_1)(H_2)(H_3)$

As above, it is evident that no theorem which has the clause H_1 as a part of its conclusion is necessarily a true theorem. Furthermore, the hypothesis of theorem 12, $(H_1)(C_2)(C_3)$, is not sufficient to establish congruency. Hence, of the above converse theorems, only theorems 10 and 11 are necessarily true theorems. Thus out of the total of 19 possible converse theorems to the original true theorem there are only eight (1, 2, 4, 5, 7, 8, 10, 11) which are necessarily true theorems.

For an illustration of inverses and contrapositives of a theorem consider the following:

Theorem. If two triangles have two sides of the one equal, respectively, to two sides of the other, but the included angle of the first greater than the included angle of the second, then the third side of the first is greater than the third side of the second.

Fig. 17-5

Hypotheses	*Conclusions*
△ ABC and $A'B'C'$.	$C \cdot b > b'$.
$H_1 \cdot a = a'$.	
$H_2 \cdot c = c'$.	
$H_3 \cdot \angle B > \angle B'$.	

This theorem is well adapted to the consideration of inverses and contrapositives because it has only one conclusion. In the discussion which follows, we shall use $\bar{H}_1$ to represent the contradiction of H_1, $\bar{H}_2$ of H_2, $\bar{H}_3$ of H_3, and $\bar{C}$ of C. Thus $\bar{H}_1$ becomes $a \neq a'$ (or $a \gtreqless a'$); $\bar{H}_2$ becomes $c \neq c'$ (or $c \gtreqless c'$); $\bar{H}_3$ becomes $\angle B \ntriangleright \angle B'$ (or $\angle B \lesseqgtr \angle B'$); and $\bar{C}$ becomes $b \ntriangleright b'$ (or $b \lesseqgtr b'$). From the definition of the inverse of a theorem it is evident that there are three inverses to the given theorem. They are:

1. Hypotheses: $\bar{H}_1$, H_2, H_3; Conclusion: $\bar{C}$.
2. Hypotheses: H_1, $\bar{H}_2$, H_3; Conclusion: $\bar{C}$.
3. Hypotheses: H_1, H_2, $\bar{H}_3$; Conclusion: $\bar{C}$.

Analysis of these three theorems establishes that theorem 3 is the only true theorem.

Similarly, there are three contrapositives of the given theorem. They are:

1. Hypotheses: $\bar{C}$, H_2, H_3; Conclusion: $\bar{H}_1$.
2. Hypotheses: H_1, $\bar{C}$, H_3; Conclusion: $\bar{H}_2$.
3. Hypotheses: H_1, H_2, $\bar{C}$; Conclusion: $\bar{H}_3$.

By the contrapositive law all three of these theorems should be true theorems. Careful analysis reveals that this is the case.

Original Exercises. The original exercise is gaining more and more recognition as an effective instructional medium in geometry. This change in emphasis is to be noted in the transition from the text with nothing but definitions, axioms, postulates, and propositions to the modern text in which much use is made of a large list of well-distributed original exercises and incomplete proofs. In fact, the modern philosophy of geometric instruction emphasizes that the pupil who does not have many opportunities for solving original exercises is missing the real opportunity to learn the nature, function, and techniques of demonstrative geometry.

Original exercises may be divided into three major divisions, viz., (1) propositions to be proved through deductive argument, (2) geometric problems to be solved through applications of algebraic or arithmetical techniques, and (3) problems calling for the construction of certain geometric configurations from given elements, using the straightedge and compass.

The propositions to be proved may be geometrical in content or entirely nonmathematical in nature. In either event the pupil must appreciate the necessity for reading the proposition carefully, for selecting the hypothesis and conclusion, for using a systematic, sound argument, and, in the case of geometric propositions, for using a compact, significant symbolism in connection with a carefully drawn figure. He must be familiar with the advantages and disadvantages of the different forms of proof. He must know how to construct a chain of reasoning and how to detect fallacious arguments and unsound hypotheses. Furthermore he must become skilled in detecting those factors of an argument which justify conclusions. The analytic-synthetic type of deduction is probably the most effective technique for discovery of unknown proofs of geometric theorems. The indirect form of argument frequently will be found to be very effective in the handling of such original exercises.

In the handling of nonmathematical propositions the emphasis of instruction is largely the same as in the geometrical type of proposition. The major differences will be in the absence of a simplifying symbolism and in the fact that the attention is centered upon the importance of the use of well-defined terms, the soundness and reasonableness of hypotheses, the evaluation of reasoning, the investigation of the evidence behind any conclusion that is drawn, the nature of converses, and the need for the careful search of an argument for unexpressed assumptions. The materials for such problems are found in advertisements, editorials, propaganda, schoolroom arguments or debates, community projects, etc.

The solving of geometric problems by algebraic and arithmetical techniques implies the use of an appropriate symbolism and a ready familiarity with the fundamental techniques of algebraic and arithmetical analysis. The pupil must not only be able to translate from geometry into algebraic and arithmetical relationships but be proficient in interpreting algebraic formulas and arithmetical results in terms of geometric figures.

There are four aspects of any construction problem in geometry: (1) Determine how to use the given elements to construct the required figure; (2) construct the figure; (3) prove that the construction is correct, i.e., prove that the constructed figure has the given elements in it, either directly or indirectly; and (4) discuss the possibilities of construction, i.e., the conditions under which the construction is possible and whether the construction, when possible, is unique. These four aspects might be more briefly labeled: (1) analysis, (2) construction, (3) proof, and (4) discussion. To illustrate, let us consider the following:

Problem. To construct a triangle, given the base, the angle opposite the base, and the sum of the other two sides.

Given. $a, b + c, \angle A$.

To construct. $\triangle ABC$.

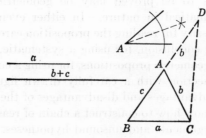

Fig. 17-6

Analysis. Suppose $\triangle ABC$ is the required triangle. How can $b + c$ be used to get the triangle? Is there an auxiliary triangle, using $b + c$ and the other given elements, which can be constructed and from which the $\triangle ABC$ can be obtained? It is to be observed that, if BA is extended to D so that $AD = AC$, then $BD = b + c$. Furthermore, since $\triangle ADC$ is isosceles, $\angle D = \frac{1}{2}\angle A$. Therefore, $\triangle BDC$ can be constructed, since two of its sides and the angle opposite one of them are known. The $\perp$ bisector of DC will then intersect BD in the point A, thus determining the required $\triangle ABC$.

Fig. 17-7

Construction

On a working line BX lay off $BD = b + c$. At D construct $\angle D = \frac{1}{2}\angle A$. With B as a center and a radius $= a$, describe a circle intersecting DY in C and C'.
Draw BC.
Erect the $\perp$ bisector of DC. It will intersect BD in A.
Draw AC.
$\triangle ABC$ is the required triangle.

Proof

1. $BC = a$.
2. $\triangle ADC$ is isosceles.

3. $AD = AC$.
4. $\therefore BA + AC = BA + AD$
   $\qquad = BD$
   $\qquad = b + c$.
5. $\angle ADC = \angle ACD$.
6. $\angle BAC = \angle ADC + \angle ACD$
   $\qquad = 2\angle ADC$.
7. $\therefore \angle BAC = \angle A$.

1. By construction.
2. A lies on $\perp$ bisector of DC by construction.
3. Legs of isosceles $\triangle$.
4. $BD = b + c$ by construction.

5. Base $\angle\!s$ of isosceles $\triangle$.
6. Ext. $\angle$ of $\triangle$ = sum of two opposite int. $\angle\!s$.
7. $\angle ADC = \frac{1}{2}\angle A$ by construction.

Discussion. For the construction to be possible, $b + c$ must be greater than a, since the sum of two sides of a triangle must be greater than the third side. In the construction of the auxiliary $\triangle BCD$, the circle with B as a center and a as a radius might intersect the line DY in two points C and C' (as in Fig. 17-7), in which case there would be two solutions for the $\triangle BCD$. If a were equal in length to the $\perp$ distance from B to DY, this circle would be tangent to DY and there would be only one $\triangle BCD$. If a were less than the $\perp$ distance from B to DY, the circle would not intersect the line DY and there would be no $\triangle BCD$ possible. From each auxiliary $\triangle BCD$ there can be obtained one and only one required $\triangle ABC$, since the $\perp$ bisector of DC will intersect the line BD in one and only one point.   Therefore, there may be two solutions, one solution, or no solution for the given problem.

No construction problem should be considered a finished product until it has been subjected to the complete treatment outlined above.   Much of the most important information concerning a construction is frequently hidden until the discussion brings it to light.   It should be emphasized that such procedure as this gives system to the attack on construction problems and eliminates a great deal of the futile effort expended and feeling of helplessness developed in the hit-or-miss, trial-and-error technique so frequently used.

Concept of Locus.   As the analysis of the above construction problem led to the consideration of certain loci, so it is with most construction problems.   In the ultimate analysis, a large majority of all constructions depend upon the intersections of loci.   In Fig. 17-7 one locus of the vertex C is the line DY and another locus is the circle with B as a center and a as a radius.   The intersection of these loci determines C.   Also, the perpendicular bisector of DC is the locus of points equidistant from D and C; hence, it locates A on BD.   The concept of locus and the methods of construction of loci which satisfy given conditions are fundamental to an intelligent approach to the study of geometric construction.

Conversely, a very effective approach to a clear understanding of locus can be made with the aid of certain elementary constructions.   Through the use of such constructions the student can frequently be made aware of the truths of certain locus theorems before he actually comes into formal contact with them.   The proper use of experimental geometry in the junior high school provides for just such an approach to the understanding of the locus concept.   A few constructions which provide experimental material suitable for this purpose are as follows:

1. Bisect the angles of a given triangle.
2. Draw the perpendicular bisectors of the sides of a given triangle.
3. Draw the altitudes of a given triangle.
4. Draw the medians of a given triangle.

Through the use of these simple constructions, the general experiences of the child, and the use of simple geometric models the introduction of the concept of locus can be made very meaningful to the pupil.   Both the dynamic and static concepts of locus should be introduced and developed. The concept of motion provides for the dynamic interpretation of locus as the path of a point moving in such a way that it satisfies certain given conditions.   In using the concept of motion, attention should be directed first to the point as it moves under the given restrictions and then to the path it generates.   Frequently it is true that this concept is easier to comprehend than is the static interpretation of locus as the place where all points which satisfy the given conditions are to be found. It is, of course, evident that the two interpretations are in no sense contradictory or mutually exclusive. They are interchangeable in nature; in the one we think of a single point moving to give us the locus, while in the other we think of the locus as a composite picture, as it were, of many points fixed in position. For example,

Dynamic

A point, moving in such a way that it is always equidistant from two given points, generates the perpendicular bisector of the line joining the two points.

Static

The locus of points equidistant from two given points is the perpendicular bisector of the line joining the two points.

The language of sets frequently affords a convenient method for describing a locus. For example, a circle might be described as the set of all points in the plane at a fixed distance from a fixed point. Also, the perpendicular bisector of a line segment might be described as the set of all points which are equidistant from the end points of the line segment. This could be a point, a line, or a plane, depending upon the dimensionality of the universe of points from which the specified set is to be selected.

It is generally recommended that locus problems be considered in conjunction with the four fundamental theorems on concurrent lines:

1. The altitudes of a triangle meet in a point.
2. The medians of a triangle meet in a point.
3. The bisectors of the angles of a triangle meet in a point.
4. The perpendicular bisectors of the sides of a triangle meet in a point.

These theorems will have been intuitively established through experimentation with the simple constructions mentioned on page 488. They form the basis for two other fundamental locus constructions, viz.,

1. Inscribe a circle within a given triangle.
2. Circumscribe a circle about a given triangle.

As an aid to general construction problems there are seven locus theorems which should be considered as fundamental and which should be thoroughly understood by everyone. These seven fundamental locus theorems are:

1. The locus of a point moving so that it is always at a given distance from a fixed point is a circle with the fixed point as the center and the given distance as the radius.
2. The locus of a point moving so that it is always at a given distance from a fixed line is a pair of lines parallel to the fixed line and the given distance from it.

3. The locus of a point moving so that it remains equidistant from two fixed points is the perpendicular bisector of the line segment joining the two fixed points.

4. The locus of a point moving so that it remains equidistant from a pair of fixed intersecting lines is a pair of lines bisecting the angles formed by the two fixed lines.

5. The locus of a point moving so that it remains equidistant from two fixed parallel lines is a line parallel to the two lines and midway between them.

6. The locus of the vertex of the right angle of a right triangle with a given fixed hypotenuse is the circumference of the circle with the hypotenuse as diameter.

7. The locus of the vertex A of the triangle ABC with fixed base BC and vertex angle A of given magnitude is the arc of a circle on BC as a chord and in which the angle A can be inscribed.

The traditional method of proving a locus problem has been to prove a theorem and one of its converses. Since the contrapositive of a theorem is true if the theorem is true, this two-way proof can also be accomplished by proving one of the contrapositives of the theorem and one of the contrapositives of the converse. The two-way method of proof of any locus problem may then be established by proving two theorems, one each from groups I and II.

Group I: Theorem and all its contrapositives

Group II: A converse of the theorem and all the contrapositives of this
    converse

Such a pairing of theorems exhausts all possibilities for a two-way proof of any locus and provides many choices of method. For example, if a given statement of a locus involves two hypotheses H_1 and H_2 and one conclusion C, we have

Group I:

 1. Theorem: $(H_1)(H_2) \rightarrow (C)$.
 2. Contrapositive: $(H_1)(\bar{C}) \rightarrow (\bar{H}_2)$.
 3. Contrapositive: $(\bar{C})(H_2) \rightarrow (\bar{H}_1)$.

Group II:

 1. Converse: $(H_1)(C) \rightarrow (H_2)$.
 2. Contrapositive: $(H_1)(\bar{H}_2) \rightarrow (\bar{C})$.
 3. Contrapositive: $(\bar{H}_2)(C) \rightarrow (\bar{H}_1)$.

Thus, since each theorem of group I may be paired with any theorem of group II, there are nine ways of giving a two-way proof of a locus problem with two hypotheses and one conclusion.[1] As an illustration, consider the following:

[1] Lazar, *op. cit.*, p. 224.

Theorem. The locus of a point equidistant from the sides of a given angle is the bisector of the angle.

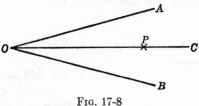

Fig. 17-8

Group I	*Group* II
Theorem. If OC is the bisector of $\angle AOB$ and P lies on OC, then P is equidistant from OA and OB.	*Converse.* If OC is the bisector of $\angle AOB$ and P is equidistant from OA and OB, then P lies on OC.
Contrapositive. If OC is the bisector of $\angle AOB$ and P is not equidistant from OA and OB, then P does not lie on OC.	*Contrapositive.* If OC is the bisector of $\angle AOB$ and P does not lie on OC, then P is not equidistant from OA and OB.
Contrapositive. If P is not equidistant from OA and OB and P lies on OC, then OC is not the bisector of $\angle AOB$.	*Contrapositive.* If P does not lie on OC and P is equidistant from OA and OB, then OC is not the bisector of $\angle AOB$.

The proof of any theorem from group I and any theorem from **group II** will constitute a two-way proof of the above locus problem. There are nine ways then of establishing the above locus by a two-way proof.

If the seven fundamental locus theorems on pages 489 to 490 are established by the two-way method, or merely postulated, then a one-way proof can be used effectively in practically all other locus situations. In order to avoid the two-way proof, some recommend that the seven fundamental loci be postulated. As an illustration of the one-way proof, two locus problems will be considered.

Problem. Find the locus of the mid-point of a rod whose ends always touch two fixed rods which are perpendicular to each other.

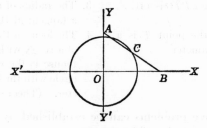

Fig. 17-9

Given. Rods XX' and YY' $\perp$ each other at O. AB a rod moving so that end A is always on YY' and end B is always on the rod XX'.

To find. The locus of C, the mid-point of AB.

Solution

1. AB in any position forms a rt. $\triangle$ with AB as hypotenuse.

2. $OC = AC = CB$.

3. $\therefore$ The locus of C is a circle with O as center and OC as radius.

1. XX' and YY' given $\perp$ each other.

2. The mid-point of the hypotenuse of a rt. $\triangle$ is equidistant from the three vertices.

3. The locus of a point moving so that it is always at a given distance from a fixed point is a circle with the fixed point as the center and the given distance as the radius. (Theorem 1, page 489.)

Problem. Find the locus of the points of contact of tangents drawn from a given point to concentric circles.

FIG. 17-10

Given. Concentric circles with center at O and tangents drawn from fixed point P.

To find. The locus of the points of contact of these tangents.

Solution

1. In any position OT will pass through O.

2. In any position PT will pass through P.

3. In any position the $\angle PTO$ is a rt. $\angle$.

4. $\therefore$ The locus of the point T is a circle on PO as diameter.

1. In each case OT is a radius of a circle.

2. Given condition.

3. The radius of a circle is always $\perp$ a tangent at the point of contact.

4. The locus of the vertex of the rt. $\angle$ of a rt. $\triangle$ with a given fixed hypotenuse is the circumference of the circle with the hypotenuse as diameter. (Theorem 6, page 490.)

Each of the above problems can be established by a two-way proof, but the directness and simplicity of the one-way method make it very desirable.

Another important aspect of the concept of locus is its power as a corre-lating link between plane and solid geometry.   Wilt states that "probably no topic offers richer materials for bringing together the content of plane and solid geometry."[1]   She suggests that we state locus problems and teach locus concepts from the points of view of both plane geometry and solid geometry simultaneously, e.g., the locus of a point equidistant from the sides of a plane angle and also from the faces of a dihedral angle, the locus of a point in the plane equidistant from two points and also the locus of a point in space equidistant from two points, etc.

Conversely, it is also suggested that the consideration of some of the more familiar space concepts might lead to a more natural and a better motivated approach to the somewhat abstract concept of locus.   The consideration of the parallel walls of a room, the parallelism of floor and ceiling, or parallel rows of trees in an orchard might lead to a more intelli-gent comprehension of the true nature of parallelism than the mere drawing of lines on paper or on the board.[2]

The close relationship existing between some of the two- and three-dimensional loci is indicated in the following discussion.   The plane locus is stated and then the concept of motion is introduced to develop the space locus.

I. The locus of a point moving in a plane so that it is always at a given distance from a fixed point is a circle with the fixed point as center and the given distance as the radius.

If in Fig. 17-11 the circle is allowed to turn on AB as an axis, we obtain the sphere of Fig. 17-12 whose diameter $A'B'$ is equal to AB.   Every point on the surface of the sphere is equidistant from O', the midpoint of $A'B'$.   Hence

Fig. 17-11   Fig. 17-12

1. The locus of a point moving in space so that it is always at a given distance from a fixed point is a sphere with the fixed point as center and the given distance as the radius.

[1] May L. Wilt, Teaching Plane and Solid Geometry Simultaneously, "Fifth Year-book" (Washington, D.C.: National Council of Teachers of Mathematics, 1930), p. 66.

[2] Gertrude E. Allen, An Experiment in the Redistribution of Materials for High School Geometry, "Fifth Yearbook" (Washington, D.C.: National Council of Teach-ers of Mathematics, 1930), pp. 73–74.

II. The locus of a point moving in a plane so that it is always at a given distance from a fixed line is a pair of lines parallel to the fixed line and at the given distance from it.

In Fig. 17-13 consider first the lines AB, CD, and EF. If the distance between CD and $AB = d =$ distance between EF and AB, then CD and EF are the lines of the plane locus II. Now, if AB moves to the position $A'B'$ and at the same time CD moves to $C'D'$ and EF to $E'F'$ and they each remain at all times the distance d from AB, then the planes $CDD'C'$ and $EFF'E'$ are each d distance from the plane $ABB'A'$. Hence

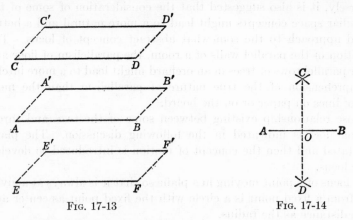

FIG. 17-13   FIG. 17-14

2. The locus of a point moving in space so that it is always at a given distance from a fixed plane is a pair of planes parallel to the fixed plane and at the given distance from it.

III. The locus of a point moving in a plane so that it remains equidistant from two fixed points is the perpendicular bisector of the line segment joining the two fixed points.

FIG. 17-15   FIG. 17-16

If in Fig. 17-14 the line AB is allowed to revolve around CD as an axis, then we obtain Fig. 17-15, in which every point on CD is equidistant from the points on the circle XYZ whose center is O and whose radius is $OA = OB$.   Furthermore, if C is a fixed point then $CA = CB$. Hence

3. The locus of a point moving in space equidistant from the points of a circle is a line perpendicular to the plane of the circle at the center of the circle.

4. The locus of a point moving in space so that it remains equidistant from the three vertices of a triangle is a line perpendicular to the plane of the triangle at the point which is the center of the circumscribed circle of the triangle.

5. The locus of a point moving in a plane so that it is at a given distance from a fixed point not in the plane is a circle whose center is the projection of the point on the plane and whose radius is the projection of the given distance upon the plane.

If in Fig. 17-14 the line CD is allowed to revolve around AB as an axis and if it is remembered that CD is unlimited in extent, then we obtain a figure represented by Fig. 17-16, in which every point in the plane RS is equidistant from the points A and B.   Hence

6. The locus of a point moving in space so that it remains equidistant from two fixed points is a plane perpendicular to the line segment joining the two points and at its mid-point.

IV. The locus of a point moving in a plane so that it remains equidistant from a pair of fixed intersecting lines is a pair of lines bisecting the angles formed by the two fixed lines.

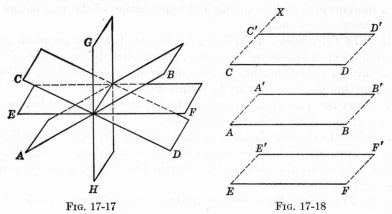

Fig. 17-17   Fig. 17-18

In Fig. 17-17 first consider the angles formed by the lines AB and CD with their bisectors EF and GH.   Then, if the lines are allowed to move so that the respective planes are generated, it follows that

7. The locus of a point moving in space so that it remains equidistant from the faces of two intersecting planes is a pair of planes bisecting the dihedral angles formed by the planes.

V. The locus of a point moving in a plane so that it remains equidistant from two parallel lines is a line parallel to the two lines and midway between them.

In Fig. 17-18 first consider the parallel lines CD and EF with AB midway between and parallel to them. Let the point C move along the line CX while the given lines move in such a way that the initial relationship remains true. Then we have

8. The locus of a point moving in space so that it remains equidistant from the faces of two parallel planes is a plane parallel to the two planes and midway between them.

Thus by using motion in space as the generalizing technique, the two- and three-dimensional concepts of locus can be shown to be closely associated with each other, and each may be effectively used to supplement the discussion of the other.

The Concept of Dependence. The dynamic concept of locus emphasizes the importance of functional dependence in the analysis of geometric configurations. This concept of the interdependence of geometrical magnitudes is by no means new. Most of the emphasis in the study of functionality on the secondary level, however, has been confined to the analysis of interdependent variation by means of algebraic techniques. In plane geometry this has resulted in a tendency to overlook the fact that there are many aspects of dependence which are not expressible in the conciseness of an algebraic formula but which are deeply significant to a fundamental understanding and appreciation of the real nature of geometrical subject matter.

In 1872 Felix Klein, in outlining his famous Erlanger program, gave the following definition of geometry: "Geometry is the study of the invariants of a configuration under a group of transformations." Thus the structure of geometry may be outlined as follows:[1]

1. Select the space, i.e., determine whether the geometry to be studied is in one, two, three, or higher dimensions.

2. Select the element, i.e., specify the undefined elements. In ordinary two- or three-dimensional geometry the undefined element is generally taken to be either the point or the straight line. This, however, is not necessary.

3. Build configurations such as triangles, quadrilaterals, circles, and polygons.

4. Select transformations. In elementary geometry, the two most frequently used groups of transformations are those of rigid motion and projection.

5. Study invariants. An invariant of a geometric configuration is a

[1] *Cf.* E. P. Lane, Definition and Classification of Geometries, *School Science and Mathematics*, **30** (1930), 50–56.

property that does not change in the process of being transformed. For example, length of a line does not change when the line is moved about in space, but it does change if the line is projected from one plane to another; hence, length is an invariant under rigid motion but not under projection.

From the above outline of the structure of geometry it is evident that the very nature of the geometry to be studied is dependent upon making certain basic choices.   In the geometry of the secondary school the space in which we are interested is either two-dimensional (plane) or three-dimensional (solid).   The undefined element is the point, and the transformations are those of rigid motion, viz., rotation and translation. Under these transformations, such geometric properties as length, distance, size of an angle, united position of point and line, and area are invariant properties. We proceed, then, to analyze the geometric configurations in terms of these invariants, for example:

1. Two triangles are congruent when their sides are of the same respective lengths.

2. Two triangles are congruent when two pairs of sides of the same respective lengths include angles of the same size.

3. A circle is the locus of a point moving at a given distance from a fixed point.

4. Two circles are congruent if their radii are of the same length.

Although the point may be taken as the undefined element of the geometry of the secondary school and all other elements defined in terms of it, from a pedagogical point of view, this is very undesirable.   It is not good psychology to crowd the young mind with so many formal definitions.   No significant mathematical rigor is lost in taking for undefined elements in secondary geometry such terms as point, line, surface, plane, solid, and space.   An intelligent comprehension of such concepts can be established intuitively, and it is pedagogically unsound to attempt to build up definitions of these concepts that could be accepted as technically correct.

In any geometric configuration there exist intrinsic interrelations among the constituent elements.   An analysis of this interdependence of elements is one of the most effective techniques for discovering the characteristic properties of the configuration and portraying its complete geometric significance. For example:

1. The area of a triangle depends upon the lengths of the altitude and base. What happens to the area when either the altitude or the base is doubled?   What happens when both are doubled?

2. How do the circumference and area of the circle depend upon the radius? Which is affected more by a change in the length of the radius?

3. In a cylinder $V = \pi r^2 h$.   Which would increase the volume more, to double h or to double r?

4. In a triangle how is a side affected by increasing the opposite angle if the lengths of the two including sides remain constant?

Questions such as these help to bring to light the exact nature of any geometric configuration under investigation. Critical analysis and intelligent interpretation of such configurational dependence will contribute to enriched geometrical comprehension.

The study of geometrical dependence is further enhanced by the principle of continuity, which asserts that a proposition that has been established in relation to a given figure will remain true when that figure changes continuously subject to the conditions controlling its initial construction. The interrelated concepts of dependence and continuity unite to replace a static, mechanical treatment of geometrical subject matter by a dynamic, functional program of instruction. It behooves every teacher of geometry to utilize the full benefits of such an approach to the study of geometrical subject matter. As an illustration of the full significance of the introduction of these dynamic concepts into the teaching of plane geometry, consider the implications for relational thinking embodied in the two following theorems:

1. The angle formed by two intersecting lines of unlimited length which meet a circle is measured by one-half the algebraic sum of the intercepted arcs.
2. In a triangle the square of the side opposite a given angle is equal to the sum of the squares of the other two sides diminished by twice the algebraic product of one of these sides by its projection upon the other.

It is true that the concept of directed line and arc lengths must be introduced in the consideration of the above theorems for their full significance. Why should we not use such concepts of directed line lengths in the teaching of plane geometry as a significant aspect of the concept of directed numbers introduced in the algebra of the junior high school? The consideration of similar groupings of significant theorems will enhance the value of these dynamic concepts of dependence and continuity as instructional mediums in plane geometry.

Since it takes only two points to determine a line, we say that three points are dependent if they are on the same line. This concept of dependence has some very interesting and important applications to the construction of geometric figures. A triangle is uniquely determined by three points not on the same line. In more general terminology this statement would read: a triangle is uniquely determined by three independent points, or still more generally, a triangle is uniquely determined by three independent elements (or conditions). The truth of this last statement is illustrated by the congruency theorems which require three independent elements.

Since the sum of angles of a triangle is always 180°, the three angles are dependent elements.   Why are two triangles whose three angles are respectively equal not necessarily congruent?   Why do three lines through the same point not determine a triangle?   Two other less evident illustrations of dependent elements are to be seen in Figs. 17-19 and 17-20.

In Fig. 17-19 it is to be noted that any angle inscribed in the arc BAC will be equal to angle A.   Hence it is evident that the elements a, A, R (radius of circumscribed circle) are dependent elements; i.e., given any two of them, the third is determined.

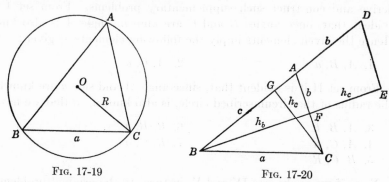

FIG. 17-19   FIG. 17-20

In the triangle ABC (Fig. 17-20) let h_b and h_c represent the altitudes upon the sides b and c, respectively.   In the rt. $\triangle$ BFC and BGC, respectively, it is evident that a, h_b, $\angle C$ and a, h_c, $\angle B$, are sets of dependent elements since, in each case, any two of the elements determine the right triangle and the third element is then uniquely determined.   Now let BA be extended to D so that $AD = AC$; then $BD = b + c$.   Draw $DE \perp BF$ extended. $DE \parallel AC$; hence $\angle D = \angle CAB$.   Also $BE = h_b + h_c$.   It then follows immediately from the right triangle BDE that the elements $b + c$, $h_c + h_b$, $\angle A$ are dependent elements.

By using both direct and indirect elements related to the unique determination of triangles, five sets of three dependent elements each have been exhibited.   They are

   I. A, B, C IV. a, h_b, C

  II. a, A, R V. a, h_c, B

III. $b + c$, $h_c + h_b$, A

Such sets of dependent elements are important aids in an effective approach to exercises in the construction of triangles.   It is the purpose of this discussion to call attention to an aspect of this concept of dependence that seems to be generally overlooked in the teaching of plane geometry.   To simplify the discussion, two specific examples will be developed in the hope that inferences will lead to the individual development of many others.

A simple construction problem that frequently comes early in the geometry course is to construct a triangle having given two angles and the included side. Let us specify that the given elements are B, C, a. After this construction has been completed, additional construction problems may be derived from it by using the dependent elements of sets I, II, IV, and V. These problems may be used as instructional aids, supplementary drill material, or as material for enriching the study of construction. It would indeed be fine instructional technique to have the students derive and construct such supplementary problems. From set I it is evident that, once angles B and C are known, angle A is also known. Hence the given elements imply the following elements as given:

1. A, B, a 2. A, C, a

From set II it is evident that, since angle A and side a are known, R, the radius of the circumscribed circle, is also known, so that we have

3. A, B, R 6. R, B, a
4. A, C, R 7. R, C, a
5. B, C, R

Now, if we apply sets IV and V, in turn, to the original problem and derived problems 1, 2, 6, and 7, we obtain

8. B, C, h_b 13. h_b, h_c, a 18. A, C, h_c
9. h_c, C, a 14. B, h_c, h_b 19. R, B, h_c
10. h_b, C, h_c 15. A, h_b, a 20. R, h_b, a
11. B, C, h_c 16. A, B, h_b 21. R, C, h_b
12. B, h_b, a 17. A, h_c, a 22. R, h_c, a

Another interpretation of set I is that, if we have given one angle of a triangle, we also know the sum of the other two. By applying this to problems 6, 7, 9, 10, 12, 14, 15, 17, 19, and 21 above, we obtain

23. R, $A + C$, a 27. $A + C$, h_b, a 30. $B + C$, h_c, a
24. R, $A + B$, a 28. $A + C$, h_c, h_b 31. R, $A + C$, h_c
25. h_c, $A + B$, a 29. $B + C$, h_b, a 32. R, $A + B$, h_b
26. h_b, $A + B$, h_c

Hence from the original set of elements there have been derived 32 additional sets of given elements with which triangles may be constructed. Each of these problems may have an individual construction which is independent of the original problem B, C, a. It is quite evident, however, that all of the problems may be reduced to the original problem. Still others may be derived.

Another illustration of interest may be found in the application of these techniques to derive additional construction problems from the one whose construction was carried out on pages 486 to 488.

From the use of set I we have the following

$$1. \ a, B + C, b + c$$

An application of set II to the original problem and to the **derived** problem gives

2. $R, A, b + c$ 4. $R, B + C, b + c$
3. $a, R, b + c$

An application of set III then gives

5. $a, h_c + h_b, b + c$ 7. $R, h_c + h_b, b + c$
6. $a, A, h_c + h_b$ 8. $R, A, h_c + h_b$

Applications of sets I and II to problems 6 and 8 give

9. $a, B + C, h_c + h_b$ 11. $R, B + C, h_c + h_b$
10. $a, R, h_c + h_b$

If it is furthermore recalled that the perimeter $2p$ is the sum of the sides, i.e.,

$$2p = a + b + c$$

the following 12 sets may be derived:

12. $2p, A, a$ 18. $2p, b + c, A$
13. $2p, R, a$ 19. $2p, R, B + C$
14. $2p, A, R$ 20. $2p, h_c + h_b, a$
15. $2p, b + c, R$ 21. $2p, h_c + h_b, A$
16. $2p, B + C, a$ 22. $2p, h_c + h_b, B + C$
17. $2p, B + C, b + c$ 23. $2p, h_c + h_b, b + c$

Thus 23 additional construction problems have been derived from the original one through successive applications of the concept of geometric dependence.

Similar possibilities exist in all construction situations in geometry. Such instructional technique not only provides the teacher with an enriched program of geometric teaching but also affords the student the opportunity for a more significant understanding of the real nature of geometric construction.

EXERCISES

1. What is meant by postulational thinking?

2. Select an editorial, news item, or advertisement and analyze it for terms that need to be defined, assumptions that are made, and conclusions that are drawn or implied.   Evaluate the validity and reliability of these conclusions.

3. In your own words distinguish between induction and deduction, synthesis and analysis.

4. What are some of the major advantages which the Commission on Mathematics ascribes to the use of coordinate geometry at the high school level of instruction?

5. Frequently we hear the expression "synthetic geometry" as contrasted with "analytic geometry." What are the implications as to technique in this contrast between synthesis and analysis?

6. What do you consider the major distinguishing characteristics between direct and indirect proof?

7. Select a problem (construction or proof), and show how the indirect form of argument may be used as an effective instrument in the analysis of the problem.

8. What is meant by the statement that demonstrative geometry is primarily a deductive science?

9. Why is it necessary that, in a deductive science, there must be a list of undefined terms and accepted assumptions?

10. Is there any significant difference in the logical and pedagogical implications of the fact that lists of undefined terms and accepted assumptions must exist?

11. Distinguish between the implications of "self-evident truth" and "accepted truth."

12. Select a nongeometrical problem, similar to the one on page 77, and show, in detail, how it might be solved by the process of indirect reasoning.

13. Given the theorem: In equal circles, equal chords are equidistant from the center. (a) What are the hypotheses and conclusions? (b) Write all converse, inverse, and contrapositive theorems. (Use these terms as defined in this chapter.) (c) Which of the theorems, part (b), are true ones?

14. Show that all the theorems relating to congruence of triangles can be derived by taking converses of any one of them. What untrue theorems are also derived?

15. Give both a static and a dynamic statement of each of the following two-dimensional locus concepts: circle, bisector of an angle, two parallel lines equidistant from a fixed line, ellipse, hyperbola, and parabola.

16. Give an extension to three-dimensional space of each of the locus concepts of exercise 15.

17. In the construction problem: To construct a triangle, given the elements a, R (radius of circumscribed circle), and h_b (altitude on the side b), show the analysis, construction, proof, and discussion.

18. Demonstrate the analytic-synthetic type of proof in proving the following theorem: If ABC is an equilateral triangle inscribed in a circle and P is any point on the arc BC, then $PA = PB + PC$.

19. What theorems of plane geometry are incorporated in theorem 1 on page 498, in theorem 2?

20. Select a group of related theorems from plane geometry and show how the concept of dependence and the principle of continuity permit the incorporation of all theorems of the group into one theorem.

21. Of the following sets of three elements of a triangle, which are sets of dependent elements? (1) a, b, c; (2) a, A, R; (3) A, B, C; (4) A, b, C; (5) A, h_c, b; (6) a, h_b, h_c; (7) a, h_b, C; (8) A, a, h_a; (9) b, R, h_c; (10) A, R, b.

22. By using sets of dependent elements, how many new construction problems can you derive from the three elements given in exercise 17?

BIBLIOGRAPHY

Allen, Frank B.: Multi-converse Concept in Geometry, *Mathematics Teacher*, **45** (1952), 582–584.

Birkhoff, G. D., and R. Beatley: A New Approach to Elementary Geometry, "Fifth Yearbook" (Washington, D.C.: National Council of Teachers of Mathematics, 1930), pp. 86–95.

Brumfiel, C. F.: The Ball State Experimental Program in Geometry and Algebra, *American Mathematical Monthly*, **66** (1959), 228–230.

Butler, Charles H.: Note on the Statements of Theorems and Assumptions, *Mathematics Teacher*, **48** (1955), 106–107.

———: Generalization in Geometry, *School Science and Mathematics*, **60** (1960), 445–449.

Christofferson, H. C.: "Geometry Professionalized for Teachers" (Oxford, Ohio: published by the author, 1933).

Commission on Mathematics, Report of: "Program for College Preparatory Mathematics" (New York: College Entrance Examination Board, 1959), pp. 38–39.

———: "Appendices" (New York: College Entrance Examination Board, 1959), pp. 109–119, 140–174.

Fawcett, H. P.: Teaching for Transfer, *Mathematics Teacher*, **28** (1935), 465–472.

———: The Nature of Proof, "Thirteenth Yearbook" (Washington, D.C.: National Council of Teachers of Mathematics, 1938).

———: Quod Erat Demonstrandum, *Mathematics Teacher*, **49** (1956), 2–6.

Fehr, Howard F.: On Teaching Trihedral Angle and Solid Angle, *Mathematics Teacher*, **51** (1958), 358–361.

Hallerberg, Arthur E.: The Geometry of the Fixed Compass, *Mathematics Teacher*, **52** (1959), 230–244.

Hamley, H. R.: Relational and Functional Thinking in Mathematics, "Ninth Yearbook" (Washington, D.C.: National Council of Teachers of Mathematics, 1934), pp. 9–193.

Hartley, Miles C.: Models in Solid Geometry, *Mathematics Teacher*, **35** (1942), 5–7.

Heinke, C. H.: Variation: A Process of Discovery in Geometry, *Mathematics Teacher*, **50** (1957), 146–154.

Henderson, Kenneth B.: The Lessons Non-Euclidean Geometry Can Teach, *Mathematics Teacher*, **33** (1940), 73–79.

Hennessey, F. P.: The Principle of Continuity, *Mathematics Teacher*, **24** (1931), 32–40.

Hess, A. L.: The Place of Geometric Constructions in Plane Geometry, *School Science and Mathematics*, **55** (1955), 594–598.

Hlavaty, Julius H.: The Nature and Content of Geometry in the High Schools, *Mathematics Teacher*, **52** (1959), 115–118.

Jones, Burton W.: Miniature Geometries, *Mathematics Teacher*, **52** (1959), 66–71.

Lankford, F. G., Jr.: Optional Proofs of Theorems in Plane Geometry, *Mathematics Teacher*, **48** (1955), 578–580.

Lazar, N.: Importance of Certain Concepts and Laws of Logic for the Study and Teaching of Geometry, *Mathematics Teacher*, **31** (1938), 99–113, 156–174, 216–240.

———: The Logic of Indirect Proof in Geometry, *Mathematics Teacher*, **40** (1947), 225–239.

Massimiano, C. C.: Influence of the Study of Plane Geometry on Critical Thinking, *Mathematics Teacher*, **49** (1956), 371–380.

Mathematics Staff of the College, University of Chicago:

A Problem on the Cutting of Squares, *Mathematics Teacher*, **49** (1956), 332–346.

———: More on the Cutting of Squares, *Mathematics Teacher*, **49** (1956), 442–454.

———: Still More on the Cutting of Squares, *Mathematics Teacher*, **49** (1956), 585–596.

———: New Exercises in Plane Geometry, *Mathematics Teacher*, **50** (1957), 125–135.

———: More New Exercises in Plane Geometry, *Mathematics Teacher*, **50** (1957), 330–339.

Meder, Albert E., Jr.: What's Wrong with Euclid? *Mathematics Teacher*, **51** (1958), 578–584.

Menger, Karl: On Necessary and Sufficient Conditions in Elementary Mathematics, *School Science and Mathematics*, **39** (1939), 631–642.

Miller, Ralph C.: A New Technique in Handling the Congruence Theorems in Plane Geometry, *Mathematics Teacher*, **36** (1943), 237–239.

Peak, Philip: Continuity in Geometry, *Mathematics Teacher*, **37** (1944), 360–362.

Pickett, Hale: Functional Thinking in Geometry, *Mathematics Teacher*, **33** (1940), 69–72.

Progressive Education Association: "Mathematics in General Education" (New York: Appleton-Century-Crofts, Inc., 1940), pp. 187–213.

Rosskopf, M. F., and R. M. Exner: Modern Emphases in the Teaching of Geometry, *Mathematics Teacher*, **50** (1957), 272–279.

Schlauch, W. S.: The Analytic Method in the Teaching of Geometry, "Fifth Yearbook" (Washington, D.C.: National Council of Teachers of Mathematics, 1930), pp. 134–144.

Schnell, L. H.: New Emphases in Teaching Geometry, "Twenty-second Yearbook" (Washington, D.C.: National Council of Teachers of Mathematics, 1954), pp. 269–276.

Serwais, W.: Equations and Geometric Loci: A Logical Synthesis, *Mathematics Teacher*, **50** (1957), 114–122.

Sleight, Norma: Geometry of the Earth's Surface, *School Science and Mathematics*, **43** (1943), 5–12.

Smith, Eugene P., and Kenneth B. Henderson: Proof, "Twenty-fourth Yearbook" (Washington, D.C.: National Council of Teachers of Mathematics, 1959), pp. 111–181.

Smith, Rolland R.: Three Major Difficulties in the Learning of Demonstrative Geometry, *Mathematics Teacher*, **33** (1940), 99–134, 150–178.

———: On the Teaching of Geometry, *Mathematics Teacher*, **42** (1949), 56–60.

Swenson, J. A.: Graphic Methods of Teaching Congruence in Geometry, "Fifth Yearbook" (Washington, D.C.: National Council of Teachers of Mathematics, 1930), pp. 96–101.

Ulrich, J. F.: Case for the Syllogism in Plane Geometry, *Mathematics Teacher*, **46** (1953), 311–315.

Wiseman, John D., Jr.: The ABC's of Geometry, *Mathematics Teacher*, **50** (1957), 327–329.

18

THE TEACHING OF TRIGONOMETRY

In the minds of many people trigonometry is associated only with the idea of college mathematics and engineering. This is doubtless true because trigonometry has not occupied a very prominent place in the mathematics program in the high schools, whereas it is universally offered and often required in college. As a consequence, comparatively few people have become really acquainted with the subject, and it has gained a reputation of being very difficult.

This reputation is in large part unmerited. It is true, of course, that certain parts of trigonometry are difficult and are suitable only for relatively mature students, but on the other hand there is much which is quite simple and which can be understood readily even by junior high school students. Indeed it has been found that some of the elementary concepts of trigonometry are more easily comprehended than much of the usual work in algebra and that the application of these principles and relationships is very interesting to children in the early years of the secondary school. Moreover, such application offers an excellent means of correlating arithmetic with certain parts of informal geometry and with the solution of simple linear equations. In addition, the early introduction and simple treatment of these elements of trigonometry may be expected to have considerable influence in counteracting the reluctance of students to undertake later the systematic study of the subject. Therefore, because of its general educational value and its motivating force, some preliminary work in trigonometry has come to be commonly offered in the junior high school. Many textbooks in ninth-grade algebra or general mathematics include a unit on numerical trigonometry, and not infrequently some of this work is given in the eighth grade.

The general maturity and mathematical experience of junior high school students is, of course, inadequate for a systematic study of trigonometry. Here the objectives are different, the subject matter more involved, the analyses more difficult, and the methods more rigorous.

505

Consequently, such a study of the subject is properly deferred until the latter years of the senior high school or the first year of college work.

Trigonometry in the Junior High School. Since it seems necessary to defer the systematic study of trigonometry until the latter years of the senior high school, those parts which are to be included in the junior high school work must find their justification in the direct contribution which they can make to the goals of general education at this level. This may be thought of as potential practical values[1] and as general educational values. By comparison, the latter are by far the more important. They make for general enrichment of the course and include extension and clarification of the concept of ratio and the use of symbolism; appreciation of the power and application of indirect measurement; understanding of the methods of accomplishing such measurement through the use of the right triangle and the tangent, sine, and cosine ratios; correlation of ideas and procedures drawn from arithmetic, algebra, and geometry; and stimulation of interest in mathematics as a whole.

Broadly speaking, the teaching of trigonometry should begin long before trigonometric ratios are considered at all. Since the ratios imply measurement, comparison, and the study of certain properties of similar figures, these activities form a potential groundwork. If properly taught, they pave the way for future work by developing concepts which later are to provide the very basis of numerical trigonometry.

The subject matter of the numerical trigonometry of the junior high school is simple; it consists primarily of instances dealing with the indirect measurement of distances. Much impetus can be given to this work by allowing the students to undertake actual field projects, but before this is done, a considerable amount of preliminary groundwork should be laid. Presumably the students will already be familiar, through their work in informal geometry, with the principles of drawing to scale and with the use of the protractor and tape for measuring angles and distances directly. This is about all that can be assumed safely. It is necessary, however, that they have clear concepts of the meaning of similar figures (especially similar triangles), of a ratio as a comparison of two quantities in the sense that one is a certain fraction of the other or that one is a certain number of times the other, and also of a ratio as a single number (fractional or integral) which may be used as a multiplier. They also need to understand the particular meanings of the tangent ratio, the sine ratio, and the cosine ratio, and they must know how to use the table of natural functions either to find the value of a particular function of a given angle or to find the value of an angle if the numerical value of one of its functions is known. They need to know the meaning of such terms as "angle of

---

[1] The term "practical" is used here in a narrow sense. Under a more liberal interpretation all genuine educational values may be regarded as practical.

elevation" and "angle of depression." They need practice in analyzing problem situations, in making working drawings, in selecting the appropriate functions to use, in setting up and solving equations involving these functions, and in substitution and evaluation. These things need to be carefully and clearly explained by the teacher. In order to develop comprehensive understanding of the techniques used in field projects, the students should work a large number of illustrative problems. Furthermore, the teacher should carefully discuss the full implications of such problems with the students.

Developing the Meaning of a Trigonometric Function. In beginning the study of numerical trigonometry the first thing to be done is to make clear the meaning of the trigonometric functions as ratios and as numbers. Probably the best way to accomplish this is to have the students actually make careful measurements of the angles and sides of right triangles and compute the numerical values of the ratios representing the tangent, sine, and cosine.

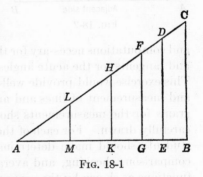

Fig. 18-1

It is well to have several students compute the values of these functions for angles of a given size so that they may compare their results. Generally, their results will show a fairly close correspondence, and the fact that they may not agree exactly offers a good opportunity to emphasize the approximate nature of measurement. Thus, any discrepancies may be attributed either to mistakes in computation or to errors in taking the measurements. This approach, through measurement and computation, to the meaning of a trigonometric function emphasizes the concept of the function both as a comparison of the lengths of two sides of a right triangle and as a single numerical quantity or quotient. Common agreement on the value to be accepted may be reached by averaging the values found by several students.

A variation of the foregoing procedure may be made by having each student make several sets of measurements and computations leading to the determination of the values of the functions of a particular angle, such as angle A in Fig. 18-1. Thus the value of the tangent of angle A might be determined by using several different ratios such as CB/AB, DE/AE, FG/AG, HK/AK, or LM/AM. This would give emphasis to the principle that the value of a given function of any angle is independent of the actual lengths of the sides of the triangle and depends only on the *ratio* of the lengths of the two sides involved.

The functions that are introduced in the study of trigonometry in the junior high school are generally limited to the tangent, sine, and cosine. The others would add nothing toward making the meaning of a function clear, and they are not needed for the solution of the simple applied problems that make up the work of this period.   For obvious reasons this work is limited to situations that involve functions of acute angles.   With this in mind, the functions of an acute angle may be defined in terms of the sides of a right triangle containing that angle.   Let angle BAC be the given angle, Fig. 18-2.

FIG. 18-2

Tangent $\angle BAC = \dfrac{\text{opposite side}}{\text{adjacent side}}$

Sine $\angle BAC = \dfrac{\text{opposite side}}{\text{hypotenuse}}$

Cosine $\angle BAC = \dfrac{\text{adjacent side}}{\text{hypotenuse}}$

An interesting and valuable exercise can now be introduced by having the class as a whole make measurements and computations necessary for the compilation of a table of sines, cosines, and tangents for the acute angles, say, which are integral multiples of 5°. This exercise would provide well-motivated practice in accurate drawing and measurement of lines and angles and in careful computation.   Diagrams for the measurements should be rather large and should be very carefully drawn.   For each of the angles considered, at least two or three students should make determinations of the functions for purposes of comparison, checking, and averaging of the results.   The values of the functions as shown by the computed results should be expressed to three significant figures.

Teaching Students How to Use the Trigonometric Functions.   The meanings of the trigonometric functions and the ways in which they are to be used will be more quickly and adequately comprehended if the meanings and uses are illustrated in problem situations.   There need be no delay about this.   As soon as the meaning of the tangent ratio has been explained to the point of understanding, the teacher should show how it is used in finding distances or angles without direct measurement.   Hypothetical or "made-up" problems will serve for this purpose quite as well as "real" problems, and perhaps better, because the assumed elements (an angle and a distance or two given distances) can be selected at will and with a view to convenience and there will be no extraneous details of actual measurement, the manipulation of instruments, or unnecessarily difficult computations to draw the students' attention from the basic principles and procedures involved.   Substantial mastery of the basic theory and procedure should be assured before the students are thrown into situations in which they will have to provide their own data. Initial interest is usually high, and the artificial motivation afforded by field projects is unnecessary at the outset. Thus, such problems as the following serve well to introduce students to the applications of the functions. The fact that convenient data are arbitrarily chosen in no way lessens the value of the problems. The steps in the solution are about in the form in which they should be explained to the students.

Example. From a point 50 feet from the base of a tree, the angle of elevation A of the top of the tree is found to be 29°. Find the height of the tree.

1. First we shall make a picture or diagram to represent the problem. On this diagram we shall indicate all data that are given, such as the distance from point A to the base of the tree and the size of the angle of elevation at A. (The diagram is made and data are indicated as shown.)

2. Since the height of the tree represents the unknown distance, we should designate it by some letter, e.g., let us use h.

3. We know that the ratio $h/50$ represents the tangent of angle A, so we may now write the equation $h/50 =$ tangent of 29°.

Fig. 18-3

4. We know that the tangent of an angle can be expressed as a number. From our table of tangents we find that the numerical value of the tangent of 29° is 0.5543. Therefore we may substitute this numerical value for the expression "tangent of 29°" and write the equation $h/50 = 0.5543$.

5. Now, if we solve this equation for h, we shall get the equation $50(h)/50 = (0.554)(50)$, or $h = 27.72$ feet, i.e., about 28 feet. Thus we know that the tree is about 28 feet high.

In presenting this explanation, the students' attention should be deliberately focused both upon the particular activities and the basic concepts presented in each of the various steps, and upon the order in which the steps are taken. The order reveals to the students a pattern for their work. This pattern not only helps them to systematize their written work and their computations but also helps them in analyzing such problems and in organizing their thinking about them. Each step stresses one important element in the analysis and solution of the problem. Drawing and lettering the figure and indicating the given data (step 1) give the problem a concrete setting and facilitate the job of translating it into an equation. The selection and indication of a literal symbol to represent the unknown part of the figure (step 2) direct attention to the fact that the object of the work is to determine the magnitude of this particular part. Writing the equation (step 3) requires analysis of the problem to determine which of the trigonometric functions is the appropriate one to use.

In this connection the following points should be stressed: (*a*) If one side and an angle of the triangle are given and it is required to find another side, that function should be selected which is represented by the ratio that involves both the unknown side and the known side. (*b*) If two sides are given and an angle is required, then that function should be selected which is represented by the ratio of one of these known sides to the other. A scheme that is slightly mechanical yet rather helpful in selecting the proper function is to emphasize that the sine and cosine should be used if one of the given sides is the hypotenuse. It should further be emphasized that the hypotenuse occurs in the denominator of each of these functions.

Fig. 18-4

The transition from the ratio concept to the numerical concept of a trigonometric function and the substitution of the numerical value for the ratio (step 4) are of vital importance in understanding the use of the functions in indirect measurement. The actual solution of the equation for the unknown part, and the reinterpretation of this in terms of the diagram or of the original problem situation (step 5), brings a realization of how the laws of algebra operate to give the required information by giving explicit form to a relationship which was merely implicit before. In the calculations involved, care should be taken to observe the rules for computation with approximate data. The order in which these steps have been indicated is the order in which they logically occur in the analysis and solution of the problem. Fortunately there is no conflict between this logical order and the natural or "psychological organization" of the analysis from the standpoint of the immature student.

The problem upon which the foregoing discussion is based involves the use of the tangent. Similar illustrative problems involving the sine and the cosine should also be used. Such problems should be selected or devised with care, but they are available in countless numbers and with many variations. The following are examples involving, respectively, the sine and cosine:

Example. A ladder 22 feet long is placed against a vertical wall so that it makes an angle of 62° with the ground. At what height above the ground does the ladder touch the wall, Fig. 18-4?

Example. To find the distance across a lake, some surveyors sighted an east-west line *AB* across the lake and then a north-south line *BC*. Then they measured the distance AC and the angle BAC. They found that $AC = 4,100$ feet and that angle $BAC = 43°$. Find how far it was from A to B, Fig. 18-5.

In setting up the earlier problems care should be taken to arrange the data so that, when the equations are set up, the symbols for the unknown parts will occur in the *numerators* of the fractions representing the trigonometric ratios or functions to be used. Later on it will be desirable to introduce some problems in which the unknown will occur in the *denominator* of the fraction. The following example will illustrate this:

Example. In order to find the distance between two points P and Q on opposite sides of a small lake, two boy scouts decided to set up a right triangle with PQ as

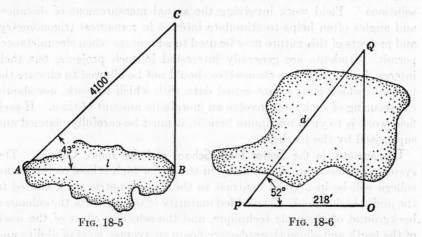

FIG. 18-5   FIG. 18-6

the hypotenuse, Fig. 18-6. They used an angle mirror to locate a point O, such that the lines OP and OQ formed a right angle. The distance from O to Q could not be measured directly, but OP was measured and found to be 218 feet. By sighting from P to O and then from P to Q, the size of angle P was established as $52°$. From these data the boys found the distance from P to Q. How far was it? (Call this distance d.)

This problem leads to the equation

$$\frac{218}{d} = \cos 52° = 0.6157$$

To simplify the solution, it may be suggested to the students that the equation can be written $218/d = 0.616/1$, that by inverting both of these fractions the equation $d/218 = 1/0.616$ will result, and that, if both members are now multiplied by 218, the equation is solved for d, the required distance, by performing the indicated division.

The work in trigonometry in the junior high school will scarcely go beyond these simple applications of the functions to the general problem of finding certain unknown parts of right triangles. If desired, the cotangent may be introduced, but it is unnecessary and little is to be gained by its use. The secant and cosecant should not be discussed.

The statement made on page 508 with reference to hypothetical problems should not be interpreted as a disparagement of field work. On the contrary, it is certain that appropriate field projects can do much to enhance the interest in the application of trigonometric methods. Students can take a plane table, field protractor, and clinometer and use them in actually performing simple surveying problems. Other instruments such as the tape, angle mirror, plane table, and alidade will also find use in connection with field problems leading to trigonometric solutions.[1] Field work involving the actual measurement of distances and angles often helps to stimulate interest in numerical trigonometry, and projects of this nature may be used to advantage when circumstances permit. Students are generally interested in such projects, but their interest in the activities themselves should not be allowed to obscure the purpose, which is to secure actual data with which to work, nor should the securing of such data involve an inordinate amount of time. If such field work is to yield maximum benefit, it must be carefully planned and supervised by the teacher.

Trigonometry in the Senior High School and the Junior College. The systematic course in trigonometry in the senior high school or the junior college will be in marked contrast to the trigonometric work offered in the junior high school. The added maturity of the students, the enhanced background of algebraic technique, and the selective effect of the work of the tenth and eleventh grades predicate an average level of ability and readiness well beyond that which can be expected in the junior high school. Moreover, the changing demands of physics, engineering, and more advanced courses in contemporary college mathematics imply a fundamental shift of emphasis in the trigonometry course. There is still an important place in the course for numerical work in the solution of triangles. But even here, relative emphasis on the ponderous accumulations of special formulas and the massive numerical work that formerly was considered so important is diminishing. On the other hand, increasing importance is being attached to the analytic aspects of the subject. Consequently, the work in trigonometry at the more advanced level will be characterized by a corresponding increase in completeness, rigor, abstractness, and generality. The students will have to accept more responsibility than before for the analysis of problems and for the mastery of a vastly expanded theory of the subject.

This does not mean, however, that the teacher is to be relieved of all

[1] For suggestions on this see C. H. Butler and F. L. Wren: "Trigonometry for Secondary Schools" (Boston: D. C. Heath and Company, 1957), pp. 241–254.

responsibility. On the contrary, there are many parts of trigonometry which many students would find inordinately difficult and time consuming to "dig out for themselves" but which can easily be made clear and meaningful by a skillful teacher. The teacher of trigonometry has the same obligation to help his class to a clear understanding of the basic principles and techniques of the subject as has the teacher of arithmetic, algebra, or geometry in the earlier years of the secondary school. With this in mind, the remainder of this chapter will be devoted to a discussion of teaching problems that arise in connection with the development of certain concepts and procedures in trigonometry. The topics which will be discussed have been selected on the basis of three criteria: (1) they are fundamental; (2) they are often troublesome; (3) they are based upon relatively simple fundamental principles which, if not properly emphasized, are easily obscured by the mass of detail attending their development but which, if set forth and perceived at the outset, will furnish a clear and helpful guide to the development. In the discussion of these topics the aim will be to present suggestions for developing them in a manner calculated to make clear the underlying principles and thus provide a basic framework around which the details of the development may be organized effectively.

Learning the Trigonometric Functions of an Acute Angle. The first thing which a student must do in beginning the study of trigonometry is get a clear understanding of the meanings and learn the names of the trigonometric functions. Suggestions for developing the meanings of the tangent, sine, and cosine of an acute angle have been given earlier in this chapter. These suggestions, made for the teaching of junior high school students, are equally applicable to senior high school or junior college students. The latter, however, must learn the meanings of the cotangent, secant, and cosecant. It may be pointed out that the functions are, after all, merely definitions of certain ratios, and the students, having learned the meanings of the sine, cosine, and tangent, will have no difficulty in understanding the meanings of the other functions in terms of the sides of a right triangle.

The student will perhaps be curious to know why the names of three of the six functions are the same as the names of the other three except for the prefix "co." The teacher should explain that the *co*-sine of an angle is the *sine of the complementary angle, which is the other acute angle in the right triangle*, and that the word "cosine" is merely a contraction and combination of the words "complement's sine." Similar explanations can be made of the corresponding relation of the *co*-tangent to the tangent of an angle and of the *co*-secant to the secant.

In case the students have any difficulty in remembering which ratios are associated with the different names, the association of the cosecant,

secant, and cotangent of an angle with the sine, cosine, and tangent of the angle can be made easy by having the students learn to recite the names of the six functions in the usual order, i.e., sine, cosine, tangent, cotangent, secant, and cosecant. If these names are then

sine A
cosine A
tangent A
———
cotangent A
secant A
cosecant A

written in a vertical column as in the diagram, it is apparent that the two functions joined by any one of the three arcs are reciprocals of each other. Thus any one of the last three can be recalled immediately by making this association with the appropriate one of the first three. This mnemonic device has two advantages. It cuts in half the amount of direct memorizing to be done at the outset and it specifies and emphasizes the reciprocal relationships existing among the functions.

Difficulties connected with the use of the inverse functions are generally due to the fact that the meanings of the functions have not been adequately explained. Also, the notation $\sin^{-1} \frac{1}{2}$, $\tan^{-1} .3802$, etc., is sometimes confusing in the beginning because there is a very definite tendency to associate this notation with the idea of an exponent. Indeed some writers hold that this notation should be entirely abandoned in favor of the expressions *arcsin*, *arctan*, etc. While there would probably be a material advantage in this, if it were universally adopted, the fact remains that both forms of notation are likely to persist in textbooks and other published works, so that students should be made familiar with both forms as a matter of practical necessity. Great care should be taken to ensure that the students will realize that the symbols $\sin^{-1} .5$, arctan .8325, etc., *represent angles rather than functions of angles.*

It should be emphasized in this connection that the periodicity of trigonometric functions creates problems of interpretation related to the inverse trigonometric functions. The relation $y = \sin x$ is clearly a function: to each value of x from the domain of the function, $-\infty < x < \infty$, there corresponds one and only one value of y from the range of the function, $-1 \leq y \leq 1$. Just as clearly, the relation $y = \sin^{-1} x$ is not a function: to each value of x from the domain of the relation, $-1 \leq x \leq 1$, there correspond infinitely many values of y from the range of the relation, $-\infty < y < \infty$. If, however, the range is restricted to its *principal values*, so that $-\frac{\pi}{2} \leq y \leq \frac{\pi}{2}$, it becomes the range of the *inverse sine function*, $y = \sin^{-1} x$, whose domain is $-1 \leq x \leq 1$. Similarly, the inverse cosine function, $y = \cos^{-1} x$, has the domain $-1 \leq x \leq 1$ and the range $0 \leq y \leq \pi$. The range of the inverse tangent function, $y = \tan^{-1} x$, is $-\frac{\pi}{2} < x < \frac{\pi}{2}$, and for the inverse cotangent function $y = \cot^{-1} x$, it is $0 < x < \pi$. The domain of each of these functions is the set of all real numbers.

In order to prevent ambiguity of meaning, some texts will capitalize the trigonometric functions when such restrictions are imposed. For example, the sine of x, when restricted as above, will be written $y = \text{Sin } x$ and read "y equals cap sin x." The inverse function may then be written as $y = \text{arcSin } x$ or $y = \text{Sin}^{-1} x$ and read "y equals inverse cap sin x." More commonly it is written as "$y = \text{Arcsin } x$."

Teaching the Functions of Special Angles. The special angles 0°, 30°, 45°, 60°, and 90° are of great importance and occur so frequently that students should be able to write down the functions of these angles without having recourse to tables. Some teachers prefer to have their students memorize the values of these functions. It is possible to do this, but it is not necessary, because they may all be immediately and easily derived from three elementary geometric considerations.

Fɪɢ. 18-7

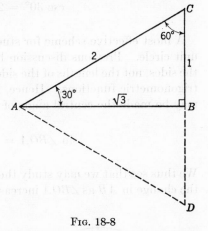

Fɪɢ. 18-8

Consider the right triangle ABC with an acute angle A of 45° and a right angle at B, Fig. 18-7. From the illustration we see at once that such a triangle is formed when a diagonal of a square is drawn. If the length of one side of the square is taken as one unit, then each leg of the triangle will be 1 unit in length, and the diagonal of the square, which is the hypotenuse of the triangle, will be found by the Pythagorean theorem to have a length of $\sqrt{2}$ units. With these numbers known, all the functions of 45° can be written down immediately. The only quantities needed are the numbers 1, 1, and $\sqrt{2}$, and even these need not be memorized, since they are immediately apparent from the fact that the triangle is formed by a diagonal and two adjacent sides of a square. The results are as follows:

$$\sin 45° = \cos 45° = \frac{1}{\sqrt{2}} \qquad \tan 45° = \cot 45° = 1$$
$$\csc 45° = \sec 45° = \sqrt{2}$$

Consider now an equilateral triangle ADC, Fig. 18-8, with angle A bisected as shown. The bisector AB forms with AC an angle of 30° and with BC a right angle. Thus we have a 30–60° right triangle ABC whose hypotenuse AC is twice as long as the leg BC (since $BC = \frac{1}{2}DC$ and $AC = DC$). If we now consider the length BC as one unit, then AC has a length of 2 units. Again, using the Pythagorean theorem, we get $AB = \sqrt{3}$ units. From Fig. 18-8 we have

$$\sin 30° = \frac{1}{2} = \cos 60°$$
$$\cos 30° = \sqrt{3}/2 = \sin 60°$$
$$\tan 30° = 1/\sqrt{3} = \cot 60°$$
$$\cot 30° = \sqrt{3} = \tan 60°$$
$$\sec 30° = 2/\sqrt{3} = \csc 60°$$
$$\csc 30° = 2 = \sec 60°$$

A most effective scheme for studying the functions of 0° and 90° is the unit circle. Previous discussion has pointed out the fact that ratios of the sides, not the lengths of the sides, determine the values of the different trigonometric functions. Hence, for convenience, the angle of reference may be made the central angle of a circle of unit radius. In Fig. 18-9

$$\sin \angle BOA = \frac{AB}{OA} = \frac{AB}{1} = AB$$

We thus see that we may study the change in the $\sin \angle BOA$ by examining the change in AB as $\angle BOA$ increases from 0° to 90°. When $\angle BOA = 0°$,

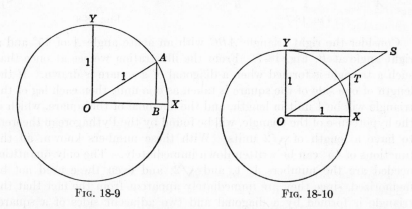

FIG. 18-9   FIG. 18-10

OA coincides with OX and $AB = 0$; when $\angle BOA = 90°$, OA and AB both coincide with OY. Thus $AB = 1$ when $\angle BOA = 90°$. Incidentally, this discussion can also be used to give significance to the use of the ratio

$$\frac{\text{Opposite side}}{\text{Hypotenuse}} = \frac{\text{ordinate}}{\text{hypotenuse}}$$

for the sine, since AB is a half chord which represents the ratio. The etymology of our word "sine" finds its beginning in the Hindi word *jyā* which Āryabhata used as an abbreviation for the word *ardhā-jyā*, meaning *half chord*.[1]

The variation of cos $\angle BOA$ may be studied by observing the behavior of the line OB in Fig. 18-9 as $\angle BOA$ varies from 0° to 90°. The extreme values are, of course, cos 0° = OX = 1 and cos 90° = 0. It is also quite evident from the figure and discussion that the cosine decreases as the sine increases.

In a similar way the line XT in Fig. 18-10 represents the tan $\angle XOT$, YS = tan $\angle SOY$ = cot $\angle XOT$, OT = sec $\angle XOT$, and OS = sec $\angle SOY$ = csc $\angle XOT$. The appropriateness of these names is immediately evident. As $\angle XOT$ decreases in size, XT decreases, while the length of YS increases without limit. The evidence of this last statement can be made clear to the pupil by drawing several positions of the terminal line OTS. As the different positions of this line make $\angle XOT$ take on values nearer to 0°, it will be evident that T approaches X along XT and YS becomes longer and longer as the line OTS approaches coincidence with OX. At the same time it can be demonstrated that sec $\angle XOT$ = OT takes on the value OX = 1 for 0°, while csc $\angle XOT$ = OS increases without limit. The symbol for "increasing without limit" is ∞, sometimes called "infinity." Thus cot 0° = ∞ and csc 0° = ∞ are convenient symbols for saying that, as the angle gets nearer and nearer to 0° in size, the cotangent and cosecant increase without limit. The student should be cautioned to remember that ∞ is merely a symbol and that it is not to be thought of as a number. It is therefore wrong to read cot 0° = ∞ as "cotangent of an angle of zero degrees is equal to infinity."

By drawing the terminal line OTS in several different positions which show $\angle XOT$ approaching 90°, it can be made apparent that

$$\tan 90° = \infty \qquad \sec 90° = \infty$$
$$\cot 90° = 0 \qquad \csc 90° = 1$$

From the foregoing considerations the values of all the functions of these special angles can be written down at once, since the relative lengths of the hypotenuse and the two legs in each of the special triangles is known. This is shown in Table 18-1.

These values (except, of course, ∞, or infinity) can be readily translated into decimal equivalents if desired. The student who learns to derive the values of the functions of these special angles in this way need never

[1] D. E. Smith, "History of Mathematics" (Boston: Ginn & Company, 1925), vol. II, pp. 615–618.

be afraid of forgetting them, because he can reconstruct them at will. Moreover, being associated directly with the triangles, they will carry for him a real functional meaning and will not be mere arbitrary and unrelated numbers.

Table 18-1. Functions of Special Angles

Function	0°	30°	45°	60°	90°
Sine.........	0	$\frac{1}{2}$	$1/\sqrt{2}$	$\sqrt{3}/2$	1
Cosine........	1	$\sqrt{3}/2$	$1/\sqrt{2}$	$\frac{1}{2}$	0
Tangent.......	0	$1/\sqrt{3}$	1	$\sqrt{3}$	∞
Cotangent....	∞	$\sqrt{3}$	1	$1/\sqrt{3}$	0
Secant........	1	$2/\sqrt{3}$	$\sqrt{2}$	2	∞
Cosecant.....	∞	2	$\sqrt{2}$	$2/\sqrt{3}$	1

Teaching the Use of the Tables and Interpolation. Students should be given special training in the use of the tables and in interpolation.   While it is not difficult to learn how to use the tables, careful explanation by the teacher and a considerable amount of practice is necessary if the students are to acquire the speed and facility required for efficient work.   Consequently it is important in the beginning, and at intervals thereafter, to supplement the incidental use of the tables by special drills particularly designed to improve the students' expertness in this phase of the work. These drills should emphasize the determination of inverse functions such as arcsin, arctan, and antilogarithm, as well as the functions themselves.   Since most tables of natural functions and logarithms of natural functions do not give values for the secant and cosecant, the students should be reminded that these functions may be found if needed by taking the reciprocals of the values given for the cosine and sine, respectively, or that the logarithms of these functions may be found by taking the *cologarithms* of the cosine and sine, respectively.   In this connection it will be well to explain and define the meaning of the term "cologarithm," if this has not been done before.   It is possible to dispense with the use of cologarithms, and some teachers prefer to do so; others find their use convenient and desirable.   Moreover, whatever may be the teacher's convictions in this respect, the students will inevitably come upon the term in their reading and will be handicapped if they do not understand its meaning.

Students often fail to realize the approximate nature of most of the values given in the tables of logarithms and natural functions.   It should be made clear to them that with comparatively few exceptions these values are not exact, but represent merely approximations to the exact values. Comparison of the tables which they commonly use with other published tables of greater or less accuracy will help to impress the students with this fact.

The greatest difficulty which most students encounter in using the tables is the determination of intermediate values by interpolation. Their difficulty in this connection resides not so much in the nature of the process as in the fact that too often it is not explained in its elemental, meaningful simplicity, but is set forth as an arbitrary, mechanical procedure. The fact is that nearly all people make intelligent use of the *principle* of linear interpolation continually in many of their everyday problems. The matter presents no material difficulty in connection with such situations as measuring, buying, and selling, because it is then related to tangible, concrete concepts and denominate quantities, and the procedure is almost intuitive. It is only when it is dissociated from denominate quantities and applied to sheer numbers that it seems to lose, for many people, this intuitive character. It is desirable to retain the association and similarity between these two kinds of situations, and this can best be done by explaining interpolation first in terms of the simple, concrete, familiar situations.

By way of illustration, consider the following problem. It can be solved, of course, by a single simple multiplication, but it may also serve to illustrate the principle of interpolation. It may be explained somewhat as outlined.

Example. If a man's wages are $1.80 an hour, how much will he earn by working 6 hours and 45 minutes?

The man worked 6¾ hours.

This is between 6 hours and 7 hours and is ¾ of the way from 6 hours to 7 hours.

His wages for 6 hours would be 6 × $1.80, or $10.80.

His wages for 7 hours would be 7 × $1.80, or $12.60.

By computation three-fourths of $1.80 is $1.35, and this must be added to the $10.80 which represents his wages for 6 hours, so that his wages for 6 hours and 45 minutes amount to $10.80 + $1.35, or $12.15.

Fig. 18-11

Example. I can buy 5 gallons of gasoline for $1.75 or 6 gallons for $2.10. How much can I buy for $2.00?

Fig. 18-12

Since the cost of 5 gallons is less than $2.00 and the cost of 6 gallons is more than $2.00, the amount I can buy must be between 5 and 6 gallons, i.e., 5 gallons and a part of another gallon.

Since $2.00 is five-sevenths of the way from $1.75 to $2.10, the number of gallons it will buy must be five-sevenths of the way from 5 gallons to 6 gallons. Thus it is easily seen that at this rate $2.00 will buy $5 + \frac{5}{7}$ gallons, or approximately 5.7 gallons.

These examples bring out four important points: (1) In interpolation we always seek to find a number which lies *between two other known numbers*. (2) We may find the wanted number by comparison with three other, corresponding numbers all of which are known. (3) The differences between the corresponding numbers in the two sets must be proportional to each other. (4) The required difference, when found, must be properly associated by addition or subtraction with the appropriate one of the known numbers between which it lies. The use of diagrams similar to those used in the foregoing examples has been found to be extremely helpful in making these points clear to the students.

Let us now take three examples from the tables.

Example. Find the value of tan 18°21′12″.

Fig. 18-13

Therefore tan 18°21′12″ = .33169 + .00006 = .33175.

Example.   Find log 327.38.

FIG. 18-14

Thus, log 327.38 = 2.51495 + .00010 = 2.51505.

Example.   Find the value of cos 38°14′29″.

FIG. 18-15

The cosine of an angle decreases as the angle increases.   Consequently, to obtain the interpolated value of this function, the difference ($^{29}\!/_{60}$ of 0.00018) must be subtracted from the value of cos 38°14′ instead of being added to it.   Thus, cos 38°14′29″ = 0.78550 − 0.00009 = 0.78541.

In many texts the tables are accompanied by sets of proportional parts of differences to facilitate and speed up the process of interpolation. These are of value after the process is thoroughly understood, but they should not be used in the beginning.   The understanding and use of these auxiliary tables constitutes a separate and distinct difficulty.   Until the student has thoroughly mastered the *principle* of linear interpolation, he should work every step of it, including the computation of the proportional parts of the differences, by himself.   Then, when he is ready to use the short cut provided by the sets of proportional parts printed with the tables, he will understand how the sets are obtained and will be able to use them with understanding.

Functions of the General Angle.   There are two points of view with regard to the introduction to the study of the functions of the general angle. Some teachers and writers believe that it is best to make this the starting point of the course, and it must be admitted that there are certain arguments which tend to support this position.   In particular, it provides a general situation in which the definitions of the functions of an acute angle, when given in terms of the sides of a right triangle, appear merely as special cases, and thus it avoids the necessity for extending the definitions after they are once made. On the other hand, there are some advantages in beginning by defining the functions of an acute angle in terms of the sides of a right triangle. In particular, these definitions are a basic part of the trigonometric background which the students bring with them from their work with numerical trigonometry in the junior high school. These definitions thus form probably the most natural point of departure in taking up the more systematic and more general treatment of trigonometric functions in the senior high school and junior college. The subsequent transition to the functions of the general angle does, of course, involve a generalization of the definition of the functions, but this need not cause any serious difficulty if it is explained carefully.

Let us assume that the students have learned to define the functions of an acute angle in terms of the sides of a right triangle as indicated earlier in this chapter.

FIG. 18-16

$$\sin A = \frac{\text{opposite side}}{\text{hypotenuse}}$$

$$\cos A = \frac{\text{adjacent side}}{\text{hypotenuse}}$$

$$\tan A = \frac{\text{opposite side}}{\text{adjacent side}}$$

Now if we draw a set of perpendicular coordinate axes such that the origin is at A with the positive X axis passing through B, we are ready to redefine the functions of the *acute* angle A in terms of the abscissa, ordinate, and distance of C, or of any other point on the terminal side of the angle. That is, the opposite side in the triangle is now y, the ordinate of C; the adjacent side is x, the abscissa of C; and the hypotenuse is r, the distance of C, Fig. 18-16. Consequently our definitions may now take the form

$$\sin A = \frac{\text{opposite side}}{\text{hypotenuse}} = \frac{\text{ordinate}}{\text{distance}} = \frac{y}{r}$$

$$\cos A = \frac{\text{adjacent side}}{\text{hypotenuse}} = \frac{\text{abscissa}}{\text{distance}} = \frac{x}{r}$$

$$\tan A = \frac{\text{opposite side}}{\text{adjacent side}} = \frac{\text{ordinate}}{\text{abscissa}} = \frac{y}{x}$$

etc.

One thing should be especially noted. Thus far we have redefined the functions *only for acute angles*. What shall we do in the case of angles greater than 90° or in the case of negative angles?

It should be made clear to the students at this point that our new definitions of the functions of acute angles give us a concept, a nomenclature, and a symbolism that will apply as readily to angles of any size, whether positive or negative, as it does to acute angles. This being the case, it has been generally agreed that these definitions, although developed originally for acute angles, will be accepted for the sake of uniformity and convenience (and for no other reason) as defining the functions of *any* angle. It is necessary only to recall the "standard position" of the angle with reference to the coordinate axes; i.e., its vertex will always be considered to be at the origin, its initial side the positive

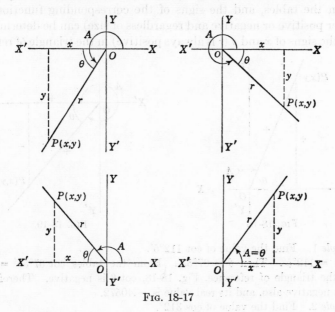

FIG. 18-17

X axis, and the position of its terminal side determined by the description of the angle or the conditions of the problem. *The functions of any angle whatever*[1] can thus be given in terms of the coordinates of any point (except the origin) on the terminal side of the angle.

In order to use these definitions, it is necessary to have some means of transforming the functions of the general angle into terms of functions of an angle in the first quadrant or at the boundaries of that quadrant. This is necessary because the tables of functions are generally given only for such angles. The method of making the required transformations may be effectively explained to the students somewhat as follows:

Let A be the given angle in standard position as shown, Fig. 18-17. If we take any point $P(x, y)$ on the terminal side of angle A and drop a

---

[1] Of course, exception is made of those functions of 0°, 90°, 180°, etc., which become infinite and so are not defined in any case.

perpendicular to the X axis, there will be formed a right triangle which is called the "triangle of reference." The values of the functions of A are determined by the lengths of the sides of this triangle, since its sides are x, y, and r, that is, the abscissa, ordinate, and distance of P, respectively.

Now, if A is known, we may also find at once the angle θ, without regard to sign. It is the smallest angle which OP makes with the X axis. This will always be the angle XOP or $X'OP$ in the triangle of reference, and its value will never exceed 90°. Thus θ becomes an angle which has the limits $0° \leqq \theta \leqq 90°$, and *the values of the functions of A will be the same as the values of the functions of θ except for sign.* The functions of θ can be found in the tables, and the signs of the corresponding functions of A (whether positive or negative and regardless of size) can be determined by noting the signs of x and y (r is always positive) in the triangle of reference.

Fig. 18-18   Fig. 18-19

Example 1. Find the value of cot 112°5'.

Let $A = 112°5'$. Then $\theta = 67°55'$. From the tables cot 67°55' = .40572. But in the triangle of reference, Fig. 18-18, cot θ is negative. Therefore, cot 112°5' is negative also, and its real value is −.40572.

Example 2. Find the value of cos 312°.

Let $A = 312°$. Thus $\theta = 48°$, Fig. 18-19. From the tables cos 48° = .66913. Therefore the value, except for sign, of cos 312° = .66913. But in the triangle of reference cos θ is positive. Therefore, cos 312° is positive also, and its real value is +.66913.

If the matter is explained and illustrated in this way, the students should have little difficulty in understanding how to find the functions of any given angle from the tables. It is well for them to work out numerous examples of the type given above and to build for themselves tables showing the signs of each of the functions when the angle is in standard position and the terminal side lies in the following eight positions:

In the first quadrant   Along the positive X axis
In the second quadrant   Along the positive Y axis
In the third quadrant   Along the negative X axis
In the fourth quadrant   Along the negative Y axis

When the students have acquired the ability to do this for themselves, they will have attained a real understanding of how the tables may be used to find the functions of any angle whatever.   They should experience no further difficulty in this respect, and there will be no need for them to memorize the signs of the functions for the various positions of the terminal side of the angle as indicated in the list given above.

Variation of the Functions.   Just as the concept of variation enriches the study of geometry and algebra, so it enriches the study of trigonometry. It is very important for the students to sense the fact that any *change* in the size of an angle is accompanied by a corresponding characteristic change in each of the functions of the angle.   This fact should be repeatedly emphasized by the teacher and should be illustrated by all available means and devices.   One such means is a thoughtful examination of the tables of functions.   It will be immediately noted that increases in the size of the angle are accompanied by characteristic increases or decreases in each of the functions.   It should be specifically pointed out that the values given in the tables merely represent particular stages in a continuous variation and that, between any two successive values given in the tables, there exists an infinitude of intermediate values. This concept of variation of the functions can be strengthened by certain mechanical devices which are available commercially, or which can be made by the teacher or students.   Perhaps the most commonly used and most effective device is the construction and study of graphs of these functions, Fig. 18-20.

A real understanding of these graphs makes clear several important things about the variation of the functions.   In particular, the following considerations are worthy of note and comment:

1. There is a general similarity in the shape of the graph of any function and its corresponding cofunction.[1]   This may be explained by the fact that, for example, the cosine of a given angle is, in fact, the sine of some other angle (in general, the complement of the given angle), and similarly for the other functions and their corresponding cofunctions.

2. The functions $\sin \theta$ and $\cos \theta$ are always finite and continuous over the entire domain of values of θ, while for certain values of θ the other functions become infinite and have points of discontinuity.   This may be explained by the fact that each of the other functions is the reciprocal of some function which may take on the value zero and, when this happens, the reciprocal obviously becomes infinite.   It should also be noted that, at each value of the angle for which a given function becomes discontinuous, the function also changes sign.

3. The sine or cosine of an angle can never be greater than 1 or less than -1, while the secant and cosecant can never have values between

---

[1] Here we speak of $\sin \theta$ and $\cos \theta$, for example, as *cofunctions of each other*.   Like reference is made to $\tan \theta$ and $\cot \theta$ and to $\sec \theta$ and $\csc \theta$.

these bounds. This is explained by the fact that the secant and cosecant of an angle are respectively reciprocals of the cosine and sine of the angle, and the reciprocal of any number which is not greater than 1 or less than −1 will have a value which must be > 1 or < −1. Numerical illustrations of these facts should be given.

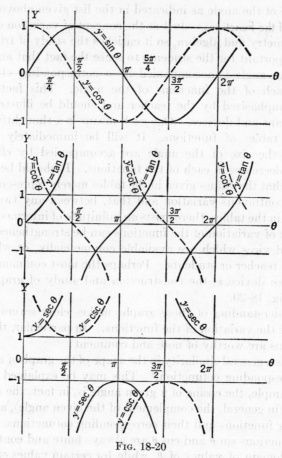

Fig. 18-20

4. From the graphs it will be seen that, when the angle is given by $k\pi + \pi/4$ for all integral values of k, any function of the angle is equal to its corresponding cofunction. The students may be asked to explain this.

5. The graph of any function, say sin θ, Fig. 18-21, is also the graph of the inverse relation, which in this case is arcsin θ. The distinction lies merely in the choice of the independent variable. This fact makes it easy to explain and emphasize the important concept of the multiple-valued nature of the inverse relations as contrasted with the single-valued nature of the functions themselves. The use of the unit circle in drawing

the graphs of the different functions is a great aid in bringing out this contrast between the functions and their inverse relations. It also gives a vivid picture of the periodicity of the functions and the nature of their respective variations.

Practically all textbooks contain graphs of the functions for reference, and in many cases the students are required to construct their own graphs. Too often, however, the attention given to the graphs of the functions is perfunctory and not very meaningful. If the graphs are to contribute much to developing the concept and the nature of the variation of the functions, considerable time will need to be spent in the interpretation of the graphs and in the discussion of their implications.

FIG. 18-21

Teaching the Functions of the Sum or Difference of Two Angles. Since there are times when the students will need to use the functions of the sum or difference of two angles, a double angle, or a half angle and perhaps certain other formulas involving two angles, it is necessary that these formulas be developed in terms of the original angles and listed for reference. This is done in practically all textbooks. It is not necessary that students memorize all of these formulas. It is desirable, however, that they see and understand the ways in which the formulas are developed and that they memorize a few which are fundamental and which will be needed frequently. Among these may be listed the following:

$$\sin (A \pm B) \qquad \cos (A \pm B) \qquad \tan (A \pm B)$$
$$\sin 2A \qquad\qquad \cos 2A \qquad\qquad \tan 2A$$

The development of a large array of these formulas is an excellent exercise in the application of algebraic technique to trigonometric functions and can be made extremely interesting to students if properly presented. After the formula

$$\sin (A + B) = \sin A \cos B + \cos A \sin B$$

has been established, all the rest of these formulas may be derived from this one through the application of fundamental algebraic and trigonometric techniques. For example:

$$\sin (A - B) = \sin [A + (-B)]$$
$$= \sin A \cos (-B) + \cos A \sin (-B)$$
$$= \sin A \cos B - \cos A \sin B$$
$$\cos (A + B) = \sin [90° - (A + B)]$$
$$= \sin [(90° - A) - B]$$
$$= \sin (90° - A) \cos B - \cos (90° - A) \sin B$$
$$= \cos A \cos B - \sin A \sin B$$

It is surprising that in the teaching of these formulas this fact is almost never emphasized either in the textbooks or by the teachers. One would

Table 18-2. Reduction Formulas

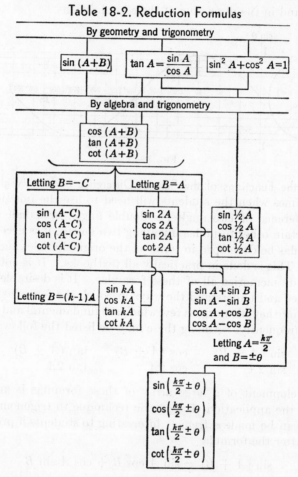

naturally expect students to be dismayed at the prospect of arbitrarily memorizing 20 or more special formulas, but one would expect them to be fascinated at seeing all 20 stem from a single one. Yet we persist in teaching them as cases unto themselves without stressing their interrelations, and thus we fail to take advantage of the most powerful of motives in our teaching, and we likewise fail to give our students that sense of organic relationship which they should feel with regard to this whole group of formulas.

As has been said, the formula for sin $(A + B)$ must be developed independently from geometric considerations. Table 18-2 shows how all the others grow out of this one.

The Solution of Triangles. The trigonometric solution of the right triangle is discussed in the first part of this chapter. The methods are so simple, obvious, and direct that they offer no difficulty and need not be discussed further here. The solution of the oblique or general triangle, however, is not so simple. It requires the development of numerous special formulas and a discriminating analysis of the given data in each particular problem to determine the method and the formulas to be used.

There are four different combinations of independent parts any one of which, with one exception which will be mentioned later, may uniquely determine a triangle. These are often referred to as the four cases of the general[1] triangle. The four combinations of parts are as follows:

Case 1.   Given two angles and any side
Case 2.   Given two sides and an angle opposite one of them
Case 3.   Given two sides and the included angle
Case 4.   Given the three sides

To handle the solution of these cases of the general triangle, various special formulas are developed; the most fundamental of them are the law of sines, the law of cosines, and the law of tangents. In addition to these there are numerous more specialized formulas connected with the triangle, including the half-angle formulas in terms of the sides and Heron's formula for the area of the triangle.

The mastery of these formulas and their use in solving the various cases of the general triangle cause a good deal of difficulty to students. The most common difficulties may be enumerated under five main types as follows:

1. Difficulty in following and understanding the derivation of the formulas
2. Difficulty in remembering the various formulas and keeping them in mind without confusing them
3. Difficulty in knowing what formulas to use in particular cases
4. Difficulty due to lack of systematic preplanning and layout of written work
5. Difficulty in checking the solution

[1] The term "general triangle" is used here instead of "oblique triangle" because the general formulas developed for these cases apply to right triangles as well as to oblique triangles.

Many teachers fail to appreciate either the seriousness of these difficulties or the extent to which failure to master them may impair the effectiveness of the students' work. Yet the teacher has a serious obligation to see that the students are adequately equipped with respect to these points.

The development of the fundamental trigonometric laws is not inherently difficult or complicated. It can be understood without great difficulty by most students if properly presented. The teacher, however, should point the way by laying out the main steps in the development in quick, bold outline just as one lays out the plan of proof for a proposition in geometry before proceeding to write down the complete synthetic proof in finished form. Some geometry teachers and textbook writers have recognized the importance of setting forth the main plan of a proof before proceeding to details. For the most part, trigonometry textbooks have not yet arrived at this point, and so the responsibility must be accepted by the teacher. For example, most students find it difficult to take the bare facts set forth in the proof of the law of cosines and to extract from them much understanding of a plan whereby the proof could be reconstructed without being literally memorized. On the other hand, a rapid "chalk-talk" explanation of the *plan* of development by the teacher will leave the student with a basis of understanding which he can fill in with the necessary details and reconstruct at will. The same may be said for the development of the law of tangents and for the other formulas involved in the solution of the general triangle. In some cases it is necessary to draw upon previously developed formulas. For example, in developing the law of tangents, it is convenient to use the relations

$$\sin A + \sin B = 2 \sin \tfrac{1}{2}(A + B) \cos \tfrac{1}{2}(A - B)$$
$$\sin A - \sin B = 2 \cos \tfrac{1}{2}(A + B) \sin \tfrac{1}{2}(A - B)$$

In such cases the teacher should specifically call attention to these substitutions in discussing the plan of development.

There are a few fundamental formulas which are used so much in the solution of oblique triangles that the student will find it advisable to memorize them. In particular, the law of sines and the law of cosines are indispensable and sufficient. The student should become as familiar with them as with the Pythagorean theorem or the fact that

$$a^2 - b^2 = (a - b)(a + b)$$

For logarithmic solutions the law of tangents is more efficient than the cosine law. Some teachers prefer to have their students memorize other formulas such as the half-angle formulas (in terms of the sides) and the area formulas. Since courses differ in emphasis, no rigid criterion can be laid down.   In general it may be said that students should be required to memorize only such formulas as are fundamental and which, in the judgment of the teacher, will be used sufficiently to warrant memorization; however, those formulas which *are* to be memorized should be memorized to the point of perfection, automatization, and permanency.

The teacher should give the students criteria for determining which formulas to use in particular cases.   One criterion is as follows: The formula to be used must be one which expresses an unknown part of the triangle completely in terms of the given parts, or from which an unknown part may be found in terms of given parts (as in the case of the law of tangents).   By adopting a standard system of notation, listing the fundamental formulas, and setting down the given parts of the triangle in a particular problem, the student may readily determine by inspection which of the formulas should be used.   If he is required to do this consistently, he will soon learn that the law of sines is the appropriate formula to use if he is given either two angles and any side or two sides and an angle opposite one of them[1] and that the law of cosines will enable him to solve triangles in which the given parts are either two sides and the included angle or the three sides.   The teacher should point out that, in place of the law of cosines, the alternative formulas for the law of tangents and for the tangents of the half angles in terms of the sides may be used when the given parts are respectively two sides and the included angle or the three sides and that these formulas are more amenable to logarithmic treatment than is the law of cosines.   The association of the appropriate formulas with the different cases would be strengthened if each formula were developed and immediately applied when the case requiring it is first taken up.   In many textbooks, however, the formulas are developed as in an intact body of theory, and the applications are left until later.

In teaching the solution of the general triangle, the teacher should show the students how to make a layout for the work and should give specific training in doing so.   Students generally are inclined to start computing as soon as they get hold of two numbers with which they can work.   However, since most problems in solving oblique triangles are somewhat long and complicated, this is uneconomical and unwise for several reasons.   There is great advantage in thinking the problem through completely and planning the entire solution in detail, but as a whole, before doing anything else.   This will ensure an understanding analysis of the problem as a whole.   It will prevent the student from becoming confused in a heterogeneous mixture of analysis and computation.   It will provide a specific step-by-step guide for all necessary com-

---

[1] The ambiguous case (given two sides and an angle opposite one of them) should be discussed at length and its geometric and trigonometric possibilities pointed out.

putation and use of the tables. It is economical of time and labor. Finally, it is conducive to orderliness, which in turn is always conducive to effective work.

The following[1] is illustrative of what may be done in this respect. The layouts will obviously vary in detail according to the conditions and the requirements of the problem, but the idea is perfectly general and can be adapted as needed.

Example. Given $a = 81.6$, $b = 121.5$, and $C = 32°18'$, find A, B, and c.

Fig. 18-22

Solution

$$B + A = 180° - C = \qquad °$$

$$\tan \tfrac{1}{2}(B - A) = \frac{b - a}{b + a} \tan \tfrac{1}{2}(B + A) \qquad \text{(to find A and B)}$$

$$c = \frac{a \sin C}{\sin A} \qquad \text{(to find c)}$$

$$c = \frac{b \sin C}{\sin B} \qquad \text{(to check the work)}$$

$a = 81.6.$		$\to$ log =	
$b = 121.5$			$\to$ log =
$b - a = 39.9.$	$\to$ log =		
$b + a = 203.1$	$\to$ colog =		
$C = 32°18'$		$\to$ log sin =	log sin =
$\tfrac{1}{2}(B + A) = 73°51'$	$\to$ log tan =		
$\tfrac{1}{2}(B - A) =$	$\leftarrow$ log tan =		
$B =$	$\leftarrow$		colog sin =
$A =$	$\leftarrow$	colog sin =	
$c =$	$\leftarrow$	log =	log =

The above outline provides a complete guide for the solution and checking of the problem. The check used in it is one of several special checks adapted to particular cases. Either of the formulas

$$\frac{a + b}{c} = \frac{\cos \tfrac{1}{2}(A - B)}{\sin \tfrac{1}{2} C} \qquad \frac{a - b}{c} = \frac{\sin \tfrac{1}{2}(A - B)}{\cos \tfrac{1}{2} C}$$

called Mollweide's equations, may be used as a general check of the solution of any triangle, since they contain all the sides and all the angles of

[1] Adapted from Davis and Chambers, "Brief Course in Plane and Spherical Trigonometry" (New York: American Book Company, 1933), pp. 60ff.

See also C. A. Ewing, "Plane Trigonometry" (New York: McGraw-Hill Book Company, Inc., 1933), pp. 49–50, 70ff.

the triangle, are well adapted to logarithmic computation, and are not used, in any of the four cases, in the solution of the triangle.

Table 18-3 gives a very concise summary of the four cases of the general triangle.

Teaching Radian Measure. The teaching of radian measure should not be difficult provided that the students have a good understanding of the

Table 18-3. Four Cases of the General Triangles*

	Case 1	Case 2	Case 3	Case 4
Given	One side and two angles	Two sides and the angle opposite one of them	Two sides and the included angle	Three sides
Solution (by logarithms)	Law of sines	Law of sines	Law of tangents	Tangent half-angle formula
Check		$\dfrac{a+b}{c} = \dfrac{\cos \frac{1}{2}(A-B)}{\sin \frac{1}{2}C}$		$A + B + C = 180°$
Solution (by natural functions)	Law of sines	Law of sines	Law of cosines†	Law of cosines†
Check		$a = b \cos C + c \cos B$	Law of sines or $A + B + C = 180°$	$A + B + C = 180°$
Area	$\dfrac{1}{2} a^2 \dfrac{\sin B \sin C}{\sin A}$		$\dfrac{1}{2} ab \sin C$	rs or $\sqrt{s(s-a)(s-b)(s-c)}$

* Adapted from Garabedian and Winston, "Plane Trigonometry" (New York: McGraw-Hill Book Company, Inc., 1929), p. 290.

† The law of cosines is usually preferable if only the third side in case 3, or one angle in case 4, is to be found.

functions of the general angle and provided that two or three fundamental concepts and conventions are made clear at the outset. In order to understand radian measure clearly, the students must first of all have a thorough understanding of the definition and meaning of a radian. The geometrical explanation and illustration should be given repeatedly until the students can readily form a mental picture similar to the one shown in Fig. 18-23. This will provide them with a concrete basis for thinking in terms of radians and for understanding the definition. It will provide a means for recalling instantly why the angle π is the same as 180°, why $\pi/2$ is the same as 90°, why $\pi/3$ is the same as 60°, why 2π is the same as 360°, etc. With this sort of picture in mind for reference the student will have no need to memorize the relations between degrees and radian measure, because he can easily figure out these relationships for himself. He is thus equipped not only with a knowledge of the facts and relationships which he will need but also with an understanding of how they are determined.

After the students have gained an understanding of the meaning of radian measure, it is well for them to have some special practice in determining the degree equivalents of angles expressed in radians and the radian equivalents of angles expressed in degrees. In this connection it may be desirable to have the degree value of one radian memorized. For the special angles 0, $\pi/2$, $\pi/3$, π, 2π, 45°, 120°, etc., the students should soon become able to give the corresponding equivalents at sight. Similar practice involving the inverse functions should be given, the principal values of the angles being given in both radians and degrees. The teacher should explain that, in expressing angles in terms of radian measure, it is customary to omit the word "radians." The student needs to be told this so that, when he encounters in his reading such expressions as sin π, tan 2, and cos $3\pi/4$, he will understand that the angles are given in radians rather than in degrees. It may be pointed out that in higher mathematics radian measure is used almost exclusively.

Fig. 18-23

One other system of angular measure should be mentioned here, though it is not so generally used nor so important theoretically as radian measure. In this system the unit is the *mil*. By definition the mil is $\frac{1}{6400}$ of a complete revolution, or $\frac{1}{1600}$ of a right angle. Thus 1 mil is about 0.000982 radian, and this is a close approximation to 0.001 radian. Its practical importance for some purposes arises from this fact. At a horizontal distance of 1000 yards, an angle of n mils subtends a vertical distance of approximately n yards, provided the angle is small. Thus under certain circumstances the measurement of angles in mils facilitates rapid calculation or estimation of distances. It is for this reason that the mil is used in field artillery work.

Teaching Trigonometric Identities and Equations. The proof of trigonometric identities and the solution of trigonometric equations are often considered to be the most difficult parts of trigonometry. Confusion over the distinction between identities and equations of condition often exists in the minds of students. Therefore, this distinction should be cleared up at the outset.

A trigonometric equation is an equation involving one or more trigonometric functions of the unknown (angle) and is true only for particular values of this unknown. In contrast to such conditional equations there is another class of trigonometric equalities which are true for *all* admissible values of the unknown. These are known as trigonometric identities. From these considerations it is evident that, in dealing with trigonometric equations, the job is to *solve* the equation, i.e., to find the value, or values, of the unknown which will satisfy the equation. On the other hand, in dealing with identities, the problem is to prove that they actually are identities, by showing that one expression can be reduced to the same form as the other, for all admissible values of the variable.

Trigonometric equations really are equations, and they are therefore subject to treatment under the algebraic laws of the equation besides being subject to the algebraic transformation of either member separately or to the trigonometric transformation of the trigonometric elements involved.

Example. Let it be required to solve $\sin 2x = \tan x$. The problem is to find an angle x for which this relation exists. A solution is as follows:

$$\sin 2x = 2 \sin x \cos x \qquad \text{(trigonometric transformation)}$$
$$\tan x = \frac{\sin x}{\cos x} \qquad \text{(trigonometric transformation)}$$
$$\therefore 2 \sin x \cos x = \frac{\sin x}{\cos x} \qquad \text{(substitution)}$$
$$2 \sin x \cos^2 x = \sin x \qquad \text{(both members multiplied by } \cos x)$$
$$2 \sin x \cos^2 x - \sin x = 0 \qquad \text{(transposition)}$$
$$\sin x(2 \cos^2 x - 1) = 0 \qquad \text{(left member factored)}$$

This can be true only (1) if $\sin x = 0$ or (2) if $2 \cos^2 x - 1 = 0$.

$\therefore$ if the equation is true, the values of x, such that $0° \leqq x < 360°$, must be

(1) $x = 0°$ or $180°$
(2) $x = 45°, 135°, 225°,$ or $315°$

Substitution in the original equation verifies these values as the required solution.

Note that the algebraic transformations which were employed to solve this example are all entirely legitimate because we started with an admitted equation and sought merely the solution of the equation.

In practically all textbooks the trigonometric identities proposed for proof are stated in the form of equations. This tends to give students a wrong feeling about the job of proving these identities. Since they are stated in the form of equations, the tendency is to feel that they may be treated legitimately under the algebraic laws of the equation. This, of course, is not so. Consider, for example, the following illustration, which is typical of the form in which these identities are proposed in the textbooks:

Prove that $\dfrac{2 - \cos x}{\cos x} = 2 \sec x - 1$ (A)

Suppose that this were regarded as an equation and treated as such in the following manner: By multiplying through by cos x, we get

$$2 - \cos x = 2 \sec x \cos x - \cos x$$
or $\qquad 2 - \cos x = 2(1) - \cos x$ (B)

This evidently gives an identity, but it is not a proof that $(2 - \cos x)/\cos x$ and 2 sec $x - 1$ are identical. Rather, it is a proof that, if equation (A) is an identity, then equation (B) is an identity. In effect, what has been done here is to assume the equality of the members of the proposed identity, to treat them algebraically under the laws of the equation, and to conclude that, since an identity is thus reached, the original pair of expressions must also have been identical.

The fallacy involved in this method of reasoning may be shown even more clearly by taking a case which is evidently absurd on the face of it but which illustrates precisely the point in question. Let it be required to test to see whether or not sin $x = -\sin x$ is an identity. By treating this as an equation and squaring both members, we do get an identity, viz., $\sin^2 x = \sin^2 x$. The foregoing line of reasoning would lead us to conclude that, since this is true, the original pair of expressions (sin x and $-\sin x$) must also have been identical. Obviously, however, we should not be justified in such a conclusion, because the equation sin $x = -\sin x$ is not true for all values of x. It holds only when $x = k\pi$ (k being any positive or negative integer or zero). The above technique can be used to discover a valid proof of an identity if the steps used prove to be reversible. Only in such a case would it be proved that one could start with the known identity and derive the unknown one. It is evident from the above discussion that this technique provides a method which may be used to derive new identities from known identities. One must be careful, however, to use only legitimate operations at each stage of the development.

In proving two trigonometric expressions identical we may legitimately work with only one of them at a time. *Either* may be changed through legitimate operations of trigonometric transformation, factoring, multiplication of factors, collection of terms, or substitution into the form of the other. When this has been done, a valid proof of the original identity results. In other cases, the same techniques may be used to change both expressions into some common expression or into two expressions which are recognized as being identically equal. Such a procedure establishes a valid proof of the original identity only if all respective steps are reversible. It should be evident that one could use the same general techniques to establish the difference of two given expressions as *identically* equal to zero and thus establish the identity of the expressions themselves. Although the textbooks are not clear at times on this matter, the students should be strongly impressed with this principle and with the important distinction between proving a trigonometric identity and solving a trigonometric equation.

Probably the greatest difficulties which students have in working with trigonometric equations and identities are (1) the lack of systematic methods of attack and (2) insufficient familiarity with the fundamental trigonometric identities. The following suggestions will be helpful to them in planning and carrying through their work:

1. If functions of multiples of an angle are involved, transform them so that they will all be expressed in terms of the same multiple of that angle. For example, in proving that $\sin 2\theta = 2 \cos \theta / \csc \theta$, one should start by expressing $\sin 2\theta$ as $2 \sin \theta \cos \theta$, so that all functions involved will be functions of the angle θ.

2. In solving equations it is generally desirable and often necessary to express all functions involved in terms of a single function by means of the fundamental identities. For example, in solving the equation

$$\cos x + \sec x = \tfrac{5}{2}$$

the first step would be to express $\sec x$ as $1/\cos x$. In many cases this is also helpful in proving identities.

3. Having reduced all functions involved in an equation to terms of a single function, transpose all terms involving this function to one side of the equation.

4. Having solved an equation for the value of some one function of the unknown (angle), it may be possible to determine the angle by inspection and consideration of the values of the functions of special angles. Otherwise, it will be necessary to refer to the table of natural functions.

5. In proving an identity, try to transform one of the members into an expression known to be identical with the other.

6. If (5) cannot be done readily, use reversible steps to transform both members separately into recognized identical expressions.

7. If other methods fail, try to obtain an identity by transforming all functions involved into terms of the sine and cosine.

Success in solving trigonometric equations or in proving identities requires close familiarity with the relations among the functions. The eight fundamental identities most commonly needed are:

$$\sin^2 x + \cos^2 x = 1 \qquad (1) \qquad\qquad \cot x = \frac{\cos x}{\sin x} \qquad (5)$$

$$\sec^2 x - \tan^2 x = 1 \qquad (2) \qquad\qquad \cot x = \frac{1}{\tan x} \qquad (6)$$

$$\csc^2 x - \cot^2 x = 1 \qquad (3) \qquad\qquad \sec x = \frac{1}{\cos x} \qquad (7)$$

$$\tan x = \frac{\sin x}{\cos x} \qquad (4) \qquad\qquad \csc x = \frac{1}{\sin x} \qquad (8)$$

These should be thoroughly memorized. The student should already be familiar with formulas (6) to (8), since they are merely the reciprocal relations pointed out in connection with the definition of the functions, and his attention should be called to the fact that formulas (2) and (3) follow immediately from formula (1). In addition to these, the student should also be familiar with the functions of the double angles.

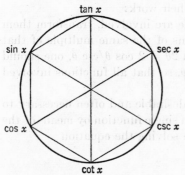

FIG. 18-24. The function hexagon.

There are other relationships which are sometimes needed but which are so numerous and so much alike that it is difficult to memorize them all. The mnemonic device of Fig. 18-24, which we shall call "the function hexagon," provides an easy means for recalling all of these fundamental identities except the first three listed above and the functions of double and half angles. The arrangement should be made exactly as shown. This is easy to remember because the sine, tangent, and secant appear in this order from left to right and each is directly above its corresponding cofunction.

1. The two functions at the ends of any diagonal are reciprocals of each other.

2. Any function is the product of the two functions between which it lies. Thus $\sin x = \tan x \cos x$; $\cot x = \cos x \csc x$; etc.

3. Any function may be expressed as a fraction in which the numerator is either of the adjacent functions and the denominator is the one on beyond that. Thus

$$\tan x = \frac{\sec x}{\csc x} \qquad\qquad \cos x = \frac{\cot x}{\csc x}$$

and so on.

4. The product of any three alternate functions is 1. Thus

$$\sin x \cot x \sec x = 1 \qquad \text{and} \qquad \cos x \tan x \csc x = 1$$

This mechanical device is so simple, economical, and powerful—giving, as it does, 26 separate identities for reference—that students will find it extremely helpful in making trigonometric transformations in their work with trigonometric identities and equations. It does not, of course, *prove* any of these identities, but the proofs are all simple and should be made by the students.

Polar Coordinates and Complex Numbers in Polar Form. Whether from lack of time or from underestimating its importance, the study of polar coordinates and of complex numbers in polar form is commonly omitted from courses in trigonometry. There are, of course, certain concepts and relations which must be understood, but the topic is not really difficult. It can be handled adequately by good high school students, and its importance in modern mathematics and science suggests that a place should be made for it in the trigonometry course, both in high school and in college.

The definition of the polar coordinates of a point is based upon superimposing a polar system, with pole, polar axis, vectorial angle, and standard position properly defined, directly upon a conventional rectangular coordinate system. This is motivated by the fact that, with respect to an initial point and direction, any point in the plane can be defined as well by a distance and a direction (its polar coordinates) as by two distances

Fig. 18-25

(its rectangular coordinates). The relations between these two coordinate systems is easily made clear by reference to a diagram such as Fig. 18-25. Evidently $x = r \cos \theta$ and $y = r \sin \theta$. Also, $r = \sqrt{x^2 + y^2}$ and $\tan \theta = y/x$, whence $\theta = \arctan y/x$. These conversion formulas are so simple and so easily reconstructed that there is no need for students to memorize them.

Once these basic relations are established, numerous exercises should be given for the purpose of strengthening understanding and developing facility in applying them. These exercises should include conversions both from rectangular to polar coordinates and from polar to rectangular coordinates. The following are samples: (1) Give the polar coordinates of the point (7, 10). (2) Give the rectangular coordinates of the point (12, $\pi/3$).

Extension of the idea of polar coordinates to polar representation of complex numbers requires setting up a one-to-one correspondence between the complex numbers and the points in a plane. This is accomplished by representing all complex numbers as vectors, or, rather, as vector sums.   Since each complex number is of the form $x + yi$, where x and y are real numbers (not excluding zero), it is necessary to designate one of the axes (usually the X axis) as the *axis of reals* and the other (the Y axis) as the *axis of imaginaries*.   Then any complex number such as $8 + 5i$ can be represented by a vector drawn from the origin (or pole) to the point (8,5) as referred to the axes.   The length, or absolute value, of this vector is known as the *magnitude* or *modulus* of the complex number. In this case the modulus is $\sqrt{8^2 + 5^2} = \sqrt{89}$.   The positive angle θ

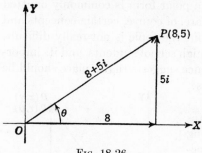

which this vector makes with the polar axis is called the *vectorial angle* or the *amplitude* of the complex number.   In this case $\tan \theta = \frac{5}{8}$, so the amplitude, or vectorial angle, is *arctan* $\frac{5}{8}$.   Hence the polar representation of the complex number $8 + 5i$ in the complex plane is $(\sqrt{89}, \text{arctan } \frac{5}{8})$.

Fig. 18-26

None of these ideas should cause any serious difficulty to students if they are carefully explained and adequately illustrated by the teacher. The only new elements are the terms "modulus" and "amplitude" and the designation of the y axis as the *axis of imaginaries*, against which the coefficients of the imaginary parts of complex numbers are plotted.   It will probably be necessary to recall to students the methods of forming the sum and product of two complex numbers and the fact that two complex numbers $a + bi$ and $c + di$ are equal if and only if $a = c$ and $b = d$.   Then they need only be reminded that (1) the sum of $a + bi$ and $c + di$ can be represented by the vector drawn from the origin to the point corresponding to the complex number $[(a + c), (b + d)]$, which is in fact their sum, and (2) the product of $a + bi$ and $c + di$ can be represented by the vector drawn from the origin to the point corresponding to the complex number $[(ac - bd), (bc + ad)]$, which is in fact their product.

Transition to trigonometric representation is now easily accomplished by recalling that in the rectangular form $x + yi$ the real numbers x and y have the polar representation $x = r \cos \theta$ and $y = r \sin \theta$, with $r > 0$. Therefore, by direct substitution $x + yi$ becomes

$$r \cos \theta + (r \sin \theta)i = r(\cos \theta + i \sin \theta)$$

From this, the passage to the formula for the product is made by direct multiplication.   Thus, let $A = r(\cos \theta + i \sin \theta)$ and

$$B = s(\cos \phi + i \sin \phi)$$

Then it needs to be shown that $AB = rs[\cos (\theta + \phi) + i \sin (\theta + \phi)]$.
Similarly, the quotient formula $A/B = \dfrac{r}{s} [\cos (\theta - \phi) + i \sin (\theta - \phi)]$
needs to be worked out directly and in detail.

The detailed work involved in developing these formulas is one of the hard spots for students. The formulas should eventually be memorized for facile use, but not until their derivation has been thoroughly explained and understood, and this is one place where the teacher's help is indispensable. Special importance is attached to these two formulas in that they provide the foundation upon which De Moivre's theorem is established.

Some Applications of Trigonometry. The interest of the students in any course in mathematics will be intensified if genuine applications of the subject are pointed out, and trigonometry has many applications in various branches of science, engineering, and technology. Some are simple, direct, and concrete. Others, such as some of the applications to mechanics and electrical theory, are implicit and abstract, but they are still genuine and important practical applications of trigonometry.

The following are a few examples, taken at random, of physical formulas which involve trigonometric functions. They are cited here merely for the purpose of giving some indication of the general usefulness of trigonometric functions. For proper use it is necessary, first, that these formulas be imbedded in the context of careful definition of units.

For a coil rotating uniformly in a magnetic field, the instantaneous induced voltage E_i is given by the formula $E_i = E_m \sin \theta$, where E_m is the maximum voltage and θ is the phase angle.

The current i, in amperes, flowing through a tangent galvanometer having n turns of radius r in the earth's field H produces an angular deflection θ. The formula for the determination of the amount of current is

$$i = \frac{Hr}{2\pi n} \tan \theta$$

The index of refraction of light n is given by the formula

$$n = \frac{\sin i}{\sin r}$$

where i is the angle of incidence and r is the angle of refraction.

For light passing at the angle of minimum deviation D through a prism whose angle is A, the index of refraction n is given by the formula

$$n = \frac{\sin \frac{1}{2}(A + D)}{\sin \frac{1}{2}A}$$

One of the basic problems of automotive engineering is the determination of the force P needed to balance a weight W on a plane inclined to the horizontal at a given angle α. This relationship is expressed in the formula $P = W \sin \alpha$.

The motion of projectiles is another general problem involving trigonometric formulas. For projectiles having an initial velocity v at an angle θ with the horizontal the following formulas hold:

Maximum height:

$$h = \frac{v^2 \sin^2 \theta}{2g}$$

Time to maximum height:

$$t = \frac{v \sin \theta}{g}$$

Total time of flight:

$$T = \frac{2v \sin \theta}{g}$$

Horizontal range:

$$R = \frac{v^2 \sin 2\theta}{g}$$

General equation of trajectory:

$$y = x \tan \theta - \frac{gx^2}{2v^2 \cos^2 \theta}$$

In geology the thickness of a rock stratum having a level outcrop may be approximately determined by finding the horizontal length of the outcrop d and the angle of dip θ. The thickness of the stratum W is then given by the formula $W = d \sin \theta$.

Most astronomical work and long-distance navigation and aviation require the application of spherical trigonometry for the determination of courses, distances, and positions. For comparatively short courses ("plane sailing" and short-distance flying) the errors due to the earth's curvature are relatively small and do not seriously affect the computations based upon the formulas of plane trigonometry.

In these days of rapid expansion of aviation many young people will be interested in air navigation. Trigonometry plays an important part in this, and those who pilot or navigate planes will need to be concerned with the mathematics of air navigation. Two important problems are the determination of the wind-correction angle and the determination of ground speed. These problems may be solved by scale drawing, or they may be solved by application of the law of sines from plane trigonometry. If, for example, the wind-correction angle is designated by x and the angle between the wind direction and the true course by y, then

$$\frac{\text{Wind velocity}}{\text{Air speed}} = \frac{\sin x}{\sin y}$$

Thus $\sin x$ (and therefore x) may be readily determined, since all the other elements in the formula presumably are known.

If the same notation is used, the formula for determining ground speed is

$$\frac{\text{Ground speed}}{\text{Air speed}} = \frac{\sin (y - x)}{\sin y}$$

The foregoing miscellaneous illustrations of the use of trigonometry may serve to suggest others. Such applications rarely fail to increase interest in the subject. Teachers will do well to be constantly on the alert for examples of the practical application of the subject, which will not only enhance the interest of the students but broaden the teacher's horizon and add zest to his teaching.[1]

Trigonometry from a Modern Viewpoint. The applications cited above are intended as illustrations of ways in which the solution of triangles and the trigonometric functions of angles enter *directly* into practical situations. It must be noted, however, that the most numerous and important applications of trigonometry to mathematics itself and to modern science and engineering are found not in solving triangles but rather in the analytic aspects of the subject. Unfortunately, the trigonometry courses taught in many high schools give undue emphasis to the solution of triangles and gravely neglect other equally important matters. Indeed, students sometimes are left with the impression that skill in the numerical solution of triangles by logarithmic methods constitutes the *summum bonum* and the peak objective, if not the sole objective, of the course.

In view of modern requirements, such a view is no longer justified, if it ever was. There are still triangles to be solved, of course, but there is need today for increased study of such analytic considerations as the variation, graphs, and composition of trigonometric functions; the inverse functions; relationships among the functions; proofs of identities; solution of trigonometric equations; polar coordinates; and complex numbers in polar (trigonometric) form; and the trigonometry of numbers as such. Of the students who take trigonometry, relatively few will have much occasion later in life to solve oblique triangles, but many will take mathematics and science in college and will need a good understanding of these analytic aspects of trigonometry. In the interests of these students, it would seem important that the course should provide increased emphasis on the analytic side of trigonometry so that a proper balance between the numerical and the analytic aspects of the subject will be maintained. In this connection Andree says:[2]

Today engineering still demands this numerical skill, but other phases of trigonometry have become so important that the numerical solution of triangles is only a minor section in a course in modern trigonometry. Some schools still spend a third or more of their time on logarithms and the solution of triangles. This is not in the best interests of students who plan to enter engineering, science,

---

[1] For additional examples of applications of trigonometry to engineering see E. M. J. Pease and G. P. Wadsworth: "Engineering Trigonometry" (Scranton, Pa.: International Textbook Company, 1946), pp. 34–68.

[2] "Modern Trigonometry," by Richard V. Andree, The University of Oklahoma, Norman, Oklahoma, *Mathematics Teacher*, **48** (February, 1955), 82–83.

or mathematics, and is certainly of little use to the student seeking a general education. Today's civilization demands a careful study of functional graphs (harmonics) and the dextrous use of identities, including the half-angle and double angle forms. The solution of trigonometric equations and identities is vital in modern science.

The engineer of today is busy with problems that were unthought of twenty years ago. As a result of this, many shop technicians are doing work which was done by the engineer twenty years ago. The technician who is to get ahead today must be mathematically prepared to accept some of the responsibility which previously rested on the shoulders of the engineer. The engineer must be prepared to reach new horizons. . . .

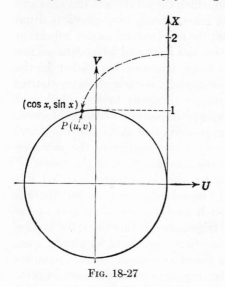

Fig. 18-27

After interviewing industrialists, scientists, engineers, technicians, and shop mechanics, my conclusion is that the trigonometry which is most needed by modern civilization is:

1. The graphs of trigonometric functions. The student must realize in graphing $y = 2x + 7 \cos 5x$ that x need not be thought of as an angle.

2. Identities. Students should be given only one member of an identity such as $(1 + \cos 2x)(\csc 2x - \cot 2x)$ to simplify as much as possible, without realizing that their goal is $\sin 2x$.

3. Trigonometric equations, especially of higher degree.

4. The inverse trigonometric functions.

5. Definitions and applications involving polar coordinates, De Moivre's theorem, and complex numbers.

6. Practical problems involving equations and identities.

7. Electrical engineers and technicians need the relationships

$$\sin \theta = (e^{i\theta} - e^{-i\theta})/2i \text{ and } \cos \theta = (e^{i\theta} + e^{-i\theta})/2$$

and their ramifications along with De Moivre's Theorem.

If your school is still teaching the trigonometry of 250 B.C., then perhaps you should learn more about the trigonometric demands of modern civilization. Your school may use one of the several excellent texts on modern trigonometry and still be giving a 250 B.C. course by slighting these important modern phases. I hope not, because much of the difficulty students encounter in calculus, mechanics, and industrial applications is traceable directly to the lack of dexterity in the manipulation of trigonometric equations and identities.

The great importance of periodic phenomena in many of the problems and considerations in modern science and engineering has led to the desirability of a definition of the circular functions in such a manner as to provide the set of real numbers as their domain.   This has been accomplished through the concept of a "wrapping process" whereby the real number line is wrapped around the unit circle.   Such a process establishes the ordered pair (cos x, sin x), where x is a real number, as the coordinates of points on the unit circle.   The complete "trigonometry" of these functions can be developed without having to make any reference to angles at any point in the development.   However, if at any time it should become desirable to compare the circular functions of real numbers with the trigonometric functions of angles, the comparison can be effected through the medium of radian measure.   The one-to-one correspondence which can thus be set up affords a simple method for the evaluation of the circular functions of real numbers.   The point should be made, however, that this is a method of evaluation used through convenience and not through necessity.   The circular functions can be evaluated without any reference to angles whatsoever.[1]

EXERCISES

1. Why should some work in numerical trigonometry be given in the junior high school?   What should it include?

2. Explain in detail, as you would in introducing the subject to a junior high school class, the meanings of the sine, cosine, and tangent of an acute angle.

3. Before trigonometric functions can be used in solving triangles, the students must understand how the tables are made up, how they are read, and how they can be used to determine either (a) the numerical value corresponding to a given function of a given angle or (b) the angle corresponding to a given numerical value of a given function.   Explain these things just as you would in introducing the subject to a junior high school class.

4. The two basic problems in solving right triangles (given sufficient data) are (a) to solve for an angle and (b) to solve for a side.   Explain in detail, as you would in introducing the subject to a junior high school class, how to use trigonometric functions and their numerical values in solving each of these two basic problems.   Use examples to illustrate your discussion.

5. Find or make up a good field project or laboratory project involving the use of right-triangle trigonometry that is suitable for junior high school students.   Describe it in detail, and show how it will exemplify the direct practical application of trigonometry.

6. Schultze (see Bibliography) calls the solution of the right triangle the "backbone of practical trigonometry," and adds that it constitutes "probably the most important chapter in the entire elementary trigonometry."   What are his arguments?   Outline his discussion.   Do you agree with him?   Why or why not?

7. The quotation from Andree (see last section in this chapter) indicates a view sharply in contrast to that expressed by Schultze.   Outline his position and give his

[1] For a more detailed discussion of circular functions of real numbers see the Report of the Commission on Mathematics, "Appendices" (New York: College Entrance Examination Board, 1959), pp. 206–213.

arguments. Try to account for the difference in the viewpoints expressed by the two men. Which do you think has the stronger case? Why?

8. Take the section on the right triangle in some recent trigonometry textbook and analyze it to determine what concepts, information, and skills of (a) arithmetic, (b) algebra, and (c) geometry are involved.

9. In a semester's course in trigonometry some teachers prefer to develop the concepts of the trigonometric functions in terms of the sides of a right triangle, and others prefer to define the functions in terms of the general angle from the outset. Give arguments for and against each of these plans.

10. Summarize the discussion of the teaching of the functions of the special angles as it is given in this chapter.

11. Show that the Pythagorean theorem is a special case of the law of cosines.

12. Examine the proof of the law of sines in five trigonometry texts. How many of the five show that the law holds when one of the angles is a right angle?

13. Why is the law of tangents often considered to be preferable to the law of cosines in solving oblique triangles? Under what circumstances might it not have this advantage? Is it ever really indispensable?

14. Do you think that in most trigonometry courses enough attention is given to studying the variation of the functions? If not, why not?

15. Why do so many students fail to get an appreciation of the real significance of the following: (a) the periodic nature of the trigonometric functions, (b) the multiple-valued nature of the inverse trigonometric relations as contrasted with the single-valued nature of the functions themselves, (c) the representation of values of functions by line values, (d) the fact that for certain angles the values of certain functions are undefined?

16. List what you feel are the important things to be learned through the study of the variation of the trigonometric functions. Why are these important?

17. Why are graphs of the functions so helpful to students in learning to appreciate the manner in which the different functions vary?

18. Demonstrate how to make graphs of the sine, cosine, and tangent of an angle by the method of projection as the angle varies continuously from 0° to 360°.

19. Explain how the graphs called for in exercise 18 can be used to determine (a) the values of the functions corresponding to given values of the angle and (b) values of the angle corresponding to given values of the functions.

20. What do the graphs show about (a) periodicity of the functions, (b) extreme values of the functions, (c) zeros of the functions, (d) domains for which the functions are increasing, (e) domains for which the functions are decreasing, (f) angles, if any, for which the functions are undefined?

21. By use of graphs of the sine, cosine, and tangent of an angle construct graphs of the cotangent, secant, and cosecant.

22. Construct a graph of $y = \sin x$. Then, by using only this graph and geometric methods, construct on the same axes graphs of the following functions: $y = 2 \sin x$, $y = \sin 2x, y = \sin \frac{1}{2}x, y = \frac{1}{2} \sin x, y = \sin (2 + x), y = 2 + \sin x, y = 1 + \frac{1}{2} \sin x$. Explain each of these constructions as you would to a class.

23. What is a radian? Discuss radian measure and the *pi* notation and explain as you would to your students how to convert from degree to radian measure and from radian to degree measure.

24. What is a mil? Discuss mil measure and explain it as you would to a class. Under what circumstances may it have a practical advantage over radian or degree measure and what is this advantage? Illustrate.

25. Most tables of trigonometric functions extend only from 0° to 90°, yet it is often necessary to find values of functions of angles not within this range. Show exactly

how you would teach students to determine values from the tables for functions such as cos 153°, tan 289°, and sin (−112°). Explain the use of the triangle of reference and show how it can be helpful in this connection.

26. Explain in complete detail how you would teach students to interpolate when using tables of natural or logarithmic functions.

27. What special cautions must students be taught to observe when interpolating in the tables for values of logarithms of functions over domains for which the functions and logarithms decrease as the angle increases? Illustrate the kind of mistake which is common in this connection.

28. It has been suggested that, since most of the data used in numerical problems in trigonometry are approximate data and nearly all the values given in the tables are also approximate, the apparent increase in accuracy obtained through interpolation is actually fictitious. If this is so, then is interpolation in such cases justified? Discuss the question.

29. What are the relative advantages and disadvantages of four- and five-place tables in the solution of trigonometric problems?

30. Is it desirable to give much work in proving identities and solving trigonometric equations in a course in trigonometry in the high school? Compare the views of different authors on this question.

31. Explain the fundamental distinction between proving identities and solving trigonometric equations. Why is it not legitimate in proving identities to use the algebraic laws of the equation and to operate as if the identity to be proved were an equation. Illustrate.

32. List the so-called eight fundamental identities of trigonometry.

33. Develop the formula for sin $(A + B)$ by means of a diagram.

34. Starting with the formula for sin $(A + B)$, develop the formulas for cos $(A + B)$ and tan $(A + B)$ and without further use of a diagram.

35. Explain and illustrate the function hexagon described in this chapter and show why it is a helpful mnemonic device.

36. List and establish all of the 26 identities which the function hexagon can "remember" for you.

37. Explain how the difference formulas, the double-angle formulas, the half-angle formulas, and the product formulas for sines and cosines can be derived, with the help of the eight fundamental identities. Refer to Table 18-2.

38. Develop the formulas for the radius of the inscribed circle and for the sines, cosines, and tangents of the half angles of a triangle entirely in terms of the sides of the triangle.

39. Take ten simple trigonometric expressions and by means of commonly known identities transform each of them into some other equivalent form. (You will then have established ten "original" trigonometric identities, proofs of which could then be assigned as exercises for your class.)

40. What advantages could students derive from establishing "original" identities themselves?

41. For what values of x in the domain $0° \leqq x \leqq 720°$ is the statement cos $x < \frac{1}{2}$ valid? For what values of x in this same domain is the statement cos $x = \frac{1}{2}$ valid?

42. For what value or values of x in the domain $90° < x \leqq 450°$ are the following statements valid? (a) 2 cos $5x = 1$; (b) 2 cos $5x > 1$.

43. Explain as you would to a class the solutions of the following equation and inequality, where $0° \leqq x \leqq 360°$: (a) sin $x = $ tan x; (b) sin $x < $ tan x. (Analysis of part (b) makes clear the great care that is needed in examining inequalities. It suggests also the importance of doing some work with inequalities and points up the interest which such work can generate.)

44. Explain, as you would to a class, the method of solving the following equation:

$$\cot^2 \theta = 5 \cot \theta - 6$$

45. Examine five recent textbooks in trigonometry and compare them with respect to their treatments of trigonometric identities and equations. Which text do you think deals most adequately with these topics? Are inequalities discussed in any of the texts?

46. Compare several textbooks in trigonometry and select the one you think is the best one for a high school class. In what ways do you think it is better than the others?

BIBLIOGRAPHY

Albert, A. A.: Suggestions for a Simplified Trigonometry, *American Mathematical Monthly*, **50** (1943), 251–253.

Amir-Moez, Ali R.: Teaching Trigonometry through Vectors, *Mathematics Magazine*, **32** (1958), 19–23.

Andree, Richard V.: Modern Trigonometry, *Mathematics Teacher*, **48** (1955), 82–83.

Aude, H. T. R.: A Project in Trigonometry, *Pentagon*, **13** (1954), 98–99.

Baker, G. A.: Multiplication Tables for Trigonometric Functions, *American Mathematical Monthly*, **64** (1957), 502–503.

Bettinger, A. K.: A Derivation for the Formulas for $\sin (\alpha + \beta)$ and $\cos (\alpha + \beta)$. *American Mathematical Monthly*, **60** (1953), 108–110.

Blackwell, Rosa: Mapping the School District: A Trigonometry Project, *Mathematics Teacher*, **45** (1952), 226–228.

Blank, Laura: Teaching Mathematics in Technicolor, *Mathematics Teacher*, **41** (1948), 229–231.

Bold, Benjamin: A Geometric Proof for a Number of Trigonometric Theories, *Mathematics Teacher*, **45** (1952), 43–44.

Boyer, Lee Emerson: "An Introduction to Mathematics for Teachers" (New York: Henry Holt and Company, Inc., 1945), pp. 415–421.

Brauer, Alfred: The Proof of the Law of Sines, *American Mathematical Monthly*, **59** (1952), 319.

Braverman, Benjamin: Changing Objectives in the Teaching of Algebra and Trigonometry in the Senior High School, *Mathematics Teacher*, **39** (1946), 314–319.

Breslich, E. R.: "Problems in Teaching Secondary-school Mathematics" (Chicago: University of Chicago Press, 1931), pp. 323–342.

Brown, Claude H.: "The Teaching of Secondary Mathematics" (New York: Harper & Brothers, 1953), pp. 267–280.

Bureau of Secondary Curriculum Development: "Mathematics 10-11-12" (Albany, N.Y.: The State Education Department, 1959).

Burg, Walter: An Experimental Construction of the Sine Curve, *School Science and Mathematics*, **44** (1944), 467–468.

Burton, L. J.: The Laws of Sines and Cosines, *American Mathematical Monthly*, **56** (1949), 550–551.

——— and E. A. Hedberg: Proofs of the Addition Formulae for Sines and Cosines, *American Mathematical Monthly*, **56** (1949), 471–473.

Carlton, Carl J.: Mathematics in the Skilled Trades, *Mathematics Teacher*, **46** (1953), 8–13, 27.

Cavins, Anna Schneider: "Teaching Approximate Computation in Secondary School Trigonometry" unpublished master's thesis Normal, Ill.: Illinois State Normal University, 1954.

Cell, John W.: The Trigonometric Functions, *Mathematics Teacher,* **43** (1950), 187–192.

Cohen, Carl: Addition Theorems for the Sine and Cosine, *American Mathematical Monthly,* **63** (1956), 248–249.

Coleman, Grace: The Signs of the Trigonometric Functions of Any Angle, *School Science and Mathematics,* **47** (1947), 81–82.

Commission on Mathematics, Report of: "Appendices" (New York: College Entrance Examination Board, 1959), pp. 176–223.

Corliss, John J., and Joseph J. Urbancek: The Law of Tangents, *School Science and Mathematics,* **40** (1940), 664–665.

Davis, David R.: "The Teaching of Mathematics" (Reading, Mass.: Addison-Wesley Publishing Company, 1951), pp. 287–292.

Dickinson, Frank G.: Some Transformations from a Unit Circle with Line Values of the Sine Function, *Mathematics Teacher,* **45** (1952), 19–24.

Dubisch, Roy: "Trigonometry" (New York: The Ronald Press Company, 1955).

Eagle, Edwin: An Improved Trigtractor, *Mathematics Teacher,* **49** (1956), 28–29.

Eves, Howard: Checking the S.A.S. Case in Trigonometry, *American Mathematical Monthly,* **52** (1945), 208–209.

Fehr, Howard F.: "Secondary Mathematics: A Functional Approach for Teachers" (Boston, D. C. Heath and Company, 1951), pp. 232–274.

Frankel, S.: Complete Approximate Solutions of the Equation $x = \tan x$, *National Mathematics Magazine,* **11** (1937), 177–182.

Fraser, J. C.: Brief Historical Review of the Development of Trigonometry, *School* (Secondary Edition), **36** (1947), 122–132.

Garabedian, Carl A.: Some Simple Logical Notions Encountered in Elementary Mathematics: II, On Proving Identities and Solving Equations, *Mathematics Teacher,* **24** (1931), 436–443.

Geer, Willard: Are High Schools Underemphasizing Trigonometry? *School Science and Mathematics,* **49** (1949), 72–75.

Greenberg, Benjamin: Transforming the Law of Cosines for Computational Purposes, *Mathematics Teacher,* **48** (1955), 308–309.

Greenwood, R.: On the Discovery of Certain Trigonometric Identities, *American Mathematical Monthly,* **47** (1940), 99–100.

Grove, Ethel, and others: Model for Introducing Trigonometry on Ninth Grade Level, *School Science and Mathematics,* **51** (1951), 296–297.

Habel, E. A.: Does the Arithmetic in Algebra Textbooks Prepare for Trigonometry? *School Science and Mathematics,* **51** (1951), 488–491.

Hassler, J. O., and R. R. Smith: "The Teaching of Secondary Mathematics" (New York: The Macmillan Company, 1930), pp. 384–391.

Jerbert, A. R.: Sine Curves, *School Science and Mathematics,* **45** (1945), 168–172.

Jones, Phillip S.: Inequalities, the Quadratic, and the Ambiguous Case, *Mathematics Teacher,* **44** (1951), 195.

————: Angular Measure: Enough of Its History to Improve Its Teaching, *Mathematics Teacher,* **46** (1953), 419–426.

Jurgensen, Ray: An Interesting Equation: $\tan 2x = \cot x$, *School Science and Mathematics,* **54** (1954), 489–490.

Karpinski, L. C.: A Problem of Presentation in Trigonometry, *National Mathematics Magazine,* **13** (1939), 240–241.

————: The Place of Trigonometry in the Development of Mathematical Ideas, *Scripta Mathematica,* **11** (1945), 268–272.

Kinney, Lucien Blair, and C. Richard Purdy: "Teaching Mathematics in the Secondary School" (New York: Rinehart & Company, Inc., 1952), pp. 152–170.

Kramer, Edna E.: The Integration of Trigonometry with Physical Science, *Mathematics Teacher*, **41** (1948), 356–361.

Lee, Herbert: Geometric Proof for the Addition Formulas for the Tangent, *Mathematics Teacher*, **44** (1951), 43–46.

Levitt, C. W.: Some Suggestions for Trigonometry, *School* (Secondary Edition), **32** (1944), 525–530.

Mathews, C. W.: Use of Mnemonic Devices in Mathematics, *School Science and Mathematics*, **49** (1949), 491–492.

Mazkewitsch, D.: Geometric Derivations of Some Trigonometric Formulae, *School Science and Mathematics*, **58** (1958), 213–216.

Mazziotta, Estelle: The Basic Concepts of Trigonometry, *Mathematics Magazine*, **22** (1949), 139–150.

Newsom, C. V., and J. F. Randolph: Trigonometry without Angles, *Mathematics Teacher*, **39** (1946), 66–68.

Nunn, T. Percy: "The Teaching of Algebra (Including Trigonometry)" (London: Longmans, Green & Co., Ltd., 1923), pp. 121–135, 261–263, 333–340, 499–514.

Nyberg, Joseph A.: Notes from a Mathematics Classroom, *School Science and Mathematics*, **42** (1942), 74, 567–568; **43** (1943), 352; **44** (1944), 81–82, 469, 572, 670; **45** (1945), 444–446; **47** (1947), 649–652; **48** (1948), 138, 479–482. (The references are to short but pointed and practically helpful articles on teaching trigonometry.)

Randolph, John F.: "Trigonometry" (New York: The Macmillan Company, 1953).

Ransom, W. R.: Guide Lines, *Mathematics Magazine*, **24** (1950), 15–18.

———: Some Mirror Trigonometry, *School Science and Mathematics*, **55** (1955), 599–600.

Read, Cecil B.: A Note on the Use of Directed Lines in Trigonometry, *School Science and Mathematics*, **42** (1942), 374–376.

——— and E. B. Wedel: Significant Figures in Trigonometry, *School Science and Mathematics*, **43** (1943), 661–664.

———, and Ferna Wrestler: Principal Values of Certain Inverse Trigonometric Functions, *American Mathematical Monthly*, **63** (1956), 184–185.

Reeve, William David: "Mathematics for the Secondary School" (New York: Henry Holt and Company, Inc., 1954), pp. 400–416.

Rine, T. E.: Integration in the Teaching of Trigonometry in the Secondary School, *School Science and Mathematics*, **53** (1953), 644–649.

Rosenberg, Herman: The Changing Concept of Trigonometry as a School Subject, *Mathematics Teacher*, **51** (1958), 246–252.

Rothman, Irwin M.: Pitfalls in the Trigonometric Solution of an Oblique Triangle, *Mathematics Teacher*, **37** (1944), 311–313.

Rutledge, W. A., and John A. Pond: "Modern Trigonometry" (Englewood Cliffs, N.J.: Prentice-Hall, Inc., 1956).

Satterly, John: Meet Mr. Tau, *School Science and Mathematics*, **56** (1956), 731–741.

Sawyer, W. W.: "Mathematician's Delight" (Baltimore: Penguin Books, Inc., 1946), pp. 161–183.

———: Trigonometry Abstractly Treated, *American Mathematical Monthly*, **64** (1957), pp. 734–737.

Schaaf, William L.: The Teaching of Trigonometry, *Mathematics Teacher*, **45** (1952), 445–450.

Schultze, Arthur: "The Teaching of Mathematics in Secondary Schools" (New York: The Macmillan Company, 1927), pp. 353–367.

Smith, D. E., and W. D. Reeve: "The Teaching of Junior High School Mathematics" (Boston: Ginn & Company, 1927), pp. 217–228.

Steinen, Ramon: Trigonometry in Grade Eight, *Mathematics Teacher*, **50** (1957), 380–383.

Thatcher, Leonard: Relations of Trigonometric Functions, *School Science and Mathematics*, **45** (1945), 365–366.

Thompson, S. L.: A Note on the Law of Cosines, *American Mathematical Monthly*, **58** (1951), 698–699.

Tierney, John A.: Trigonometric Functions of Real Numbers, *Mathematics Teacher*, **50** (1957), 38–39.

Trigg, C. W.: A Proof of the Law of Cosines, *School Science and Mathematics*, **54** (1954), 370.

Tuckey, C.: Diagram for the Study and Solution of Triangles, *Mathematical Gazette*, **23** (1939), 150–154.

Vance, Elbridge P.: Teaching Trigonometry, *American Mathematical Monthly*, **54** (1947), 36–37.

———: "Trigonometry" (Reading, Mass.: Addison-Wesley Publishing Company, 1954).

Wagner, R. W.: A Substitution for Solving Trigonometric Equations, *American Mathematical Monthly*, **54** (1947), 219.

Wayne, Alan: Some Light Trigonometry, *School Science and Mathematics*, **45** (1945), 453–456.

Williams, K.: Note Concerning Some Trigonometrical Inequalities, *American Mathematical Monthly*, **44** (1937), 579–583.

Wolfe, J. M.: Proximity of Prerequisite Learning and Success in Trigonometry in College, *Mathematics Teacher*, **49** (1956), 605–606.

Wylie, C. R., Jr.: "Plane Trigonometry" (New York: The McGraw-Hill Book Company, Inc., 1955).

Young, Frederick H.: sin $(A + B)$, *Mathematics Magazine*, **27** (1954), 208–209.

———: The Addition Formulas, *Mathematics Teacher*, **50** (1957), 45–48.

Young, J. W. A.: "The Teaching of Mathematics" (New York: Longmans, Green & Co., Inc., 1924), pp. 287–291.

19

THE TEACHING OF ANALYTIC GEOMETRY

Analytic geometry is a borderline subject between the high school courses and the more rigorous work in the calculus and subsequent college courses in mathematics. It contributes to the mathematical development and background of students in at least three important ways. It embraces a body of subject matter which is interesting and beautiful in its own right. Also, by bringing powerful algebraic concepts and techniques to bear upon geometrical problems, it links algebra and geometry together into a unified mathematical structure. Finally, it develops mathematical formulas and techniques, many of which are needed for subsequent work in mathematics, and thus provides an important tool for the mathematician. Analytic geometry may be viewed, therefore, as a mathematical structure, as a method, or as a tool, and it is something of each of these.

Some students find analytic geometry easier than other branches of mathematics which they have studied, but a good many find it harder. While little has been written on the teaching of analytic geometry, the fact that the subject is beginning to find a significant place in the mathematics programs of some high schools implies that there ought to be some published source to which teachers can turn for suggestions. Hence, consideration is given in this chapter to some of the key concepts of analytic geometry and to some of the characteristic difficulties which students often have with the subject.

Analytic Geometry and the High School Program. In the past, analytic geometry has been the typical offering for the second half of the freshman year of college mathematics. Until quite recently, few attempts have been made to introduce even its simplest concepts and terminology into the usual courses in high school algebra and geometry, although these subjects afford numerous opportunities for the introduction. To be sure, some work with graphs is included in all algebra courses, but the usual treatment can hardly be said to be analytic; all too often the work has stressed only the point-by-point plotting of graphs, with little emphasis on their interpretation. Except for occasional discussion of the slope of a straight line and of the slope-intercept equation of a line, the standard textbooks in high school algebra and geometry have been practically devoid of any reference to the concepts, notation, or method of analytic geometry.

There are, however, certain forces now beginning to be felt which look toward the injection of some new ideas into the high school courses. There was a time when trigonometry was rarely taught in high schools, and then only as a separate course in some of the larger schools. But by the end of the first quarter of this century textbooks in ninth-grade algebra and plane geometry were beginning to include chapters or units dealing with simple trigonometric ideas and methods and problems. Today nearly all textbooks for these courses include such units, and trigonometry has come to be commonly offered as a standard course in the third or fourth year of the high school.

It is too early to predict that the same kind of thing will happen to analytic geometry, but there is some indication that it might. The 1957 revised program in mathematics for the high schools in New York State gives some attention to analytic geometry in the regular work in grades 10 and 11 and in a special course being tried out experimentally in grade 12. In the tenth grade it forms one of the seven main divisions of the course. The range of topics is somewhat extended in the eleventh grade. The experimental twelfth-grade course reviews the topics developed earlier and includes study of the conic sections in standard position, study of the properties and type equations of the sections, and some work on polar coordinates and parametric equations.[1]

Subsequently (1959) the Commission on Mathematics of the College Entrance Examination Board included a substantial unit on coordinate geometry as one of the six units comprising its recommended program in mathematics for the tenth grade. The topics proposed for this unit include rectangular coordinates and one-to-one correspondence between points of a plane and ordered number pairs, and rather systematic analytic study of some of the important properties of the straight line and the circle. Emphasis is placed upon the concept of sets, e.g., a locus as a set of points satisfying given conditions and solution sets for equations or inequalities as sets of values satisfying these equations or inequalities. The use of methods of coordinate geometry in proving theorems and solving numerical problems of plane geometry is encouraged.[2]

[1] For further details on this, see the following documents: "Instruction in Mathematics and Science in New York State Schools" (Albany, N.Y.: State Education Department, 1957), p. 3; "Tenth Grade Mathematics—Coordinate Geometry" *ibid.*, p. 1; "An Experimental Course in Mathematics for the Twelfth Year" *ibid.*, pp. 25–27.

[2] Report of the Commission on Mathematics, "Program for College Preparatory Mathematics" (New York: College Entrance Examination Board, 1959), p. 39, and "Appendices" *ibid.*, pp. 120–139.

In view of the current interest in strengthening the mathematics curriculum in the high school, these innovations might gain widespread acceptance. If they do, analytic geometry may come to be recognized, in due course, as an accepted part of the high school program, as trigonometry has. This, however, is still in the realm of speculation.

In the remainder of this chapter some of the key topics of analytic geometry will be considered and certain associated instructional problems discussed.

Some Elementary Concepts. In beginning the study of analytic geometry the students will not encounter immediately any geometric ideas that are essentially new. On the contrary, the introductory work usually consists of a reexamination of the Cartesian coordinate system with which they should already be familiar through their earlier work with graphs. In many cases, however, this earlier work will have been rather casual and not very systematic. Therefore, it is generally advisable at the start to review and refurbish the concepts, terms, and notation associated with rectangular coordinates. This can be done quickly through a little supervised work on plotting points. A few illustrations done at the blackboard, together with a modicum of practice in plotting points and indicating coordinates in conventional form, will suffice to clear up any questions the students may have.

The concept of ordered pairs of numbers should be stressed in this connection. It should be emphasized that the location of a point in a coordinate system depends not alone on the numerical values of its coordinates but also upon their order and that the point whose coordinates are (a,b) is not, in general, the same point as the one whose coordinates are (b,a). There is no difficulty involved here, and it would be unnecessary to mention this except that students sometimes get careless about this convention. It is well, however, to stress the importance of giving conscious and explicit attention both to the concept of order in naming the coordinates of a point and to the conventional notation used. Any carelessness or any departure from the accepted notation will induce mistakes in representation and communication. Moreover, it may be pointed out at this time that the modern definition of *function* is given in terms of ordered pairs of elements and that the ordering and its proper representation will be of prime importance throughout all subsequent work in mathematics.

Other matters which probably should be reviewed and clarified in the introductory part of the course include the concept of projections on a line and the notion of directed line segments. Neither of these should require much time or entail any difficulty. The importance of reviewing them at this time lies in the fact that they are basic concepts which must be used continually. Fuzzy conceptions about these terms or the associated notation is likely to lead to fuzzy thinking and uncertainty in their application.

Associated with line segments and projections is the idea of *length* of a line segment, or *distance* from one point to another. The measure of this distance is made through direct application of the Pythagorean theorem to a right triangle, a concept with which the students are already familiar. In connection with any given line segment no difficulty is involved in showing that an associated right triangle may be formed by taking lines respectively parallel to the axes, one through each end of the given segment, and that the projections of the segment on these lines are the legs of the triangle, the segment itself being the hypotenuse. The very simplicity of this concept may tend to throw teachers off guard. It must be remembered that, while it is very elementary, it is also completely fundamental. It needs to be adequately illustrated. Moreover, even after the underlying idea is clearly understood by the students, the general relation needs to be explicitly formulated in terms of the coordinates of the ends of the segment:

$$d = \sqrt{(x_1 - x_2)^2 + (y_1 - y_2)^2} = \sqrt{(x_2 - x_1)^2 + (y_2 - y_1)^2}$$

This is easy to explain and illustrate by a diagram, but it is also the point at which students sometimes begin to become uncertain and confused. Their formulas of synthetic geometry will not usually have involved the use of coordinates, yet from here on they must both make and interpret their formulations in the notation of coordinates. If they can be made to understand both the rationale and the notation of this formula, a long step will have been made in the direction of understanding.

The point-of-division formulas are examples of formulas of analytic geometry which students often attempt to memorize without having a clear understanding of why they are as they are. Like the distance formula, they depend directly on theorems of high school geometry, and the concept is easily explained on this basis. Students bog down on it not because the concept is difficult but because they are unaccustomed to the notation. At this early stage in the course they will not yet have learned either to use or to interpret this notation very readily, and the formulas look forbidding to them. Hence, instead of attempting to interpret the formulas in terms of a figure and then reconstruct them in the new notation, the students often resort to memorizing the formulas. Usually it is not the geometric ideas that trouble them. It is the notation. This is new. It is fundamental and it must become the student's tool and servant throughout this and subsequent courses. It is important, therefore, to give a good deal of attention to this matter of notation in the early part of this work. It may even spell the difference between success and failure in the course.

The mid-point formulas, of course, are merely special cases of the point-of-division formulas, but (again in terms of notation) they are usually stated differently, so that the relation is not immediately apparent. Teachers, on the other hand, may tend to assume that the connection is so obvious as not to require any comment. It is desirable to point out this relation explicitly from a geometric viewpoint, and also to show how the mid-point formulas can be derived analytically from the point-of-division formulas. This not only serves to clarify this particular case but provides a simple and good illustration of the application of algebraic techniques to geometric problems.

Loci and Their Equations. The associated concepts of loci and their equations are central throughout analytic geometry. In high school mathematics courses little has been done to point up this association, though there are some good opportunities to do this even in ninth-grade algebra. The equation is thought of as being a part of algebra, and even the study of graphs of equations is often rather casual and perfunctory. The concept of a locus, on the other hand, is seldom encountered and clarified until the course in plane geometry, and even there the study of loci is confined mainly to its geometrical aspects. Little effort is made to bring the two together in any systematic manner until the course in analytic geometry, when that becomes the central theme. The conditions or restrictions imposed on the points forming a given locus are now expressed analytically or algebraically by equations which specify particular relations among the coordinates of each point in the locus and for no other points. Frequently the loci studied in analytic geometry are described verbally in terms of geometric conditions, but before they can be studied analytically these conditions have to be translated into equations.

The first serious difficulty which students are likely to encounter stems from this fact. Up to this point they have not been accustomed to identify geometric conditions with algebraic forms. Now they must not only learn to make this identification but go even further. In order to be proficient, they must actually learn to think in terms of these forms. For the common and rather simple loci studied, the form of the equation must come to suggest the associated locus, and conversely, the geometric conception of the locus must come to suggest the form of the associated equation. From the outset it should be made clear and kept continually before the students that there is a duality of form and a dual purpose in analytic geometry. The students should be reminded continually that every locus studied is represented by an equation and that every basic equation studied represents a locus. The two fundamental problems of analytic geometry are (1) to learn to associate with each locus studied the characteristic form of its equation and (2) to learn to infer from the type

form of the equation the nature and properties of the locus which it represents.   These fundamental considerations are not always made clear to
students, yet they form the very foundation of understanding.   To learn
that the equation $(x - h)^2/a^2 + (y - k)^2/b^2 = 1$ represents an ellipse is
certainly necessary, but it is not sufficient.   Unless the student understands what a and b and h and k represent geometrically, he will have
little conception of the form or the properties of the ellipse whose equation
is given him as $(x - 5)^2/37 + y^2/10 = 1$.   On the other hand, unless
he does know this type of equation, he will not be able to write down
readily the equation of the ellipse whose center is at $(5,0)$ and whose
major and minor axes have lengths of $2\sqrt{37}$ and $2\sqrt{10}$, respectively.
Each kind of locus studied in elementary analytic geometry has a characteristic form of equation.   The association between the properties of the
locus and the form of its type equation needs to be emphasized continually.   Indeed, broadly speaking, one may say that this association constitutes one of the fundamental objectives of the course.

The moment a student attains real appreciation of how a statement of
geometric restrictions can be translated into an equation, and of the fact
that the one is the counterpart of the other, he has made a major break-
through.   If he really understands what has taken place, it should then
be apparent to him that a powerful new instrument has been added to his
working equipment.   Once the geometric problem has been translated
into algebraic terms, he has at his command all the formal rules and
procedures of algebra to assist him.   He may manipulate the equation
formally and at will without, for the moment, giving any thought to the
geometric implications.   Then if in the end he can reinterpret the results
of his algebraic work back into terms of geometric relations, he will
have accomplished his geometric investigation by analytic methods,
and these often are more powerful than the direct methods of synthetic
geometry.

To some students this concept comes quickly; to others it does not.
Yet it is so much the essence of analytic geometry that every effort should
be made to ensure that all the students come to appreciate it.   Repeated
explanations and illustrations will doubtless be necessary, and penetrating
questions can often do much to clarify this dual representation and give
point to the analytic treatment of geometric problems.   Accomplishment
of this will give the students genuine insight into the method of analytic
geometry.   Without such insight they often resort to mere profitless
memorization and miss the whole point of the course.

Determining the Locus of an Equation.   In the beginning, the locus of an
equation is usually determined by plotting a considerable number of
points whose coordinates satisfy the equation and then drawing a smooth
curve through the points.   Students have no trouble with this because

they have had some experience with graphing and they understand what they are doing. However, despite the fact that constructing the graph of a given equation is one of the fundamental problems of analytic geometry, this method of point-by-point plotting has severe and fundamental limitations. One of them is that it is tedious and slow, and in general one can never plot all the points on the locus. Another is that it is inexact, and exactness is often of great importance, as, for example, in determining the coordinates of points of intersection of loci. Thus, by meticulous point-by-point plotting, a student might obtain carefully made graphs of the loci represented by the equations $x^2 + y^2 + 4x - 5 = 0$ and $y = 1 + 2x$. If the graphs are very carefully made to a large scale, he might well conclude that the one represents a circle and the other a straight line. Indeed, he might decide from observation that the circle has its center at $(-2,0)$, that its radius is 3 units in length, and that one of its points of intersection with the straight line is $(-2,-3)$. He might even make a good estimate of the coordinates of the other point of intersection.

Nobody would question the value of this intuitive observational type of analysis on the part of the students. It should by all means be encouraged, because it offers a splendid means for clarifying concepts and interpretations and for stimulating interest in the work. But on the other hand, the students must not be left with the impression that this is sufficient. They must be made to realize that even if all these conjectures were exactly correct (and they might well be so in this case), the graph itself could offer no confirmation of such exactness and that the only way the exact values can be known, or the estimates can be tested for exactness, is through solving simultaneously the equations of the two loci. It should be pointed out also that this observational method cannot bring to light the essential relations between the form of the equation and the general and special properties of the curve.

This is but a single example of the fundamental limitations inherent in this point-by-point plotting of the graphs of equations. Its weakness is that it does not utilize algebraic considerations to determine the characteristics of the locus or to relate them to the form of the equation. It should be explained that the objective of the course is to learn how to apply analytic methods which are at the same time less tedious, more powerful, and more revealing than those of point-by-point plotting and mere observational analysis of graphs. Such analytic methods can bring to light not only the exact coordinates of intersection points but also such characteristics as the coordinates of intercepts, limitations on the extent of the locus if such limitations exist, symmetry or lack of symmetry with respect to either axis, and discontinuities in the case of horizontal or vertical asymptotes.

Determining the Equation of a Locus. The general problem of setting up the equation of a locus which is described geometrically usually implies an ordered sequence of steps. The details are sometimes a bit complicated but the pattern is not, at least in the case of the simpler loci studied in elementary analytic geometry.

The first step consists in making a suitable sketch or working drawing. This is done by drawing a pair of axes to represent the coordinate plane, sketching in all given fixed points or lines with their coordinates or equations shown, drawing in a representative point of the locus with variable coordinates (x,y) indicated, and drawing suitable line segments connecting the point (x,y) with the fixed points or lines described in the given conditions. Lengths of these segments may now be denoted (often through their projections on the axes) in terms of the coordinates of the fixed points and the general point of the locus, or in terms of the distances of the general point (x, y) from given fixed lines.

Once these details are depicted in a reasonably good sketch, it is not difficult to translate the required conditions from their verbal form into an equation. This equation will always involve the coordinates of the representative point of the locus and the coordinates of some given fixed point or points described in the initial conditions. The actual setting up of the equation in this manner constitutes the second and final step; for the simpler loci it is usually an easy matter. Ordinarily it will involve distances which will be denoted on the sketch and which are either to be equated to each other or set into an equation with given constants. Once the student has identified these distances on the sketch and has noted their forms in terms of coordinates, it is a simple matter to translate them directly into the required equation.

The essential simplicity of this procedure, however, may not be immediately apparent to the students. Through their very familiarity with the subject, teachers are prone to assume too much on this score. These ideas are still new and unfamiliar to most students, and it cannot be assumed that the students will assimilate and use them successfully without help. A few who have unusual perception and insight will have no difficulty, but for most students the topic will probably require careful and repeated explanation, pointed questions, numerous illustrations, and a considerable amount of supervised practice with well-chosen problems.

Example. Determine the equation of the locus of points the sum of whose distances from two fixed points is 10 units.

$$\text{Distance from } P_1 + \text{distance from } P_2 = 10$$
$$d_1 + d_2 = 10$$
$$\sqrt{(x - x_1)^2 + (y - y_1)^2} + \sqrt{(x - x_2)^2 + (y - y_2)^2} = 10$$

Thus the equation is set up without difficulty. To be sure, it is not yet in its simplest form, but the rest is a matter of routine algebraic detail which can be carried on as such, without any further immediate concern about geometric considerations.

One other matter which may well be clarified at this time is the question, which some student will probably ask: "Why shouldn't we write $d_2 = \sqrt{(x_2 - x)^2 + (y - y_2)^2}$ instead of $\sqrt{(x - x_2)^2 + (y - y_2)^2}$?" This often bothers students, and the question is a good one which deserves careful attention. There are two ways of answering it. One is that d_1 and d_2 are thought of here as undirected distances, so we are concerned only with the absolute values of their components, and $|x - x_1| = |x_1 - x|$.

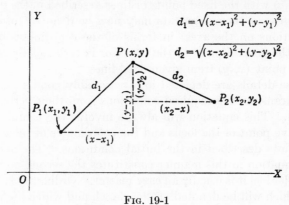

FIG. 19-1

In this case, then, the order of the subscripts makes no difference. If we were concerned with d_1 and d_2 as directed distances with correspondingly directed components, the forms $x_2 - x$ and $y_2 - y$ would be the proper ones to use so long as the point P was in a position such as that shown in the diagram above. In this case, for example, $x - x_1$ would be positive, while $x - x_2$ would be negative. It should be pointed out, however, that P might be in such a position that both $x - x_1$ and $x - x_2$ could both be positive, or both negative. In any case, since only the squares of these distances are involved, the order of subscripts would be immaterial, because obviously $(x - x_2)^2 = (x_2 - x)^2$. Since this is true, by keeping the subscripts in the same order, the form of the equation is made somewhat simpler and easier to remember.

There is one other matter that should be discussed in connection with this problem. It should be pointed out that in the above diagram the positions of P, P_1, and P_2 were taken essentially at random and so lead to the most general form of the equation. However, unless the coordinates of the fixed point are definitely specified, no harm is done by taking the axes in the most convenient position with respect to the given points. This is usually done in textbooks in developing the type form of the equation for this locus.   If the given points P_1 and P_2 are taken on an axis with the origin midway between them, then the form of the equation is simplified and important properties of the locus come to light readily from inspection of the equation.

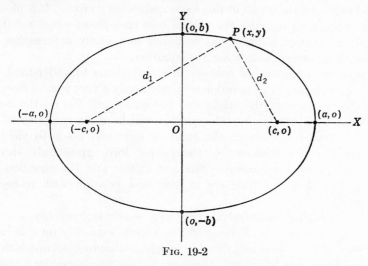

Fɪɢ. 19-2

Thus, by using conventional notation and assuming that d_1 and d_2 are not both zero, the fixed points may be designated as $(c,0)$ and $(-c,0)$, so that the distance between them is $2c$.   Then if the sum $d_1 + d_2$ is designated as $2a$ for convenience, we immediately have $d_1 + d_2 = 2a$, and, unless $d_1 = 0$ or $d_2 = 0$, this means that $2a > 2c$.   Then

$$d_1 + d_2 = 2a = \sqrt{(x + c)^2 + y^2} + \sqrt{(x - c)^2 + y^2}$$

By straight algebraic manipulation this yields the equation

$$\frac{x^2}{a^2} + \frac{y^2}{a^2 - c^2} = 1$$

and by designating $a^2 - c^2 = b^2$, the equation becomes $x^2/a^2 + y^2/b^2 = 1$.

Not only is this the simplest form for the equation of an ellipse, but the equation itself yields directly some important geometrical information about the locus.   If $|a| \neq |c|$ and if $y = 0$, the equation becomes $x^2/a^2 = 1$, which yields the coordinates of the vertexes as $(a,0)$ and $(-a,0)$.   If we take $x = 0$, we get $y = \pm b$, and we have the ordinates of the points where the locus intersects the y axis.   Thus with the equation in the form indicated above, the intercepts on the axes are known at a glance, and the coordinates of the foci are immediately determined from the defining relation $c = \sqrt{a^2 - b^2}$.   The extent of the locus is readily determined, since if $|x| > |a|$ or if $|y| > |b|$, the values of y and x, respectively, become imaginary. The form of the equation makes it clear that there are no horizontal or vertical asymptotes, and the absence of any odd powers of either variable shows that the locus is symmetrical with respect to both axes. Hence this equation provides immediately all information needed to sketch the graph of this locus and locate its foci. It is of interest, in passing, to consider the special case that arises when $c = 0$ and the ellipse becomes a circle and to notice how easily one reaches this conclusion by merely inspecting the equation.

It is most important, of course, for the students to understand that this simplest form of the equation represents only a very special case, i.e., when the center is at the origin and the major axis lies on the x axis. Under other circumstances the equation will be more complicated and can be thrown into this simple standard form and made to yield the geometrical information which the simple form gives only through the laborious work of referring the coordinates and the equation to a new system of axes which *are* in standard position with respect to the curve.

In the beginning most students need some supervised practice in setting up equations of loci. A little extra time spent explicitly on this in the early part of the course can develop insight and appreciation which will pay good dividends later on. The same insight which enables a student to translate geometrical conditions into algebraic equations is likely also to be a powerful aid to him in inferring geometrical conditions when the equations are given.

The Straight Line. The objectives for the study of the straight line may be set down as follows:

1. To understand that a straight line is uniquely determined if any of the following pairs of conditions is specified:
   a. Two fixed points through which it passes.
   b. One fixed point through which it passes with a given slope.
   c. Its intercepts on the two axes, provided these are not both zero. This is a special case of (a).
   d. Its slope and its intercept on one of the axes. This is a special case of (b).
   e. Its slope and its directed distance from the origin.
2. To know and be able to write or redevelop the type equation of a straight line for each of these sets of conditions.
3. To recognize and identify the equation of a straight line from the form and the characteristic constants in its equation.
4. To be able to convert the equation of a line from one type form into another type form.

Development of the formulas for the first four sets of conditions given under (1) should involve little difficulty; it requires only the proportionality property of similar triangles and the concept of slope as the tangent of the angle of inclination. Nearly all students can follow the details of these developments readily when they are given by the instructor. A good many, however, do not know how to proceed if they are called on to redevelop these formulas, and the common reason is that they do not have clearly in mind where the details are leading. They have seen the trees but not the forest. They have verified the details without sensing clearly the goal and the plan. If in their explanation instructors would rapidly sketch out the objective and the plan of each development before filling in the details, it would do much to clarify the derivations in the students' minds and give point and direction to the sequence of detailed steps.

Students should learn and use the names commonly given to these formulas: the two-point form, the point-slope form, the intercept form, the slope-intercept form, the normal form. These names are helpful in at least three ways. First, the name suggests the proper approach to the derivation of that particular formula because it indicates the geometric considerations which define the line and so suggests the form of equation which is stated in terms of those characteristics. Second, if a line is known to satisfy a given pair of independent conditions and if the student knows the various forms, the appropriate one can be written down at once. The given conditions can then be inserted to complete the equation of the particular line in question. Third, if the type form of a given equation can be recognized, the associated name suggests at once what geometrical characteristics of the line can be inferred directly from the equation.

Of course the importance of the type forms of the equation of a straight line lies not only in setting up specific equations from given geometric conditions but also in interpreting particular equations in terms of geometric properties of the locus. This consists in identifying certain constants in the equation directly with the particular geometric information which they afford. Thus the equation $y + 7 = (5/9)(x - 4)$ should yield at once the information that this particular line passes through the point $(4, -7)$ and that its slope is $5/9$. Students need practice in this sort of interpretation, but as a rule they get too little of it. Such interpretation can do a great deal to build understanding and appreciation of the geometrical significance of key elements in the equation of a locus, and this is one of the over-all objectives of analytic geometry. It need not take a great deal of time, but it does need to be given more attention than it has customarily received in the past.

The normal form for the equation of a straight line will require some special attention to both its derivation and its interpretation. Here a new element, the *normal axis*, is introduced, and along with it the meanings of the *normal intercept* and the *normal angle* (the angle of inclination of the normal axis). Different textbooks exhibit somewhat different methods of deriving the normal equation of a line. A few writers favor the use of direction cosines as the counterpart of what is done in solid analytic geometry, but most textbooks develop the formula in terms of the sine and cosine of the normal angle. These are subsequently transformed into terms of numbers which form the constants in the equivalent linear form of the equation.

Derivation of the normal form is not so simple as the derivation of the other four forms. Here the students may experience difficulty even in following some of the details. However, this difficulty again can be traced in large measure to their failing to sense the aim and the plan, i.e., to their failing to see what this form of the equation can tell them that the other forms cannot. This is one of the hard spots in this course, but the normal form is also one of the most important of all the formulas, since it gives the distance from a straight line to a given point. Few students can successfully get all that they should about it merely from the discussion in their textbooks. Whether the students are held responsible for redeveloping this formula or not, they need to know its form, understand the geometrical significance of its elements, and understand how to reduce an ordinary linear equation in two variables to its normal form in order to find the normal angle and the normal intercept of the straight line which it represents. These aims will be achieved about in proportion to the clearness of the instructor's explanations and the opportunity afforded to the students for interpretation of particular equations.

Families of Straight Lines: Parameters. The equation of any straight line, given in one of the standard forms, contains certain constants, and these constants determine which one of all the straight lines in the coordinate plane is represented by that equation. When all the necessary constants are explicitly given, the line is determined uniquely. For example, the equation $y = 7x - 2$ represents the one line whose slope is 7 and whose y intercept is -2. The equation $y = 7x + 1$ represents a different line. It has the same slope as the first one but a different y intercept. Similarly, the equation $y = 4x - 2$ represents still another line. This line has the same y intercept as the first one but a different slope.

The general form of the slope-intercept equation of a line is usually written $y = mx + b$, where m and b represent constants which in turn represent respectively the slope and the y intercept of the line. In this general form, however, it is not specified what constant values m and b have. Numerical values may be assigned to m and b at will, and the particular values assigned to them determine respectively the slope and the y intercept of the line. By assigning different values to b, we can arbitrarily represent many lines having different y intercepts. Similarly, by assigning different values to m, we can arbitrarily represent many lines having different slopes.   By keeping m fixed while assigning different values to b, we represent a set of lines having different y intercepts but the same slope.   In other words, we represent a set of parallel lines— one line for each value assigned to b.   On the other hand, if we keep b fixed but assign different values to m, we represent a set of lines all having the same y intercept but different slopes.   If m is allowed to take on all possible values while b is kept fixed, say at 2, then the equation $y = mx + 2$ represents all the lines in the plane (except, of course, the y axis, which has no slope) which pass through the point $(0,2)$.   For each value assigned to m, one particular line of this whole set is defined.   From similar considerations it is seen that, if m is kept fixed, say at $\frac{1}{2}$, while b is allowed to take on all possible values, then the equation $y = \frac{1}{2}x + b$ represents the set of all lines in the plane whose slope is $\frac{1}{2}$.

Letters such as m and b in the slope-intercept formula are called *arbitrary constants*, or *undetermined constants*, or *parameters* in the formulas. Whenever a slope-intercept equation contains a single such parameter, as, for example, $y = 7x + b$ or $y = mx + 5$, it represents a whole *set* or *system* or *family* of lines.   These will all differ in the one characteristic ascribable to that parameter, and they will all be alike in the characteristic determined by the fixed constant.   Such a system is a *one-parameter* family of lines.   If both m and b are allowed to take on all admissible values, we get a *two-parameter* family of lines which clearly includes every line in the plane except the y axis and those lines parallel to it.   No value for m can be ascribed to these lines.

These notions represent generalizations which are important for more than one reason.   In the first place, they are important because they *are* generalizations.   As such they can deepen the student's understanding and expand his mathematical horizons.   Moreover, if properly explained, they seem to fascinate many students and increase interest in the subject as a whole.   They afford unlimited opportunity and variety for illustrations which are easy to give and which can be most illuminating.   Then, too, the notions of parameters and families of loci are pervasive concepts which will play important roles later on in this and subsequent courses. They should be solidly established and firmly clinched here where they are first encountered.

The Circle.   Of all the loci studied in elementary analytic geometry, the circle probably offers the least difficulty to students.   Once they have grasped the idea of how the equations of loci are set up in terms of coordinates from given geometric conditions, they are not likely to experience difficulty either in setting up the equation from given geometric conditions or in inferring the essential geometric properties of the locus from its equation.

Once the coordinates of the center and the length of the radius are known, a sketch shows clearly that a single application of the distance formula is sufficient to give the equation. The right triangle constructed as shown in Fig. 19-3 here yields at once the equation

$$(x - h)^2 + (y - k)^2 = r^2$$

which is the generalized standard form in terms of these parameters. It is probably best to derive the equation in this generalized form first, and it should be pointed out that h, k, and r in this formula are parameters.

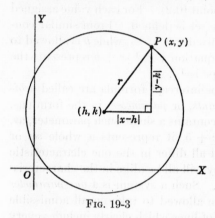

Fig. 19-3

The formula thus represents the family of all circles. This is a three-parameter family of circles.

When a fixed value is assigned to just one of these parameters, say to r, the equation still defines a family of circles in the plane, but this is a two-parameter family of circles because, although r is fixed, both h and k may take on any values whatever. It is the family of all circles lying in the plane and having a fixed radius but arbitrary centers. There are also one-parameter families of circles in the plane. For example, if r is arbitrary while both h and k are fixed, we get the family of concentric circles whose center is at (h,k). Thus when specific values are assigned to one or two of the three parameters, the family of circles defined by the equation is less inclusive than that defined when all three parameters are left arbitrary. On the other hand, when all three parameters are assigned particular values, a single or unique circle is defined. With these understandings established, it is easy for students to see why the simplest form of all is obtained when both h and k are assigned the value zero.

This, in turn, provides motivation for study of the translation of axes, which may well be undertaken at this time. It should involve no serious difficulty on the part of the students, provided the instructor makes three things clear: (1) the reason for making the translation (to simplify the equation of the locus), (2) the fact that the general coordinates (x,y) must now be replaced by expressions involving coordinates (x',y') referred to the new axes, and (3) why, in the case of the circle, these replacements are of the form $x = x' + h$, $y = y' + k$, where h and k are the coordinates of the center as referred to the original axes. Once these points are grasped, and with h and k being known, the translation is easily effected and the simplified equation is obtained.

It must be remembered, however, that this is but one side of the coin. Interpretation of the new equation is no less important than its derivation, and there can be little assurance of full understanding unless both receive proper emphasis. Suppose, for example, that the equation of a particular circle is given as $(x - 4)^2 + (y + 1)^2 = 26$ and that through the usual transformation procedures associated with the translation of axes the students arrive at the simpler equation $x'^2 + y'^2 = 26$. Unless they can interpret this new form correctly, little will have been gained. They need to be made to understand that this change in the form of the equation does not imply any change in the characteristics of the circle itself (the location of the center and the length of the radius) because these remain invariant for any particular circle; that $x'^2 + y'^2 = 26$ should be interpreted as $(x' - 0)^2 + (y' - 0)^2 = 26$, and that the constants in this equation and in the form $(x - 4)^2 + (y + 1)^2 = 26$ provide information about these characteristics when the circle is referred to certain axes and would provide different information if the circle were referred to other sets of respectively parallel axes; in a word, the students must understand that the equations $(x - 4)^2 + (y + 1)^2 = 26$ and $x'^2 + y'^2 = 26$ are merely two representations of the same circle when referred to two sets of respectively parallel axes one of which has its origin at the center of the circle.

There are certain problems associated with the study of circles which do sometimes prove troublesome for students. Among those which commonly are included in current textbooks may be mentioned the following:

1. Deriving the equation of the circle through three given points not on a line (understanding why it takes three such points to provide the necessary data, why these data are also sufficient, and why the routine work of deriving the equation takes the form it does)

2. Finding the equation of a family of circles through the points of intersection of two given circles

3. Finding the length of a tangent to a given circle from a given point outside the circle

This catalog of associated problems is by no means exhaustive but it is representative. It may be expected that each of the problems mentioned will prove troublesome to some students. Also, it is almost certain that trouble with such problems stems from lack of insight, i.e., from failure to understand what the problem really is, what the given conditions imply, and what the plan is for using what is known to establish what is required.

To explain the approach to these problems successfully, attention should be focused first on the things of major concern rather than upon details of notation. By rapidly sketching out the problem and the plan of attack in broad, bold, rapid strokes, it should be possible to get across to the students a basic understanding of both in a very short time. The explanation may be lacking in elegance, and it may be superficial from the standpoint of rigor and completeness of detail. Elegance and rigor can come later. The important consideration at the moment is that the explanation shall present clearly and as simply as possible the essential considerations and the line of argument leading to the conclusion or solution. Any student who has a modicum of skill in algebraic technique can fill in the necessary details and the proper notation once the essential framework has been built in his mind. Textbooks, however, too seldom use this approach. Authors do not always bother to make clear this framework and plan at the outset, and this is probably responsible for much of the trouble which students experience in this subject. Most

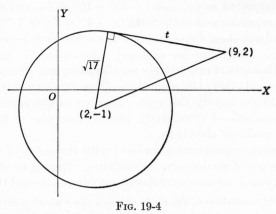

Fig. 19-4

students can supply necessary detail to complete a proof or to solve a problem when they have the plan of work well in mind more successfully than they can discover the plan by studying the detail.

As a single example of a broad quick outline of a plan, we shall consider the problem of finding the length of a tangent, say, from the point $(9,2)$ to the circle $(x - 2)^2 + (y + 1)^2 = 17$. A sketch can be quickly made to show that the required distance t is merely one leg of a right triangle, Fig. 19-4. The length of the other leg, being the radius of the circle, is known, and the length of the hypotenuse can be found immediately by use of the distance formula. It is clear then that

$$t^2 + (\text{radius})^2 = (\text{hypotenuse})^2,$$

and this equation can easily be solved to give the length t which is required.

This explanation can be given in about two minutes at the chalkboard. It involves no subtleties. There is no need for students to ask, "Why do you do it that way?" It lays out the essential plan for attacking this problem in simple, familiar terms, and once the students grasp the plan they should have no trouble in supplying the details needed for the numerical solution.

The Conic Sections.   Study of the conic sections has traditionally occupied a place of prominence in analytic geometry.   It represents an important class of loci, and the study of these loci affords excellent opportunity for applying analytic methods as well as for determining the properties of the loci and their equations.   The latter should include awareness of both the common characteristics which bind them together in a class and the special characteristics which distinguish them from each other.

If the coordinate axes are chosen to give the equations of these loci in simplest form, if the definitions are given very clearly and are supplemented by good illustrations, and if the geometrical meanings and the notation of the characteristic elements are made perfectly clear, then any intelligent student should attain these objectives without serious difficulty.   The explanations of the instructor, however, are very important here, as, indeed, they are throughout this course.   Many students do not read very effectively.   Moreover, diagrams in the textbooks are necessary and good as far as they go, but they are static.   It is hard even to suggest motion and variation in a textbook diagram.   On the other hand this can be done well by the instructor sketching at the blackboard and actually building the diagram and discussing it at the same time. In this way he can give the locus a dynamic character and can highlight the things he wants to emphasize much more effectively than an author can simply by placing an already-made diagram in the textbook.   Thus the ability of the instructor to "chalk-talk" effectively is a tremendous asset, and it can do a great deal to promote understanding and facilitate learning.

There is practically complete uniformity among textbooks in their definitions of the parabola, which invariably seem to be in terms of the equality of two distances.   The ellipse and the hyperbola are initially defined in most textbooks in terms of the sum or difference of two distances, but this is not always the case.   Some authors prefer to define first the eccentricity in terms of the *ratio* of two distances and then the ellipse and hyperbola in terms of the eccentricity.   Doubtless each of these approaches has its advantages, and it is not possible to state categorically that either is better than any other.

Logically the two approaches have equal validity.   From the viewpoint of the immature learner there are some considerations which seem to favor the former.   Perhaps this is because the sum or difference of two distances can be visualized and apprehended more readily than their ratio.   Also, this way of defining these loci stresses the fact, from the outset, that an ellipse or hyperbola has two foci.   On the other hand, the directrixes play no part in this definition.   In contrast, the second approach ensures that these concepts are established at the outset but gives no hint of the important property upon which the first definition is based.   If time permits, it is well, at least for one of these curves, to give derivations from both definitions and to point out that the equations and the properties at which one arrives in the two cases are equivalent.

Study of the hyperbola involves some special features which have to be given special attention.   In the ellipse both axes terminate in the curve itself; in the hyperbola they do not.   Moreover, in the ellipse the major axis (the segment joining the vertices) is always longer than the minor axis; their counterparts (the transverse and conjugate axes) in the hyperbola are not subject to this condition.   The length of the conjugate axis can be depicted only by means of an auxiliary rectangle which in turn is determined by the curve and its asymptotes.   The asymptotes themselves and their relation to the locus require special definition and study, and the considerations involved are often troublesome to students.   The directrixes of a hyperbola lie between the vertexes, but the vertexes of an ellipse lie between the directrixes.   Every hyperbola has associated with it a conjugate hyperbola, but there is no counterpart of this for the ellipse.

Students sometimes forget or confuse these numerous and special characteristics and the conventional notation generally used.   It has been found helpful to have them make type diagrams showing these things geometrically in typical form and actually refer to these diagrams if they need to do so when working problems.   A specimen diagram of this sort is shown in Fig. 19-5.

The general equation of the second degree in x and y takes the form $Ax^2 + Bxy + Cy^2 + Dx + Ey + F = 0$, and always represents a conic section or a degenerate or limiting case of a conic, provided A, B, and C are not all zero.   In an equation of this kind the coefficients can reveal much information about the nature of the locus, sometimes even through casual examination, if the students have been taught how to discover it. This fact needs to be emphasized.   Thus if $B = 0$ while A and C are not equal and neither is zero, the curve will be an ellipse or hyperbola.   If A and C have like signs, the curve will be an ellipse; if they have unlike signs, the curve will be a hyperbola.   In either case the principal axes of the locus will be parallel to the coordinate axes.   If $B = 0$ and either $A = 0$ or $C = 0$ but not both, the curve is a parabola with its axis parallel to one of the coordinate axes.

On the other hand, if $B \neq 0$, then the locus is a conic with its principal axis inclined at some angle θ to the x axis.   In such cases the product term can be removed and the equation correspondingly simplified by the transformation known as rotation of axes.   This is not inherently difficult, but it is a long, laborious process if done by direct substitution

of the transformation formulas and the subsequent algebraic work necessary to determine the angle θ for which $B = 0$.   The labor of simplifying
such equations can be greatly reduced by having the students use the
not-too-well-known   relation $\tan 2\theta = B/(A - C)$.   This   should   be
proved, of course, and most textbooks contain proofs of this theorem,
but the relation is often neglected, even though it provides an efficient
means for simplifying such equations.

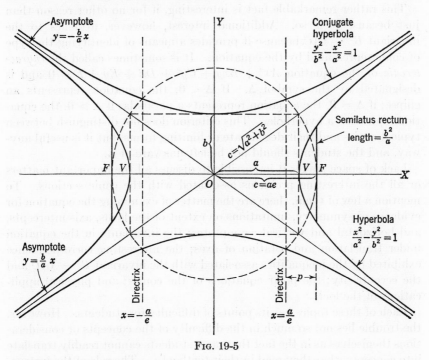

Asymptote
$y=-\frac{b}{a}x$

Conjugate
hyperbola
$\frac{y^2}{b^2}-\frac{x^2}{a^2}=1$

Semilatus rectum
length $=\frac{b^2}{a}$

$c=\sqrt{a^2+b^2}$

$c=ae$

Hyperbola
$\frac{x^2}{a^2}-\frac{y^2}{b^2}=1$

Asymptote
$y=\frac{b}{a}x$

Directrix

Directrix

$x=-\frac{a}{e}$

$x=\frac{a}{e}$

Fig. 19-5

With one exception[1] both the translation and rotation of axes have the
effect of changing the coordinates of every point on the locus, and consequently of changing the form of the equation of the locus.   On the other
hand, these transformations do not change the metric or geometrical
properties of the locus at all.   These properties are said to be *invariant*
under the transformations indicated.   It is also true that, when the equation is written in the general form

$$Ax^2 + Bxy + Cy^2 + Dx + Ey + F = 0$$

the values of certain expressions involving some of the coefficients remain

[1] The single exception is that the coordinates of the origin are not changed under
rotation about the origin.

unaltered by these transformations. Thus the coefficients of the second-degree terms are invariant under the translation of axes. Under rotation, the sum of the coefficients $A + C$ of the terms in x^2 and y^2 is invariant, and the value of the expression $B^2 - 4AC$ is also invariant under rotation. In view of the fact, noted above, that A, B, and C are individually invariant under translation, it follows that the values of the expressions $A + C$ and $B^2 - 4AC$ are invariants under both transformations.

This rather remarkable fact is interesting, if for no other reason than just because it is so. Additional interest, however, attaches to the invariant $B^2 - 4AC$ because it provides a means of identifying the type of conic represented by the equation. It is sometimes called the *characteristic* of the equation $Ax^2 + Bxy + Cy^2 + Dx + Ey + F = 0$ and is designated by the symbol Δ. If $\Delta < 0$, the equation represents an ellipse; if $\Delta = 0$, the equation represents a parabola; if $\Delta > 0$, the equation represents a hyperbola. This criterion does not distinguish between typical conics and their degenerate or limiting forms, but it is useful anyway, and the students should not be left unaware of it.

Lack of space makes it impossible to discuss all the important matters or all the interesting problems associated with the conic sections. To mention a few of them, there are the matter of examining the equation for evidence of symmetry, limitations on extent of the locus, axis intercepts, and horizontal and vertical asymptotes; the invariants in the equation under translation and rotation of axes; the interesting correspondence exhibited by the inequalities associated with the invariant $B^2 - 4AC$ and the eccentricity; the polar equations of the conics; and physical applications of the loci.

Each of these topics has its points of difficulty for students. However, the trouble lies not so much in the difficulty of the concepts or considerations themselves as in the fact that most students cannot readily translate into concepts what they read in their textbooks. The role of the instructor as an expositor in helping to make these ideas emerge and stand out is most important. The instructor who is able to highlight key ideas and help his students crystallize them and make them stand out in their minds will have contributed greatly to their understanding.

The many interesting aspects and properties of the conics could easily lead one to devote a disproportionate amount of time to their study. It must not be forgotten, however, that there are other parts of the course which are also interesting and important and which must not be neglected. Therefore, in the study of the conic sections it may be necessary at times to sacrifice the merely interesting to make time for things that are relatively more important in relation to subsequent work.

Polar Coordinates. Probably the key to success in working with polar coordinates and polar equations is to develop clear understandings of the meaning and terminology and the relations between polar and rectangular coordinate systems.   To this end it is a good thing to start by sketching a set of axes as for an ordinary rectangular system and putting in a single point P in a representative position, giving it the usual rectangular coordinates (x,y).   The pole and the polar axis are identified with the origin and the positive half of the x axis.   The line segment joining P with the origin is the radius vector r, and the angle it makes with the polar axis is the vectorial angle θ.   Reference to the diagram, Fig. 19-6, gives at once the fundamental relations between the two systems of coordinates.   It

FIG. 19-6

should be pointed out, however, that whereas the rectangular coordinates of a point are unique, the polar coordinates are not.   For example, the point whose rectangular coordinates are (1,1) has infinitely many pairs of polar coordinates: $(\sqrt{2},45°)$, $(\sqrt{2},405°)$, $(\sqrt{2},-315°)$, $(-\sqrt{2},225°)$, etc.

With these things in mind students should easily convert an equation from rectangular form to polar form simply by making the appropriate substitutions.   Thus $y^2 = 3 + 6x$ becomes $(r \sin \theta)^2 = 3 + 6(r \cos \theta)$. In similar fashion one may convert an equation from polar form to rectangular form.   Thus $r = 10 \cos \theta$ becomes $\sqrt{x^2 + y^2} = 10x/\sqrt{x^2 + y^2}$, whence $x^2 + y^2 - 10x = 0$.

It is usually easier for students to make these conversions than to plot the graphs of equations in polar form.   Typically, constructing a graph requires a point-by-point plotting of enough points to give a good sketch of the locus, and this in turn requires the construction of a table of values of θ and r.   Except for the simplest equations this table may need several columns.   For example, let it be required to plot the graph of

$$r = 1 + 4 \cos 2\theta$$

The table should be similar to the accompanying one.

θ	2θ	$\cos 2\theta$	$4 \cos 2\theta$	$1 + 4 \cos 2\theta$
0°	0°	1	4	5
30°	60°	½	2	3
45°	90°	0	0	1
60°	120°	−½	−2	−1
		etc.		

A good many students have to be shown how to plan and construct such a table. Also, they frequently need to be reminded that, as in the present case, even if r is given as a function of 2θ, the values of r must be plotted against the corresponding values of θ itself, and not against the values of 2θ. The use of polar-coordinate paper facilitates the actual plotting, though good sketches can often be made by use of a protractor or even by careful estimates of the sizes of the angles.

Certain additional considerations may be helpful to students in determining characteristics of some loci given in polar coordinates, and they should be explained to students:

1. If r occurs only in the form r^2, then the curve will be symmetrical with respect to the pole.

2. If an equivalent equation is obtained when θ is replaced by $180° - \theta$, then the curve is symmetrical with respect to the 90° axis. An example of this situation occurs with the locus of the equation $r = 3 \sin \theta$.

3. If an equivalent equation is obtained when θ is replaced by $-\theta$, then the curve is symmetrical with respect to the polar axis. Thus the locus of $r = 3 \cos \theta$ is symmetrical in this way.

4. The intercepts on the lines whose equations are $\theta = 0°$, 90°, 180°, 270°, and 360° can usually be found readily.

5. Sometimes values of θ for which r becomes infinite can be found easily, and this fact may be very helpful in sketching.

6. Finding maximum and minimum values of r, with the corresponding values of θ, can be helpful in determining the extent of the curve. Limitations on the extent of the curve may also often be determined by solving the equation for r in terms of θ to see whether there are any values of θ that will make r imaginary. Thus, for the locus $r^2 = \cos \theta$ we find that r is imaginary for $90° < \theta < 270°$.

7. Sometimes the form of the locus is revealed by converting the equation from polar to rectangular form. Thus the equation $r = 10 \cos \theta$ becomes

$$x^2 + y^2 = 10x$$

which is clearly the equation of a circle.

To determine points of intersection of the graphs of two polar equations, one may solve the equations simultaneously for the two variables, as is done with equations in rectangular form. However, in seeking common solutions for two polar equations it is always advisable to plot the graphs of the equations. This may suggest at once solutions that can be tested directly in the equations. But even more importantly, it will sometimes reveal one or more points of intersection that are not brought to light in the algebraic solution of the equations. A simple example of this is the pair of equations $r = 2 \sin \theta$ and $r = 2 \cos \theta$. Algebraic solution gives $\tan \theta = 1$, $\theta = 45°$, $r = 2$. Thus it yields only a single point of intersection, $(2,45°)$. The graph will show, however, that the pole also lies on both curves.

Parametric Equations. The one concept which will be essentially new or unfamiliar to students when they take up the study of parametric equations is the notion of a parameter. In previous work there has been exhibited a direct relation between the independent and dependent variables, the one being expressible as a function of the other. It is not at all hard for students to recognize that each of the original variables, say x and y, may in certain cases be defined as some function of a third variable; it simply is a new idea to which they need to become accustomed. The best way to bring about this feeling of familiarity is by having tables and graphs made for several rather simple cases. Such pairs of equations as $x = t$, $y = 1/t$ or $x = t^2$, $y = 3 + t$ can be used to illustrate how the table of values is to be formed and the corresponding values of x and y are to be used to plot points on the locus.

Converting a pair of parametric equations into an equivalent equation in rectangular form by eliminating the parameter is usually interesting to students. It strengthens the feeling of a direct relation between the original variables, even though it may not be apparent in the parametric forms in which they are both expressed. For some loci this rectangular form of the equation may be very simple. For example, the parametric equations $x = 5 \cos \theta$, $y = 5 \sin \theta$ yield the equation $x^2 + y^2 = 25$, which is recognizable immediately as a circle with center at the origin and radius 5 units. But even though the rectangular form will not always be simple, it is well worthwhile to have students work out a number of such cases as a means of giving explicit form to the implicit relation between the original variables. A useful by-product of this is some excellent incidental practice in algebraic manipulation and equation solving.

Students often ask, "Why use the parametric form at all? Why not simply use the rectangular form?" In answer to this question it should be pointed out that there may be several possible advantages in using the parametric equations. For one thing, the parametric equations may sometimes convey more information than the rectangular equations, as in the case of the trajectory of a projectile. Thus they are often needed in physics and engineering. Again, in calculus the derivatives of some functions can be obtained more easily from parametric equations of the loci than from the rectangular equations. However, the principal reason for the use of parametric equations in analytic geometry lies in the fact that for certain loci the parametric equations are simpler than the rectangular equations. Indeed, for some loci parametric equations can be set up directly from the geometrical descriptions of the loci, although it may be impossible to set up the rectangular equations for the loci directly. In such cases the rectangular equation may be derived from the parametric equations if the parameter can be eliminated. The cycloid curves are fairly simple examples of such loci.

Loci in Three-dimensional Space. Lack of time usually imposes severe limitations on the study of space loci in analytic geometry, and justice can be done to this topic only in a separate course. At the same time it is highly desirable that some topics from three-dimensional geometry be included in the elementary course. In particular, if time permits, it is desirable to give some attention to the analytic geometry of the straight line, the plane, cylindrical surfaces and projections on the coordinate planes, surfaces of revolution, and discussion of surfaces from their traces and their intercepts. This admittedly is a large order, and it can be regarded as realistic only if time is economized in the earlier part of the course, but it is a worthwhile goal to attempt to reach.

There are a good many places in solid analytic geometry where students may be expected to have difficulty. Many of these difficulties stem from three general limitations which are common to many students: (1) poor space imagination and inability to visualize three-dimensional figures well, (2) inability to sketch good diagrams to represent space configurations realistically, and (3) difficulty in translating given geometric conditions into algebraic form and in interpreting the latter in terms of the former. Lacking adequate skill in these things, students are tempted to rely on sheer memorization, and this contributes nothing to understanding. There are, of course, certain formulas which do need to be memorized in the interest of economy, but to memorize a formula without understanding how it is derived and what it means is of little lasting benefit. The ability of the instructor to draw good diagrams and to explain how the formulas are derived, what they mean, and how they are used is of crucial importance.

Textbooks on analytic geometry are remarkably uniform in respect to the topics of solid analytic geometry which they include. These may be listed substantially as follows:

General

Projections of a line segment on the coordinate axes
Distance between two points
Direction cosines of a straight line
Direction numbers of a straight line

Angle between two lines
Conditions for parallel and perpendicular lines
Definition of a locus in space

The Plane

Normal equation of a plane
General equation of a plane
Conditions for parallel and perpendicular planes
Intercepts and traces of a plane
Angle between two planes
Distance from a plane to a point
Intercept equation of a plane

The Straight Line

Projection equations of a line
Symmetric equations of a line
Two-point equations of a line

Nonplanar Surfaces

Cylindrical surfaces; projecting cylinders
Surfaces of revolution
Quadric surfaces in standard position
Study of surfaces through their traces and their intercepts

There is a high degree of essential sequence in the development of these topics, and thorough development of all of them would require more time than is available in many cases.   Often a choice may be forced upon the instructor, and such a choice is not easy.   It would require careful weighing of the topics with respect to their relative importance in future use.   From this viewpoint the following would surely find a place among those chosen: (1) the general forms and significance of the equations of the plane, cylindrical surfaces, and the standard quadric surfaces; (2) the characteristics of a surface of revolution, as these are exhibited through the equation of the surface; (3) the study of surfaces through study of their intercepts and their traces in the coordinate planes and in other, parallel planes.

Solid analytic geometry is rather hard for most students.   Nearly every topic will have its potential difficulties.   In view of the pressure of time, it is especially important that the instructor examine each topic in detail and plan his discussion to highlight the important ideas, bypass the nonessential ideas, and try to find ways to make the hard parts understandable.

Analytic Geometry and Calculus.   Since about the middle of the century there has been a growing tendency to merge analytic geometry and calculus into a single course.   Actually, some attempts at this were made even earlier, but the effort has become more pronounced since that time, and the movement has been marked by the appearance of a number of textbooks. The close relation of the two subjects and the role of analytic geometry in calculus provides a strong argument for such a combination. The principal advantages claimed for fusing the two into a single course appear to be about as follows:

1. It makes possible an earlier introduction of some of the fundamental notions, techniques, and applications of calculus, thus making calculus available as an instrument for the study of physics earlier than would otherwise be the case.

2. Certain parts of the work in analytic geometry itself can be simplified by the use of derivatives.

3. Many of the topics of analytic geometry that are needed in calculus can be taken up just before they are needed, and in this way time can be gained.

4. The simultaneous study of the two subjects gives the students a feeling of their interrelation.

These arguments present a good case for a combined course, and there is some evidence that it is being viewed with increasing favor. However, upon examination of some of the textbooks, it is not always apparent that there is much organic correlation of the two subjects. Frequently the parts on analytic geometry are distinctly subordinated to the calculus, and sometimes their relation to immediately subsequent parts of the calculus is far from clear. Probably the intention in these books is to consider the calculus course as the prime objective and develop only such parts of the analytic geometry as are needed for the calculus. Undoubtedly some time can be saved in such an arrangement.

It can be expected that the combined course will be tried out extensively in the years ahead, and that new and better textbooks will appear. Eventually more will be known about the merits of the combined course than is known now. In the meantime, and until there is clear evidence of the superiority of such a course, analytic geometry and calculus will undoubtedly continue to be offered widely as separate courses.

EXERCISES

1. Why should stress be laid on the concept of *ordered* pairs of numbers in connection with the coordinates of points in a plane, and of *ordered* triples of numbers in connection with the coordinates of a point in three-space?

2. Give a brief but clear exposition of the derivation of the formula for the distance from one point to another in terms of the coordinates of these points (*a*) in a plane and (*b*) in three-dimensional space. Use the chalkboard and make clear the importance of the notion of the projection of one line on another in this connection.

3. Explain the derivation of the general point-of-division formulas for the coordinates of a point dividing a given line segment in a given ratio. Show why the midpoint formulas are merely special cases of the general formulas.

4. One main problem of analytic geometry is to infer certain geometric properties of loci from the equations of these loci without actually drawing the graphs.   Give an example.   Point out what elements of the equation provide geometric information directly and list information they provide.

5. What advantage is there in reducing the equations of straight lines, circles, and conic sections to standard forms?   Illustrate the advantage.

6. Describe the loci represented by the following equations:

$$y = \tfrac{3}{4}x - 2 \qquad x/5 + y/8 = 1 \qquad (x - 5)^2 + (y + 2)^2 = 9$$

7. It has been said that one really understands the method of analytic geometry when and only when he has attained a genuine appreciation of the interrelations between loci and their equations.   Comment on this.

8. Explain and illustrate the steps to be taken in setting up the equation of a locus when the geometrical conditions are specified.

9. Set up the equation for the locus of a point which is three units further from the point $(2,3)$ than it is from the point $(9,6)$.   Follow the outline of steps described in the preceding exercise.

10. If (x_1,y_1) and (x_2,y_2) are two points, the distance between them can be found by using either of these formulas: $d^2 = (x_1 - x_2)^2 + (y_1 - y_2)^2$ or $d^2 = (x_2 - x_1)^2 + (y_2 - y_1)^2$.   Explain why the order of the subscripts makes no difference in this case.

11. What geometric information about a conic section is yielded by the equation $x^2/a^2 + y^2/(a^2 - c^2) = 1$?   Be explicit.

12. Write the five type forms for the equation of a straight line.   In each of these identify the two parameters and explain what information each parameter gives about the line.

13. What advantage is there in knowing how to write or how to interpret the equation of a straight line in the various forms called for in exercise 12.   Be specific.

14. Write the intercept form and the slope-intercept form for the equation of the line $7x + 2y + 1 = 0$.   What geometric information would each provide?

15. Derive the normal form for the equation of a straight line and interpret it. Illustrate your interpretation by an example.

16. Describe the locus of points represented by each of the following: $y = 3 + \tfrac{1}{2}x$, $y < 3 + \tfrac{1}{2}x$; $y > 3 + \tfrac{1}{2}x$; $y \leqq 3 + \tfrac{1}{2}x$.

17. Why does the family of lines represented by $y = mx + b$ not include the y axis or any straight line perpendicular to the x axis?   Does it include all other straight lines in the plane?   Explain.

18. Write the equation of the family of circles whose centers are at $(-3,8)$.

19. Describe the family of circles represented by the inequality

$$(x - 5)^2 + (y - 2)^2 \leqq 4$$

20. Describe the family of circles represented by the inequality

$$(x - a)^2 + (y - b)^2 \neq 12$$

Does this include all circles in the plane?

21. Explain how to find the length of a tangent from a fixed point to a given circle whose equation is given.

22. What is meant by the eccentricity of a conic section?   What is the numerical value of the eccentricity of a circle?

23. The general equation of the second degree in x and y can be written in the form $Ax^2 + Bxy + Cy^2 + Dx + Ey + F = 0$.   Give the name of the locus in each of the following cases: $B = 0$, $A > 0$, $C < 0$; $B = 0$, $A = C$; $B = 0$, $A > 0$,

$C > 0$, $A \neq C$; $B = 0$, $C = 0$, $A \neq 0$. Are the principal axes of all these curves necessarily parallel to the coordinate axes?

24. In the general equation above, let $B \neq 0$ and $A \neq C$. What information does this provide about the principal axis of the curve? Can the curve be a circle?

25. Derive and explain the transformation formulas for the translation of axes. For what purposes are these used in simplifying equations of the second degree in two unknowns? Illustrate.

26. Derive and explain the transformation formulas for the rotation of axes. For what purpose are these used?

27. What is meant by saying that the geometric or metric properties of a locus are invariant under translation and rotation of axes?

28. The expression $B^2 - 4AC$ is invariant under these transformations. Explain how the value of this invariant provides a means for identifying at once the kind of conic section represented by any particular equation of the second degree in x and y.

29. Take the equation of some locus given in rectangular coordinates and translate it into polar coordinates.

30. Translate the equation $r = 5 - 3 \cos \theta$ into rectangular coordinates. Note that the polar equation is the simpler of the two.

31. Assume that you are teaching a course in analytic geometry and that you have time for about twelve lessons on solid analytic geometry at the end of the course. What topics do you think you would include?

32. Much of the study of three-dimensional surfaces is made through studying the intercepts of these surfaces on the axes and the traces of these surfaces in the coordinate planes and planes parallel to the coordinate planes. Take the equation of some nonplanar surface and show how this can be done.

BIBLIOGRAPHY

Ballard, Joe R.: The Line, Circle, and Parabola Using Complex Numbers, *Pentagon*, **13** (1954), 91–95.

Bourne, Samuel: Coordinate Geometry from the Vector Point of View, *American Mathematical Monthly*, **59** (1952), 245–248.

Boyer, C. B.: History of Analytic Geometry, *Scripta Mathematica* (1956).

Bureau of Secondary Curriculum Development, "Mathematics 10-11-12" (Albany, N.Y.: The State Education Department, 1959), pp. 12, 19, 30–32, 69, 72–74.

Commission on Mathematics, Report of: "Program for College Preparatory Mathematics" (New York: College Entrance Examination Board, 1959), pp. 25–28.

————: "Appendices" (New York: College Entrance Examination Board, 1959), pp. 36–58, 120–139.

Gallego-Diaz, J.: A Note on the Conics, *American Mathematical Monthly*, **66** (1959), 225–228.

Greenspan, Donald: On Rapid Sketching of Polar Curves, *Mathematics Teacher*, **50** (1957), 267–271.

Karst, O. J.: Two Methods for Finding the Angle of Rotation, *American Mathematical Monthly*, **63** (1956), 416–417.

Lange, Luise: Deriving the Equations of the Sections of a Cone, *American Mathematical Monthly*, **63** (1956), 488–491.

Porges, Arthur: The Rotation of Axes, *American Mathematical Monthly*, **64** (1957), 37.

————: Rapid Sketching of a Conic, *American Mathematical Monthly*, **64** (1957), 41–42.

20

THE TEACHING OF CALCULUS

Except for a few scattered articles in one or two professional magazines, very little has been written on the teaching of calculus. This is doubtless due to the fact that calculus has always been regarded as essentially a college subject. For various reasons efforts looking toward the improvement of the teaching of mathematics have been very largely confined to the courses of the elementary school and the junior and senior high schools. The journals dealing with college mathematics give expositions of subject matter but rarely concern themselves with pedagogical considerations.

That this should be so is not hard to understand. In general, college students are presumed to be intellectually more mature and more highly selected than students in the junior or senior high schools and may reasonably be expected to assume more responsibility for the mastery of their work. The subject matter which they study is increasingly rigorous and exacting. Most important of all, their instructors have, as a rule, far more extensive academic training than the teachers in the lower schools. Their viewpoints are more specialized, and they tend to be more interested in the logical aspects of their courses than in the manner in which the subject matter is most effectively learned. For these reasons, among others, the literature on the teaching of mathematics has included very little discussion of the teaching of college mathematics.

On the other hand, the mortality among students of college mathematics is relatively high. It is probably higher than it needs to be, and higher than it would be if instructors would give more attention to the careful development of the various topics, to diagnosis and remedial teaching, and to a study of the particular difficulties which are characteristically encountered by their students. Calculus, in particular, has acquired the reputation of being extremely difficult, and many students approach it with fear and trembling. That it involves substantial difficulties nobody would deny, but most of them can be considerably mitigated by good teaching.

Calculus in the High School. Since the turn of the century, various leaders in mathematical education have advocated that elements of the calculus be introduced in the last year of the senior high school. It was not contemplated that this work should comprise the complete course in differential and integral calculus usually offered in the junior college. Obviously, such a course would require more adequate mastery of algebra, trigonometry, and analytic geometry than could be reasonably expected at the end of the eleventh grade. Rather, the idea is that just as there are certain parts of trigonometry that are simple enough to be successfully understood by junior high school students, so there are certain parts of calculus which can be understood by twelfth-grade students, even if they do not have all the prerequisites for a complete systematic course.

This position was well stated in the suggestions of the National Committee on Mathematical Requirements regarding calculus in the high school:[1]

In connection with the recommendations concerning the calculus, such questions as the following may arise: Why should a college subject like this be added to a high school program? How can it be expected that high school teachers will have the necessary training and attainments for teaching it? Will not the attempt to teach such a subject result in loss of thoroughness in earlier work? Will anything be gained beyond a mere smattering of the theory? Will the boy or girl ever use the information or training secured? The subsequent remarks are intended to answer such objections as these and to develop more fully the point of view of the committee in recommending the inclusion of elementary work in the calculus in the high school program.

By the calculus we mean for the present a study of *rates* of change. In nature all things change. How much do they change in a given time? How fast do they change? Do they increase or decrease? When does a changing quantity become largest or smallest? How can rates of changing quantities be compared?

These are some of the questions which lead us to study the elementary calculus. Without its essential principles these questions cannot be answered with definiteness.

The following are a few of the specific replies that might be given in answer to the questions listed at the beginning of this note: The difficulties of the college calculus lie mainly outside the boundaries of the proposed work. The elements of the subject present less difficulty than many topics now offered in advanced algebra. It is not implied that in the near future many secondary school teachers will have any occasion to teach the elementary calculus. It is the culminating subject in a series which only relatively strong schools will complete and only then for a selected group of students. In such schools there should always be teachers competent to teach the elementary calculus here intended. No superficial study of calculus should be regarded as justifying any substantial sacrifice of thoroughness. In the judgment of the committee the introduction of elementary calculus

[1] Report of the National Committee on Mathematical Requirements, "The Reorganization of Mathematics in Secondary Education" (Boston: Houghton Mifflin Company, 1923), pp. 57–59.

necessarily includes sufficient algebra and geometry to compensate for whatever diversion of time from these subjects would be implied.

The calculus of the algebraic polynomial is so simple that a boy or girl who is capable of grasping the idea of limit, of slope, and of velocity, may in a brief time gain an outlook upon the field of mechanics and other exact sciences and acquire a fair degree of facility in using one of the most powerful tools of mathematics, together with the capacity for solving a number of interesting problems. Moreover, the fundamental ideas involved, quite aside from their technical applications, will provide valuable training in understanding and analyzing quantitative relations—and such training is of value to everyone.

With reference to the content of such a course as was contemplated, the committee stated[1]

The work should include:

a. The general notion of a derivative as a limit indispensable for the accurate expression of such fundamental quantities as velocity of a moving body or slope of a curve.

b. Applications of derivatives to easy problems in rates and in maxima and minima.

c. Simple cases of inverse problems; e.g., finding distance from velocity, etc.

d. Approximate methods of summation leading up to integration as a powerful method of summation.

e. Applications to simple cases of motion, area, volume, and pressure.

Work in the calculus should be largely graphic and may be closely related to that in physics; the necessary technique should be reduced to a minimum by basing it wholly or mainly on algebraic polynomials. No formal study of analytic geometry need be presupposed beyond the plotting of simple graphs.

It is important to bear in mind that, while the elementary calculus is sufficiently easy, interesting, and valuable to justify its introduction, special pains should be taken to guard against any lack of thoroughness in the fundamentals of algebra and geometry; no possible gain could compensate for a real sacrifice of such thoroughness.

It should also be borne in mind that the suggestion of including elementary calculus is not intended for all schools nor for all teachers in any school. It is not intended to connect in any direct way with college entrance requirements. The future college student will have ample opportunity for calculus later. The capable boy or girl who is not to have the college work ought not on that account to be prevented from learning something of the use of this powerful tool. The applications of elementary calculus to simple concrete problems are far more abundant and interesting than those of algebra. The necessary technique is extremely simple.

This Report of the National Committee gave some impetus to the inclusion of certain ideas and work from calculus in the high school. The attempts, however, were scattered and sporadic, and, while a certain

[1] *Ibid.,* pp. 54–55.

amount of interest and success was reported in some instances, there appears to have been little general enthusiasm for it, and as a subject calculus never has attained a position of any prominence in the senior high school. No important subsequent report has recommended a systematic course in calculus for the high school, though the Joint Commission, in its 1940 report, suggested "introducing study of differentiation, limited to polynomials, with applications to slopes, maxima and minima, rates of change, velocity, acceleration, and related problems" in connection with algebra in the twelfth grade.[1] Much more recently (1959) the College Entrance Examination Board's Commission on Mathematics pointed out that few high schools at present are sufficiently well staffed to teach a full course of college-level calculus effectively. The commission deprecated the practice of exposing high school students to formal calculus for a short time.[2]

From these indications it appears that calculus as a subject probably is not destined to find a place in the high school curriculum but will in all likelihood remain distinctively a college subject. There are numerous opportunities in high school work, however, in connection with algebra, geometry, trigonometry, graphical work, and physics to bring about the preliminary development of fundamental concepts which will be needed in the subsequent study of calculus. Much can be done to illustrate such concepts as rates of change, maxima and minima, slopes, independent and dependent variables and functions, limits, and approximate methods of summation. If time permits, it is easily possible even to develop the notion of a derivative and rules for differentiating simple algebraic functions. Simple applications involving time rates, maxima and minima, etc., will add interest to this work, as will the mention of how calculus may be used as a powerful means of summation to find areas, volumes, pressures, and the like. The student who approaches his college calculus equipped with such a background will certainly find the work easier and more meaningful than it would be otherwise. The high school teacher of mathematics who is able to give his students the advantage of such a springboard will have done much to enrich their conception of the subject and to ensure their success in it.

In the remainder of this chapter the teaching of various parts of the calculus will be considered primarily from the standpoint of the systematic course in calculus in the junior college.

[1] Joint Commission of the Mathematical Association of America and the National Council of Teachers of Mathematics: "The Place of Mathematics in Secondary Education," *Fifteenth Yearbook* (Washington, D.C.: National Council of Teachers of Mathematics, 1940), pp. 97–98.

[2] College Entrance Examination Board: Report of the Commission on Mathematics (New York: College Entrance Examination Board, 1959), pp. 14–15.

Importance of Emphasizing Fundamental Concepts.   Any thorough mastery of the calculus has two fundamental aspects, viz., (1) the understanding of the basic concepts that are involved in the development of the subject and familiarity with the many special formulas that are needed and (2) the acquisition of ability and ready facility in the use of these special formulas and methods.   Both are fundamental to a balanced mastery of the subject.

It is possible for an individual to acquire a high degree of skill in the latter aspect of the work without understanding much about what he is doing or why he is doing it.   Indeed this situation is often found.   The relatively enormous amount of formal work that must be done begets a tendency on the part of instructors to emphasize this aspect, often to the detriment of understanding.   Many students acquire high proficiency in performing difficult feats of formal differentiation or integration without having any clear conception of the meaning of a derivative or an integral or of the real significance of what they are doing.   Proficiency in this mechanical aspect of the work, although it is indispensable, tends to produce complacency on the part of both student and teacher.   This is not unnatural, but it is unfortunate.   Such a one-sided development indicates not a balanced mastery of the subject, but rather mere proficiency in rote performance.   It is precisely the sort of thing against which so much criticism of the teaching of elementary algebra has been directed.   The reason why we hear so little of this criticism leveled at the teaching of calculus is simply that the matter of improving the teaching of college mathematics has as yet received too little attention, at least in the way of published suggestions.

It is true that most of the actual work of differentiation and integration must be carried on by formal methods and that these must be learned and mastered by the students.   At the same time, these formal methods and devices can be developed in such a way as to give them meaning, and this should be regarded as a major responsibility of the instructor.   The student who gains a real understanding of the meanings of function,[1] variation, increment, limits,[2] infinitesimals, continuity, derivative, rates, maxima and minima, an integral as an antiderivative and as a summation, indefinite and definite integrals, and other basic concepts will derive a far richer experience and a far more adequate basis for further work in either applied or theoretical mathematics than the student who works by rote alone.

The Teaching of Variables, Limits, and Infinitesimals.   Variables, limits, and infinitesimals are primary concepts in calculus, and serious effort

---

[1] See "Insights into Modern Mathematics," *Twenty-Third Yearbook* (Washington, D.C.: *National Council of Teachers of Mathematics*, 1957), chap. 8.

[2] *Ibid.*, chap. 7.

should be made to ensure that the students will have a good understanding of their meanings. Normally the students will have gained considerable familiarity with the meanings of "function" and "variable" through their previous work in trigonometry and algebra. Care should be taken that variables and constants are thought of as symbols and not as quantities: a *variable* is a symbol which may represent any one of a set of values called its *domain;* a *constant* is a symbol which represents the same value throughout a particular discussion.

The student should become familiar with the concept of a set (domain, range) of values and with the nature of, and the distinction between, *arbitrary constants (parameters)* and *absolute constants.*

It is important that a clear distinction between independent and dependent variables be made. Furthermore, when these concepts are used in the context of a defined functional relation, they should be associated respectively with the domain and the range of the function.

Consider a set of ordered pairs (x,y) and define a function as a rule which specifies the functional relationship between the members of the set of first elements x and the members of the set of second elements y, or which associates with each element of the set of first elements exactly one element from the set of second elements. Then a symbol (in this case x) which may represent any member of the set of first elements is called the *independent variable,* and a symbol (in this case y) which may represent any member of the set of second elements is called the *dependent variable.*

The function itself (defined above as a rule) may also be thought of as the set of ordered pairs (x,y), where for each x in the domain of the function (i.e., each value of the independent variable) the corresponding element y in the range of the function (i.e., the corresponding value of the dependent variable) is determined by the rule which defines the function. Thus the dependent variable represents the set of values of the function over its domain.

In spite of the presumption of familiarity with these notions, it is advisable at the beginning of the course in calculus to review them, giving numerous and varied illustrations involving both algebraic and transcendental functions. It is not anticipated that students will have much difficulty in establishing these concepts, but as a means of ensuring understanding, some practice should be given in identifying independent variables and dependent variables and in building tables and making graphs to illustrate the variation of each of these and the relationship of functions to their independent variables. The student should also become thoroughly familiar with the generalized functional notation. He should learn to recognize $f(x)$ in all its variations and with all its implications.

The concepts of a limit[1] and an infinitesimal and the application of these concepts are vital to an understanding of the calculus and are indeed the foundation stones upon which the calculus is built. Because of logical difficulties, formal treatment of the subject of limits is usually omitted from high school mathematics. At most, this subject is sometimes taken up in a sort of intuitive way. Evidence of this is found in the common omission of incommensurable cases from the textbooks in elementary geometry. However, in the study of calculus it is very important that there be a careful treatment of limits and infinitesimals. In this connection McKelvey says:[2]

The student's previous mathematical study has been built entirely upon the elementary principles of algebra and plane geometry. The notion of a function approaching a limit has appeared only in occasional problems. In contrast with this state of affairs, throughout both Differential and Integral Calculus, the limit concept appears as a fundamental principle. This one feature, more than any other, sets the subject of Calculus apart from the student's previous field of study and requires that he enlarge his group of mathematical operations and become familiar with new methods of approach to a mathematical problem.

The difficulty which students most often experience in this connection is not so much in acquiring intuitive concepts of limits and infinitesimals as in understanding the technical definitions. The concept of a limit can be illustrated by various situations drawn from elementary geometry or algebra. For example, let there be a polygon inscribed in or circumscribed about a circle. As the number of sides is increased, the difference between the length of the perimeter of the polygon and the circumference of the circle obviously becomes less than it was at the outset. As the process is indefinitely continued, the difference between these two lengths becomes and remains less than any value we may care to assign; i.e., the difference approaches zero as a limit. In other words, the length of the perimeter of the polygon becomes always more nearly equal to the circumference of the circle; the one approaches the other as a limit.

Again, let there be a series of terms of the form $1/2^n$, where $n = 0, 1, 2, 3, 4$, etc. The first term of this series is 1, and, if successive terms are added, the sum of the series becomes $1 + \frac{1}{2} + \frac{1}{4} + \frac{1}{8} + \cdots$. The addition of successive terms brings the sum nearer and nearer to 2. No finite number of terms can make the sum equal to 2, but by taking n sufficiently large, the difference between the sum of the series and 2 can be made as small as desired. Thus we say that, as the number of terms is indefinitely increased, the sum approaches 2 as a limit.

[1] *Ibid.*, chap. 7.
[2] From Joseph Vance McKelvey, "Calculus" (New York: The Macmillan Company, 1937), p. v. By permission of The Macmillan Company, publishers.

The fundamental idea involved in these illustrations is that of a variable difference, diminishing progressively toward zero, between the value of the varying function and the constant which it approaches as a limit. This idea should be emphasized in all the illustrations that are used, because it is only when it is well understood that the somewhat technical definition of a limit, as it is usually given, takes on real meaning. In general, when a variable or function approaches zero as a limit, it is called an "infinitesimal." It must be made clear that an infinitesimal is not merely "a very small quantity" but a *variable* quantity which can be made smaller than any previously assigned value, no matter how small this value may be; i.e., it approaches zero as a limit. It was the failure to sense this distinction which prevented the ancients from understanding the real nature of continuous variation, and it is precisely the conception of this distinction which enables us to understand the nature of continuity, infinitesimals, and limits, which are the very taproots of calculus.

With this concept of an infinitesimal clearly in mind, the limit of a variable may now be technically defined as follows: If x is a variable and a is a constant and if it is true that, as the values which x may take so change that $|x - a|$ becomes and remains less than h, where h is an arbitrarily small positive quantity, then x is said to approach a as a limit.[1]

Evidently this definition can be extended to define the limit of a function. Thus: If $f(x)$ is a function of x, and a and A are constants, and if for any arbitrarily chosen small positive quantity d there exists another small positive quantity h such that, when $|x - a| < h$, it is true that $|f(x) - A| < d$, then $f(x)$ is said to approach A as a limit as x approaches a as a limit.

Every effort should be made to make these definitions meaningful to the students. To this end graphic and numerical illustrations should be used in the explanations, which should be more than perfunctory. These definitions are of great importance in that they provide the analytical means of defining the important property of continuity of a function or a variable as well as the indispensable concept of a derivative.

The students should be made familiar with the customary notation used in connection with limits. They should also become familiar with certain theorems concerning limits. These may be, and usually are, given without proof, but their statements should be accompanied by ample illustrative explanation to ensure that their meanings are really understood by the students.

Teaching the Meaning of a Derivative and a Differential. The late Prof. Louis Ingold once said that whoever really understands the meaning of a

---

[1] The symbol $|x - a|$ is to be read "the absolute value of $x - a$" or "the numerical value of $x - a$." It is to be interpreted as meaning the difference between x and a without regard to sign.

derivative has learned the most of calculus.   He referred, of course, not to operational facility, but rather to the fact that an understanding of the derivative underlies the conception of what calculus is all about. The importance of the concept of a derivative and the associated concept of a differential cannot be too greatly emphasized.   Therefore, if calculus is to be taught with the idea of giving the students something more than a rote mastery of its techniques, it is highly important that every effort be made to give them at the outset a clear understanding of these two fundamental concepts.

A derivative might be thought of as the instantaneous rate of change of a function with respect to its independent variable.   The usual method of defining the derivative in terms of increments, ratios, and limits, with variation in details, is substantially the same in nearly all textbooks. Like many careful definitions, however, this one is difficult for many students to comprehend.   There seems to be something mysterious about the process of passing to the limit and of determining the limiting value of the ratio of the increment of the function to the increment of the independent variable when the latter approaches zero as a limit.   The student reasons that, if the one increment approaches zero, the other will also approach zero, and the ratio will be reduced in this way to the form $0/0$ which, in form, appears meaningless because of the division by zero.

In order to clarify this concept, it is absolutely necessary to make the student understand that the increment of the dependent variable can and must be expressed *in terms of the independent variable and its increment* and that the ratio of the increment of the dependent variable to the increment of the independent variable thus becomes a function of the increment of the independent variable.   Furthermore, it should be emphasized that it is the limit of this ratio that is sought and not the ratio of the limits of the numerator and denominator as separate functions. Thus let $y = f(x)$ be a continuous function of x.   If x takes on an increment Δx, then y will also take on an increment Δy, such that

$$y + \Delta y = f(x + \Delta x)$$

or $\Delta y = f(x + \Delta x) - y$, or $\Delta y = f(x + \Delta x) - f(x)$.   In this way Δy is expressed entirely in terms of x and Δx.   Then the ratio $\Delta y/\Delta x$ becomes $[f(x) + \Delta x) - f(x)]/\Delta x$, which is reducible in general to a determinate form and should be so reduced *before the limit is taken*.   Graphic representations such as are given in nearly all textbooks help greatly in giving concreteness to the concepts of these increments and ratios, and full advantage should be taken of this means of illustrating and clarifying the concepts.

The notation also is confusing to the students, who are puzzled about such questions as these: What is the distinction between Δy and dy and between Δx and dx? Why is it that Δy is not in general equal to dy, while Δx is in general equal to dx? How does Δy become dy? What does dy mean? If dy/dx is defined as the limit of $\Delta y/\Delta x$ as Δx approaches zero, why can it not be thought of as a quotient? Are dy and dx infinitesimals? Are Δy and Δx infinitesimals? What is the distinction between an infinitesimal and an increment, and between an increment and a differential?

It is recommended that the notation dy/dx not be used for the derivative until after the concept of differential is developed. A good notation for the derivative of y with respect to x is $D_x y$; similarly, the derivative

FIG. 20-1

of $f(x)$ with respect to x would be $D_x f(x)$. There are other good notations that do not introduce the confusion of thinking of a quotient where there is no quotient. It seems probable that a good deal of the confusion and uncertainty concerning the distinction between increment, differential, and derivative could be avoided if, contrary to custom, at least an intuitive notion of the meaning of a differential were to be developed along with the discussion of the derivative. This can easily be done by means of geometric considerations and an arbitrary definition. In Fig. 20-1 suppose that P is some point (x,y) on the curve $y = f(x)$. If x takes on an increment Δx, then y must take on an increment Δy whose value depends upon the value of Δx. Therefore the ratio $\Delta y/\Delta x$ would give the average rate of change of y with respect to x over the interval Δx, but not the instantaneous rate of change at the beginning of the interval. The instantaneous rate of change at any point on the curve is given by the slope of the curve at that point, and the slope of a curve at a given point is defined as the slope of the tangent to the curve at that point. Thus the derivative of a function at a point, which is defined to be

$\lim\limits_{\Delta x \to 0} \dfrac{\Delta y}{\Delta x}$ and which gives the instantaneous rate of change for the corresponding value of the dependent variable, also gives the slope of the tangent to the curve at that point.

If we draw PT tangent to the curve at $P(x,y)$, the distance dy, as shown in Fig. 20-2, represents the increment which y would have taken if its rate of change with respect to x had become constant exactly at the point $P(x,y)$. As P' moves along the curve to the position of P, Fig. 20-2,

Fig. 20-2

both Δx and Δy approach zero as a limit. If the ratio $\Delta y/\Delta x$ represents the average rate of change for any of the intervals Δx and the ratio dy/dx the rate of change for the tangent line PT, it is evident that $\Delta y/\Delta x$ is changing in value as Δy and Δx approach zero, while dy/dx is remaining constant. For each new position of P', the Δx and dx are the same in value, while Δy and dy differ. Furthermore, $\lim\limits_{\Delta x \to 0} \dfrac{\Delta y}{\Delta x} = \dfrac{dy}{dx}$. By agreement we shall call dx, which is the same as Δx, *the differential of x,* and we shall call dy *the differential of y* corresponding to dx. We have shown that the ratio dy/dx of the differentials dy and dx is the same as the *derivative of y with respect to x.* The value of this ratio will vary accordingly as P takes different positions on the curve, but for any particular position of P (i.e., for any given value of x) the value of the derivative dy/dx remains constant and is entirely independent of the value of dx.

Now, if we wish to let dx become an infinitesimal and approach zero as a limit, dy will also become an infinitesimal and approach zero as a limit, but the ratio dy/dx remains the same, even in the limit. However, it is no longer necessary to regard the differentials dy and dx as infinitesimals unless we so wish. They may be regarded simply as tangible, finite increments, dx being any arbitrary increment of x, and dy being the increment which y *would take on* if the slope of the curve (or the rate of change of y with respect to x) had become constant at the point $P(x,y)$.

It is believed that an approach to the concept of the derivative along with this intuitive notion of the differential as a finite, measurable quantity rather than an infinitesimal would dispel much of the mystery and uncertainty so often associated with the meaning of derivatives and differentials. The student's understanding will be strengthened if he is asked to take various curves, select arbitrary values and arbitrary increments for the independent variable, and by drawing and actual measurement determine dx, $f(x)$, $f(x + \Delta x)$, Δy, and dy. Then by actual division, dy/dx, he can get approximations to the values of the derivatives. To develop the rules for differentiation, of course, the usual analytic procedure will need to be employed. However, if a preliminary approach such as has just been described can make this analytic procedure more meaningful to the student, it will be exceedingly worthwhile.

Teaching the Rules for Differentiation. The student will soon find that the process of finding the derivative of a function by the graphical method gives only approximations at isolated points and does not give any general expression for the derivative. He will also find that the detailed application of the formula

$$D_x y = \lim_{\Delta x \to 0} \frac{f(x + \Delta x) - f(x)}{\Delta x}$$

while it does give a general and exact expression for the derivative, is a clumsy and laborious process. The practical limitations of time demand that he learn and use the special rules or formulas which are available for differentiating various kinds of functions.

There are two points of view with regard to the introduction, learning, and use of these rules for differentiation. Considered solely from the standpoint of logical sequence and mathematical consistency, it would seem necessary that each of these formulas should be completely developed and proved before being used. This is the position taken by the authors of most textbooks on calculus. On the other hand, there are some authors and many teachers who hold that it is a sounder and more economical pedagogical procedure to introduce without proof certain of these rules in which the meaning is clear and to let the students use these empirically for the time being, the proofs being reserved until later, and special attention being given at the time only to the matter of making sure that the concepts involved are understood by the students. Professor Huntington writes:[1]

Now the simplest function is the polynomial,

$$y = A + Bx + Cx^2 + Dx^3 + \cdots$$

I should begin the second day, therefore, by stating, without proof, the rule for differentiating a polynomial, namely:

$$dy = (B + 2Cx + 3Dx^2 + \cdots) \, dx$$

Equipped with this rule, we can proceed at once to solve a multitude of problems in maxima and minima, which serve better than anything else to convince the student that here is a new tool which is mighty convenient to have at hand. . . .

The study of the polynomial naturally leads to problems involving the quotient of two polynomials, and to problems involving the solution of a quadratic equation. In order to handle such problems, it is well to introduce at this point the statement, without proofs, of the general rules for differentiating a sum, a product, and a quotient, and also the special rules

$$d\left(\frac{1}{x}\right) = -\frac{1}{x^2} \, dx, \qquad d(\sqrt{x}) = \frac{dx}{2\sqrt{x}}$$

in which x may be the independent variable, or itself a function of some other variable. . . .

If the meaning of a theorem is clear, as in the case of the rules for differentiation, the formal proof may often be postponed to advantage, but . . . the meaning of a new concept cannot safely be postponed. . . .

With regard to the subsequent proofs of the rules for differentiation, Professor Huntington later writes:[2]

If the time-saving program above outlined has been followed, the student should now have a good working knowledge of the properties of all the elementary functions including the rules for differentiation. If he has a spark of scientific curiosity, he will be interested to know how these rules, whose utility he has come to appreciate, were ever discovered, and how we know they are true. . . .

To indicate how much time can be saved, by taking up the proofs in the most effective order, I may say that the proofs of all the rules for differentiation can easily be disposed of in two classroom periods. First establish the rule for the sine and the rule for the logarithm, for the general case of a function of a function. Then the rules for kx, x^n, e^x, uv, u/v, cos x, tan x, and the inverse functions follow by a turn of the hand.

[1] Edward V. Huntington, Teaching the Calculus, Four Papers on the Teaching of Mathematics, *Bulletin* 19 (Lancaster, Pa.: Society for the Promotion of Engineering Education, 1932) pp. 39, 40, 41.

[2] *Ibid.*, pp. 46–47.

This will doubtless be regarded by many teachers as an overstatement and an oversimplification of the situation, and it may be that it is.   There are also those who will object to it on the grounds that it lacks the sequential rigor of the prove-as-you-go plan, though the basis for this objection may be more apparent than real.   However, regardless of whether or not one subscribes wholly to the suggestions made by Professor Huntington, it seems probable that whatever sacrifice of mathematical order they would entail might be largely compensated by increased interest and operational efficiency.

If the student is to use the differentiation formulas with efficiency and dispatch, he will need to memorize them and memorize them thoroughly.   As soon as a rule is given, whether with or without proof, it should be applied immediately, and considerable practice should be given in finding derivatives of functions under this rule.   This will do a great deal toward enabling the student to fix the rule in his mind.   However, as the number of new formulas increases, the difficulty of keeping them straight becomes greater, and the student will in general have to resort to actual and thorough memorization.   Careful inspection of a tabulated list of the formulas will perhaps enable the student to discover certain relationships among them and to set up various mnemonics to aid in remembering them and to avoid confusing them with each other.

Some of the formulas are special cases of others.   For example, $D_x(cu)$ is a special case of $D_x(uv)$; $D_x(e^u)$ is a special case of $D_x(a^u)$; and other similar instances may be found.   Again, certain similarities may be found among the derivatives of certain related inverse functions.   The derivative of the arccos x is minus the derivative of the arcsin x; that of the arccot x is minus that of the arctan x; and that of the arccsc x is minus that of the arcsec x.

These and perhaps other relationships that might be found among the formulas will reduce the amount of sheer memorizing that will need to be done, and the very search for such mnemonic devices is itself an excellent exercise in familiarizing the students with the formulas.

Some Critical Points in Developing the Proofs of Certain Rules for Differentiation.   We have already discussed the matter of teaching the meanings of derivative and differential.   A clear concept of the meanings of these terms is prerequisite to any real understanding of the proofs of the formulas for the elementary derivatives.   These concepts, in turn, involve an understanding of the meanings of increments, limits, and infinitesimals, which have also been discussed.   It is probable that teachers, in developing the formulas for derivatives, are inclined to be too generous in their assumptions regarding the students' mastery of the meanings of these concepts.

The general method of finding a derivative needs to be stressed.   Its almost mechanical form and the one-two-three order of its steps, together with the reasons for this order, need to be explained and illustrated, not once, but numerous times, until the students are able to apply it independently and with facility to simple functions.   It is easy for them to follow and verify, step by step, the illustration of it, but it is by no means equally apparent to them *why* the particular steps are taken in that particular order.   Consider the typical order in the general development:

(1) $$y = f(x)$$
(2) $$y + \Delta y = f(x + \Delta x)$$
(3) $$\Delta y = f(x + \Delta x) - y = f(x + \Delta x) - f(x)$$
(4) $$\frac{\Delta y}{\Delta x} = \frac{f(x + \Delta x) - f(x)}{\Delta x}$$
(5) $$\lim_{\Delta x \to 0} \frac{\Delta y}{\Delta x} = \lim_{\Delta x \to 0} \frac{f(x + \Delta x) - f(x)}{\Delta x} = D_x y = D_x f(x)$$

(by definition)

From a synthetic standpoint it is perfect, each step being a justified consequence of the preceding one.   However, it cannot be said that each step *suggests* the following one, and herein lies the rub.   The steps and their order suggest themselves only if one has in mind the end toward which he is working.   It must be the task of the teacher to point out what this goal is and how and why this particular sequence of steps does lead to it.   It is well to carry along this general synthesis with the illustrations of its application to particular functions while pointing out the parallel development and repeatedly calling attention to the reason for performing each step in its particular place.

The explanation may be somewhat as follows: Let us assume that we have given a variable y which is a function of x.   Our task is to find the derivative of y with respect to x, or to find D_x.   By definition $D_x y$ means $\lim_{\Delta x \to 0} \frac{\Delta y}{\Delta x}$.   We must therefore find some way of getting an expression $\Delta y / \Delta x$ in terms of x and Δx in order that we may determine its limit and thus find the derivative.

General Case

$$y = f(x)$$
$$y + \Delta y = f(x + \Delta x)$$

Example

$$y = 3x + 7$$
$$y + \Delta y = 3(x + \Delta x) + 7$$

Since we want to get an expression $\Delta y / \Delta x$, we must first get an expression for Δy itself.   This we can do by subtracting y from each member of the above equation:

$$\Delta y = f(x + \Delta x) - y \qquad \Delta y = 3(x + \Delta x) + 7 - y$$

We may now substitute for y its value $f(x)$ (or $3x + 7$) and express Δy entirely in terms of x and Δx.

$$\Delta y = f(x + \Delta x) - f(x) \qquad \Delta y = 3(x + \Delta x) + 7 - (3x + 7)$$
$$= 3x + 3\Delta x + 7 - 3x - 7$$
$$= 3\Delta x$$

Now in order to get an expression for $\Delta y / \Delta x$, we must divide both members of the equation by Δx.

$$\frac{\Delta y}{\Delta x} = \frac{f(x + \Delta) - f(x)}{\Delta x} \qquad \frac{\Delta y}{\Delta x} = \frac{3\Delta x}{\Delta x} = 3$$

Finally, since we want $D_x y$, and since this means $\lim\limits_{\Delta x \to 0} \dfrac{\Delta y}{\Delta x}$, we must take the limit of $\Delta y / \Delta x$ as Δx approaches zero as a limit.

$$D_x y = \lim_{\Delta x \to 0} \frac{\Delta y}{\Delta x} \qquad\qquad D_x y = \lim_{\Delta x \to 0} \frac{3\Delta x}{\Delta x}$$
$$= \lim_{\Delta x \to 0} \frac{f(x + \Delta x) - f(x)}{\Delta x} \qquad = \lim_{\Delta x \to 0} 3(1)$$
$$= \lim_{\Delta x \to 0} 3 = 3$$

Several illustrations carried through in this manner, with specific attention to the order of procedure and the reasons that each step comes in its particular place, will be extremely helpful to the students. It will go far toward giving them a real understanding of the fundamental meaning and method of finding derivatives and developing the general derivative formulas.

Proof of the Formula for the Derivative of a Logarithm. This is one of the particularly tough spots which students encounter. The method is perfectly general, but the proof involves certain facts and relations with which students often lack familiarity, although presumably they will have encountered them beforehand. We shall give a proof of the general formula and then analyze some of its difficulties.

(1)   Let $y = \log_a u$, where u is a function of x

(2) $y + \Delta y = \log_a (u + \Delta u)$

(3) $\Delta y = \log_a (u + \Delta u) - y$

(4) $= \log_a (u + \Delta u) - \log_a u$

(5) $= \log_a \dfrac{u + \Delta u}{u}$

(6) $= \log_a \left(1 + \dfrac{\Delta u}{u}\right)$

$$(7) \qquad \frac{\Delta y}{\Delta u} = \frac{1}{\Delta u} \log_a \left(1 + \frac{\Delta u}{u} \right)$$

$$(8) \qquad = \frac{1}{u} \cdot \frac{u}{\Delta u} \log_a \left(1 + \frac{\Delta u}{u} \right)$$

$$(9) \qquad = \frac{1}{u} \log_a \left(1 + \frac{\Delta u}{u} \right)^{u/\Delta u}$$

$$(10) \qquad D_u y = \lim_{\Delta u \to 0} \frac{\Delta y}{\Delta u} = \frac{1}{u} \log_a \left[\lim_{\Delta u \to 0} \left(1 + \frac{\Delta u}{u} \right)^{u/\Delta u} \right]$$

$$= \frac{1}{u} \log_a e$$

$$(11) \qquad = \frac{1}{u} \cdot \frac{1}{\log_e a}$$

$$(12) \qquad D_x y = D_u y \cdot D_x u = \frac{1}{u \log_e a} \cdot D_x u$$

The first four steps involve no particular difficulties, but throughout the rest of the proof there are several places where the development is likely to be hard for students to follow. The first of these trouble spots occurs in step 5. Here the student must learn to recognize the application of the principle $\log m - \log n = \log m/n$. The principle itself will be familiar, but there is possibility that in this unfamiliar dress the student may fail to recognize it unless it is pointed out by the teacher.

In step 6 the reason for the change of form is not obvious, and perhaps it can be made entirely clear only after the next four steps are given. It may be explained at the time that the aim is to arrive at an expression for e. It must then be recalled that

$$e = \lim_{x \to 0} (1 + x)^{1/x}$$

and that the expression $\lim_{\Delta u \to 0} (1 + \Delta u/u)^{u/\Delta u}$, which appears in step 10 and to which the expression $1 + \Delta u/u$ in step 6 contributes, is precisely of this form.

Step 7 involves no difficulty, nor does step 8 except that the reason for the change of form from the expression in step 7 should be explained.

The transition from step 8 to step 9 involves passing from a product form to an exponential expression. This process should be familiar to the students, but since the expressions are somewhat unusual, it will probably be necessary, and certainly helpful, to point out the identification with the customary form $m \log n = \log (n)^m$.

In step 10, as has been said, it is extremely likely that some of the students will not recognize that $\lim_{\Delta u \to 0} (1 + \Delta u/u)^{u/\Delta u} = e$. Although the proof of the existence of this limit is too difficult to be presented at this level of instruction, a satisfactory intuitive justification of the fact that $\lim_{x \to 0} (1 + x)^{1/x} = 2.718 \ldots$, approximately, can be given either algebraically or geometrically.

Substitution of e for this limit leads to the formula of step 11 for $D_u y$. However, since we are required to find $D_x y$ and since u is a function of x, we must make use of the formula for the derivative of a function of a function: $D_x y = D_u y \cdot D_x u$. We may assume that this has been previously developed, so that in passing to step 12 we need only recall this rule and point out its application in the present situation.

Finally, it should be pointed out that we have developed the formula for the most general case: $y = \log_a u$. If we take e as the base (as a special case of a), then $\log_e a$, in the denominator of 12, becomes $\log_e e$, and the formula itself becomes

$$D_x (\log_e u) = \frac{1}{u} \cdot D_x u$$

since $\log_e e = 1$. This is the form in which it is usually found and in which it is generally used.

We have thus seen that the proof of this formula holds numerous specific difficulties for students. In addition to these it has the general difficulty of being somewhat long and involving numerous transformations and substitutions, the reasons for which are not immediately obvious to the students. Only a few of the better students will be able to dig it all out for themselves. Whether the majority really get it or not will depend largely upon how skillfully and clearly it is explained by the teacher.

The proof of the formula for the derivative of the exponential $y = a^u$ follows easily after the formula for the derivative of a logarithm has been established. Conversely, if the formula for the derivative of the exponential is independently developed first, as can be done, it may be used to simplify the development of the formula for the derivative of a logarithm. The order varies with different textbooks. Either may be used. In general it may be said that the one which is developed first, and independently of the other, will be more difficult for the students than the one which makes use of the first. The formulas depend ultimately upon the evaluation of

$$\lim_{x \to 0} \frac{a^x - 1}{x} = \log_e a \quad \text{or} \quad \lim_{x \to 0} (1 + x)^{1/x} = e$$

Proof of the Formula for the Derivative of the Sine of an Angle. This is another of the basic derivatives and a proverbial trouble spot for students. The steps in the proof may be given as follows:

(1)   Let $y = \sin u$, where u is some function of x

(2) $y + \Delta y = \sin (u + \Delta u)$

(3) $\Delta y = \sin (u + \Delta u) - y$

(4) $= \sin (u + \Delta u) - \sin u$

(5) $= \sin u \cos \Delta u + \cos u \sin \Delta u - \sin u$

(6) $\dfrac{\Delta y}{\Delta u} = \dfrac{\cos u \sin \Delta u}{\Delta u} - \dfrac{\sin u(1 - \cos \Delta u)}{\Delta u}$

(7) $= \cos u \dfrac{\sin \Delta u}{\Delta u} - \sin u \dfrac{1 - \cos \Delta u}{\Delta u}$

(8) $D_u y = \lim\limits_{\Delta u \to 0} \dfrac{\Delta y}{\Delta u} = \cos u \left[\lim\limits_{\Delta u \to 0} \dfrac{\sin \Delta u}{\Delta u} \right]$
$$- \sin u \left[\lim\limits_{\Delta u \to 0} \dfrac{1 - \cos \Delta u}{\Delta u} \right]$$

(9) $= \cos u(1) - (0)$
$$= \cos u$$

(10) $D_x y = D_u y \cdot D_x u = \cos u \cdot D_x u$

The first four steps involve no difficulty whatever. In step 5 there is a substitution to be made, and in steps 6 and 7 there are certain rearrangements of terms and the insertion of the divisor Δu, but these, again, involve no special difficulty so far as the operations themselves are concerned. There is, however, the question *why* these particular substitutions and rearrangements are made, and the reasons should be explained clearly to the students. In order to present these reasons, however, one must recall that it is necessary, in setting up the derivative, to evaluate $\lim\limits_{\Delta u \to 0} \dfrac{\Delta y}{\Delta u}$. It should be explained that, in order to do this, we need to use $\lim\limits_{\Delta u \to 0} \dfrac{\sin \Delta u}{\Delta u}$ and $\lim\limits_{\Delta u \to 0} \dfrac{1 - \cos \Delta u}{\Delta u}$ because these expressions can be evaluated and their use affords the only way to evaluate $\lim\limits_{\Delta u \to 0} \dfrac{\Delta y}{\Delta u}$. Indeed, the limiting values of these expressions will already have been determined, but as a matter of refreshing the minds of the students on these points it will be well to review them before substituting them in the formula. As a matter of fact, the two most difficult parts of the whole proof are (a) the preliminary establishment of the limiting values of these two expressions, and (b) sensing the role which they play in the proof. Step 9 merely involves the substitution of the numerical limiting values for these expressions.

It will be noted that this development gives the derivative of y with respect to u, where u is some function of x. In order to get the derivative of y with respect to x, we must again make use of the relation

$$D_x y = D_u y \cdot D_x u$$

This is done in step 10, which completes the proof.

Successive Differentiation; Maxima and Minima. A few illustrations will suffice to make it clear to the students that in general the derivative of a function of x with respect to x is itself a function of x which may in turn be differentiated and that, by differentiating successive derivatives in this way, there are obtained the so-called higher derivatives of the function. The students should be made acquainted with the various forms of notation for these higher derivatives, and in particular they should be given an interpretation of the second derivative as the rate at which the first derivative is changing, or graphically, as the rate of change of the slope of the curve. That is, the student should come to understand that, if the second derivative is positive at a given point, it means that the first derivative is increasing at that point; a negative value of the second derivative indicates a decreasing first derivative; and a zero value of the second derivative indicates that the first derivative is neither increasing nor decreasing.

The most important immediate application of the second derivative is in connection with the determination of maximum, minimum, and inflection points. It will be obvious to the student from a consideration of the graphs of functions that the first derivative at a maximum or a minimum point must be zero. The converse does not necessarily hold true, however, and even if it did, this would not enable one to distinguish between a maximum and minimum. In order to make a certain test of this, the second derivative must also be employed. The student must be shown that, if $f'(x) = 0$ and is decreasing (i.e., if at the same time $f''(x)$ is negative), then a maximum is indicated at that point, while if $f'(x) = 0$ and is increasing (i.e., if at the same time $f''(x)$ is positive), then a minimum is indicated. If $f'(x) = 0$ and $f''(x) = 0$, also, then at that point the function has neither a maximum nor a minimum, but a point of inflection. Careful explanation of these matters should be given and should be accompanied by graphical illustrations to ensure that the students understand them clearly.

The students should be warned against concluding wrongly that $f'(x)$ for a certain x, or at a certain point, will necessarily be zero just because $f''(x)$ is zero. Since $f''(x) < 0$ indicates that the curve is *concave downward* and $f''(x) > 0$ indicates it is *concave upward*, it follows that, at the point where the sense of concavity changes, $f''(x) = 0$ if it has a value. This point is called a point of inflection, or flex point. That these are not sufficient conditions for a flex point may be seen by examining the curves

$f(x) = x^4$ and $f(x) = x^{\frac{2}{3}}$. A simple illustration of how $f'(x)$ and $f''(x)$ may be used in graphing a function is the graph of $f(x) = 3x^3 - 2x + 5$ given in Fig. 20-3.

The study of maxima and minima offers a wealth of interesting applications of the theory to geometrical and physical situations. These problems not only give practice in formal differentiation but also give

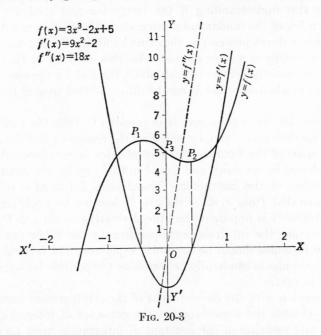

$f(x) = 3x^3 - 2x + 5$
$f'(x) = 9x^2 - 2$
$f''(x) = 18x$

FIG. 20-3

to the work a high degree of motivation and afford excellent training in interpreting geometric and physical situations and in translating these into the formal language of the derivative.

The Indefinite Integral; Formal Integration. Up to the present we have considered only matters which are related to derivation and differentiation of functions. We must now give some attention to that part of calculus which is concerned with the inverse problem of finding a primitive function of which the given function is the derivative. It should be pointed out to the students that many of the most important applications of calculus give rise to problems of this nature, particularly those involving definite integrals. No student should have any difficulty in understanding the meaning of integration if it is explained simply as the process of antidifferentiation; i.e., if it is clearly pointed out that in differentiation we are given the function and required to find the derivative, while in integration we are given the derivative and required to find the function.

The two processes are absolutely inverse to each other, just as division and multiplication or addition and subtraction are. Either one *undoes* the other.

In taking up the study of integration, then, the first task of the instructor should be to make this clear to the students so that their work in integration will not be devoid of meaning. It will help greatly toward achieving this understanding if the instructor and students together work out a few of the fundamental integrals. The finding of a derivative is, of course, a direct process; on the other hand, the finding of an integral form is essentially a matter of trial. In view of the fact that the two processes are exactly inverse to each other, the test for the correctness of an integral is whether or not it can be differentiated to give the original expression.

By using this basic principle, it is possible to take the fundamental formulas for derivatives and, by reversing the reasoning and the notation, arrive at some of the fundamental formulas for integration. A number of these should be set down and tested in this way by the students with the assistance of the instructor. Thus, since $D_x(\sin x) = \cos x$, it is seen at once that $\int (\cos x)\, dx = \sin x + C$, because by applying the test for an integral it is apparent that the derivative of $\sin x + C$ is $\cos x$. In like manner the integrals corresponding to the other fundamental derivative formulas should be set down, explained, and verified. If this is done, the students can hardly help sensing the relation between derivatives and integrals.

In connection with the development of these integration formulas the student will note the appearance of the constant of integration. The necessity and meaning of the constant of integration must be carefully explained by the instructor. This may be done by use of the theorem "If two functions have the same derivative, they differ only by a constant" and its converse; these may easily be illustrated by examples. It should be pointed out that in many of the applications of integration the determination of the constant of integration to satisfy initial conditions is of extreme importance.

Use of the Table of Integrals. There are a few of the fundamental integrals with which the student should become perfectly familiar. The lists of these vary in different textbooks, the number usually being between 12 and 25 and depending mainly upon the author's inclination toward generalization or specialization of the forms. The discussion of these forms in each textbook will presumably be consistent with the author's views in this respect, so that the precise number of formulas listed in any case is of less consequence than the fact that there *are* certain of these which the student must know thoroughly. These formulas should be tested by differentiation and should be memorized.

In addition to these fundamental integrals there are many special integrals which are often useful. Textbooks usually contain more or less extensive lists or tables of these special integrals. Separately published tables, which are much more complete even than those given in the textbooks, are also available. There is no general agreement among instructors on the extent to which students should use these tables of special integrals. Some feel that, since much of integration is formal anyway, the free use of the tables speeds up the work and allows more to be accomplished without any detriment to the student. Others feel that the student will gain more insight and understanding if he performs most of these integrations for himself by means of the fundamental integrals. Nobody knows just what the optimum is with regard to this question, but it would seem that a middle ground or reasonable balance of these views would perhaps be more defensible than either extreme position. To this end, the suggestion of Professor Huntington that "no formula in the table should be used until it has at least been verified by 'differentiating back'"[1] seems appropriate.

In using an extensive table of integrals, the student will need to familiarize himself with the way in which the integrals are classified, so that he may readily locate and identify the form corresponding to any given integrand.

Sometimes it may be impossible to find in the table a formula which corresponds to the given integrand. In such cases it is sometimes possible to transform the given expression into usable form through such special devices as resolution of the expression into partial fractions, the substitution of a new variable, application of the rule for integration by parts, or use of the reduction formulas. These special devices involve special procedures the reasons for which, and the real significance of which, will probably not be clear to the students unless the underlying principles and considerations are carefully explained by the instructor. In order that the students may appreciate and become familiar with the nature of these devices, ample illustration and explanation of them should be given. In connection with trigonometric substitutions and the transformation of trigonometric expressions into integrable forms, it may be advisable to give again a brief summary and review of certain of the trigonometric identities, notably the addition formulas and the functions of half angles and double angles. The extreme generality of the reduction formulas makes it desirable that illustrative examples be worked out by the instructor to familiarize the students with the precise manner in which these formulas are applied to particular functions and with the effect which is produced in the integrand through the application of these formulas.

[1] Huntington, *op. cit.*, p. 55.

The Definite Integral. As in the case of the indefinite integral, many students employ the definite integral without clearly understanding its nature and interpretation. The indefinite integral was defined merely as an antiderivative. The definite integral, on the other hand, is to be interpreted in a different way, viz., as a summation of elements having the characteristic form $f(x) \, \Delta x$, or, more precisely, as the limit of the sum of these elements as Δx approaches zero as a limit. The justification for identifying the limit of such a sum with an integral rests, of course, upon the fundamental theorem for definite integrals, and this must be made clear to the students in due time. Here is a case, however, in which the concept of the definite integral may justifiably be developed, explained,

FIG. 20-4

illustrated, defined, associated with its characteristic symbolism, and actually used before proceeding to a proof of the fact that its use is justified.

In general there are three phases to problems involving definite integrals: (1) setting up the element of integration, (2) performing the formal integration, and (3) substituting limits and evaluating the integral. The third of these is mere labor. The second involves the knowledge and ability required to perform the integration correctly. This presumably will have been developed in connection with the work on indefinite integrals. The first phase, setting up the formula for the element of integration, is the part of the work which is likely to cause the students the most difficulty. Since ideas seem to be most readily acquired and assimilated when they are associated with graphic representations, the most effective illustration of the method of setting up the formula for the element of integration is probably in connection with the problem of finding the area under a curve, Fig. 20-4. Here it is apparent that the element of area, ΔA or $ABCD$, is approximately equal to the area of the rectangle $ABED$, this area being given by $y \, \Delta x$, or $f(x) \, \Delta x$. On passing to the differential notation, we have $dA = f(x) \, dx$, which is the characteristic form for the differential of area or the element of integration, whence $A = \int dA = \int f(x) \, dx$. The important thing here is that the element of integration is always of the form $dA = f(x) \, dx$, and the area itself is given as $A = \int f(x) \, dx$, or $F(x)$. If $x = a$, we have $A = F(a)$; if $x = b$, we have $A = F(b)$. The area under the curve and *between* the ordinates erected at a and b will evidently be $F(b) - F(a)$, which, as we have seen, is given by

$$\int_{x=b} f(x)\ dx - \int_{x=a} f(x)\ dx.$$

It is to be noted that the constant of integration would appear in both of these integrals but would disappear in the subtraction, so that it may be disregarded.

The customary notation for the definite integral, $\int_a^b f(x)\ dx$, should be clearly explained, and the student should observe and keep in mind the meaning of every detail of this notation.   In particular, the student should be aware of the fact that, for a given function $f(x)$, the value of the definite integral $\int_a^b f(x)\ dx$ depends entirely upon the values of a and b.

It should be pointed out to the student that in general the element of integration for any solid can be readily set up provided it is possible to get a characteristic expression for the area of all the sections made by planes parallel to a given plane.   If the solid is cut into slices of thickness dh by planes parallel to this plane and if the sections thus made are all similar to each other, then, denoting a typical section by A_i, the element of integration is given by $A_i\ dh$.   The meaning of this should be made clear by drawings, as should the fact that, if A_i can now be expressed in terms of h, then a definite integral for the volume can be set up.   Probably the most common and simplest application of this is in connection with solids of revolution.

Other type forms for the element of integration are encountered in problems involving length of arc, surfaces of solids, plane areas in polar coordinates, moments of mass and inertia, and centroids.   Whenever a new type form is to be considered, the instructor should make a special point of explaining and illustrating how the new special form fits into, and in fact derives from, the fundamental concept and definition of an element of integration.   If this is done, the student will gradually acquire the ability to interpret problems and set up integrals for himself, and the application of the definite integral will come to have meaning for him instead of seeming to be merely an assortment of tricks to be learned. If the student once gets a clear concept of the meaning of the element of integration for single definite integrals, the subsequent extension to double, triple, or multiple integrals in general will be plausible and comparatively easy for him.

The foregoing discussion has dealt mainly with the matter of developing meanings and concepts.   The illustrations used have dealt with simple functions, and rigorous treatment has not been attempted.   This is not to say that rigorous work has no place in connection with the advanced study of the definite integral.   On the contrary, if one is to justify completely the use of this important mathematical tool, it is absolutely necessary that a rigorous proof of the fundamental theorem be given.

It should be kept in mind, however, that there is an important distinction between understanding and using this tool and justifying its use. As has been said before, it seems that in this case there is a substantial advantage to be gained by undertaking a thorough development of the concept and application of the definite integral before, or perhaps even without, requiring a rigorous analytical proof of the theorem which justifies its use. Indeed, most elementary textbooks make no pretense of giving a rigorous proof of the theorem but rest the case upon explanations which give understanding and plausibility but which involve a considerable amount of intuition.

All students should be required to understand the line of reasoning which underlies the proof of the fundamental theorem. If the customary geometrical interpretation is used as a basis for the explanation, the problem resolves itself essentially into showing that the area bounded by the curve $y = f(x)$, the X axis, and the perpendiculars erected to the X axis at the points $x = a$ and $x = b$ is exactly equal to the area given by the limit of the sum

$$f(x_1) \, \Delta x_1 + f(x_2) \, \Delta x_2 + f(x_3) \, \Delta x_3 + \cdots + f(x_n) \, \Delta x_n$$

as n becomes infinite and each Δx approaches zero as a limit; i.e., $\lim\limits_{n \to \infty} \sum\limits_{i=1}^{n} f(x_i) \, \Delta x_i$, where $\Delta x_i \to 0$ as $n \to \infty$. This is done by showing

1. That a certain area, say A, is given by $F(b) - F(a)$, where a and b are particular values of x, and $F(x) = \int f(x) \, dx$

2. That $\lim\limits_{n \to \infty} \sum\limits_{i=1}^{n} f(x_i) \, \Delta x_i$ gives *precisely* this same area A

Thus the students should come to see that the summation process may at any time be replaced by the definite integral and that the symbols $\lim\limits_{n \to \infty} \sum\limits_{i=1}^{n} f(x_i) \, \Delta x_i$ and $\int_{x_1}^{x_2} f(x) \, dx$ may be regarded as interchangeable, provided the function is continuous over the interval.

It should be pointed out that neither the conclusion embodied in the theorem nor the line of reasoning leading to it is limited to or dependent upon geometrical considerations, although a geometrical illustration was used and the problem was set up in terms of the summation of elements of area. This is done (1) because the graphic or geometric representation helps to give tangibility and concreteness to a situation otherwise highly abstract and (2) because functions may be represented graphically and interpreted geometrically even though they refer to nongeometric variables such as forces, heat, and work. It should be emphasized that the definite integral may be used to determine any kind of magnitude, provided the characteristic function can be set up in conformity with the requirements stated above.

Improvement of Prerequisite Concepts and Skills. In addition to adding a whole new branch of mathematics to the student's equipment, the study of calculus holds tremendous possibilities for extending and deepening his understanding of the branches previously studied, and the perfection of his skills in them. This is especially the case with reference to algebra, trigonometry, and analytic geometry. It has been said that the place where these subjects are really learned is in calculus. That this is more than a mere figure of speech will be evident from a consideration of the completeness with which the concepts and operations peculiar to these branches underlie and permeate the whole structure of calculus. Algebraic processes find application in innumerable connections throughout the course. Indeed, one of the main problems of formal integration is the algebraic transformation of functions into integrable forms. Trigonometric functions, identities, and transformations are also much in evidence, and a good understanding of analytic geometry is certainly a prime requisite, not only in setting up functions and equations for many of the applied problems but in giving the student tangible geometric interpretations of the fundamental concepts of calculus.

Functions of many kinds are met with and are made the subject of various investigations and operations. Incidentally, it may be noted that calculus gives the student a more comprehensive concept of the nature of a function than he will have been able to get in his previous study. He will already have gained an understanding of the general meaning of a function and will have made some study of the variation of functions, but in calculus, for the first time, he will make a systematic study of a new aspect of functions, viz., the rate of change of a function with respect to its independent variable.

The student who, in taking up a study of calculus, lacks an adequate background in algebra, trigonometry, and analytic geometry will find himself at a great disadvantage.[1] Indeed, it is not improbable that a large share of the difficulty which students experience in calculus may be directly traceable to inadequate mastery of the prerequisite branches. On the other hand, nowhere could there be found a finer opportunity for

[1] W. H. Fagerstrom, Mathematical Facts and Processes Prerequisite to the Study of the Calculus, *Contributions to Education* 572 (New York: Bureau of Publications, Teachers College, Columbia University, 1933).

well-motivated review and application of their concepts and techniques. Every student should be made conscious of this and should be urged as a matter of enlightened self-interest to put forth every effort to perfect himself in these concepts and techniques. For students who have difficulty, the instructor may be able to perform a real service by helping them to diagnose their troubles and suggesting appropriate remedial exercises. The importance of perfecting the skills and having ready mastery of the concepts and relationships of algebra, trigonometry, and analytic geometry is a matter which should receive continual emphasis.

Mathematical Rigor in Calculus. The discussion in this chapter has admittedly given special emphasis to the matter of developing concepts and understandings, because it has been felt that in general the teaching of calculus more often falls short in this respect than in any other. Intuitive concepts, however, do not provide sufficiently sound mathematical justification for the conclusions upon which much of calculus is based. Moreover, by the time the student has come through a study of calculus, he should have acquired a feeling for the nature of and the necessity for mathematical rigor *as such*. There can be no real appreciation of the nature of mathematical thinking, nor any sound basis for the exploration of higher mathematics, apart from an understanding of what is implied by a rigorous examination of the foundations of mathematics, the nature of the processes employed, and the consequences of given conditions.

Calculus stands more or less in the position of a border-line subject with respect to the matter of mathematical rigor. The courses which precede it are concerned mainly with the development of concepts, the acquisition of rules for operation, and the perfection of skills, although at some points there is an approach to real rigor in the treatment of certain theorems. On the other hand, the higher analytical courses are characterized by essentially rigorous and formal treatment of the subject matter. Thus, whether the student expects to "top off" his work in mathematics with calculus or go on into the domain of higher mathematics, it is important that his study of calculus provide him, both as a matter of appreciation and as a matter of training, with some opportunity for really rigorous examination of certain topics.

Calculus offers numerous opportunities for such work in the analytical definitions associated with the concepts of limits, infinitesimals, continuity, differentials, derivatives, and the like and in the proofs of certain theorems such as Rolle's theorem, the theorem of the mean, the fundamental theorem of definite integrals, Taylor's theorem, and Maclaurin's theorem.

It is undoubtedly true that there are many students who will be able to do little with this kind of work, and it must not be assumed merely on this account that the course is worthless to them. This, after all, is but one of the objectives of the course; it must not be forgotten that the use of a theorem and the proof of that same theorem are two entirely different matters and that things may often be extremely useful without being completely understood. On the other hand, students who are able to appreciate the significance of this type of analysis and follow its development will find a satisfying sense of security and finality in their work which must otherwise be lacking. Those who expect to go further in mathematics will find the training afforded in this sort of rigorous treatment of the foundations and theorems of calculus to be of inestimable value to them in their later work.

EXERCISES

1. What have been the main arguments for the introduction of some work in calculus in the high school?

2. Why, in your opinion, has calculus not been more extensively taught in the high school?

3. The opinion has sometimes been advanced that much of the difficulty which students have in calculus is due to inability to handle basic elementary algebra and trigonometric identities with facility and assurance. Comment on this.

4. To what extent do you think students' difficulties in calculus stem from their inability to read and interpret readily the explanations and discussions in their calculus textbooks? Present some examples of material taken from a calculus textbook which you feel might involve difficulty of this nature, and explain what the difficulty is.

5. Select a passage from a calculus textbook which you think might be hard for students to understand and then rewrite it in such a way that the difficulty would, in your opinion, be obviated or reduced.

6. Summarize MacDuffee's article (see Bibliography) on the objectives for a course in calculus.

7. What do you consider the most serious indictment of the teaching of calculus in colleges and engineering schools?

8. Explain and present illustrations of the following: variable, constant, parameter, domain of a variable, infinitesimal.

9. Give an intuitive explanation or illustration and also a formal definition of what is meant by saying that a variable approaches a constant as a limit. What difficulties do students have with the formal definition?

10. Give a formal definition of a derivative, using the notation of the textbook you use. Then explain and clarify this, using various illustrations.

11. What is a differential? Give three physical illustrations of the differentials of functions.

12. List from your calculus book several applied problems in which approximate solutions are to be found by means of differentials. Present the solutions of three of these to the class.

13. If $y = f(x)$, explain as you would to a class why it is that $\Delta x = dx$, while in general $\Delta y \neq dy$. Under what circumstances does $\Delta y = dy$?

14. Present arguments to justify or refute the assertion that in calculus the trigonometric identities play a more important role than the solution of triangles.

15. By using the definition and assuming the existence of the number e, present to the class a complete derivation of the formula for $D_x y$, where $y = \log_a x$, and show

how this formula is simplified when a is taken to be e. (Note that this is where the number e really comes into the mathematical picture as an important constant.)

16. Show how the formula for the derivative of an exponential follows easily from the formula for the derivative of a logarithm.

17. Present to the class a full derivation of the formula for D_xy, where $y = \sin x$.

18. By taking u as a function of x and using the formulas for the derivative of $\sin u$ and the derivative of a fraction, show how to obtain the formulas for the derivatives of $\cos x$ and $\tan x$ with respect to x.

19. By using the formulas for the derivatives of the trigonometric functions, show how to obtain the formulas for the derivatives of the inverse trigonometric functions.

20. Give a symbolic statement of the law of the mean. Then, using a diagram, explain and illustrate clearly the meaning of this formula. Give one instance in which this important law is used.

21. Give a clear explanation of the role of first and second derivatives in the matter of locating and classifying critical points (relative maxima and minima and inflection points) on the graph of a function.

22. Explain clearly the meaning of an indefinite integral as an antiderivative. Why must an indefinite integral contain a constant of integration?

23. Explain clearly the meaning of a definite integral as the limit of a summation process. Show that the constant of integration is actually accounted for in the process of evaluating a definite integral.

24. Show how the law of the mean is used in establishing L'Hôpital's rule for evaluating indeterminate forms. Give some examples of the application of this rule.

25. By using the trapezoidal rule, find the approximate area bounded by the curve $y = 3x^2$, the x axis, and the ordinates at $x = 2$ and $x = 7$. Use $\Delta x = 1$. Check your result by integration. Explain your work to the class.

26. Give a good, clear geometric interpretation of a partial derivative, and explain your diagram in detail. Do the same thing for a directional derivative.

27. Enumerate five tests for the convergence of infinite series. Explain how and why each of these works and why it is really a test.

28. Find five applications of calculus to problems in your textbook in college physics.

29. Select a problem in physics in the solution of which a definite integral is involved. Explain to the class just how you would set up the element of integration and the integral and how you would establish the limits of integration.

30. Cite a problem involving an improper integral and show how it should be solved.

31. Discuss the role of mathematical rigor in the course in calculus.

32. Examine several textbooks in calculus and, after careful consideration, decide which one in your opinion gives the most satisfactory treatment of each of the following topics: (*a*) limits, infinitesimals, and continuity; (*b*) derivatives and differentiation; (*c*) increments and differentials; (*d*) integration as antidifferentiation; indefinite integrals; (*e*) integration as summation; definite integrals; (*f*) infinite series, including tests for convergence and divergence.

33. Prepare a talk, as for a mathematics club, in which you will review the ideas set forth in Chapter 15 of Hooper's book "The River Mathematics" (see Bibliography).

34. Discuss the suggestions made in Humbert's article (see Bibliography) and give your opinion about them. Do you think the course in calculus would be more effective if teachers would follow these suggestions?

35. Pick out five things which seemed to you to present special difficulty when you were taking calculus. Try now to locate and identify the precise reasons why these

things caused you difficulty.   Then try to devise teaching procedures by which you
would hope to make them clearer to your own students.

BIBLIOGRAPHY

Abbott, P.: "Teach Yourself Calculus" (London: The English Universities Press,
Ltd., 1946).

Anderson, A. G.: The Derivative of cos x, American Mathematical Monthly, **60** (1953),
255–256.

Apostol, T. M.: Term-wise Differentiation of Power Series, American Mathematical
Monthly, **59** (1952), 323–326.

Association of Assistant Masters in Secondary Schools: "The Teaching of Mathematics" (London: Cambridge University Press, 1957), pp. 115–123.

Barton, A.: Differentials from a New Viewpoint, Mathematical Gazette, **29** (1945),
193–199.

Bonnell, Charles R.: A Tangential Approach to the Area under a Curve by Integration, Pentagon, **14** (1954), 30–33.

Boyer, Carl: "The Concepts of the Calculus" (New York: Columbia University
Press, 1939).

————: History of the Derivative and Integral of the Sine, Mathematics Teacher, **40**
(1947), 267–275.

————: Analysis: Notes on the Evolution of a Subject and a Name, Mathematics
Teacher, **47** (1954), 450–462.

Brand, Louis: The Fundamental Theorem of the Calculus, American Mathematical
Monthly, **62** (1955), 440–441.

Bryan, Noah: An Outline of High School Calculus, School Science and Mathematics,
30 (1930), 937–944.

Burton, W. W., and W. G. Miller: The Integral Powers of the Secant and Cosecant,
American Mathematical Monthly, **48** (1941), 544–545.

Clair, Harry S.: The Theorem of the Mean and Its Application to Problems of Maxima
and Minima, School Science and Mathematics, **57** (1957), 468–472.

Coffman, Raphael T.: An Elementary Approach to the Use of the Rate of Change
Concept for Solving Problems, Mathematics Magazine, **30** (1956), 81–90.

Coxeter, H. S. M.: The Area of a Hyperbolic Sector, Pentagon, **14** (1954), 39.

Dragoo, R. C.: Teaching the Calculus, National Mathematics Magazine, **19** (1945),
186–193.

Eaves, J. C.: Off the Beaten Path with Some Differentiation Formulas for the Trigonometric, Exponential, and Logarithmic Functions, Mathematics Magazine, **26**
(1953), 147–152.

Fagerstrom, W. H.: "Mathematical Facts and Processes Prerequisite to the Study of
the Calculus," Contributions to Education 572 (New York: Bureau of Publications,
Teachers College, Columbia University, 1933).

Farmer, Susie B.: The Place and Teaching of Calculus in Secondary Schools, Mathematics Teacher, **20** (1927), 181–202.

Fehr, Howard F.: "Secondary Mathematics: A Functional Approach for Teachers"
(Boston: D. C. Heath and Company, 1951) pp. 168–190, 315–337.

Folley, K. W.: Integration by Parts, American Mathematical Monthly, **54** (1947), 542.

Fort, M. K.: Differentials, American Mathematical Monthly, **59** (1952), 392–395.

Fulton, Curtis M.: Differentiation of Logarithms, Mathematics Magazine, **28** (1954), 8.

Gans, David: Angle of Inclination and Curvature, Mathematics Magazine, **31** (1957),
31–32.

Graesser, R. F.: Note on Integration by Parts, *School Science and Mathematics*, **51** (1951), 602.

Hanna, J. Ray: Alternate Formulas for First, Second, and other Moments of an Area, *School Science and Mathematics*, **51** (1951), 286–288.

Hildebrand, F. B.: A Simple Problem in Cylindrical Coordinates, *American Mathematical Monthly*, **64** (1957), 194–195.

Hooper, Alfred: "The River Mathematics" (New York: Henry Holt and Company, Inc., 1945), pp. 340–379.

Hoyt, J. P.: A Natural Approach to the Fundamental Theorem of the Integral Calculus, *American Mathematical Monthly*, **61** (1954), 413–415.

————: A Proof of the Moment-Area Problem, *Mathematics Magazine*, **30** (1956), 95–97.

Humbert, R.: Wanted: Better Mathematics Instruction, *School Science and Mathematics*, **48** (1948), 534–535.

Huntington, Edward V.: "Teaching the Calculus: Four Papers on the Teaching of Mathematics," *Bulletin* 19 (Lancaster, Pa.: Society for the Promotion of Engineering Education, 1932), pp. 35–70.

Ingersoll, B. M.: Geometric Derivation of the Formula for Integration by Parts, *National Mathematics Magazine*, **18** (1944), 280–283.

James, Glenn: The Gist of the Calculus, *Mathematics Magazine*, **22** (1948), 29–46.

Jerbert, A. R.: The Art of Summation, *School Science and Mathematics*, **46** (1946), 703–707.

Johnson, C. A.: Coordinating Calculus Instruction in the Engineering Program, *Journal of Engineering Education*, **41** (1951), 537–541.

————: A Reflective Approach in the Teaching of Mathematics, *Mathematics Magazine*, **26** (1952), 35–38

Karst, Otto J.: The Limit, *Mathematics Teacher*, **51** (1958) 443–449.

Kasner, Edward, and James Newman: "Mathematics and the Imagination" (New York: Simon and Schuster, Inc., 1940), pp. 299–356.

Kramer, Edna: "The Main Stream of Mathematics" (New York: Oxford University Press, 1951), pp. 209–240.

Lange, Luise: More Stress on General Formulations in Calculus Problems, *American Mathematical Monthly*, **57** (1950), 181–183.

Laws, L. S.: A Simplification of the Second Derivative Test, *American Mathematical Monthly*, **54** (1947), 543.

Leader, S.: On the Definition of ln a, *American Mathematical Monthly*, **66** (1959), 622–623.

Lubin, C. I.: Differentiation of the Trigonometric Functions, *American Mathematical Monthly*, **54** (1947), 465–467.

MacDuffee, C. C.: Objectives in Calculus, *American Mathematical Monthly*, **54** (1947), 335–337.

————: What Mathematics Shall We Teach in the Fourth Year of High School? *Mathematics Teacher*, **45** (1952), 1–5.

MacNeish, H. F.: Logarithmic Integration, *American Mathematical Monthly*, **56** (1949) 25–27.

Mathematical Association (England): "The Teaching of Calculus in Schools" (London: G. Bell & Sons, Ltd., 1951). (A report prepared for the Mathematical Association.)

Moore, J. H., and J. A. Mira: "The Gist of Mathematics" (Englewood Cliffs, N.J.: Prentice-Hall, Inc., 1942), pp. 560–579

Myers, Sheldon: The Meaning of Derivative and Integral Illustrated by the Speedometer, *Mathematics Teacher*, **45** (1952), 58–59.

National Council of Teachers of Mathematics: "Insights into Modern Mathematics," *Twenty-third Yearbook* (Washington, D.C.: National Council of Teachers of Mathematics, 1957), pp. 200–272, 404–427.

Newsom, C. V.: The Teaching of Collegiate Mathematics, *School Science and Mathematics*, **52** (1952), 130–132.

Nicholas, C. P.: More on Taylor's Theorem in a First Course, *American Mathematical Monthly*, **60** (1953), 329–331.

———: Another Look at the Probability Integral, *American Mathematical Monthly*, **64** (1957), 739–741.

Ogilvy, C. S.: A Calculus Problem with Overtones in Related Fields, *American Mathematical Monthly*, **65** (1958), 765–767.

Olds, C. D.: Remarks on Integration by Parts, *American Mathematical Monthly*, **56** (1949), 29–30.

———: The Evaluation of Two Infinite Integrals, *American Mathematical Monthly*, **63** (1956), 575–576.

Olds, Edwin G.: A Fresh Start, *National Mathematics Magazine*, **12** (1937–1938) 290–293.

Osborn, Roger: A Note on Indeterminate Forms, *American Mathematical Monthly*, **59** (1952), 549–550.

Parker, F. D.: Integrals of Inverse Functions, *American Mathematical Monthly*, **62** (1955), 439–440.

Parker, J. E.: The Teaching Objectives in a First Course in the Calculus, *Mathematics Teacher*, **37** (1944), 347–349.

Pascual, M. J.: On the $\lim_{\theta \to 0} \cos \theta$, *American Mathematical Monthly*, **62** (1955), 252–253.

———: The Derivatives of the Trigonometric Functions, *Mathematics Magazine*, **31** (1957), 39–40.

Phipps, C. G.: The Relation of Differential and Delta Increments, *American Mathematical Monthly*, **59** (1952), 395–398.

Prenowitz, Walter: Insight and Understanding in the Calculus, *American Mathematical Monthly*, **60** (1953), 32–37.

Punga, V.: Transformation of Standard Integrals, *American Mathematical Monthly*, **62** (1955), 363–364.

Ransom, W. R.: A Geometrical Meaning for $f''(x)$, *School Science and Mathematics*, **43** (1943), 600.

———: Introducing $e = 2.718 +$, *American Mathematical Monthly*, **55** (1948), 572.

———: The Fundamental Theorem of the Differential Calculus, *American Mathematical Monthly*, **62** (1955), 361–363.

Reynolds, J. B.: Undetermined Coefficients in Integration, *American Mathematical Monthly*, **54** (1947), 37–38.

Richardson, M.: "Fundamentals of Mathematics" (New York: The Macmillan Company, 1946), pp. 288–333.

Robbins, Charles K. (Editor): Some Notes on the Limit Concept, *Mathematics Magazine*, **25** (1952), 163–165.

Rosenberger, Noah B.: An Outline of High School Calculus, *School Science and Mathematics*, **30** (1930), 937–944.

Satterly, John: The Trisection of the Area of a Circle, *School Science and Mathematics*, **53** (1953), 124–130.

Sawyer, W. W.: "Mathematician's Delight" (Baltimore: Penguin Books, Inc., 1946), pp. 107–160.

Schaaf, William L.: Calculus in the Classroom [bibliography], *Mathematics Teacher*, **45** (1952), 525–527.

Smith, H. W.: Some Integral Formulas, *American Mathematical Monthly*, **56** (1949), 27–28.

Spiegel, M. R.: Some Interesting Series Resulting from a Certain Maclaurin Expansion, *American Mathematical Monthly*, **60** (1953), 243–247.

———: Derivatives of Implicit Functions, *American Mathematical Monthly*, **61** (1954), 120–121

———: L'Hospital's Rule and Expansion of Functions in Power Series, *American Mathematical Monthly*, **62** (1955), 358–360.

———: Remarks Concerning the Probability Integral, *American Mathematical Monthly*, **63** (1956), 35–37.

Sutton, Richard M.: The "Steinmetz Problem" and School Arithmetic, *Mathematics Teacher*, **50** (1957), 434–435.

Walker, A. W.: An Elementary Integral, *American Mathematical Monthly*, **59** (1952), 103–104.

Walsh, J. L.: A Rigorous Treatment of the First Maximum Problem in the Calculus, *American Mathematical Monthly*, **54** (1947), 35.

Ward, J. A.: An Extension of Plane Analytic Geometry, *American Mathematical Monthly*, **59** (1952) 463–464.

Weiner, L. M.: On the Computation of Definite Integrals, *American Mathematical Monthly*, **61** (1954), 254–255.

Whitman, E. A.: The Use of Models while Teaching Triple Integration, *American Mathematical Monthly*, **47** (1940), 45–48.

———: The Film—A Triple Integral, *American Mathematical Monthly*, **49** (1942), 399–400.

Wolfe, James: A Proof of Taylor's Formula, *American Mathematical Monthly*, **60** (1953), 415.

———: An Adjusted Trapezoidal Rule Using Function Values within the Range of Integration, *American Mathematical Monthly*, **66** (1959), 125–127.

Wren, F. L., and J. A. Garrett: The Development of the Fundamental Concepts of Infinitesimal Calculus, *American Mathematical Monthly*, **40** (1933), 269–281.

Yates, R. C.: Differentiating the Logarithm, *American Mathematical Monthly*, **61** (1954), 120.

———: Developments in Power Series, *American Mathematical Monthly*, **61** (1954), 256–258.

———: The Logarithm and Its Inverse, *Mathematics Teacher*, **51** (1958), 105–106.

———: The Trigonometric Functions, *Mathematics Teacher*, **51** (1958), 191–193.

Zeitlin, David: An Application of the Mean Value Theorem, *American Mathematical Monthly*, **64** (1957), 427.

———: On Plane Area in Polar Coordinates, *American Mathematical Monthly*, **66** (1959), 135-136.

Index